$$\int_{-\infty}^{\infty} e^{-x^2} dx = \sqrt{\pi}$$

$$\int_{0}^{\infty} \frac{\sin x}{x} dx = \frac{\pi}{2}$$

$$\int_{0}^{\infty} \frac{1 - \cos ax}{x^2} dx = \frac{\pi}{2}|a|$$

$$\int_{0}^{\infty} e^{ix^a} dx = \Gamma\left(\frac{1}{a} + 1\right) e^{i\pi/2a} \quad \text{if } 1 < a < \infty$$

$$\int_{0}^{\infty} \cos x^2 dx = \int_{0}^{\infty} \sin x^2 dx = \sqrt{\pi/8} \qquad \text{FRESNEL}$$

$$\int_{0}^{1} x^{a-1}(1-x)^{b-1} dx = \frac{\Gamma(a)\Gamma(b)}{\Gamma(a+b)} \qquad \text{BETA FUNCTION}$$

$$2\int_{0}^{\pi/2} \sin^{2a-1}\theta \cos^{2b-1}\theta d\theta = \frac{\Gamma(a)\Gamma(b)}{\Gamma(a+b)}$$

$$e^{-a|x|^2} * e^{-b|x|^2} = \left(\frac{\pi}{a+b}\right)^{n/2} e^{-\frac{ab}{a+b}|x|^2}$$

$$\sum_{n=1}^{\infty} \frac{1}{n^2} = \frac{\pi^2}{6}, \qquad \sum_{n=1}^{\infty} \frac{1}{(2n-1)^2} = \frac{\pi^2}{8}$$

$$\sum_{n=0}^{\infty} \frac{\sin(2n+1)x}{2n+1} = \frac{\pi}{4} \quad \text{for } 0 < x < \pi \qquad \text{SQUARE WAVE}$$

$$\sum_{n=1}^{\infty} \frac{\sin nx}{n} = \frac{\pi - x}{2} \quad \text{for } 0 < x < 2\pi \qquad \text{SAWTOOTH WAVE}$$

$$\sum_{n=1}^{\infty} \frac{\cos nx}{n^2} = \frac{x^2}{4} - \frac{\pi x}{2} + \frac{\pi^2}{6} \quad \text{for } 0 \leq x \leq 2\pi$$

Lebesgue Integration

on

Euclidean Space

————Jones and Bartlett Books in Mathematics————

Beltrami, E., *Mathematical Models in the Social and Biological Sciences*

Jones, F., *Lebesgue Integration on Euclidean Space*

Loomis, L.H., and Sternberg, S., *Advanced Calculus*

Protter, M.H., and Protter, P.E., *Calculus, Fourth Edition*

Redheffer, R., *Differential Equations: Theory and Applications*

Redheffer, R., *Introduction to Differential Equations*

Ruskai, M.B., *et al.*, *Wavelets and Their Applications*

Lebesgue Integration
on
Euclidean Space

Frank Jones

Department of Mathematics
Rice University
Houston, Texas

Jones and Bartlett Publishers
Boston   *London*

Editorial, Sales, and Customer Service Offices
Jones and Bartlett Publishers
One Exeter Plaza
Boston, MA 02116

Jones and Bartlett Publishers International
P.O. Box 1498
London W6 7RS
England

Copyright © 1993 by Jones and Bartlett Publishers, Inc.

All rights reserved. No part of the material protected by this copyright notice may be reproduced or utilized in any form, electronic or mechanical, including photocopying, recording, or by any information storage and retrieval system, without written permission from the copyright owner.

Library of Congress Cataloging-in-Publication Data

Jones, Frank, 1936.
    Lebesgue integration on Euclidean space / Frank Jones.
       p.   cm.
    Includes bibliographical references.
    ISBN 0-86720-203-3
    1. Measure theory.   2. Title
    QA312.I58   1993   92-25592
    515$'$.42--dc20   CIP

Printed in the United States of America
96 95 94 93   10 9 8 7 6 5 4 3 2 1

Contents

Preface

"Though of real knowledge there be little, yet
of books there are plenty"
–Herman Melville, *Moby Dick*, Chapter XXXI.

The treatment of integration developed by the French mathematician Henri Lebesgue (1875–1944) almost a century ago has proved to be indispensable in many areas of mathematics. Lebesgue's theory is of such extreme importance because on the one hand it has rendered previous theories of integration virtually obsolete, and on the other hand it has not been replaced with a significantly different, better theory. Most subsequent important investigations of integration theory have extended or illuminated Lebesgue's work.

In fact, as is so often the case in a new field of mathematics, many of the best consequences were given by the originator. For example, Lebesgue's dominated convergence theorem, Lebesgue's increasing convergence theorem, the theory of the Lebesgue function of the Cantor ternary set, and Lebesgue's theory of differentiation of indefinite integrals.

Naturally, many splendid textbooks have been produced in this area. I shall list some of these below. They are quite varied in their approach to the subject. My aims in the present book are as follows.

1. To present a *slow* introduction to Lebesgue integration. Most books nowadays take the opposite tack. I have no argument with their approach, except that I feel that many students who see only a very rapid approach tend to lack strong intuition about measure and integration. That is why I have made Chapter 2, "Lebesgue measure on $\mathbb{R}^n$," so lengthy and have restricted it to Euclidean space, and why I have (somewhat inconveniently) placed Chapter 3, "Invariance of Lebesgue measure," before Fubini's theorem. In my approach I have omitted much important material, for the sake of concreteness. As the title of the book signifies, I restrict attention almost entirely to Euclidean space.

2. To deal with n-dimensional spaces from the outset. I believe this is preferable to one standard approach to the theory which first thoroughly treats integration on the real line and then generalizes. There are several reasons for this belief. One is quite simply that significant figures are frequently easier to sketch in $\mathbb{R}^2$ than in $\mathbb{R}^1$! Another is that some things in $\mathbb{R}^1$ are so special that the generalization to $\mathbb{R}^n$ is not clear; for example, the structure of the most general open set in $\mathbb{R}^1$ is essentially trivial — it must be a disjoint union of open intervals (see Problem 2.6). A third is that coping with the n-dimensional case from the outset causes the learner to realize that it is not significantly more difficult than the one-dimensional case as far as many aspects of integration are concerned.

3. To provide a thorough treatment of Fourier analysis. One of the triumphs of Lebesgue integration is the fact that it provides definitive answers to many questions of Fourier analysis. I feel that without a thorough study of this topic the student is simply not well educated in integration theory. Chapter 13 is a very long one on the Fourier transform in several variables, and Chapter 14 also a very long one on Fourier series in one variable.

4. To prepare the student to become a "worker" in real analysis. I do not mean that he should become a researcher, but instead that he be able to *apply* to other areas of interest to him the things he has seen in this book. As a certain sort of analyst myself, I have chosen to include those topics which I have found to be of primary importance in my own research. This purpose partially explains the inclusion of the two long Chapters 15 and 16 on differentiation theory. They are also here because of their beauty and depth.

This last aim seems to be ever growing in its importance, as we mathematicians are seeing more and more students from other disciplines taking our advanced courses. It is now commonplace to find engineering graduate students, for example, taking courses in integration theory, differential geometry, etc.

I have written this book under the assumption that the student either is already familiar with certain basic concepts or has a teacher. Thus, the introductory chapter on the basic facts about $\mathbb{R}^n$ is extremely brief, except that I have tried to give a fairly careful account of compactness (in $\mathbb{R}^n$). (I have done so because compactness is a serious stumbling block for many students.)

I confess that I am proud of the problems in this book. There are 600 of them, and I think most of them are interesting and neither trivial nor impossibly difficult. There are a few that are "challenging," and this is another reason for the utility of having a teacher. I have chosen to spread the problems throughout the text, in order to encourage the student and teacher to use them as an integral part of their study. Thus, when a problem appears as a subject is being developed, the indication to the student is that he is now ready for this exercise to check his knowledge and to strengthen his understanding of what is being discussed.

Bibliography

I am placing this in such a prominent position in order to acknowledge some debts and to encourage the reader to engage in further reading.

* Paul R. Halmos, *Measure Theory,* Springer-Verlag, 1988.

* H.L. Royden, *Real Analysis,* third edition, Macmillan, 1988.

The two books just cited are standard texts. They concentrate on theoretical aspects, especially the Carathéodory construction of measurable sets. They contain important topics which are not discussed at all in my book. For example, the Radon-Nikodym theorem, Egorov's theorem, the dual space of L^p.

* Richard L. Wheeden and Antoni Zygmund, *Measure and Integral,* Dekker, 1977.

This excellent book has similar aims to mine (it is quite concrete in its approach), but also concentrates on many technical aspects which I have not included.

* Walter Rudin, *Real and Complex Analysis*, third edition, McGraw-Hill, 1987.

* Herbert Federer, *Geometric Measure Theory*, Springer-Verlag, 1969. Federer's book is perhaps the ultimate text on this subject. It seems to contain everything but Fourier analysis, including a complete course on measure theory in Chapter Two, "General measure theory." The really serious student should find great benefit in working through this chapter.

* de la Vallée Poussin, *Intégrales de Lebesgue*, Gauthier-Villars, 1950. When I first learned this subject from Professor Bray in 1958, this was the text he used. A beautiful source for the generalization of the Fourier transform to distributions is

* L. Hörmander, *The Analysis of Linear Partial Differential Operators I*, Springer Study Edition, Springer-Verlag, 1990. Chapter VII, "The Fourier transformation," contains a wealth of material, and the exercises in the Springer Study Edition are marvelously illuminating.

One deficiency of my book that I am sorely aware of is the dearth of historical information. A very thorough source of such material may be found in the work of

* Thomas Hawkins, *Lebesgue's Theory of Integration*, Univ. of Wisconsin Press, 1970. I highly recommend the reader of my book to become acquainted with Hawkins' interesting book.

Finally, I have greatly benefited from two papers of Dale E. Varberg concerning differentiation theory. His influence is especially seen in Chapter 15. The references are

* "On absolutely continuous functions," *Amer. Math. Monthly 72* (1965), 831–841;

* "On differentiable transformations in $\mathbb{R}^n$," *Amer. Math. Monthly 73* (1966, Number 4, Part II), 111–114.

Acknowledgments

The mathematicians who first introduced me to the subject of this book were Hubert E. Bray and Jim Douglas, Jr. Much of which I have included I originally learned from them. But I must say that it was Professor Bray to a much greater extent, as I took a year-long course from him on integration theory and Fourier series in 1958–59. Professor Bray (1889–1978) earned the first Ph.D. which Rice Institute ever awarded. His 1918 thesis was entitled, *A Green's Theorem in Terms of Lebesgue Integrals*. He was a faculty member of the Rice Department of Mathematics from then until his death. I still have on my shelf the splendid notes I took from his course over thirty years ago.

Many of my students have contributed significantly to this work. I am not going to name them all, but some of them are Jim Fox, Bob Hasse, Randy Mitchell, and Eric Swartz.

I am indebted to Calixto Calderón for discussions about Section 15.I.

I especially am indebted to the following people, who encouraged me to have this book published, and who constantly provided more-or-less friendly goading: John Brickner, Robert Burckel, John Cannon, Beverly Jones, Todd Simpson, and Mary Wheeler. Of these, Professors Burckel and Cannon each provided a detailed reading and very constructive criticism of earlier manuscripts. Just last year, Professor Burckel in fact reread the entire manuscript and provided me with many, many clever and useful observations and suggestions. I gladly acknowledge his splendid assistance.

Special thanks go to Janie McBane, the mathematical typist currently in the Rice mathematics department, and her teamwork with David Mallis; their major tool is a Macintosh computer and software called "TEX." And very special thanks to Anita Poley, who originally typed my manuscript many years ago, on bond paper, using an IBM Model D typewriter (pre-Selectric) and Typ-its!!! Both Janie and Anita are superb craftsmen (craftswomen?) at what they do, and they always do it *cheerfully*! They are absolute delights to work with!

I am most humbly grateful to have been a faculy member here at Rice since 1962. Working in our Department of Mathematics is the most wonderful occupation I can imagine. I have always been blessed with marveleous friendly stimulating colleagues both on the faculty and staff, and have been privileged to teach many truly remarkable and interesting students. Many of the latter have been guinea pigs for earlier drafts of this book.

Our current department coordinator, Sharon McDonough, is the greatest!

Carl Hesler of Jones and Bartlett has been a delight to work with.

Since I originally was taught by Professor Bray, it is especially thrilling to me recently to have had his grandsons Hubert L. Bray and Clark B. Bray as my students at Rice. In fact, young Hubert read my manuscript during a recent summer in order to learn the subject for himself and last year Clark was my student in this very course. I feel especially honored to have been the mediator between Hubert E. Bray and the brothers Bray as the grandfather taught the grandsons this beautiful subject.

To the most important people in my life:

Beverly, my wife
Marianna (and husband Jerry), Elaine, and David, our children
Nathan, Kara, Lauren, and Caroline, our grandchildren
Elizabeth, my mother

and the man who purchased us with his own blood
two thousand years ago.

Introduction to $\mathbb{R}^n$

A. Sets

The real number system will be denoted $\mathbb{R}$. We shall be working on $\mathbb{R}^n$, the set of ordered n-tuples of real numbers, and shall use a notation such as x for points in $\mathbb{R}^n$: $x = (x_1, \ldots, x_n)$. If $n = 1$ we shall simply write x instead of x_1; and if $n = 2$ we shall frequently use the notation (x, y) instead of (x_1, x_2).

In general there is a notion of *Cartesian product*: If A_1, A_2, ..., A_N are sets, then

$$A_1 \times A_2 \times \cdots \times A_N$$

is the set of all ordered N-tuples $(a_1, a_2, \ldots, a_N)$ with $a_k \in A_k$ for $k = 1, 2, \ldots, N$. In particular, $\mathbb{R}^n = \mathbb{R} \times \cdots \times \mathbb{R}$ (n factors). We shall not hesitate to write the equality $\mathbb{R}^l \times \mathbb{R}^m = \mathbb{R}^{l+m}$, although, strictly speaking, these two sets are not equal.

Given a set A contained in $\mathbb{R}^n$, the *complement* of A is the set

$$A^c = \{x \in \mathbb{R}^n \mid x \notin A\}.$$

Let $\emptyset$ denote the empty set. Then $(\mathbb{R}^n)^c = \emptyset$ and $\emptyset^c = \mathbb{R}^n$. It is always true that $A^{cc} = A$.

If A and B are sets, and if every member of A is also a member of B, then we say that A is *contained* in B, and we write $A \subset B$. We also write $B \supset A$. Since two sets are equal if and only if they have the same members, a proof that $A = B$ frequently follows the pattern of proving that $A \subset B$ and also that $B \subset A$.

If A and B are sets in $\mathbb{R}^n$, the *union* of A and B is the set

$$A \cup B = \{x \in \mathbb{R}^n \mid x \in A \quad \text{or} \quad x \in B\},$$

and the *intersection* of A and B is the set

$$A \cap B = \{x \in \mathbb{R}^n \mid x \in A \quad \text{and} \quad x \in B\}.$$

The sets A and B are said to be *disjoint* if $A \cap B = \emptyset$.

The *difference* $A \sim B$ is the set

$$A \sim B = A \cap B^c.$$

Now we shall generalize the notions of union and intersection to arbitrary collections of sets. To do this, let the symbol $\mathcal{I}$ stand for an arbitrary set used for indexing. The indices will be denoted by the letter i. Suppose that for each $i \in \mathcal{I}$ there corresponds a set A_i. Then the *union* of these sets is the set

$$\bigcup_{i \in \mathcal{I}} A_i = \{x \mid \text{there exists } i \in \mathcal{I} \text{ such that } x \in A_i\},$$

and the *intersection* is the set

$$\bigcap_{i \in \mathcal{I}} A_i = \{x \mid \text{for every } i \in \mathcal{I}, \ x \in A_i\}.$$

We could also denote the union as $\cup\{A_i \mid i \in \mathcal{I}\}$ and the intersection as $\cap\{A_i \mid i \in \mathcal{I}\}$.

We say the sets are *disjoint* if $i \neq i' \Rightarrow A_i \cap A_{i'} = \emptyset$.

The system of *natural numbers* will be denoted $\mathbb{N} = \{1, 2, 3, \dots\}$. In case the index set is $\mathbb{N}$, we shall usually write

$$\bigcup_{k=1}^{\infty} A_k \quad \text{and} \quad \bigcap_{k=1}^{\infty} A_k$$

for the union and intersection, respectively.

Problem 1 (DE MORGAN'S LAWS).
   Prove that

$$\left(\bigcup_{i \in \mathcal{I}} A_i\right)^c = \bigcap_{i \in \mathcal{I}} A_i^c$$

and

$$\left(\bigcap_{i \in \mathcal{I}} A_i\right)^c = \bigcup_{i \in \mathcal{I}} A_i^c.$$

Problem 2. *limsup and liminf.*

(a) For a sequence of sets A_1, A_2, ..., prove that

$$\bigcap_{j=1}^{\infty} \left(\bigcup_{k=j}^{\infty} A_k \right) = \{x \mid x \in A_k \text{ for infinitely many } k\}.$$

This set is designated $\limsup_{k \to \infty} A_k$ or simply $\limsup A_k$.

(b) Derive a similar equation for the set

$$\bigcup_{j=1}^{\infty} \left(\bigcap_{k=j}^{\infty} A_k \right) = \{x \mid \text{ ?? }\}.$$

This set is designated $\liminf_{k \to \infty} A_k$ or simply $\liminf A_k$.

(c) Prove that $\liminf A_k \subset \limsup A_k$.

(d) Prove that $(\limsup A_k)^c = \liminf A_k^c$. Do this by two methods: First, apply De Morgan's laws to the formal expressions used to define $\limsup$ and $\liminf$; second, use the descriptions of $\limsup$ and $\liminf$ on the right sides of (a) and (b).

(e) Prove that $\limsup(A_k \cup B_k) = \limsup A_k \cup \limsup B_k$.

(f) Prove that $\liminf(A_k \cap B_k) = \liminf A_k \cap \liminf B_k$. Do this problem by combining (d) and (e).

(g) We say that the sequence of sets is *decreasing* if $A_1 \supset A_2 \supset A_3 \supset \cdots$. Prove that if the sequence is decreasing, then

$$\limsup A_k = \liminf A_k = \bigcap_{k=1}^{\infty} A_k.$$

(h) Prove the analogous result for an *increasing* sequence of sets.

Problem 3. Give an example of a decreasing sequence of nonempty sets in $\mathbb{R}$ whose intersection is empty.

B. Countable Sets

We say that a set is *countable* if it is finite or if there exists a one-to-one correspondence between it and the natural numbers. That is, the set A is countable if A is finite or if there exists a function $\mathbb{N} \xrightarrow{f} A$ which is one-to-one and onto. The function f is said to be a *bijection*. Another way of thinking about this is to say that A is countable if its members can be listed: $A = \{x_1, x_2, x_3, \ldots\}$. With this point of view, the set A is finite if and only if the list terminates. This idea of listing the members of A should be of great help to you in working the next few problems.

Problem 4. Suppose there exists a function $\mathbb{N} \xrightarrow{f} A$ which is onto. This means that for every $x \in A$ there exists $n \in \mathbb{N}$ such that $f(n) = x$. (The function f is said to be a *surjection*.) Prove that A is countable.

Problem 5. Suppose there exists a function $A \xrightarrow{f} \mathbb{N}$ which is one-to-one. This means that if x and y are in A and $x \neq y$, then $f(x) \neq f(y)$. (In this case f is said to be an *injection*.) Prove that A is countable.

Problem 6. Prove that any subset of a countable set is also countable.

Problem 7. Prove that any infinite set contains a countable infinite subset. (In your proof you will invoke the *axiom of choice*, probably without noticing it. Don't worry about it unless you want to.)

Problem 8. Prove that $\mathbb{N} \times \mathbb{N}$ is countable.

Problem 9. Let $\mathbb{Q}$ be the set of *rational* real numbers. Prove that $\mathbb{Q}$ is countable.

Problem 10. Prove that the union of a countable collection of countable sets is also countable.

It is true that $\mathbb{R}$ is not countable. Here is the elegant proof of Georg Cantor. Assume that $\mathbb{R}$ is countable. Then the open interval $(0, 1)$ is also countable, and can be written $(0, 1) = \{x_1, x_2, x_3, \ldots\}$. Write down the unique nonterminating decimal expansions of these numbers:

$$x_1 = 0.a_{11}a_{12}a_{13}\ldots,$$
$$x_2 = 0.a_{21}a_{22}a_{23}\ldots,$$

etc. Now define a number $y = 0.b_1 b_2 b_3 \ldots$ by setting

$$b_k = \begin{cases} 7 & \text{if } a_{kk} = 1, \\ 1 & \text{if } a_{kk} \neq 1, \end{cases}$$

for $k = 1, 2, 3, \ldots$.

Problem 11. Prove that $0 < y < 1$ and that $y \neq x_k$ for any k.

Thus there is a contradiction.
   We shall later see in Problem 2.13 a different proof that $\mathbb{R}$ is uncountable.

C. Topology

We use the Euclidean *norm* on $\mathbb{R}^n$,

$$|x| = \sqrt{x_1^2 + \cdots + x_n^2}.$$

Problem 12 (TRIANGLE INEQUALITY).
   Prove that

$$|x + y| \leq |x| + |y|.$$

(This property is important. If you have not seen a proof, you might have a difficult time with this problem. An algebraic proof may be given as follows: Square both sides to show that the triangle inequality is equivalent to

$$x_1 y_1 + \cdots + x_n y_n \leq |x||y|.$$

This inequality is known as the *Schwarz inequality*. By squaring again, show that it follows from the inequality

$$\sum_{i,j=1}^{n} x_i y_i x_j y_j \leq \sum_{i,j=1}^{n} x_i^2 y_j^2.$$

Finally show that the difference of the two sides of this inequality is

$$\sum_{1 \le i < j \le n} (x_i y_j - x_j y_i)^2.)$$

A different proof of the Schwarz inequality will be given in Section 13.E.

We shall be using the standard *vector space* structure of $\mathbb{R}^n$: $x + y$ and $-x$ are defined coordinatewise, as is ax for $a \in \mathbb{R}$ and $x \in \mathbb{R}^n$. The origin is $0 = (0, 0, \ldots, 0)$. Then $\mathbb{R}^n$ with the Euclidean norm is an example of what is called a *normed space*. Every normed space has a natural *metric*. In the case of $\mathbb{R}^n$ we denote this metric by d, so that the *distance* between x and y is $d(x, y) = |x - y|$.

Problem 13. Prove that $|x + y| = |x| + |y|$ if and only if one of x and y is a nonnegative scalar multiple of the other.

Problem 14. The metric d satisfies the following properties which characterize metrics:

(a) $d(x, y) \ge 0$.

(b) $d(x, y) = 0 \iff x = y$.

(c) $d(x, y) = d(y, x)$.

(d) $d(x, y) \le d(x, z) + d(z, y)$.

Prove these properties are valid.

Problem 15. Prove the inequality $|d(x, y) - d(x, z)| \le d(y, z)$.

For $x \in \mathbb{R}^n$ and $0 < r < \infty$ we define the *open ball with center x and radius r* to be the set

$$B(x, r) = \{y \in \mathbb{R}^n \mid d(x, y) < r\}.$$

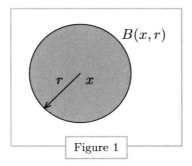

Figure 1

Problem 16. Prove that the open balls $B(x,r)$ and $B(x',r')$ are disjoint $\Longleftrightarrow r + r' \leq d(x, x')$.

Problem 17. Prove that $B(x,r) \subset B(x',r') \Longleftrightarrow d(x,x') \leq r' - r$.

Definition: Let $x \in A \subset \mathbb{R}^n$. Then x is an *interior point* of A if there exists $r > 0$ such that $B(x,r) \subset A$.

Definition: Let $A \subset \mathbb{R}^n$. Then A is an *open* set if every point of A is an interior point of A.

Problem 18. Establish the following properties of open sets:

(a) $\emptyset$ is open.

(b) $\mathbb{R}^n$ is open.

(c) The union of any collection of open sets is open.

(d) The intersection of any finite collection of open sets is open.

Because of these properties, the open sets are said to form a *topology* for $\mathbb{R}^n$.

We shall not require the actual definition of the word "topology," even though that is the title we have given to this section, but we shall sometimes use the word for emphasis.

Problem 19. Give an example illustrating why the adjective "finite" is needed in Problem 18(d).

We have a potentially embarrassing situation here. Namely, we first spoke of "open balls" and then of "open sets." But what if an open ball were not necessarily an open set? Then our terminology would be atrocious. The next problem shows that we haven't made such a mistake.

Problem 20. Prove that any open ball is an open set.

We have stressed this point for a reason: In Chapter 2 we shall meet several redundancies of this sort, and each time they arise we shall have to check for consistency.

Definition: If $A \subset \mathbb{R}^n$, the *interior* of A is the set of all the interior points of A. The interior of A is denoted A° or $\mathring{A}$:

$$A^\circ = \{x \mid x \text{ is an interior point of } A\}.$$

Problem 21. Prove the following properties of interior:

(a) A is open $\Longleftrightarrow A^\circ = A$.

(b) A° is open.

(c) $A^{\circ\circ} = A^\circ$.

(d) $(A \cap B)^\circ = A^\circ \cap B^\circ$.

(e) It is not true in general that $(A \cup B)^\circ = A^\circ \cup B^\circ$.

(f) $A^\circ = $ the union of all open subsets of A.

(g) $A^\circ = $ the largest open subset of A (i.e., A° is an open subset of A, and if B is any open subset of A, then $B \subset A^\circ$).

Definition: A subset of $\mathbb{R}^n$ is *closed* if (and only if) its complement is open.

De Morgan's laws imply immediately from Problem 18:

Problem 22. Prove the following properties of closed sets:

(a) $\mathbb{R}^n$ is closed.

(b) $\emptyset$ is closed.

(c) The intersection of any collection of closed sets is closed.

(d) The union of any finite collection of closed sets is closed.

Warning: Many students fall into the trap of thinking that if a set is not closed, then it must be open. Don't believe such nonsense! (Exhibit a counterexample.)

Definition: Let $x \in \mathbb{R}^n$ and $A \subset \mathbb{R}^n$. Then x is a *limit point* of A if for every $r > 0$ there exists $y \neq x$ such that $y \in A \cap B(x, r)$.

Problem 23. Prove that x is a limit point of $A \iff$ for every $r > 0$ the set $A \cap B(x, r)$ is infinite.

Problem 24. Prove that a set is closed $\iff$ it contains all its limit points.

Definition: For any $A \subset \mathbb{R}^n$, the *closure* of A is the set which consists of the points of A and the limit points of A. The closure of A is denoted A^- or $\overline{A}$:

$$A^- = \{x \mid x \in A \text{ or } x \text{ is a limit point of } A\}.$$

Problem 25. Prove that $x \in A^- \iff$ for every $r > 0$ the set $A \cap B(x, r) \neq \emptyset$.

Problem 26. Prove that $x \in A^- \iff$ there exists a sequence x_1, x_2, ... such that $x_k \in A$ for all k and $\lim_{k \to \infty} x_k = x$. (The last equation just means that $\lim_{k \to \infty} d(x_k, x) = 0$.)

Problem 27. Is it true in general that $A^{\circ c} = A^{c-}$? Justify your answer. That is, if the statement is true, prove it; if it is false, give a counterexample.

Problem 28. The seven assertions of Problem 21 all have analogs for closure. State them in the corresponding order and prove them.

Problem 29. Prove that

$$B(x, r)^- = \{y \mid d(x, y) \leq r\}$$

and
$$\{y \mid d(x,y) \le r\}^\circ = B(x,r).$$

Problem 30. Problem 29 shows that if A is an open ball, then $A^{-\circ} = A$. Is it true that for any open set A the equation $A^{-\circ} = A$ holds? Justify your answer.

Problem 31. Prove that if A is both open and closed, then $A = \emptyset$ or $A = \mathbb{R}^n$.

We shall need the following concept in the next section. We place the definition here, even though it does not, strictly speaking, belong to "topology."

Definition: A set $A \subset \mathbb{R}^n$ is *bounded* if A is contained in some open ball. It is easy to see that this is equivalent to the existence of a number $M > 0$ such that $x \in A \Rightarrow |x| \le M$.

Convention: Hereafter we shall strive for consistency in denoting open sets with the letter G and closed sets with the letter F. Obviously, any two letters would do, but tradition is on the side of G and F. In German the noun *Gebiet* means region, and in French the adjective *fermé* means closed.

D. Compact Sets

This subject is actually part of topology, but will be so important that we give it a separate section. We shall now give a definition with which you may not be familiar. Study it carefully and learn it well.

Definition: A set $A \subset \mathbb{R}^n$ is *compact* if the following statement is true:

> Whenever A is contained in a union of open sets, then A is contained in the union of finitely many of these sets.

In symbols:

Whenever $A \subset \bigcup_{i \in \mathcal{I}} G_i$ and each G_i is open, then there exist

$i_1, \ldots, i_N \in \mathcal{I}$ such that $A \subset \bigcup_{k=1}^{N} G_{i_k}$.

To help digest this definition, work the following easy

Problem 32. Prove that:

(a) $\emptyset$ is compact.

(b) Any finite set is compact.

(c) If A and B are compact, then so is $A \cup B$.

(d) Any finite union of compact sets is compact.

(e) $B(x, r)$ is not compact.

(f) $\mathbb{R}^n$ is not compact.

The definition of compact sets appears to be quite unwieldy. You may wonder whether such a strange condition could be worth anything. How could a person ever check for a given set A whether it satisfies the definition? Fortunately, there is a classic theorem which does just that. It is the main theorem of this chapter. The fact that every closed and bounded set is compact is the significant part of the theorem. Its proof makes *essential* use of the *completeness* property of the real number system, which could be phrased in the following way: Every bounded increasing sequence of real numbers converges to a limit.

Heine-Borel Covering Theorem: *A set in $\mathbb{R}^n$ is compact $\Longleftrightarrow$ it is closed and bounded.*

Proof: First we prove the easy implication: Assume A is compact. We must then prove that A is closed and bounded. In order to show that A is closed, we prove that A^c is open. Let $x \in A^c$. Then define the open sets

$$G_k = \{y \mid d(x, y) > k^{-1}\}, \qquad k = 1, 2, \dots .$$

Since the union of the G_k's is $\mathbb{R}^n \sim \{x\}$, it follows that A is contained in this union. Since A is compact, it must be contained in the union of a finite number of the G_k's. Since these sets form an increasing sequence, there exists k such that $A \subset G_k$. But this implies $G_k^c \subset A^c$. That is, $\{y \mid d(x, y) \leq k^{-1}\} \subset A^c$. Therefore, x is an interior point of A^c, and we have shown that A^c is open.

Problem 33. By a similar argument, prove that if A is compact, then A is bounded.

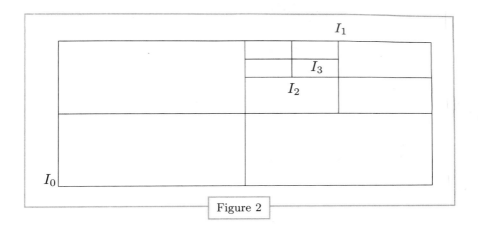

Figure 2

The converse is much more difficult, and is the useful part of the theorem. For its proof we assume A is closed and bounded, and we also assume that A is *not* compact. We seek to derive a contradiction. If A is not compact, then there exists a collection of open sets G_i such that $A \subset \bigcup_{i \in \mathcal{I}} G_i$, but no finite collection of the G_i's has a union which contains A. Since A is bounded, there exists a closed n-dimensional "rectangle" $I_0 = [a_1, b_1] \times \cdots \times [a_n, b_n]$ which contains A. The crux of the proof is to subdivide I_0 into 2^n congruent closed rectangles by using the midpoints of the factors $[a_i, b_i]$. See Figure 2, p.12 in case $n = 2$.

We notice that if each of these 2^n closed rectangles has an intersection with A which is contained in a finite union of the G_i's, then A itself has the same property. Since this is not true, there exists at least one of these rectangles, which we designate I_1, with the property that $A \cap I_1$ is not contained in a finite union of the G_i's. Now apply the same procedure to I_1, etc. As a result of this inductive construction, we obtain a sequence of closed rectangles $I_0 \supset I_1 \supset I_2 \cdots$ whose edges are half those of the preceding, having the property that for all k the intersection $A \cap I_k$ is not contained in a finite union of the G_i's. The *completeness* property of $\mathbb{R}$ implies that there exists $x \in \bigcap_{k=0}^{\infty} I_k$. Since each $A \cap I_k$ is not empty, there is also a sequence of points $x_k \in A \cap I_k$; since the sides of I_k converge to 0 as $k \to \infty$, also $\lim_{k \to \infty} x_k = x$. Thus, $x \in A^-$. Since A is closed, $x \in A$.

Now we are ready to demonstrate the contradiction. Since $x \in A$, there exists $i_0 \in \mathcal{I}$ such that $x \in G_{i_0}$. Since G_{i_0} is open and the I_k's are "converging" to x, there exists k such that $I_k \subset G_{i_0}$. But then $A \cap I_k \subset G_{i_0}$; and that is a contradiction, for $A \cap I_k$ is not contained in a finite union of the G_i's (and we have shown it is contained in just one G_{i_0}!).   **QED**

In Chapter 2 we shall be considering compact subsets of open sets. In such situations we need to assert that the compact set is "well inside" the open set. The next three results treat this problem.

Lemma: *Let K be compact and let K be covered by a collection of open sets G_i:*

$$K \subset \bigcup_{i \in \mathcal{I}} G_i.$$

Then there exists $\epsilon > 0$ with the following property: For every $x \in K$ there exists $i \in \mathcal{I}$ such that

$$B(x, \epsilon) \subset G_i.$$

(This number ϵ is called a Lebesgue number *for the covering $\{G_i \mid i \in \mathcal{I}\}$ of K.)*

Proof: If $x \in K$, then there exists $i(x) \in \mathcal{I}$ such that $x \in G_{i(x)}$. Since the latter set is open, there exists $r(x) > 0$ such that

$$B(x, 2r(x)) \subset G_{i(x)}.$$

Obviously, K is contained in the union of the open balls $B(x, r(x))$ for $x \in K$. Since K is compact, there exist $x_1, \ldots, x_N \in K$ such that

$$K \subset \bigcup_{j=1}^{N} B(x_j, r(x_j)).$$

Let $\epsilon = $ minimum of $r(x_j)$ for $1 \leq j \leq N$.

Now suppose $x \in K$. Then there exists j such that $x \in B(x_j, r(x_j))$. Thus, $d(x, x_j) < r(x_j) \leq 2r(x_j) - \epsilon$. Therefore, Problem 17 implies

$$B(x, \epsilon) \subset B(x_j, 2r(x_j)) \subset G_{i(x_j)}.$$

                                                                      QED

Corollary: *Let K be a compact set and G an open set, with $K \subset G$. Then there exists $\epsilon > 0$ such that for all $x \in K$,*

$$B(x, \epsilon) \subset G.$$

Proof: Apply the lemma with the single open set G.   **QED**

Corollary: Let K be a compact set and F a closed set, with $K \cap F = \emptyset$. Then there exists $\epsilon > 0$ such that for every $x \in K$, $y \in F$,

$$d(x, y) \geq \epsilon.$$

Proof: Apply the preceeding corollary with $G = F^c$. Thus, there exists $\epsilon > 0$ such that for every $x \in K$, $B(x, \epsilon) \subset F^c$. This implies that for every $y \in F$, $y \notin B(x, \epsilon)$. That is, $d(x, y) \geq \epsilon$.   **QED**

Problem 34. Show that there exist disjoint closed sets A, B in $\mathbb{R}$ such that there is no positive ϵ with the property that $x \in A$, $y \in B \implies d(x, y) \geq \epsilon$.

Problem 35. Prove that if F_1 and F_2 are disjoint closed sets in $\mathbb{R}^n$, then there exist disjoint open sets G_1 and G_2 such that $F_1 \subset G_1$ and $F_2 \subset G_2$.

We conclude this section with the important

Bolzano-Weierstrass Theorem: Every bounded infinite subset of $\mathbb{R}^n$ has a limit point.

Proof: We prove this by contradiction. Suppose $A \subset \mathbb{R}^n$ is bounded and has no limit point. Then we shall show that A is finite. Since A has *no* limit points, Problem 24 implies that A is closed. The Heine-Borel theorem implies that A is compact. Now if $x \in A$, then since x is not a limit point of A, there exists an open ball B_x with center x such that $A \cap B_x$ consists of just the point x. Since $A \subset \bigcup_{x \in A} B_x$ and A is compact, there exist $x_1, \ldots, x_N \in A$ such that $A \subset \bigcup_{k=1}^{N} B_{x_k}$ (or else $A = \emptyset$). But then the choice of the B_x's shows that $A = \{x_1, \ldots, x_N\}$.   **QED**

Problem 36. Use this theorem to prove the following version of it: *Every bounded sequence in $\mathbb{R}^n$ has a convergent subsequence.*

E. Continuity

Definition: Assume A is a nonempty subset of $\mathbb{R}^n$ and let $f : A \to \mathbb{R}^m$ be a function defined on A with values in $\mathbb{R}^m$. Let $x_0 \in A$. Then f is *continuous at* x_0 if for every $\epsilon > 0$ there exists $\delta > 0$ such that $x \in A$ and $d(x, x_0) < \delta$ imply $d(f(x), f(x_0)) < \epsilon$.

Problem 37. In the situation described in the definition, f can be expressed in terms of the coordinates in $\mathbb{R}^m$ as $f(x) = (f_1(x), \ldots, f_m(x))$. Prove that f is continuous at $x_0 \Longleftrightarrow$ all the components $f_1, \ldots, f_m$ are continuous at x_0.

Definition: In case $f : A \to \mathbb{R}^m$ is continuous at x_0 for every $x_0 \in A$, then f is *continuous on* A. For short, f is also said to be *continuous* if A is understood.

Problem 38. Let $f : \mathbb{R}^2 \to \mathbb{R}$ be the function given by

$$
f(x) = \begin{cases} \dfrac{x_1^2 x_2}{x_1^4 + x_2^2} & \text{if } x \neq 0, \\[2mm] 0 & \text{if } x = 0. \end{cases}
$$

(a) Prove that for each $x \in \mathbb{R}^2$, $f(tx)$ is a continuous function of $t \in \mathbb{R}$.

(b) Prove that f is not continuous at 0.

Problem 39. Why does Problem 15 imply that for any fixed $x \in \mathbb{R}^n$, the function $f(y) = d(x, y)$ is continuous on $\mathbb{R}^n$?

The first result will show that the continuity of f on A can be described completely in terms of open sets. Before stating it, some notation is required. If $f : A \to B$ is any function and $X \subset A$, then

$$
f(X) = \{f(x) \mid x \in X\},
$$

and if $Y \subset B$, then

$$
f^{-1}(Y) = \{x \in A \mid f(x) \in Y\}.
$$

The set $f(X)$ is called the *image* of X and the set $f^{-1}(Y)$ is called the *inverse image* of Y.

Problem 40. Prove the following properties:

(a)
$$f^{-1}\left(\bigcup_{i\in\mathcal{I}} Y_i\right) = \bigcup_{i\in\mathcal{I}} f^{-1}(Y_i).$$

(b)
$$f^{-1}\left(\bigcap_{i\in\mathcal{I}} Y_i\right) = \bigcap_{i\in\mathcal{I}} f^{-1}(Y_i).$$

(c)
$$f\left(\bigcup_{i\in\mathcal{I}} X_i\right) = \bigcup_{i\in\mathcal{I}} f(X_i).$$

(d)
$$f\left(\bigcap_{i\in\mathcal{I}} X_i\right) \subset \bigcap_{i\in\mathcal{I}} f(X_i).$$

(e)   The inclusion in (d) might not be equality.

Problem 41. Prove the following properties for $f : A \to B$.

(a) $f(f^{-1}(Y)) = Y \cap f(A)$.

(b) $f^{-1}(f(X)) \supset X$.

(c) Equality holds in (b) if f is one-to-one.

Theorem: *Let $A \subset \mathbb{R}^n$ and let $f : A \to \mathbb{R}^m$. Then f is continuous on $A \iff$ for every open set $G \subset \mathbb{R}^m$ there exists an open set $H \subset \mathbb{R}^n$ such that $f^{-1}(G) = A \cap H$.*

Proof: First assume f has this property. Let $x_0 \in A$ and let $\epsilon > 0$. Then $B(f(x_0), \epsilon)$ is an open subset of $\mathbb{R}^m$, so there exists an open set $H \subset \mathbb{R}^n$ such that $f^{-1}(B(f(x_0), \epsilon)) = A \cap H$. That is,

$$\{x \in A \mid d(f(x), f(x_0)) < \epsilon\} = A \cap H.$$

This shows that $x_0 \in H$. Since H is open, there exists $\delta > 0$ such that $B(x_0, \delta) \subset H$. Therefore,

$$x \in A \quad \text{and} \quad d(x, x_0) < \delta \Rightarrow x \in A \cap H$$
$$\Rightarrow d(f(x), f(x_0)) < \epsilon.$$

Therefore, f is continuous at x_0. Since x_0 is arbitrary, f is continuous on A.

Conversely, assume f is continuous on A, and let $G \subset \mathbb{R}^m$ be open. For any $x \in f^{-1}(G)$, $f(x) \in G$ and there exists $\epsilon(x) > 0$ such that $B(f(x), \epsilon(x)) \subset G$. Since f is continuous at x, there exists $\delta(x) > 0$ such that

$$y \in A \quad \text{and} \quad d(x, y) < \delta(x) \Rightarrow d(f(x), f(y)) < \epsilon(x).$$

Define

$$H = \bigcup \{ B(x, \delta(x)) \mid x \in f^{-1}(G) \}.$$

As it is a union of open sets (balls), H is open. Clearly, if $y \in f^{-1}(G)$, then $y \in A$ and $y \in B(y, \delta(y)) \subset H$. This proves that $f^{-1}(G) \subset A \cap H$. On the other hand, suppose $y \in A \cap H$. Then there exists $x \in f^{-1}(G)$ such that $y \in B(x, \delta(x))$. Therefore, $d(f(x), f(y)) < \epsilon(x)$, proving that $f(y) \in G$. That is, $y \in f^{-1}(G)$. This proves that $A \cap H \subset f^{-1}(G)$.

QED

Problem 42. Prove that the theorem remains valid if the word "open" is replaced by the word "closed" in both occurrences.

Problem 43. Give an example of a continuous function $f : \mathbb{R} \to \mathbb{R}$ for which G open does not imply $f(G)$ is open.

Problem 44. Give an example of a continuous function $f : \mathbb{R} \to \mathbb{R}$ for which F closed does not imply $f(F)$ is closed.

Definition: Suppose $A \subset \mathbb{R}^n$ and $B \subset \mathbb{R}^m$ and $f : A \to B$ is a bijection of A onto B. If both f and its inverse f^{-1} are continuous functions, f is said to be a *homeomorphism* of A onto B.

Problem 45. Suppose A and B are open sets and f is a homeomorphism of A onto B. (A deep theorem of topology then implies that $m = n$.) Prove that f establishes a bijection of the open subsets of A with the open subsets of B.

Problem 46. Repeat Problem 45 with the word "open" replaced by "closed."

A significant modification of the statement of Problem 44 produces an important result, which we now state.

> **Theorem:** *Let $A \subset \mathbb{R}^n$ and let $f : A \to \mathbb{R}^m$ be continuous. Let K be a compact subset of A. Then $f(K)$ is compact.*

Proof: The restriction of f to the compact set K is continuous on K. Therefore, we do not need to consider the set A at all, and we might as well assume $A = K$. Suppose $f(K)$ is covered by open sets:

$$f(K) \subset \bigcup_{i \in \mathcal{I}} G_i,$$

where each $G_i \subset \mathbb{R}^m$ is open. Problems 41(b) and 40(a) imply

$$K \subset f^{-1}(f(K))$$
$$\subset \bigcup_{i \in \mathcal{I}} f^{-1}(G_i).$$

By the preceding theorem, there exist open sets $H_i \subset \mathbb{R}^n$ for all $i \in \mathcal{I}$ such that $f^{-1}(G_i) = K \cap H_i$. Therefore,

$$K \subset \bigcup_{i \in \mathcal{I}} K \cap H_i$$
$$\subset \bigcup_{i \in \mathcal{I}} H_i.$$

Since K is compact, there exist $i_1, \ldots, i_N \in \mathcal{I}$ such that

$$K \subset \bigcup_{k=1}^{N} H_{i_k}.$$

Problems 40(c) and 41(a) imply

$$f(K) = f\left(\bigcup_{k=1}^{N} K \cap H_{i_k} \right)$$
$$= \bigcup_{k=1}^{N} f(K \cap H_{i_k})$$
$$= \bigcup_{k=1}^{N} f(f^{-1}(G_{i_k}))$$
$$= \bigcup_{k=1}^{N} G_{i_k} \cap f(K)$$
$$\subset \bigcup_{k=1}^{N} G_{i_k}.$$

This shows that $f(K)$ satisfies the definition of compactness.   **QED**

Problem 47. Give an example of a continuous function $f : \mathbb{R} \to \mathbb{R}$ for which K compact does not imply $f^{-1}(K)$ is compact.

Corollary: *Let $K \subset \mathbb{R}^n$ be compact and let $f : K \to \mathbb{R}$ be continuous. Then f attains a maximum and a minimum value on K.*

Proof: Let $a = \sup\{f(x) \mid x \in K\}$. Since $f(K)$ is compact, it is bounded. Therefore, $a \in \mathbb{R}$. Since $f(K)$ is compact, it is closed. Therefore, $a \in f(K)$. That is, there exists $x_0 \in K$ such that $a = f(x_0)$. Since $a \geq f(x)$ for all $x \in K$, the statement about the maximum value is proved. Obviously, the existence of a minimum value is assured as well.
                                                                          QED

We conclude this section with a brief discussion of uniform continuity.

Definition: Let $A \subset \mathbb{R}^n$ and $f : A \to \mathbb{R}^m$. Then f is *uniformly continuous (on A)* if for every $\epsilon > 0$ there exists $\delta > 0$ such that x and y in A and $d(x, y) < \delta$ imply $d(f(x), f(y)) < \epsilon$.

Problem 48. Obviously, a uniformly continuous function is continuous. Give an example of a bounded continuous function $f : \mathbb{R} \to \mathbb{R}$ which is not uniformly continuous.

Problem 49. A function $f : A \to \mathbb{R}^m$ is said to satisfy a *Lipschitz condition* if there exists a constant C such that for each x and y in A

$$d(f(x), f(y)) \leq C d(x, y).$$

(See Problem 16.23.) Prove that such a function is uniformly continuous.

Theorem: *Let K be compact and let $f : K \to \mathbb{R}^m$ be continuous. Then f is uniformly continuous.*

Proof: Let $\epsilon > 0$. For every $x \in K$ there exists $\delta(x) > 0$ such that

$$y \in K \quad \text{and} \quad d(x, y) < \delta(x) \Rightarrow d(f(x), f(y)) < \tfrac{1}{2}\epsilon.$$

Obviously,

$$K \subset \bigcup\{B(x, \tfrac{1}{2}\delta(x)) \mid x \in K\}.$$

Since K is compact, there exist $x_1, \ldots, x_N \in K$ such that

$$K \subset \bigcup_{k=1}^{N} B(x_k, \tfrac{1}{2}\delta(x_k)).$$

Let

$$\delta = \min\{\tfrac{1}{2}\delta(x_1), \ldots, \tfrac{1}{2}\delta(x_N)\}.$$

Now suppose x, $y \in K$ and $d(x,y) < \delta$. Since $x \in K$, there exists k such that $x \in B(x_k, \tfrac{1}{2}\delta(x_k))$. Since $d(x,y) < \delta \leq \tfrac{1}{2}\delta(x_k)$, also $y \in B(x_k, \delta(x_k))$. Therefore, we have both the inequalities

$$d(f(x), f(x_k)) < \tfrac{1}{2}\epsilon,$$
$$d(f(y), f(x_k)) < \tfrac{1}{2}\epsilon.$$

The triangle inequality implies

$$d(f(x), f(y)) < \epsilon.$$

This establishes the uniform continuity.   **QED**

F. The Distance Function

Definition: Assume A is a nonempty subset of $\mathbb{R}^n$. The *distance* from x to A is the number

$$d(x, A) = \inf\{d(x,y) \mid y \in A\}.$$

Proposition: *If A is a nonempty subset of $\mathbb{R}^n$ and $x \in \mathbb{R}^n$, then there exists $x_0 \in A^-$ such that*

$$d(x, A) = d(x, x_0).$$

Proof: By definition of $d(x, A)$, there exists $y_k \in A$ such that

$$\lim_{k \to \infty} d(x, y_k) = d(x, A).$$

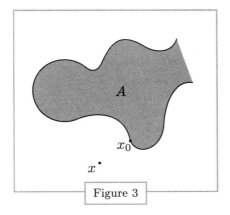

Figure 3

In particular, $d(x, y_k)$ is bounded independently of k. Since the sequence y_k is bounded, the Bolzano-Weierstrass theorem (rather, Problem 36) implies that a subsequence converges. Let us rename the subsequence and call it y_k again. Thus, there exists $x_0 \in \mathbb{R}^n$ such that $\lim\limits_{k \to \infty} y_k = x_0$. Since $y_k \in A$, it follows that $x_0 \in A^-$. And since $d(x, y)$ is a continuous function of y (by Problem 39), $d(x, x_0) = \lim\limits_{k \to \infty} d(x, y_k) = d(x, A)$. **QED**

Corollary: *If A is closed and nonempty, there exists $x_0 \in A$ such that*

$$d(x, A) = d(x, x_0).$$

Problem 50. Prove that $x \in A^- \iff d(x, A) = 0$.

Problem 51. Prove that if $\emptyset \neq A \subset B$, then $d(x, A) \geq d(x, B)$.

Problem 52. Prove that $d(x, A) = d(x, A^-)$.

Problem 53. Prove that $A^- = B^- \iff d(x, A) = d(x, B)$ for every $x \in \mathbb{R}^n$.

Proposition: *Assume $A \neq \emptyset$. Then $d(x, A)$ is a continuous function of x.*

Proof: Given x, $x' \in \mathbb{R}^n$, the triangle inequality shows that for every $y \in A$

$$d(x, A) \leq d(x, y) \leq d(x, x') + d(x', y).$$

This shows that $d(x, A) - d(x, x')$ is a lower bound for the set $\{d(x', y) \mid y \in A\}$. Therefore, the definition of $d(x', A)$ implies

$$d(x, A) - d(x, x') \leq d(x', A).$$

That is,

$$d(x, A) - d(x', A) \leq d(x, x').$$

By symmetry,

$$d(x', A) - d(x, A) \leq d(x', x).$$

The last two inequalities are equivalent to

$$\mid d(x, A) - d(x', A) \mid \ \leq \ d(x, x').$$

QED

Notice that the last inequality is a generalization of Problem 15.

Theorem: *Assume F is closed and G is open with $F \subset G \subset \mathbb{R}^n$. Then there exists a continuous function $f : \mathbb{R}^n \to \mathbb{R}$ such that*

$$\begin{aligned}
0 \leq f(x) \leq 1 \qquad &\textit{for all } x \in \mathbb{R}^n, \\
f(x) = 1 \qquad &\textit{for all } x \in F, \\
f(x) = 0 \qquad &\textit{for all } x \in G^c.
\end{aligned}$$

Proof: The theorem is trivial if either F or G^c is empty. Eliminating this case, we simply define

$$f(x) = \frac{d(x, G^c)}{d(x, G^c) + d(x, F)}.$$

The continuity of f follows from the preceding proposition and the fact that the denominator never vanishes — for if $d(x, F) = 0$, then $x \in F$ by Problem 50, and thus $x \in G$ and thus $d(x, G^c) > 0$ (also by Problem 50).

QED

Definition: The function f in the above theorem is called an *Urysohn function* for the pair of sets $F \subset G$.

Problem 54. Use an Urysohn function to give a solution of Problem 35.

Another important number associated with a set in $\mathbb{R}^n$ is its diameter:

Definition: Let A be a nonempty subset of $\mathbb{R}^n$. The *diameter* of A is

$$\text{diam}(A) = \sup\{d(x,y) \mid x,y \in A\}.$$

Of course, $0 \leq \text{diam}(A) \leq \infty$.

Problem 55. Prove that $\text{diam}(A) = 0 \Longleftrightarrow A$ consists of a single point.

Problem 56. Prove that $\text{diam}(A) < \infty \Longleftrightarrow A$ is bounded.

Problem 57. Prove that $\text{diam}(A) = \text{diam}(A^-)$.

Problem 58. Prove that $\text{diam}(B(x,r)) = 2r$.

Problem 59. Prove that if $\text{diam}(A) < \infty$, then there exist x, $y \in A^-$ such that $\text{diam}(A) = d(x,y)$.

Problem 60. Prove that if $0 < d = \text{diam}(A) < \infty$, then there exists $x \in \mathbb{R}^n$ such that $A \subset B(x,d)^-$.

The preceding problem does not provide the best possible result. A sharp result is Jung's theorem, which states that

$$A \subset B\left(x, \sqrt{\frac{n}{2(n+1)}}\, d\right)^-.$$

Problem 61. Show that Jung's theorem gives the best possible result in case A is an equilateral triangle in $\mathbb{R}^2$.

Problem 62. Show that Jung's theorem gives the best possible result in case A is a regular tetrahedron in $\mathbb{R}^3$.

Jung's theorem is not extremely difficult to prove. A proof can be found in the book of Federer (see the Preface), p. 200.

Lebesgue Measure on $\mathbb{R}^n$

2

A. Construction

Before we shall be ready to study integration, we shall need to possess a method for measuring subsets of $\mathbb{R}^n$. This method will have to be quantitative and will have to be carefully defined. It will not be possible to measure every subset of $\mathbb{R}^n$, but a large class of sets will turn out to be "measurable." For such a measurable set $A \subset \mathbb{R}^n$ the measure of A will be a nonnegative real number or ∞, and will be denoted $\lambda(A)$. This number $\lambda(A)$ will be called *the Lebesgue measure* of A.

Since we shall usually work in the context of subsets of $\mathbb{R}^n$ with n fixed, the notation $\lambda(A)$ will not have to indicate explicitly the value of n. In the rare exceptions to this situation, the notation $\lambda_n(A)$ will be used. In case $n = 1$, the measure $\lambda(A)$ should be thought of as the *length* of $A \subset \mathbb{R}$. If $n = 2$, $\lambda(A)$ is the *area* of $A \subset \mathbb{R}^2$. If $n = 3$, $\lambda(A)$ is the *volume* of $A \subset \mathbb{R}^3$. These statements will become clear after the initial definition of $\lambda(A)$ for special rectangles.

The definition of $\lambda(A)$ will now be given. We shall give the definition in six stages, progressing to more and more complicated classes of subsets of $\mathbb{R}^n$.

STAGE 0: The empty set.

$$\lambda(\emptyset) = 0.$$

STAGE 1: Special rectangles.

We use the notation $[a, b]$ for the closed interval $a \leq x \leq b$ in $\mathbb{R}$. In $\mathbb{R}^n$ a *special rectangle* is a set of the form

$$I = [a_1, b_1] \times \cdots \times [a_n, b_n]$$
$$= \{x \in \mathbb{R}^n \mid a_i \leq x_i \leq b_i \quad \text{for } 1 \leq i \leq n\}.$$

Define

$$\lambda(I) = (b_1 - a_1) \ldots (b_n - a_n).$$

Here is a figure for $n = 2$:

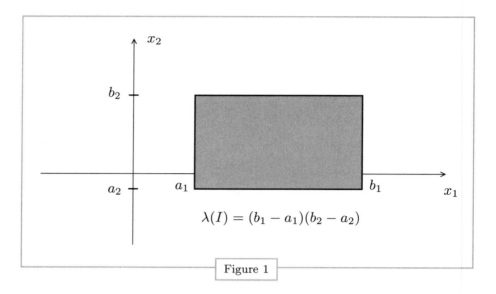

$$\lambda(I) = (b_1 - a_1)(b_2 - a_2)$$

Figure 1

Of course the formula for $\lambda(I)$ is purely a definition. At this stage of the construction we do not give a formula for $\lambda(I)$ in case I is a rectangle which is not special, as in this figure:

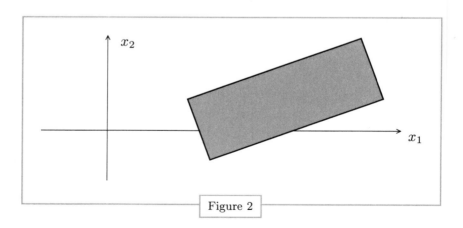

Figure 2

We shall eventually be able to calculate the measure of any rectangle, of course, but at this primitive stage of the theory it is necessary to confine our discussion to special rectangles.

Problem 1. Let I be a special rectangle in $\mathbb{R}^n$. Prove that the following conditions are equivalent:

(a) $\lambda(I) = 0$.

(b) $I^\circ = \emptyset$.

(c) I is contained in an affine subspace of $\mathbb{R}^n$ having dimension smaller than n. (An affine subspace is any set of the form $\{x_0 + x \mid x \in E\}$, where $x_0 \in \mathbb{R}^n$ is fixed and E is a subspace of the vector space $\mathbb{R}^n$. Its dimension is equal to the dimension of E.)

STAGE 2:   Special polygons.

A *special polygon* is a finite union of special rectangles each of which has nonzero measure. (Or, each of which has nonzero edge lengths. By the way, a special rectangle which is degenerate in the sense of Problem 1 is not called a special polygon.) Here is an example of a special polygon in $\mathbb{R}^2$:

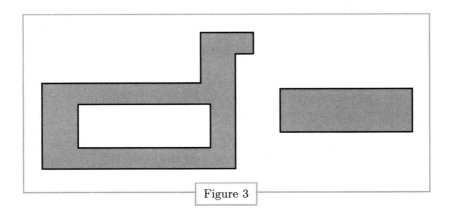

Figure 3

Notice that all the special polygons have "sides" parallel to the coordinate axes. Thus, the set in Figure 2 is not a special polygon.

Also notice that the special polygons are *compact* subsets of $\mathbb{R}^n$. This is so because we chose the special rectangles to be closed and bounded sets; therefore the special polygons also are closed and bounded. The Heine-Borel theorem implies that they are compact.

Now we are going to define the measure of a special polygon. If P is a special polygon, first decompose P into a finite union of *nonoverlapping* special rectangles:

$$P = \bigcup_{k=1}^{N} I_k,$$

where the rectangles are *nonoverlapping* in the sense that their interiors are disjoint. Then define

$$\lambda(P) = \sum_{k=1}^{N} \lambda(I_k).$$

This definition is obviously motivated by two considerations: We want the measure function λ to be additive on disjoint unions, and we expect that the boundaries of the rectangles I_k will have no effect on the measure of P.

But there are two difficulties with this definition. First, we must check that it is indeed possible to express every special polygon as a finite union of nonoverlapping rectangles. Second, we must prove that the expression defining $\lambda(P)$ yields a number which is independent of the particular expression of P as a finite union of nonoverlapping special rectangles. These are important considerations. We would otherwise have no candidate at all for the number $\lambda(P)$, and even if we did have, we would not know that $\lambda(P)$ represented an intrinsic property of P. We could possibly produce several different numbers which we would like to call $\lambda(P)$. That would be chaos. Happily, it is a completely elementary task to show that the definition of $\lambda(P)$ does make sense (we say that $\lambda(P)$ is *well defined*). But to write out all the details is extremely tedious. For this reason, and because it is intuitively clear that $\lambda(P)$ is well defined, I have relegated the proof to the appendix to this chapter. It is not expected that anyone will ever read this appendix, but it is there as a service to honesty. The important things are that (1) you understand how $\lambda(P)$ is defined and why it is defined that way, (2) you intuitively understand the definition, and (3) you realize there is a minor problem in proving that the definition makes sense.

At each stage of the construction, we want to list some of the important properties which λ enjoys up to that moment. At the present time we mention just two:

Properties

P1 $P_1 \subset P_2 \implies \lambda(P_1) \le \lambda(P_2)$.

P2 P_1 and P_2 nonoverlapping $\implies \lambda(P_1 \cup P_2) = \lambda(P_1) + \lambda(P_2)$.

The proof of these properties has also been placed in the appendix, since they seem intuitively clear.

Problem 2. In the plane $\mathbb{R}^2$ consider the unit square $I = [0,1] \times [0,1]$. Partition I into nine nonoverlapping squares of side $\frac{1}{3}$, as shown in Figure 4. Let G_1 be the middle one of these nine squares, taken to be *open*: $G_1 = (\frac{1}{3}, \frac{2}{3}) \times (\frac{1}{3}, \frac{2}{3})$. Then $I \sim G_1$ is a special polygon represented as eight nonoverlapping squares, with $\lambda(I \sim G_1) = \frac{8}{9}$. Now take each of the remaining eight closed squares, partition each into nine squares as in the first step, and let G_2 be the union of the eight open middle squares. $I \sim G_1 \sim G_2$ is a special polygon represented as 64 nonoverlapping squares, with $\lambda(I \sim G_1 \sim G_2) = \frac{64}{81}$.

The problem is for you to describe the general stage of a construction which begins like Figure 4, and calculate the measure of the special polygon which remains after N steps, $I \sim \bigcup_{k=1}^{N} G_k$. (We shall soon return to this type of example.)

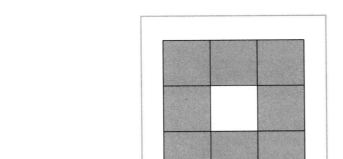

Figure 4

STAGE 3:   Open sets.

We now return to our construction of λ by defining the measure of an arbitrary open set in $\mathbb{R}^n$. We do this by "approximating" the set from within by polygons. This procedure works well because of the topological nature of open sets.

If $G \subset \mathbb{R}^n$ is an open set and if $G \neq \emptyset$, we define

$$\lambda(G) = \sup\{\lambda(P) \mid P \subset G, P \text{ a special polygon}\}.$$

Since G is open and nonempty, it has interior points, and thus there are polygons contained in G. It is therefore possible to consider the least upper bound of the set of numbers $\lambda(P)$ for $P \subset G$. In case this set is bounded, then $0 < \lambda(G) < \infty$. In case it is not a bounded set of numbers, then we interpret the definition to produce $\lambda(G) = \infty$. In particular, $\lambda(\mathbb{R}^n) = \infty$.

Problem 3. If G is open and P is a special polygon with $P \subset G$, prove there exists a special polygon P' such that $P \subset P' \subset G$ and $\lambda(P) < \lambda(P')$.

Problem 4.

(a) Prove that if G is a bounded open set, then $\lambda(G) < \infty$.

(b) In the plane $\mathbb{R}^2$ let

$$G = \{(x, y) \mid 1 < x \text{ and } 0 < y < \frac{1}{x}\}.$$

Prove that $\lambda(G) = \infty$.

(c) In the plane $\mathbb{R}^2$ let

$$G = \{(x, y) \mid 0 < x \text{ and } 0 < y < e^{-x}\}.$$

Prove that $\lambda(G) = 1$.

(d) In the plane $\mathbb{R}^2$ let

$$G = \{(x, y) \mid 1 < x \text{ and } 0 < y < x^{-a}\},$$

where a is a real number satisfying $a > 1$. Prove that $\lambda(G) = \frac{1}{a-1}$.

In working this problem, you must play by the rules. You are not allowed to use the methods of calculus to the extent that you work (d), say, by writing

$$\lambda(G) = \int_1^\infty x^{-a} dx = \frac{1}{a-1}.$$

One of the results of this theory will enable you to do this, but at this stage you must use the actual definition of $\lambda(G)$. The purpose of the problem is to give you practice with the definition.

Properties

O1 $0 \leq \lambda(G) \leq \infty$.

O2 $\lambda(G) = 0 \Longleftrightarrow G = \emptyset$.

O3 $\lambda(\mathbb{R}^n) = \infty$.

O4 $G_1 \subset G_2 \Rightarrow \lambda(G_1) \leq \lambda(G_2)$.

O5 $\lambda \left(\bigcup_{k=1}^{\infty} G_k \right) \leq \sum_{k=1}^{\infty} \lambda(G_k)$.

O6 If the open sets G_k are disjoint,

$$\lambda \left(\bigcup_{k=1}^{\infty} G_k \right) = \sum_{k=1}^{\infty} \lambda(G_k).$$

O7 If P is a special polygon, $\lambda(P) = \lambda(P^\circ)$.

Proof:

O1 Trivial.

O2 If $G \neq \emptyset$, then there exists a special polygon $P \subset G$. Thus $\lambda(G) \geq \lambda(P) > 0$.

O3 For any $0 < a < \infty$, $[-a, a] \times \cdots \times [-a, a]$ is a special polygon contained in $\mathbb{R}^n$. Thus $\lambda(\mathbb{R}^n) \geq (2a)^n$ for all a.

O4 This is an easy principle which will be employed several times. Since $G_1 \subset G_2$,

$$\{\lambda(P) \mid P \subset G_1\} \subset \{\lambda(P) \mid P \subset G_2\}.$$

Since $\lambda(G_2)$ is the least upper of the set of numbers on the right, it is an upper bound for the same set. Therefore, $\lambda(G_2)$ is also an upper bound for the *smaller* set on the left. As $\lambda(G_1)$ is the least upper bound of this set, $\lambda(G_1) \leq \lambda(G_2)$.

O5 The proof of this property contains a beautiful argument; as it should, since this property has significant depth. Notice first that the property at least makes sense, since $\bigcup_{k=1}^{\infty} G_k$, being a union of open sets, is also an open set.

Let P be any special polygon which is allowed to enter the definition of the measure of the union:

$$P \subset \bigcup_{k=1}^{\infty} G_k.$$

Since P is compact, the lemma on p.13 guarantees the existence of a *Lebesgue number* $\epsilon > 0$ for the covering of P by the G_k's. Therefore, for every $x \in P$ there exists k such that

$$B(x, \epsilon) \subset G_k.$$

By further subdivisions of the rectangles which constitute P (if necessary), we can assume that

$$P = \bigcup_{j=1}^{N} I_j,$$

where the I_j's are nonoverlapping rectangles each of which has diameter less than 2ϵ. Consider any I_j, and denote its center by x_j. Then

$$I_j \subset B(x_j, \epsilon) \subset G_k$$

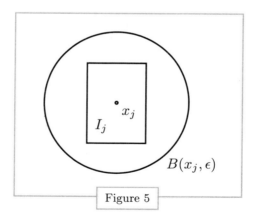

Figure 5

for some k. Thus, each I_j is entirely contained in at least one of the open sets G_k. Now let P_1 be the union of all I_j's such that $I_j \subset G_1$. In general, we define P_k to be the union of all I_j's such that $I_j \subset G_k$

and $I_j \not\subset G_1, G_2, \ldots$, or G_{k-1}. Since each I_j is contained in one of $G_1, G_2, \ldots$, $P = \bigcup\limits_{k=1}^{\infty} P_k$. As each I_j can belong to just one of the P_k's, at most N of the P_k's are nonempty. The nonempty P_k's are polygons and $P_k \subset G_k$. Also the P_k's are nonoverlapping special polygons. Therefore, Property P2 implies

$$\lambda(P) = \sum_k \lambda(P_k) \le \sum_k \lambda(G_k).$$

The notation $\sum\limits_k$ signifies a finite summation which includes only the terms with $P_k \ne \emptyset$. Therefore,

$$\lambda(P) \le \sum_{k=1}^{\infty} \lambda(G_k).$$

Since P is an arbitrary special polygon contained in $\bigcup\limits_{k=1}^{\infty} G_k$, we obtain by definition

$$\lambda\left(\bigcup_{k=1}^{\infty} G_k\right) \le \sum_{k=1}^{\infty} \lambda(G_k).$$

O6 Here is an easy argument of a very standard nature. Suppose that $P_1, \ldots, P_N$ are arbitrary special polygons such that $P_k \subset G_k$ for $1 \le k \le N$. Then the P_k's are disjoint since the G_k's are, and $\bigcup\limits_{k=1}^{N} P_k \subset \bigcup\limits_{k=1}^{N} G_k \subset \bigcup\limits_{k=1}^{\infty} G_k$. Thus Property P2 implies

$$\sum_{k=1}^{N} \lambda(P_k) = \lambda\left(\bigcup_{k=1}^{N} P_k\right) \le \lambda\left(\bigcup_{k=1}^{\infty} G_k\right).$$

Since $P_k \subset G_k$ is arbitrary,

$$\sum_{k=1}^{N} \lambda(G_k) \le \lambda\left(\bigcup_{k=1}^{\infty} G_k\right).$$

Since N is arbitrary,

$$\sum_{k=1}^{\infty} \lambda(G_k) \le \lambda\left(\bigcup_{k=1}^{\infty} G_k\right).$$

This finishes the proof, as O5 contains the reverse inequality.

O7 First we show that for a special rectangle I, $\lambda(I^\circ) \geq \lambda(I)$. It is clear that for any $\epsilon > 0$ there exists a rectangle I' just slightly smaller than I in the sense that

$$I' \subset I^\circ \quad \text{and} \quad \lambda(I') > \lambda(I) - \epsilon.$$

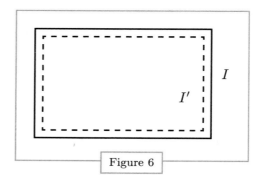

Figure 6

Thus, $\lambda(I^\circ) \geq \lambda(I') > \lambda(I) - \epsilon$. Since ϵ is arbitrary, we conclude that $\lambda(I^\circ) \geq \lambda(I)$. Now if P is a special polygon represented with nonoverlapping special rectangles in the form

$$P = \bigcup_{k=1}^{N} I_k,$$

then $P^\circ \supset \displaystyle\bigcup_{k=1}^{N} I_k^\circ$, a disjoint union, so that O6 implies

$$\lambda(P^\circ) \geq \sum_{k=1}^{N} \lambda(I_k^\circ) \geq \sum_{k=1}^{N} \lambda(I_k) = \lambda(P).$$

On the other hand, if Q is any special polygon such that $Q \subset P^\circ$, then also $Q \subset P$ and Property P1 implies $\lambda(Q) \leq \lambda(P)$. Since Q is arbitrary, $\lambda(P^\circ) \leq \lambda(P)$.

QED

Problem 5. Let G_i, $i \in \mathcal{I}$, be a collection of disjoint open sets in $\mathbb{R}^n$. Prove that only countably many of these sets are nonempty.

(**HINT**: If G_i is not empty, show that it contains a point of $\mathbb{Q}^n$.)

Problem 6. *The structure of open sets in* $\mathbb{R}$.
Prove that every nonempty open subset of $\mathbb{R}$ can be expressed as a countable disjoint union of open intervals:

$$G = \bigcup_k (a_k, b_k),$$

where the range on k can be finite or infinite. Furthermore, show that this expression is unique except for the numbering of the component intervals.

(**HINT**: for any $x \in G$, show that there exists a largest open interval A_x such that $x \in A_x$ and $A_x \subset G$.)

Problem 7. In the notation of Problem 6, prove that $\lambda(G) = \sum_k (b_k - a_k)$.

Problems 6 and 7 together provide an elegant method for constructing the measure of an open set in $\mathbb{R}$: Find the component intervals of the set and form the sum of their lengths. This approach is taken in some texts. Problem 8 indicates that this method will not work in $\mathbb{R}^n$ for $n \geq 2$. But Problems 9 and 10 indicate a modification that is sometimes used.

Problem 8. Prove that the open disk $B(0,1)$ in $\mathbb{R}^2$ cannot be expressed as a disjoint union of open rectangles.

Problem 9. Prove that every nonempty open subset of $\mathbb{R}^n$ can be expressed as a countable union of nonoverlapping special rectangles, which may be taken to be cubes:

$$G = \bigcup_{k=1}^{\infty} I_k.$$

The range on k must be infinite. Why?

(**HINT**: First pave $\mathbb{R}^n$ with cubes of side 1. Select those cubes which are contained in G. Then bisect the sides of the remaining cubes to obtain cubes with side $\frac{1}{2}$. Select those cubes which are contained in G. Etc.)

Problem 10. In the notation of Problem 9, prove that $\lambda(G) = \sum\limits_{k=1}^{\infty} \lambda(I_k)$.

Problem 11. In the notation of Problem 2, calculate the measure of the totality of discarded open sets. That is, calculate $\lambda\left(\bigcup\limits_{k=1}^{\infty} G_k\right)$.

Problem 12. Let $\epsilon > 0$. Prove that there exists an open set $G \subset \mathbb{R}$ such that $\mathbb{Q} \subset G$ and $\lambda(G) < \epsilon$. (This result will probably surprise you: Although G is open and contains every rational number, "most" of $\mathbb{R}$ is in G^c.)

Problem 13. Use your method of working Problem 12 to give a proof that $\mathbb{R}$ is uncountable (cf. Section 1B).

STAGE 4: Compact sets.

We now define the measure of an arbitrary compact set in $\mathbb{R}^n$. We do this by "approximating" the set from without by open sets. This procedure is satisfactory because of the topological nature of open sets.

If $K \subset \mathbb{R}^n$ is a compact set, we define

$$\lambda(K) = \inf\{\lambda(G) \mid K \subset G, G \text{ an open set}\}.$$

We are immediately confronted with a problem of possible ambiguity. Namely, if K is a compact set which is also a special polygon, we must show that our new definition of $\lambda(K)$ gives the same number for the measure of K as the old definition in Stage 2 gives. In order to do this, suppose P is a special polygon and for the moment let

$$\alpha = \text{``old } \lambda(P)\text{''} \text{ (defined in Stage 2)},$$
$$\beta = \text{``new } \lambda(P)\text{''} = \inf\{\lambda(G) \mid P \subset G = \text{ open set}\}.$$

If $P \subset G$, the definition of $\lambda(G)$ implies $\alpha \leq \lambda(G)$. As G is arbitrary, $\alpha \leq \beta$. On the other hand, suppose

$$P = \bigcup_{k=1}^{N} I_k$$

is an expression for P involving nonoverlapping special rectangles I_k. For any $\epsilon > 0$ choose special rectangles I_k' such that

$$I_k \subset I_k'^{\circ}$$

and

$$\lambda(I'_k) < \lambda(I_k) + \frac{\epsilon}{N}.$$

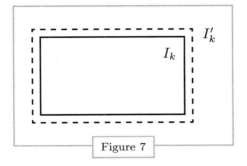

Figure 7

(This is the reverse of the situation depicted in Figure 6.) Now let

$$G = \bigcup_{k=1}^{N} I'^{\circ}_k.$$

The set G is open and $P \subset G$, so that

$$\beta \leq \lambda(G)$$

$$\leq \sum_{k=1}^{N} \lambda(I'^{\circ}_k)$$

$$= \sum_{k=1}^{N} \lambda(I'_k)$$

$$< \sum_{k=1}^{N} (\lambda(I_k) + \frac{\epsilon}{N})$$

$$= \alpha + \epsilon.$$

Since ϵ is arbitrary, $\beta \leq \alpha$. Therefore, $\alpha = \beta$, and it follows that the new definition is consistent with the old.

Properties

C1 $0 \le \lambda(K) < \infty$.

C2 $K_1 \subset K_2 \Rightarrow \lambda(K_1) \le \lambda(K_2)$.

C3 $\lambda(K_1 \cup K_2) \le \lambda(K_1) + \lambda(K_2)$.

C4 If the compact sets K_1 and K_2 are disjoint, $\lambda(K_1 \cup K_2) = \lambda(K_1) + \lambda(K_2)$.

Proof:

C1 Trivial.

C2 This is clear because every open set which contains K_2 also contains K_1.

C3 If $K_1 \subset G_1$ and $K_2 \subset G_2$, then $K_1 \cup K_2 \subset G_1 \cup G_2$, and this implies

$$\lambda(K_1 \cup K_2) \le \lambda(G_1 \cup G_2)$$
$$\le \lambda(G_1) + \lambda(G_2) \quad \text{(Property O5)}.$$

Since G_1 and G_2 are arbitrary,

$$\lambda(K_1 \cup K_2) \le \lambda(K_1) + \lambda(K_2).$$

C4 By the second corollary in Section 1D, there exists $\epsilon > 0$ such that $x \in K_1$, $y \in K_2 \Rightarrow d(x,y) \ge \epsilon$. Now suppose G is any open set such that $K_1 \cup K_2 \subset G$. Define

$$G_i = G \cap \bigcup_{x \in K_i} B(x, \frac{\epsilon}{2}) \quad \text{for} \quad i = 1, 2.$$

Then G_i is an open set. Obviously, $K_i \subset G_i \subset G$. Furthermore, the choice of ϵ guarantees that $G_1 \cap G_2 = \emptyset$. Therefore,

$$\lambda(K_1) + \lambda(K_2) \le \lambda(G_1) + \lambda(G_2)$$

$$= \lambda(G_1 \cup G_2) \quad \text{(Property O6)}$$

$$\le \lambda(G).$$

Since G is arbitrary, $\lambda(K_1) + \lambda(K_2) \le \lambda(K_1 \cup K_2)$. The reverse inequality already being known, C4 is proved.

QED

The Cantor Ternary Set

Before we advance any further in the construction of Lebesgue measure, we need to consider at least one significant example. The one we have chosen is not only a good example, but is extremely important in its own right. The example is a set situated on the real line and is the one-dimensional analog of the construction indicated in Problems 2 and 11.

The set will be a subset of $[0, 1] \subset \mathbb{R}$. Let $G_1 = \left(\frac{1}{3}, \frac{2}{3}\right)$, the open interval which we call the open middle third of the original interval $[0, 1]$. Then $[0, 1] \sim G_1$ consists of two disjoint closed intervals each of length $\frac{1}{3}$. Let $G_2 = \left(\frac{1}{9}, \frac{2}{9}\right) \cup \left(\frac{7}{9}, \frac{8}{9}\right)$, the union of the two open middle thirds of the two intervals in $[0, 1] \sim G_1$. Then $[0, 1] \sim \bigcup\limits_{k=1}^{2} G_k$ consists of four disjoint closed intervals each of length $\frac{1}{9}$. Repeat this construction

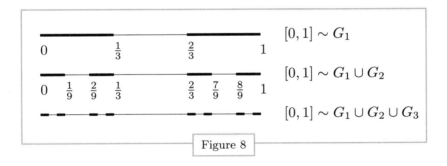

$$[0, 1] \sim G_1$$
$$[0, 1] \sim G_1 \cup G_2$$
$$[0, 1] \sim G_1 \cup G_2 \cup G_3$$

Figure 8

indefinitely. Then the *Cantor ternary set* is defined to be

$$C = [0, 1] \sim \bigcup_{k=1}^{\infty} G_k.$$

Thus, C is *compact*. We shall see later that the cardinal number of C is the same as that of $\mathbb{R}$. This means that there exists a one-to-one correspondence of C and $\mathbb{R}$. In spite of this,

$$\lambda(C) = 0.$$

To see this, note that for any $N \geq 1$, $C \subset [0,1] \sim \bigcup\limits_{k=1}^{N} G_k$. The larger set in this inclusion is actually one of our special polygons in $\mathbb{R}$, consisting of precisely 2^N disjoint closed intervals of length 3^{-N} each. Thus, $\lambda(C) \leq \left(\frac{2}{3}\right)^N$. Since N is arbitrary, $\lambda(C) = 0$.

Connection with ternary expansions. Every real number can of course be represented by a decimal expansion, as you well know. Instead of using base 10, any number 2, 3, 4, ... could be used as the base, and then every real number could be represented by an expansion in that base. We shall have occasion to use 2 and 3 as bases. If we use base 2, we call the representation of a number in this base its *binary* expansion. Likewise, we call the representation of a number in base 3 its *ternary* expansion. In particular, every $x \in [0,1]$ can be written

$$x = \sum_{j=1}^{\infty} \frac{\alpha_j}{3^j},$$

where for all j, $\alpha_j = 0$, 1, or 2. To simplify the notation we express this equation symbolically in the form

$$x = .\alpha_1\alpha_2\alpha_3 \ldots \quad \text{(ternary)}.$$

The ternary expansion is unique except for a certain type of ambiguity: A number has two different ternary expansions if and only if it has a ternary expansion which *terminates* (meaning that only finitely many α_j's are different from 0). The typical ambiguity is of the form

$$\frac{4}{9} = .11000\ldots$$
$$= .10222\ldots\,.$$

The reason for the ambiguity is of course the geometric series

$$\sum_{j=1}^{\infty} \frac{2}{3^j} = 1.$$

Now we re-examine the construction of the Cantor set C. At the first stage we remove the middle third $G_1 = \left(\frac{1}{3}, \frac{2}{3}\right)$. If $x \in [0,1]$ and if $x = .\alpha_1\alpha_2\alpha_3 \ldots$ is a ternary expansion, then $\frac{1}{3} < x < \frac{2}{3} \Leftrightarrow \alpha_1$ *must* be equal to 1. At the second stage we assume

$x \in [0,1] \sim G_1$. Thus, $x = .0\alpha_2\alpha_3\ldots$ or $x = .2\alpha_2\alpha_3\ldots$. We then observe that in either case the value of α_2 determines which of the three new subintervals contains x. Thus, $x \in G_1 \cup G_2 \Leftrightarrow$ at least one of α_1 and α_2 must be equal to 1. Repeating this argument yields the

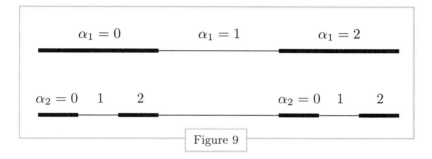

Figure 9

following result:

> **_Theorem:_** *Let $x \in [0,1]$. Then x belongs to the Cantor ternary set $C \Longleftrightarrow x$ has a ternary expansion consisting only of 0's and 2's.*

Problem 14. Finish the proof of this theorem.

Notice that the theorem does not say that if $x \in C$, then "the" ternary expansion of x must have only 0's and 2's. For instance, $\frac{1}{3} = .1000\ldots$ does belong to C, as does $\frac{2}{3} = .1222\ldots$. But the point is that in cases like these, the numbers do have ternary expansions of the required form: $\frac{1}{3} = .0222\ldots$ and $\frac{2}{3} = .2000\ldots$.

Problem 15. Let $x \in C$. Prove that x is an end point of some extracted interval belonging to some $G_k \Longleftrightarrow x$ has two different ternary expansions.

Problem 16. Frequently students think that after removing all the open intervals in the construction of C, the only points left to belong to C are end points of the extracted open intervals.

Show this is not the case by proving that $\frac{1}{4} \in C$ and that $\frac{1}{4}$ is not an end point of any of the intervals in the G_k's. Do the same for $\frac{1}{10}$.

Problem 17. Prove that $x \in C \Leftrightarrow 1 - x \in C$. Give two proofs — one based on geometric intuition and the other based on ternary expansions.

Problem 18. Which of these numbers belong to C: $\frac{1}{249}$, $\frac{1}{252}$, $\frac{31}{121}$?

Problem 19. Find all x such that both x and $2x$ belong to C.

Problem 20. Find all x such that both x and $2x - 1$ belong to C.

Problem 21. If x, $y \in C$, then obviously $x + y \in [0, 2]$. Prove conversely that if z is any number in $[0, 2]$, then there exist x, $y \in C$ such that $x + y = z$.

(**HINT:** Consider the ternary expansion of $z/2$.)

Problem 22. Likewise, prove that if $w \in [-1, 1]$, then there exist x, $y \in C$ such that $x - y = w$.

Problem 23. Prove that C is uncountable.

In Chapter 4 we shall again take up a study of the Cantor ternary set in much greater detail.

Definition: Let $A \subset \mathbb{R}^n$ be an arbitrary set. Then

$\lambda^*(A) =$ the *outer measure* of $A = \inf\{\lambda(G) \mid A \subset G = \text{open set}\}$;

$\lambda_*(A) =$ the *inner measure* of $A = \sup\{\lambda(K) \mid A \supset K = \text{compact set}\}$.

These important functions of sets have been introduced to enable us to define the concept of "measurable" set in Stages 5 and 6.

Notice again the roles played by open sets *larger* than A and compact sets *smaller* than A.

Properties

*1 $\lambda_*(A) \leq \lambda^*(A)$.

*2 $A \subset B \Rightarrow \lambda^*(A) \leq \lambda^*(B)$ and $\lambda_*(A) \leq \lambda_*(B)$.

*3 $\lambda^* \left(\bigcup_{k=1}^{\infty} A_k \right) \leq \sum_{k=1}^{\infty} \lambda^*(A_k)$.

*4 If the A_k's are disjoint, $\lambda_* \left(\bigcup_{k=1}^{\infty} A_k \right) \geq \sum_{k=1}^{\infty} \lambda_*(A_k)$.

*5 If A is open or compact, $\lambda^*(A) = \lambda_*(A) = \lambda(A)$.

Proof:

*1 This holds because $K \subset A \subset G \Rightarrow K \subset G \Rightarrow \lambda(K) \leq \lambda(G)$ by definition of $\lambda(K)$.

*2 Clear, as in O4 and C2.

*3 If $\epsilon > 0$, then there exist open sets $G_k \supset A_k$ such that
$$\lambda(G_k) < \lambda^*(A_k) + \epsilon 2^{-k}.$$
Then Property O5 implies

$$\lambda^* \left(\bigcup_{k=1}^{\infty} A_k \right) \leq \lambda \left(\bigcup_{k=1}^{\infty} G_k \right)$$

$$\leq \sum_{k=1}^{\infty} \lambda(G_k)$$

$$< \sum_{k=1}^{\infty} [\lambda^*(A_k) + \epsilon 2^{-k}]$$

$$= \sum_{k=1}^{\infty} \lambda^*(A_k) + \epsilon.$$

Since ϵ is arbitrary, the result follows.

*4 If $K_1, \ldots, K_N$ are any compact subsets of $A_1, \ldots, A_N$, respectively, then they are disjoint. Therefore, Property C4 implies

$$\lambda_* \left(\bigcup_{k=1}^{\infty} A_k \right) \geq \lambda \left(\bigcup_{k=1}^{N} K_k \right)$$

$$= \sum_{k=1}^{N} \lambda(K_k).$$

Since the K_k's are arbitrary,

$$\lambda_* \left(\bigcup_{k=1}^{\infty} A_k \right) \geq \sum_{k=1}^{N} \lambda_*(A_k).$$

Since N is arbitrary, Property *4 is proved.

*5 First, assume A is open. Clearly, $\lambda^*(A) = \lambda(A)$. If P is any special polygon with $P \subset A$, then P is compact and we conclude that $\lambda(P) \leq \lambda_*(A)$. Since P is arbitrary, the definition of $\lambda(A)$ implies $\lambda(A) \leq \lambda_*(A)$. Therefore, we have $\lambda^*(A) = \lambda(A) \leq \lambda_*(A) \leq \lambda^*(A)$, and thus all these numbers are equal.

Second, assume A is compact. Clearly, $\lambda_*(A) = \lambda(A)$, but the definition of $\lambda(A)$ shows that $\lambda(A) = \lambda^*(A)$.   **QED**

STAGE 5:   Sets having finite outer measure.

We are almost ready for the conclusion. We want to assign a measure to every set which has the property that it can be well approximated from within by compact sets and from without by open sets. That is why we have introduced inner measure and outer measure, respectively. We should like to say that a set A is *measurable* if $\lambda^*(A) = \lambda_*(A)$. But if A is so "large" that $\lambda_*(A) = \infty$, then this definition would not restrict A at all. This minor problem is only a technicality and will be treated in the sixth stage.

Definition: Let $A \subset \mathbb{R}^n$ be a set having finite outer measure: $\lambda^*(A) < \infty$. Then we say that $A \in \mathcal{L}_0$ if $\lambda^*(A) = \lambda_*(A)$.

(We shall later say that A is *measurable*, but we prefer to wait until the sixth stage to introduce that term.) Thus, we have defined

$$\mathcal{L}_0 = \{A \subset \mathbb{R}^n \mid \lambda^*(A) = \lambda_*(A) < \infty\}.$$

In case $A \in \mathcal{L}_0$, we define the *measure* of A to be the number

$$\lambda(A) = \lambda^*(A) = \lambda_*(A).$$

Proposition: $\mathcal{L}_0$ *contains all open sets which have finite measure and all compact sets. The newly defined measure on such sets agrees with the measure defined in Stages 3 and 4.*

Proof: This is an immediate consequence of Property *5.   **QED**

Lemma: *If A and $B \in \mathcal{L}_0$ and are disjoint, then $A \cup B \in \mathcal{L}_0$ and*

$$\lambda(A \cup B) = \lambda(A) + \lambda(B).$$

Proof: By Properties *3, *4, and *1,

$$\begin{aligned}
\lambda^*(A \cup B) &\leq \lambda^*(A) + \lambda^*(B) \\
&= \lambda(A) + \lambda(B) \\
&= \lambda_*(A) + \lambda_*(B) \\
&\leq \lambda_*(A \cup B) \\
&\leq \lambda^*(A \cup B).
\end{aligned}$$

QED

Theorem on Approximation: *Let $A \subset \mathbb{R}^n$ satisfy $\lambda^*(A) < \infty$. Then $A \in \mathcal{L}_0 \iff$ for every $\epsilon > 0$ there exist a compact set K and an open set G such that*

$$K \subset A \subset G$$

and

$$\lambda(G \sim K) < \epsilon.$$

Proof: First assume $A \in \mathcal{L}_0$. By definition of outer and inner measure, it follows that for any $\epsilon > 0$ there exist K and G such that

$$\begin{aligned}
A \subset G \quad &\text{and} \quad \lambda(G) < \lambda^*(A) + \tfrac{\epsilon}{2} = \lambda(A) + \tfrac{\epsilon}{2}, \\
K \subset A \quad &\text{and} \quad \lambda(K) > \lambda_*(A) - \tfrac{\epsilon}{2} = \lambda(A) - \tfrac{\epsilon}{2}.
\end{aligned}$$

The lemma implies that $\lambda(G) = \lambda(K) + \lambda(G \sim K)$. Therefore,

$$\begin{aligned}
\lambda(G \sim K) &= \lambda(G) - \lambda(K) \\
&< \left(\lambda(A) + \tfrac{\epsilon}{2}\right) - \left(\lambda(A) - \tfrac{\epsilon}{2}\right) \\
&= \epsilon.
\end{aligned}$$

Conversely, assume that for any $\epsilon > 0$ there exist sets K and G as specified in the statement of the theorem. Then the lemma implies that

$$\begin{aligned}
\lambda^*(A) &\leq \lambda(G) \\
&= \lambda(K) + \lambda(G \sim K) \\
&< \lambda(K) + \epsilon \\
&\leq \lambda_*(A) + \epsilon.
\end{aligned}$$

Since ϵ is arbitrary, it follows that $\lambda^*(A) \le \lambda_*(A)$ and therefore that $A \in \mathcal{L}_0$.   **QED**

Corollary: *If A, $B \in \mathcal{L}_0$, then also the sets $A \cup B$, $A \cap B$, and $A \sim B$ belong to $\mathcal{L}_0$.*

Proof: We first deal with $A \sim B$, and then the others will follow easily. Let $\epsilon > 0$. The theorem on approximation allows us to write, with obvious notation,

$$K_1 \subset A \subset G_1, \quad \lambda(G_1 \sim K_1) < \epsilon/2;$$
$$K_2 \subset B \subset G_2, \quad \lambda(G_2 \sim K_2) < \epsilon/2.$$

Define $K = K_1 \sim G_2$ and $G = G_1 \sim K_2$. It is clear that K is compact, G is open, and

$$K \subset A \sim B \subset G.$$

Moreover, it is a simple matter to verify that

$$G \sim K \subset (G_1 \sim K_1) \cup (G_2 \sim K_2).$$

Thus,

$$\lambda(G \sim K) \le \lambda(G_1 \sim K_1) + \lambda(G_2 \sim K_2) < \epsilon,$$

and the theorem on approximation shows that $A \sim B \in \mathcal{L}_0$.
It now follows immediately that $A \cap B \in \mathcal{L}_0$, since

$$A \cap B = A \sim (A \sim B).$$

And the lemma shows that $A \cup B \in \mathcal{L}_0$, since

$$A \cup B = (A \sim B) \cup B.$$

                                                                                 QED

Problem 24. Give another proof that $A \cap B$ and $A \cup B \in \mathcal{L}_0$, using the same type of argument that was employed to prove that $A \sim B \in \mathcal{L}_0$.

Theorem on Countable Additivity: *Assume* $A_k \in \mathcal{L}_0$ *for* $k = 1$, $2, \ldots$. *Let* $A = \bigcup\limits_{k=1}^{\infty} A_k$, *and assume* $\lambda^*(A) < \infty$. *Then* $A \in \mathcal{L}_0$ *and*

$$\lambda(A) \leq \sum_{k=1}^{\infty} \lambda(A_k).$$

In addition, if the A_k's *are disjoint, then*

$$\lambda(A) = \sum_{k=1}^{\infty} \lambda(A_k).$$

Proof: We first take up the case in which the A_k's are disjoint. By Properties *3 and *4,

$$\lambda^*(A) \leq \sum_{k=1}^{\infty} \lambda^*(A_k)$$
$$= \sum_{k=1}^{\infty} \lambda(A_k)$$
$$= \sum_{k=1}^{\infty} \lambda_*(A_k)$$
$$\leq \lambda_*(A) \leq \lambda^*(A).$$

Therefore, these numbers are all equal, proving both assertions of the theorem in this case.

In the general case there is a standard method of writing A as a *disjoint* union and using the case we have just treated. Define new sets B_k by the formulas

$$B_1 = A_1,$$
$$B_k = A_k \sim (A_1 \cup \cdots \cup A_{k-1}) \quad \text{for } k = 2, 3, \ldots .$$

By the corollary, each $B_k \in \mathcal{L}_0$. Moreover, the sets B_k are disjoint, $B_k \subset A_k$, and $\bigcup\limits_{k=1}^{\infty} B_k = A$. By the previous case it follows that $A \in \mathcal{L}_0$

and

$$\lambda(A) = \sum_{k=1}^{\infty} \lambda(B_k)$$

$$\leq \sum_{k=1}^{\infty} \lambda(A_k).$$

QED

STAGE 6:   Arbitrary measurable sets.

This will be the final step in our construction of Lebesgue measure. All we have to accomplish in this stage is the removal of the restriction to sets with finite outer measure. This will be done in a rather straightforward way. Throughout the discussion of Stage 6 we shall use the notation M to denote an arbitrary set belonging to $\mathcal{L}_0 : \lambda^*(M) = \lambda_*(M) < \infty$.

Definition: Let $A \subset \mathbb{R}^n$. Then A is *measurable* (or *Lebesgue measurable*, for emphasis) if for all $M \in \mathcal{L}_0$, $A \cap M \in \mathcal{L}_0$. In case A is measurable, the *measure* (or *Lebesgue measure*) of A is

$$\lambda(A) = \sup\{\lambda(A \cap M) \mid M \in \mathcal{L}_0\}.$$

We denote by $\mathcal{L}$ the class of all measurable sets $A \subset \mathbb{R}^n$. Thus,

$$A \in \mathcal{L} \Longleftrightarrow A \cap M \in \mathcal{L}_0 \quad \text{for all} \quad M \in \mathcal{L}_0.$$

As we have had to do before, we must run a consistency check before proceeding further. For if $\lambda^*(A) < \infty$, then we have given two definitions of $\lambda(A)$ (in case it can be defined): One comes from Stage 5 in case $A \in \mathcal{L}_0$, and the other from Stage 6 in case $A \in \mathcal{L}$. These two situations are identical, as we now prove.

Proposition: *Let $A \subset \mathbb{R}^n$ and assume $\lambda^*(A) < \infty$. Then $A \in \mathcal{L}_0 \Longleftrightarrow A \in \mathcal{L}$. Moreover, in case $A \in \mathcal{L}$, then the definitions of $\lambda(A)$ in Stages 5 and 6 produce the same number.*

Proof: If $A \in \mathcal{L}_0$, then the corollary in Stage 5 implies that $A \cap M \in \mathcal{L}_0$ for all $M \in \mathcal{L}_0$, so we conclude that $A \in \mathcal{L}$. Conversely, assume $A \in \mathcal{L}$. Then since the ball $B(0, k) \in \mathcal{L}_0$, the set $A_k = A \cap B(0, k)$ belongs to $\mathcal{L}_0$. Since $A = \bigcup_{k=1}^{\infty} A_k$, the theorem on countable additivity in Stage 5 implies that $A \in \mathcal{L}_0$.

Now assume $A \in \mathcal{L}$ (and $\mathcal{L}_0$). Let $\tilde{\lambda}(A)$ stand for the measure of A which we have introduced in Stage 6:

$$\tilde{\lambda}(A) = \sup\{\lambda(A \cap M) \mid M \in \mathcal{L}_0\}.$$

Since $A \cap M \subset A$, then $\lambda(A \cap M) \leq \lambda(A)$ and we conclude that $\tilde{\lambda}(A) \leq \lambda(A)$. On the other hand, we can actually choose $M = A$ since $A \in \mathcal{L}_0$, and this yields $\tilde{\lambda}(A) \geq \lambda(A)$. Therefore, $\tilde{\lambda}(A) = \lambda(A)$.   **QED**

We shall now finish this chapter by listing the important properties of measurable sets which will be used in the remainder of this book. A remark is in order. We have been very careful in this chapter to do things in the correct order. Once the measure has been constructed, however, and all the following properties have been established, you can virtually forget where it all came from and how the final results came about. This makes Lebesgue measure rather easy to use — easier to use than to construct!
Because these properties are so many and are so important, we prefer to place them in a new section.

B. Properties of Lebesgue Measure

M1 $A \in \mathcal{L} \Rightarrow A^c \in \mathcal{L}$.

M2   Countable unions and countable intersections of measurable sets are measurable.

M3 $A, B \in \mathcal{L} \Rightarrow A \sim B \in \mathcal{L}$.

M4   If the sets $A_1, A_2, \ldots$ are all measurable, then

$$\lambda \left(\bigcup_{k=1}^{\infty} A_k \right) \leq \sum_{k=1}^{\infty} \lambda(A_k).$$

If in addition the sets are disjoint,

$$\lambda \left(\bigcup_{k=1}^{\infty} A_k \right) = \sum_{k=1}^{\infty} \lambda(A_k).$$

(λ is said to be *countably additive*.)

M5 If the A_k's are measurable and $A_1 \subset A_2 \subset A_3 \subset \ldots$, then

$$\lambda \left(\bigcup_{k=1}^{\infty} A_k \right) = \lim_{k \to \infty} \lambda(A_k).$$

M6 If the A_k's are measurable and $A_1 \supset A_2 \supset A_3 \supset \ldots$, and if $\lambda(A_1) < \infty$, then

$$\lambda \left(\bigcap_{k=1}^{\infty} A_k \right) = \lim_{k \to \infty} \lambda(A_k).$$

M7 All open sets and all closed sets are measurable.

M8 If $\lambda^*(A) = 0$, then A is measurable (and $\lambda(A) = 0$).

M9 APPROXIMATION PROPERTY. A is measurable $\Longleftrightarrow$ for every $\epsilon > 0$ there exist a closed set F and an open set G such that

$$F \subset A \subset G \quad \text{and} \quad \lambda(G \sim F) < \epsilon.$$

M10 If A is measurable, $\lambda^*(A) = \lambda_*(A) = \lambda(A)$.

M11 If $A \subset B$ and B is measurable, then

$$\lambda^*(A) + \lambda_*(B \sim A) = \lambda(B).$$

M12 (Carathéodory) A is measurable $\Longleftrightarrow$ for every set $E \subset \mathbb{R}^n$,

$$\lambda^*(E) = \lambda^*(E \cap A) + \lambda^*(E \cap A^c).$$

Proof: In the following arguments we continue to employ the generic notation $M \in \mathcal{L}_0$.

M1 $A^c \cap M = M \sim A = M \sim (A \cap M) \in \mathcal{L}_0$ by the corollary in Stage 5. As M is arbitrary, $A^c \in \mathcal{L}$.

M2 If $A_k \in \mathcal{L}$ and $A = \bigcup_{k=1}^{\infty} A_k$, then $A \cap M = \bigcup_{k=1}^{\infty} A_k \cap M$. Since $\lambda^*(A \cap M) \le \lambda(M) < \infty$, the theorem on countable additivity in

Stage 5 implies $A \cap M \in \mathcal{L}_0$. As M is arbitrary, $A \in \mathcal{L}$. De Morgan's laws together with M1 give the result for intersections:

$$\bigcap_{k=1}^{\infty} A_k = \left(\bigcup_{k=1}^{\infty} A_k^c\right)^c.$$

M3 $A \sim B = A \cap B^c$.

M4 Let $A = \bigcup_{k=1}^{\infty} A_k$. By the theorem on countable additivity,

$$\lambda(A \cap M) = \lambda\left(\bigcup_{k=1}^{\infty} A_k \cap M\right)$$

$$\leq \sum_{k=1}^{\infty} \lambda(A_k \cap M)$$

$$\leq \sum_{k=1}^{\infty} \lambda(A_k).$$

Taking the least upper bound of $\lambda(A \cap M)$ for all M yields

$$\lambda(A) \leq \sum_{k=1}^{\infty} \lambda(A_k).$$

Now assume the sets A_k to be disjoint. Let $N \in \mathbb{N}$ be arbitrary, and let $M_1, \ldots, M_N$ be arbitrary sets in $\mathcal{L}_0$. Then define $M = \bigcup_{k=1}^{N} M_k$. By the theorem on countable additivity,

$$\lambda(A) \geq \lambda(A \cap M)$$

$$= \sum_{k=1}^{\infty} \lambda(A_k \cap M)$$

$$\geq \sum_{k=1}^{N} \lambda(A_k \cap M)$$

$$\geq \sum_{k=1}^{N} \lambda(A_k \cap M_k).$$

Since the M_k's are arbitrary, it follows that

$$\lambda(A) \geq \sum_{k=1}^{N} \lambda(A_k).$$

Since N is arbitrary,

$$\lambda(A) \geq \sum_{k=1}^{\infty} \lambda(A_k).$$

M5 Express $\displaystyle\bigcup_{k=1}^{\infty} A_k$ as a *disjoint* union:

$$\bigcup_{k=1}^{\infty} A_k = A_1 \cup \bigcup_{k=2}^{\infty} (A_k \sim A_{k-1}).$$

Then M4 implies

$$\lambda\left(\bigcup_{k=1}^{\infty} A_k\right) = \lambda(A_1) + \sum_{k=2}^{\infty} \lambda(A_k \sim A_{k-1})$$

$$= \lim_{N\to\infty} \left[\lambda(A_1) + \sum_{k=2}^{N} \lambda(A_k \sim A_{k-1})\right]$$

$$= \lim_{N\to\infty} \lambda\left(A_1 \cup \bigcup_{k=2}^{N}(A_k \sim A_{k-1})\right)$$

$$= \lim_{N\to\infty} \lambda(A_N).$$

Problem 25. Prove M6. (You must use the assumption $\lambda(A_1) < \infty$.)

Problem 26. Give an example to show why the assumption $\lambda(A_1) < \infty$ is needed in Property M6.

M7 Any open set G is a countable union of the bounded open sets $G \cap B(0, k)$, and these sets are measurable by the proposition in Stage 5. Thus, G is measurable by M2. If F is closed, then F^c is open and therefore measurable. M1 then implies F is measurable.

M8 $0 \leq \lambda_*(A) \leq \lambda^*(A) = 0$. Therefore, $A \in \mathcal{L}_0$ and $\lambda(A) = 0$. (Only Stage 5 information is required for this.)

M9 First assume that A has the approximation property described in the statement of M9. Then for any $k \in \mathbb{N}$ there exist a closed set F_k and an open set G_k such that $F_k \subset A \subset G_k$ and $\lambda(G_k \sim F_k) < k^{-1}$. Define $B = \bigcup_{k=1}^{\infty} F_k$. Then B is measurable and $B \subset A$, and, for every k,

$$A \sim B \subset G_k \sim B \subset G_k \sim F_k.$$

Thus, $\lambda^*(A \sim B) \leq \lambda(G_k \sim F_k) < k^{-1}$. Since k is arbitrary, $\lambda^*(A \sim B) = 0$. By M8, $A \sim B$ is measurable. Therefore, $A = (A \sim B) \cup B$ is measurable.

Conversely, assume A is measurable. We select some convenient measurable partition of $\mathbb{R}^n$, such as the sets defined for $k \in \mathbb{N}$ by

$$E_k = B(0, k) \sim B(0, k - 1)$$
$$= \{x \mid k - 1 \leq\mid x \mid< k\}.$$

By the theorem on approximation in Stage 5, for any $\epsilon > 0$ there exist a compact set K_k and an open set G_k such that

$$K_k \subset A \cap E_k \subset G_k,$$
$$\lambda(G_k \sim K_k) < \epsilon 2^{-k}.$$

Define

$$F = \bigcup_{k=1}^{\infty} K_k \quad \text{and} \quad G = \bigcup_{k=1}^{\infty} G_k.$$

Clearly, G is open; though unions of countably many closed sets are not necessarily closed, in this case it is easy to check that F is closed. For any limit point of F must already be a limit point of some finite union $\bigcup_{k=1}^{N} K_k$, and the latter is closed. Clearly, $F \subset A \subset G$. Finally,

$$G \sim F = \bigcup_{k=1}^{\infty} (G_k \sim F) \subset \bigcup_{k=1}^{\infty} (G_k \sim K_k),$$

and we thus conclude

$$\lambda(G \sim F) \leq \sum_{k=1}^{\infty} \lambda(G_k \sim K_k)$$

$$< \sum_{k=1}^{\infty} \epsilon 2^{-k}$$

$$= \epsilon.$$

M10 If $\lambda^*(A) < \infty$, then we have already proved the truth of this statement in our discussion of consistency at the beginning of this stage. Therefore, we may assume that A is measurable and $\lambda^*(A) = \infty$. If it were true that $\lambda(A) < \infty$, then M9 would produce $F \subset A \subset G$ such that $\lambda(G \sim F) < 1$, and we would have

$$\lambda(G) = \lambda(G \sim A) + \lambda(A)$$
$$\leq \lambda(G \sim F) + \lambda(A)$$
$$< 1 + \lambda(A)$$
$$< \infty,$$

contradicting $\lambda^*(A) = \infty$. Therefore, $\lambda(A) = \infty$.

By Property M5,

$$\lim_{k \to \infty} \lambda(A \cap B(0, k)) = \infty.$$

Since $\lambda(A \cap B(0, k)) < \infty$, we have

$$\lambda(A \cap B(0, k)) = \lambda_*(A \cap B(0, k)) \leq \lambda_*(A).$$

Since this is true for all k, $\lambda_*(A) = \infty$.

M11 For any open set G with $G \supset A$,

$$\lambda(G) + \lambda_*(B \sim A) \geq \lambda(B \cap G) + \lambda_*(B \sim A)$$
$$\geq \lambda(B \cap G) + \lambda_*(B \sim G)$$
$$= \lambda(B \cap G) + \lambda(B \sim G)$$
$$= \lambda(B).$$

Since G is arbitrary, $\lambda^*(A) + \lambda_*(B \sim A) \geq \lambda(B)$. On the other hand, if K is any compact set with $K \subset B \sim A$, then

$$\lambda^*(A) + \lambda(K) \leq \lambda^*(B \sim K) + \lambda(K)$$
$$= \lambda(B \sim K) + \lambda(K)$$
$$= \lambda(B).$$

Since K is arbitrary, $\lambda^*(A) + \lambda_*(B \sim A) \leq \lambda(B)$.

M12 First assume that A is measurable. If G is any open set which contains E, then

$$\lambda(G) = \lambda(G \cap A) + \lambda(G \cap A^c)$$
$$\geq \lambda^*(E \cap A) + \lambda^*(E \cap A^c).$$

Since G is arbitrary, $\lambda^*(E) \geq \lambda^*(E \cap A) + \lambda^*(E \cap A^c)$. The reverse inequality follows from Property *3 (whether or not A is measurable).

Conversely, assume the equation in the statement of M12 to be valid for all E. Let $M \in \mathcal{L}_0$ and substitute $E = M$:

$$\lambda(M) = \lambda^*(M \cap A) + \lambda^*(M \cap A^c).$$

Next use M11 with B replaced by M and A replaced by $M \cap A^c$:

$$\lambda(M) = \lambda_*(M \cap A) + \lambda^*(M \cap A^c).$$

Comparing these two equations, we discover that $\lambda^*(M \cap A) = \lambda_*(M \cap A)$. Thus, $M \cap A \in \mathcal{L}_0$. Since M is arbitrary, A is measurable.

QED

Remark: The last property in the list, M12, turns out to be quite significant. It shows us that the knowledge of the properties of *outer* measure alone is sufficient to decide which sets are measurable. And knowing λ^* is tantamount to knowing $\lambda(G)$ for open sets G. In fact, we could even dispense with the knowledge of the measure of open sets and define λ^* entirely in terms of $\lambda(I)$ for special rectangles I. Thus, immediately after the trivial Stage 1 we could jump all the way to λ^* and define measurable sets by Property M12. Then we would derive all the properties of Lebesgue measure mentioned up until now. This would be a fine way to develop Lebesgue measure, and is the quickest way to proceed. But I believe the slow and deliberate development we have given is preferable for the beginner.

The method of Carathéodory outlined in the preceeding paragraph is discussed and developed in quite a number of text books on integration. The next problem shows explicitly how λ^* may be defined directly from Stage 1.

Problem 27. Let $A \subset \mathbb{R}^n$ be arbitrary. Prove that

$$\lambda^*(A) = \inf \left\{ \sum_{k=1}^{\infty} \lambda(I_k) \mid A \subset \bigcup_{k=1}^{\infty} I_k \right\},$$

where the I_k's are special rectangles.

(HINT: If $A \subset \bigcup_{k=1}^{\infty} I_k$, then $\lambda^*(A) \leq \sum_{k=1}^{\infty} \lambda(I_k)$ (why?). This will establish that $\lambda^*(A) \leq \inf\{\ \}$. To establish the reverse inequality, consider a well chosen $G \supset A$, and apply Problem 9.)

This section will conclude with some problems giving further properties of Lebesgue measure.

Problem 28. Suppose that $A \cup B$ is measurable and that

$$\lambda(A \cup B) = \lambda^*(A) + \lambda^*(B) < \infty.$$

Prove that A and B are measurable.

Problem 29. Prove that if A and B are measurable, then

$$\lambda(A) + \lambda(B) = \lambda(A \cup B) + \lambda(A \cap B).$$

Problem 30. Prove that in general

$$\lambda^*(A) + \lambda^*(B) \geq \lambda^*(A \cup B) + \lambda^*(A \cap B)$$

and

$$\lambda_*(A) + \lambda_*(B) \leq \lambda_*(A \cup B) + \lambda_*(A \cap B).$$

Problem 31. Prove that if A is countable, then $\lambda(A) = 0$. (In particular, $\lambda(\mathbb{Q}) = 0$.)

Problem 32. Let $a \in \mathbb{R}$ be fixed. Prove that

$$\lambda(\{a\} \times \mathbb{R}^{n-1}) = 0.$$

Problem 33. Let $A = \{x = (x_1, \ldots, x_n) \mid$ for some i, $x_i \in \mathbb{Q}\}$. Prove that $\lambda(A) = 0$.

Problem 34. Students sometimes err by believing that if a measurable set has positive measure, then that set must contain an interior point. Of course, the example of the irrational numbers $\mathbb{R} \sim \mathbb{Q}$ shows that this belief is not valid. But then one might think that the problem is just that the irrationals are not a closed set. Construct a *closed* subset of $[0, 1]$ whose measure is positive and whose interior is empty.

(**HINT:** Try the complement of the set G of Problem 12. A more sophisticated example, a "fat Cantor set," will be constructed in Chapter 4.)

Problem 35. Does there exist a closed subset A of $[0, 1]$ whose measure is 1 and whose interior is empty? Substantiate your answer.

Problem 36. (Difficult) Prove that $\mathbb{R}^n$ can be decomposed into a countable union of the form

$$\mathbb{R}^n = N \cup \bigcup_{k=1}^{\infty} B(x_k, r_k)^-,$$

where $\lambda(N) = 0$ and the closed balls $B(x_k, r_k)^-$ are disjoint.

Problem 37. Prove that if $E \subset \mathbb{R}^n$ and $\lambda^*(E) < \infty$, then a *measurable* set A exists such that

$$E \subset A \quad \text{and} \quad \lambda^*(E) = \lambda(A).$$

(The set A is called a *measurable hull* of E.)

(**HINT:** Choose open sets G_k such that $\lambda(G_k) < \lambda^*(E) + k^{-1}$ and $E \subset G_k$. Then let $A = \bigcap_{k=1}^{\infty} G_k$.)

Problem 38. Let $\lambda^*(E) < \infty$, $E \subset A \in \mathcal{L}$. Prove that A is a measurable hull of $E \iff \lambda_*(A \sim E) = 0$.

Problem 39. In general, if $E \subset \mathbb{R}^n$ (and even if $\lambda^*(E) = \infty$), a set A is called a *measurable hull* of E if A is measurable, $E \subset A$ and $\lambda_*(A \sim E) = 0$. Prove that every set has a measurable hull.

(**HINT:** Choose some measurable partition of $\mathbb{R}^n$, such as $E_k = B(0, k) \sim B(0, k - 1)$. Show that there exists a measurable hull A_k for the set $E \cap E_k$ with the additional property that $A_k \subset E_k$. Let $A = \bigcup_{k=1}^{\infty} A_k$.

Suppose K is an arbitrary compact set such that $K \subset A \sim E$. Prove that $\lambda(K \cap E_k) = 0$.)

Problem 40. Prove that if $E_1 \subset E_2 \subset E_3 \subset \ldots$, then

$$\lambda^* \left(\bigcup_{k=1}^{\infty} E_k \right) = \lim_{k \to \infty} \lambda^*(E_k).$$

(**HINT:** Let A_k be a measurable hull of E_k, and define $B_k = \bigcap_{j=k}^{\infty} A_j$. Then B_k is also a measurable hull of E_k, and, furthermore, $B_1 \subset B_2 \subset B_3 \subset \ldots$. Apply Property M5.)

Problem 41. Suppose $A_1, A_2, A_3, \ldots$ are measurable sets and that

$$\sum_{k=1}^{\infty} \lambda(A_k) < \infty.$$

Prove that $\lambda(\limsup A_k) = 0$.

Problem 42. Suppose $A_1, A_2, A_3, \ldots$ are measurable sets and suppose $d \in \mathbb{N}$ and that each point $x \in \mathbb{R}^n$ belongs to no more than d of the A_k's. Prove that

$$\sum_{k=1}^{\infty} \lambda(A_k) \leq d\lambda \left(\bigcup_{k=1}^{\infty} A_k \right).$$

(If $d = 1$ this is just Property M4.) (See also Problem 6.42.)

(**HINT:** This property should look obvious after consideration of a few diagrams. If you have trouble writing out a rigorous argument, you might like to try the following. Let $\mathcal{E}$ be the collection of all nonempty subsets of $\mathbb{N}$ which contain no more than d numbers. For any $\mathcal{S} \in \mathcal{E}$ define a set A_S in the following manner:

$$\text{If } S = \{k_1, \ldots, k_l\} \quad \text{and} \quad S^c = \{j_1, j_2, \ldots\} \quad (\text{so } l \leq d),$$

let

$$A_S = A_{k_1} \cap \cdots \cap A_{k_l} \cap A_{j_1}^c \cap A_{j_2}^c \ldots .$$

Show that the sets A_S are disjoint and that $\displaystyle\bigcup_{k=1}^{\infty} A_k = \bigcup_{S \in \mathcal{E}} A_S$. Then justify all the following steps:

$$\sum_{k=1}^{\infty} \lambda(A_k) = \sum_{k=1}^{\infty} \left(\sum_{\substack{S \in \mathcal{E} \\ k \in S}} \lambda(A_S) \right)$$

$$= \sum_{S \in \mathcal{E}} \left(\sum_{\substack{k=1 \\ k \in S}}^{\infty} \lambda(A_S) \right)$$

$$= \sum_{S \in \mathcal{E}} \lambda(A_S) \times \ \text{(number of elements of } S)$$

$$\leq \sum_{S \in \mathcal{E}} \lambda(A_S) d = d\lambda \left(\bigcup_{k=1}^{\infty} A_k \right) .)$$

Problem 43. Suppose that the measurable sets $A_1, A_2, \ldots$ are "almost disjoint," in the sense that $\lambda(A_j \cap A_k) = 0$ if $j \neq k$. Prove that

$$\lambda \left(\bigcup_{k=1}^{\infty} A_k \right) = \sum_{k=1}^{\infty} \lambda(A_k).$$

Problem 44. Conversely, suppose the measurable sets $A_1, A_2, \ldots$ satisfy

$$\lambda \left(\bigcup_{k=1}^{\infty} A_k \right) = \sum_{k=1}^{\infty} \lambda(A_k) < \infty.$$

Prove that the sets are almost disjoint.

Problem 45. Suppose that A_i is a measurable set in $\mathbb{R}^n$ for each i belonging to an index set $\mathcal{I}$, and suppose that the A_i's are disjoint and that $\lambda(A_i) > 0$ for all i. Prove that $\mathcal{I}$ is countable.

(**HINT:** First assume that all the A_i's are contained in some fixed ball $B(0, k)$; how many A_i's can have $\lambda(A_i) \geq j^{-1}$ for a fixed $j \in \mathbb{N}$?)

Problem 46. For a sequence of real numbers $a_1, a_2, a_3, \ldots$, we define

$$\limsup_{k \to \infty} a_k = \lim_{k \to \infty} \left[\sup\{a_k, a_{k+1}, a_{k+2}, \ldots\} \right],$$

$$\liminf_{k \to \infty} a_k = \lim_{k \to \infty} \left[\inf\{a_k, a_{k+1}, a_{k+2}, \ldots\} \right].$$

Prove that if $A_1, A_2, A_3, \ldots$ is a sequence of measurable sets, then

$$\lambda(\limsup_{k \to \infty} A_k) \geq \limsup_{k \to \infty} \lambda(A_k) \quad \text{if } \lambda\left(\bigcup_{k=1}^{\infty} A_k \right) < \infty;$$

and

$$\lambda(\liminf_{k \to \infty} A_k) \leq \liminf_{k \to \infty} \lambda(A_k).$$

Also produce an example showing why the condition $\lambda\left(\bigcup_{k=1}^{\infty} A_k \right) < \infty$ is needed to insure the first inequality.

Problem 47. Let $A_1, A_2, A_3, \ldots$ be a sequence of measurable sets contained in the ball $B(0,1) \subset \mathbb{R}^n$. Assume that for some $\epsilon > 0$ it is true that $\lambda(A_k) \geq \epsilon$ for all k. Prove that there is some point which belongs to infinitely many A_k's.

Problem 48. Let $A \subset \mathbb{R}^n$ be measurable. Prove that there exists a sequence of compact sets $K_1 \subset K_2 \subset \cdots \subset A$ such that $\lambda\left(A \sim \bigcup_{j=1}^{\infty} K_j \right) = 0$.

C. Appendix: Proof of P1 and P2

In Stage 2 of the construction of Lebesgue measure we defined the measure of special polygons. At that time we omitted the proofs of several assertions: the proof that every polygon is a finite union of nonoverlapping rectangles; the proof that $\lambda(P)$ is well defined; P1; and P2.

We first prove that every special polygon is a finite union of nonoverlapping special rectangles. Suppose that $P = \bigcup_{k=1}^{N} I^k$, where

$$I^k = [a_1^k, b_1^k] \times \cdots \times [a_n^k, b_n^k].$$

For each $i \in [1, n]$ let $c_i^1 < c_i^2 < \cdots < c_i^{m_i}$ be the list of all the distinct numbers among a_i^k and b_i^k for $1 \leq k \leq N$. Denote by $\mathcal{L}$ any n-tuple of the form

$$\mathcal{L} = (l_1, \ldots, l_n),$$
$$1 \leq l_i < m_i.$$

Then denote

$$I^{\mathcal{L}} = [c_1^{l_1}, c_1^{l_1+1}] \times \cdots \times [c_n^{l_n}, c_n^{l_n+1}].$$

Figure 10 gives an illustration of a special polygon in $\mathbb{R}^n$; to its right is an illustration of the resulting $I^{\mathcal{L}}$'s. There are 36 $I^{\mathcal{L}}$'s which result in this example, and we have shaded each of the 24 of these which are actually contained in P.

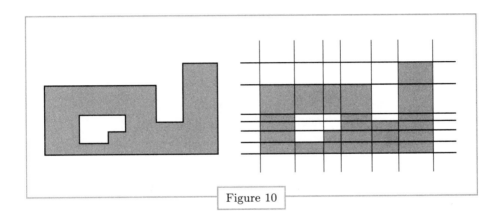

Figure 10

Clearly, the $I^{\mathcal{L}}$'s are nonoverlapping. We have to prove that any $I^{\mathcal{L}}$ which has an interior point in common with P is actually contained in P, and that P is the union of such $I^{\mathcal{L}}$'s.

Suppose then that $I^{\mathcal{L}\circ} \cap I^k \neq \emptyset$. If x is a point of this intersection, then $c_i^{l_i} < x_i < c_i^{l_i+1}$ and $a_i^k \leq x_i \leq b_i^k$ for $i \in [1, n]$. By the choice of the c_i's, this implies $a_i^k \leq c_i^{l_i}$ and $c_i^{l_i+1} \leq b_i^k$. Thus, $I^{\mathcal{L}} \subset I^k \subset P$.

On the other hand, suppose $x \in P$. Then for some k, $x \in I^k$, so that $a_i^k \leq x_i \leq b_i^k$. By the choice of the c_i's, there exists l_i such that $a_i^k \leq c_i^{l_i} \leq x_i \leq c_i^{l_i+1} \leq b_i^k$. Thus, $x \in I^{\mathcal{L}} \subset I^k$, and, furthermore, $I^{\mathcal{L}\circ} \subset I^{k\circ}$ so that $I^{\mathcal{L}}$ has an interior point in common with P.

Thus, $P = \cup I^{\mathcal{L}}$, where the union is taken only over those $I^{\mathcal{L}}$ which have an interior point in P.

We still have three things to prove: $\lambda(P)$ is well defined; P1; and P2. It is obvious that P2 is a consequence of the fact that $\lambda(P)$ is well defined. For if P_1 and P_2 are both represented as nonoverlapping unions of rectangles and P_1 and P_2 are nonoverlapping, then clearly $P_1 \cup P_2$ is automatically represented as a union of nonoverlapping rectangles (those used for P_1 and those used for P_2) and $\lambda(P_1 \cup P_2) = \lambda(P_1) + \lambda(P_2)$. Thus, we have to prove $\lambda(P)$ is well defined and P1.

These two facts can be proved simultaneously by proving the following: suppose P and P' are special polygons represented as nonoverlapping unions of special rectangles:

$$P = \bigcup_{k=1}^{N} I_k, \quad P' = \bigcup_{k=1}^{N'} I'_k.$$

Suppose that

$$P \subset P'.$$

Then

$$\sum_{k=1}^{N} \lambda(I_k) \leq \sum_{k=1}^{N'} \lambda(I'_k).$$

The fact that P1 holds is then clear, and the fact that $\lambda(P)$ is well defined follows simply by letting $P = P'$.

To prove this we refer to the above argument. We regard $P' = \bigcup_{k=1}^{N} I_k \cup \bigcup_{k=1}^{N'} I'_k$ and we obtain a large collection of rectangles $I^{\mathcal{L}}$. Then

$$P = \cup\{I^{\mathcal{L}} \mid I^{\mathcal{L}\circ} \cap P \neq \emptyset\},$$
$$P' = \cup\{I^{\mathcal{L}} \mid I^{\mathcal{L}\circ} \cap P' \neq \emptyset\}.$$

Clearly, then, the sum of $\lambda(I^{\mathcal{L}})$ for those $I^{\mathcal{L}}$'s in the representation of P is not greater than the sum of $\lambda(I^{\mathcal{L}})$ for those $I^{\mathcal{L}}$'s in the representation of P'. What must be proved is then simply

$$\sum_{k=1}^{N} \lambda(I_k) = \sum_{I^{\mathcal{L}\circ} \cap P \neq \emptyset} \lambda(I^{\mathcal{L}\circ})$$

and likewise for P'. This reduces to showing that for each I_k

$$\lambda(I_k) = \sum_{I^{\mathcal{L}\circ} \cap I_k \neq \emptyset} \lambda(I^{\mathcal{L}})$$

and likewise for I'_k. This is something which can clearly be handled. We have reduced the proof to showing that if $I = [a_1, b_1] \times \cdots \times [a_n, b_n]$, and if

$$a_i = c_i^1 < c_i^2 < \cdots < c_i^{m_i} = b_i,$$

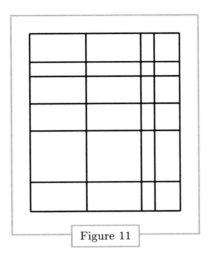

Figure 11

then

$$\lambda(I) = \sum_l \lambda(I^{\mathcal{L}}).$$

This situation is illustrated in Figure 11. The equation to be verified can be written as follows. Let

$$d_i^k = c_i^{k+1} - c_i^k \quad \text{for } 1 \leq k < m_i.$$

Then we must show

$$\prod_{i=1}^n \sum_{k=1}^{m_i-1} d_i^k = \sum_{\mathcal{L}} \prod_{i=1}^n d_i^{l_i}.$$

But this is valid by the simplest algebra. We just need to think of calculating the product on the left side by choosing for each i one term $k = l_i$, multiplying these terms together to obtain $d_1^{l_1} \ldots d_n^{l_n}$, and then summing over all possible choices. The result is precisely the right side.

Invariance of Lebesgue Measure

3

Our construction of the measure λ has a serious potential defect — it seems to depend on a particular coordinate system for $\mathbb{R}^n$. We admitted this in the preceding chapter in the discussion of special rectangles. There we remarked that we do not have a formula for the measure of a rectangle whose edges are not oriented in the directions of the coordinate axes, as in Figure 2.2. The purpose of the present chapter is to remedy this situation, and much more will be accomplished as a result.

Here is a typical situation which we illustrate in $\mathbb{R}^2$:

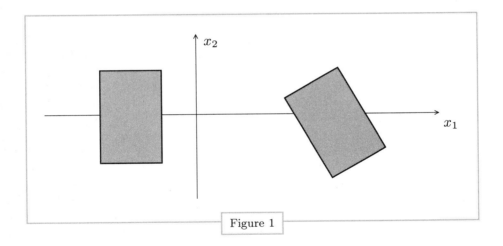

Figure 1

These two rectangles are "congruent" in a fairly obvious sense. The one on the left is special, so we know how to calculate its measure. Suppose its measure is 5. The rectangle on the right is not special, so we do not know how to calculate its measure. But it is a measurable set (it's *compact*), and thus it has a measure. Of course, we expect that its measure is also 5.

In order to prove things like this, we must first define the term "congruent." Since we also want to do more than this, we shall spend the first section of this chapter discussing a bit of linear algebra.

A. Some Linear Algebra

We shall be using $n \times n$ matrices of real numbers. If T is an $n \times n$ matrix, we denote by t_{ij} the entry of T which is in row number i and column number j. We then also write $T = (t_{ij})$, or we display the matrix

$$
T = \begin{pmatrix}
t_{11} & t_{12} & \cdots & t_{1n} \\
t_{21} & t_{22} & \cdots & t_{2n} \\
\vdots & \vdots & & \vdots \\
t_{n1} & t_{n2} & \cdots & t_{nn}
\end{pmatrix} .
$$

The *identity* matrix will be denoted id:

$$
\text{id} = \begin{pmatrix}
1 & 0 & \cdots & 0 \\
0 & 1 & \cdots & 0 \\
\vdots & \vdots & & \vdots \\
0 & 0 & \cdots & 1
\end{pmatrix} .
$$

If T is an $n \times n$ matrix $x \in \mathbb{R}^n$, then we define another point $Tx \in \mathbb{R}^n$ by the formula for the ith coordinate of Tx:

$$
(Tx)_i = \sum_{j=1}^{n} t_{ij} x_j .
$$

This construction defines a *linear* function $x \rightarrow Tx$ of $\mathbb{R}^n$ into itself. Notice that id $x = x$ for all $x \in \mathbb{R}^n$.

In general, a function F which maps one vector space into another is said to be *linear* if

$$
F(ax + by) = aF(x) + bF(y)
$$

for all vectors x and y and all scalars a and b.

Problem 1. Prove that if F is a linear function from $\mathbb{R}^n$ to $\mathbb{R}^n$, then there is a unique matrix T such that

$$
F(x) = Tx \qquad \text{for all } x \in \mathbb{R}^n .
$$

Problem 2. Generalize Problem 1 to the case of a linear function from $\mathbb{R}^n$ to $\mathbb{R}^m$ (T will have to be an $m \times n$ matrix).

Problem 3. Say that a function F which maps one vector space into another is *affine* if

$$F(ax + (1 - a)y) = aF(x) + (1 - a)F(y)$$

for all vectors x and y and all scalars a. Prove that F is affine $\Longleftrightarrow$ there exists a linear function F_0 and a fixed vector x_0 such that

$$F(x) = x_0 + F_0(x) \qquad \text{for all } x.$$

Prove that F_0 and x_0 are uniquely determined by F.

These matrices can be multiplied: If S and T are $n \times n$ matrices, then we define another $n \times n$ matrix ST by the formula

$$ST = \left(\sum_{k=1}^{n} s_{ik} t_{kj} \right) .$$

In general, it is not true that $ST = TS$. But the multiplication is associative: $R(ST) = (RS)T$. Therefore, we do not need to insert parentheses in writing a product of several $n \times n$ matrices. Notice that $\operatorname{id} T = T \operatorname{id} = T$.

Problem 4. Show that this definition of matrix multiplication is not optional, in the following sense. Let F and G be the linear functions

$$F(x) = Sx,$$
$$G(x) = Tx.$$

The composition $F \circ G$ is linear, and is thus given by matrix multiplication according to Problem 1. Prove that the matrix is precisely ST.

Problem 5. Suppose that S is a matrix such that $ST = TS$ for all matrices T. Prove that there exists $c \in \mathbb{R}$ such that

$$S = \begin{pmatrix} c & 0 & \cdots & 0 \\ 0 & c & \cdots & 0 \\ \vdots & \vdots & & \vdots \\ 0 & 0 & \cdots & c \end{pmatrix} .$$

In general, if $c \in \mathbb{R}$ we define $cT = (ct_{ij})$. Thus, in Problem 5 the conclusion is that $S = c \operatorname{id}$.

A matrix T is *invertible* if there exists a matrix S such that $ST = TS =$ id. In this case the matrix S is unique, and is called the *inverse* of T. The usual notation is $S = T^{-1}$.

We now *describe* determinants, though we shall not give a definition (and therefore shall not prove any of the properties). It is possible to assign to every (real) $n \times n$ matrix T a real number; this number is the *determinant* of T and will be denoted $\det T$. The determinant has the following properties:

1. Switching two rows of T produces a matrix whose determinant is $-\det T$.

2. Multiplying any row of T by a real number c produces a matrix whose determinant is $c \det T$.

3. Adding a real multiple of any row of T to a different row produces a matrix whose determinant is $\det T$.

4. Properties 1, 2, and 3 also hold with the word "row" replaced by "column."

5. $\det$ id $= 1$.

6. $\det(ST) = \det S \det T$.

7. T is invertible $\iff \det T \neq 0$.

8. If a matrix T has $t_{ij} = 0$ for all $i < j$, then $\det T = t_{11}t_{22}\ldots t_{nn}$.

9. Let T^{tr} be the *transpose* of T : $T^{\mathrm{tr}} = (t_{ji})$. Then $\det T^{\mathrm{tr}} = \det T$.

We remark that properties 2, 3, and 5 uniquely determine determinants. Notice that $\det(T^{-1}) = (\det T)^{-1}$ in case T is invertible.

A matrix T is said to be an *orthogonal* matrix if T is invertible and $T^{-1} = T^{\mathrm{tr}}$.

An equivalent definition of orthogonal matrices can be given in terms of the Euclidean *inner product* for $\mathbb{R}^n$:

$$x \cdot y = \sum_{k=1}^{n} x_k y_k \qquad \text{for } x, y \in \mathbb{R}^n \ .$$

Then the equivalent definition is the following:

Problem 6. T is an orthogonal matrix $\iff Tx \cdot Ty = x \cdot y$ for all x, $y \in \mathbb{R}^n$.

Elementary matrices. There are two special kinds of matrices we want to discuss and use. In all cases k and l stand for fixed integers between 1 and n.

Multiplying. This is any matrix of the following form. Let $c \neq 0$. Let M be defined by

$$
\begin{aligned}
m_{ii} &= 1 && \text{if } i \neq k, \\
m_{kk} &= c, \\
m_{ij} &= 0 && \text{if } i \neq j.
\end{aligned}
$$

Note that $\underline{\det M = c}$ and that M^{-1} is also a multiplying matrix with c replaced by c^{-1}. Illustration $(k = 1)$:

$$
\begin{pmatrix}
c & 0 & \cdots & 0 \\
0 & 1 & \cdots & 0 \\
\vdots & \vdots & & \vdots \\
0 & 0 & \cdots & 1
\end{pmatrix}.
$$

Adding. In this case let $k \neq l$ and let $c \in \mathbb{R}$. Let the matrix A be defined by

$$
\begin{aligned}
a_{ii} &= 1, \\
a_{kl} &= c, \\
a_{ij} &= 0 && \text{for all other } (i, j).
\end{aligned}
$$

Note that $\underline{\det A = 1}$ and that A^{-1} is another adding matrix, with c replaced by $-c$. Illustration $(k = 1, l = 2)$:

$$
\begin{pmatrix}
1 & c & 0 & \cdots & 0 \\
0 & 1 & 0 & \cdots & 0 \\
\vdots & \vdots & \vdots & & \vdots \\
0 & 0 & 0 & \cdots & 1
\end{pmatrix}.
$$

Now notice the effect of multiplying a given matrix on the *left* by these elementary matrices:

   Multiplying. MT is the matrix obtained from T by multiplying row k by the number c.

   Adding. AT is the matrix obtained from T by adding c times row l to row k.

Problem 7. Describe what happens to T after multiplication on the right in each of these two cases.

We now state the main result of this section.

Lemma: *Every invertible matrix can be expressed as a product of elementary matrices.*

Proof: Let T be an arbitrary $n \times n$ invertible matrix. We first want to obtain the entry 1 in the $(1,1)$ position. There are two possibilities. If $t_{11} \neq 0$, then there exists a unique multiplying matrix M such that MT has the desired property. If $t_{11} = 0$, then the fact that T is invertible implies that some $t_{i1} \neq 0$, and thus there exists an adding matrix A such that AT has the desired property. We describe both possibilities by saying that there exists an elementary matrix E such that ET has the form

$$ET = \begin{pmatrix} 1 \underline{\hspace{3cm}} \\ \underline{\hspace{3cm}} \\ \vdots \end{pmatrix} .$$

Then there exists a sequence of adding matrices A_k such that

$$A_{n-1} A_{n-2} \ldots A_1 \, ET = \begin{pmatrix} 1 & \underline{\hspace{2cm}} \\ 0 & \underline{\hspace{2cm}} \\ \vdots & \vdots \\ 0 & \underline{\hspace{2cm}} \end{pmatrix} .$$

By Problem 7, another sequence of adding matrices $\widetilde{A}_k$ can be found such that

$$A_{n-1} \ldots A_1 \, ET \, \widetilde{A}_1 \ldots \widetilde{A}_{n-1} = \begin{pmatrix} 1 & 0 & \cdots & 0 \\ 0 & \underline{\hspace{2cm}} \\ \vdots & \vdots \\ 0 & \underline{\hspace{2cm}} \end{pmatrix} .$$

This new matrix contains an invertible $(n-1) \times (n-1)$ submatrix, to which we can apply the same procedure. This will not disturb the 1 or the 0's which are displayed above. Therefore, after n stages we arrive at a formula which can be expressed symbolically as

$$E_r E_{r-1} \ldots E_2 E_1 T \, F_1 F_2 \ldots F_{s-1} F_s = \text{id} ,$$

where all the E's and F's are elementary matrices of the two kinds. Multiplying by their inverses in the correct way produces the formula

$$T = E_1^{-1} E_2^{-1} \ldots E_r^{-1} F_s^{-1} \ldots F_2^{-1} F_1^{-1} .$$

Since the inverses are also elementary matrices, the lemma is proved.

QED

Problem 8. There is a third kind of elementary matrix which could be used, called a *switching* matrix. Let $k \neq l$. Then S is a switching matrix if ST is the matrix obtained from T by interchanging rows k and l of T. From this description, calculate the entries of S.

Problem 9. Prove that every switching matrix S can be expressed as a product of the form $M A_1 A_2 A_3$.

This problem implies that we do not need to use switching matrices in our theory (though it may be convenient at times to do so).

Problem 10. Prove that the representation produced in the lemma can be achieved with no more than n^2 elementary matrices. Why is n^2 "obviously" the least number of elementary matrices that can be employed in general?

Problem 11. Write out explicitly the representation of 2×2 matrices as products of elementary matrices.

Problem 12. For this problem only agree that multiplying matrices as defined above are allowed to have $\det M = c = 0$. Then prove that every $n \times n$ matrix can be expressed as a product of elementary matrices. In fact, prove this can be achieved with no more than $n^2 - 1$ elementary matrices in case the matrix is not invertible.

B. Translation and Dilation

First we introduce some convenient notation. If A and B are subsets of $\mathbb{R}^n$, we define their *algebraic* sum and difference respectively by the expressions

$$A + B = \{x + y \mid x \in A \quad \text{and} \quad y \in B\},$$
$$A - B = \{x - y \mid x \in A \quad \text{and} \quad y \in B\}.$$

Note for example that in $\mathbb{R}$ we have $[3,5] + (-1,0) = (2,5)$ and $(-1,4) - (5,6) = (-7,-1)$. Also Problems 2.21 and 2.22 show that if C is the Cantor ternary set, then

$$C + C = [0, 2], \quad C - C = [-1, 1].$$

If $A \subset \mathbb{R}^n$ and $z \in \mathbb{R}^n$, then we define

$$z + A = \{z + x \mid x \in A\},$$

and we call this set a *translation* of A. Also if $t \in \mathbb{R}$ and $t > 0$, then we define

$$tA = \{tx \mid x \in A\},$$

and we call this set a *dilation* of A.

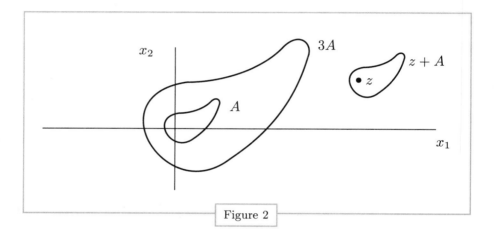

Figure 2

If $I = [a_1, b_1] \times \cdots \times [a_n, b_n]$ is a special rectangle, then

$$z + I = [z_1 + a_1, z_1 + b_1] \times \cdots \times [z_n + a_n, z_n + b_n],$$

and

$$tI = [ta_1, tb_1] \times \cdots \times [ta_n, tb_n].$$

Therefore, we conclude that

$$\lambda(z + I) = \lambda(I),$$
$$\lambda(tI) = t^n \lambda(I).$$

Now by following the stages in the construction of λ in Chapter 2, these two relations can be extended to special polygons, then to open sets, then to compact sets, and we ultimately obtain the following properties:

1. For any $A \subset \mathbb{R}^n$,

$$\lambda^*(z + A) = \lambda^*(A) \quad \text{and}$$
$$\lambda_*(z + A) = \lambda_*(A).$$

2. For any $A \subset \mathbb{R}^n$ and $0 < t < \infty$,

$$\lambda^*(tA) = t^n \lambda^*(A) \quad \text{and}$$

$$\lambda_*(tA) = t^n \lambda_*(A).$$

3. For any $A \subset \mathbb{R}^n$, $z \in \mathbb{R}^n$, and $0 < t < \infty$, A is measurable $\iff z + A$ is measurable $\iff tA$ is measurable. In case A is measurable,

$$\lambda(z + A) = \lambda(A) \quad \text{and}$$

$$\lambda(tA) = t^n \lambda(A).$$

Problem 13. Here is a set related to the Cantor ternary set. Let A be the set of numbers in $[0, 1]$ whose ternary expansions have only finitely many 1's. Prove that $\lambda(A) = 0$.

Problem 14. Let A be the set of real numbers in $[0, \infty)$ whose decimal expansions contain only finitely many 7's. Prove that $\lambda(A) = 0$.

C. Orthogonal Matrices

In this section we shall finally learn that the Lebesgue measure of a set really is independent of its position relative to the coordinate axes of $\mathbb{R}^n$. The precise way to say this is the following: If $A \subset \mathbb{R}^n$ is measurable and B results from A by a *rigid motion*, then B is measurable and $\lambda(B) = \lambda(A)$. Of course, we must also define "rigid motion."

Definition: A function $\mathbb{R}^n \xrightarrow{\Phi} \mathbb{R}^n$ is a *rigid motion* if there exists $z \in \mathbb{R}^n$ and an orthogonal matrix T such that

$$\Phi(x) = z + Tx \qquad \text{for all} \ \ x \in \mathbb{R}^n.$$

Problem 15. Prove that the rigid motions on $\mathbb{R}^n$ form a group if the group multiplication is composition of functions. This group is called the *Euclidean group*. (In case you are not familiar with the word "group," what you must prove are the following properties:

(a) If Φ and Ψ are rigid motions, so is the composition $\Phi \circ \Psi$.

(b) If Φ, Ψ, and Θ are rigid motions, then

$$(\Phi \circ \Psi) \circ \Theta = \Phi \circ (\Psi \circ \Theta).$$

(c) If id is the rigid motion which is the identity, then

$$\Phi \circ \mathrm{id} = \mathrm{id} \circ \Phi = \Phi$$

for every rigid motion Φ.

(d) If Φ is a rigid motion, there exists a rigid motion Ψ such that

$$\Phi \circ \Psi = \Psi \circ \Phi = \mathrm{id} .)$$

If Φ is a rigid motion as in the above definition, and $A \subset \mathbb{R}^n$, then we sometimes write the image $\Phi(A) = z + TA$.

The result we are after will now be stated.

Theorem: *Let Φ be a rigid motion of $\mathbb{R}^n$ and let $A \subset \mathbb{R}^n$. Then*

$$\lambda^*(\Phi(A)) = \lambda^*(A),$$
$$\lambda_*(\Phi(A)) = \lambda_*(A).$$

If A is measurable, then $\Phi(A)$ is measurable and

$$\lambda(\Phi(A)) = \lambda(A).$$

This theorem is a special case of a more general theorem we are going to prove in the following section. Therefore, we do not prove it at the present time. We have singled it out because of its importance and the especially intuitive nature of its statement.

We do remark that if Φ has the form $\Phi(x) = z + Tx$, where T is an orthogonal matrix, then $\Phi(A) = z + TA$, and the results of Section B already show that $\lambda^*(\Phi(A)) = \lambda^*(TA)$, etc. Therefore, when we give the proof we may as well assume that $z = 0$.

Problem 16. The definition of rigid motion in this section requires that Φ be affine. This problem and the next show that this assumption is not actually necessary. First prove the following lemma: If x, y, $z \in \mathbb{R}^n$ and $|x - y| = |x - z| + |z - y|$, then z is on the line segment connecting x and y. This means that for some $t \in [0, 1]$, $z = (1 - t)x + ty$.

(**HINT**: See Problem 1.13.)

Problem 17. Here is a potentially more generous definition of rigid motion: Say that a function $\mathbb{R}^n \overset{\Phi}{\longrightarrow} \mathbb{R}^n$ is a rigid motion if Φ is an *isometry*:

$$|\Phi(x) - \Phi(y)| = |x - y| \quad \text{for all} \quad x, y \in \mathbb{R}^n.$$

Prove that Φ must then be a rigid motion in the previous sense.

(**HINT**: Show that you can assume $\Phi(0) = 0$. Use Problem 16 to show that if $0 \le s \le 1$ and x, $y \in \mathbb{R}^n$, then there exists $t \in [0, 1]$ such that

$$\Phi((1 - s)x + sy) = (1 - t)\Phi(x) + t\Phi(y).$$

Then prove that $s = t$. The rest should be straightforward.)

Problem 18. Here is a different way to obtain the conclusion of Problem 17. Assume Φ is an isometry in the above sense and, with no loss of generality, $\Phi(0) = 0$. First prove that $\Phi(x) \cdot \Phi(y) = x \cdot y$, using the fact that

$$2x \cdot y = |x|^2 + |y|^2 - |x - y|^2.$$

Now let $\varepsilon_1, \ldots, \varepsilon_n$ be an orthonormal basis of $\mathbb{R}^n$. Prove that $\Phi(\varepsilon_1), \ldots, \Phi(\varepsilon_n)$ also form an orthonormal basis. For any $x \in \mathbb{R}^n$, $\Phi(x) \cdot \Phi(\varepsilon_k) = x \cdot \varepsilon_k$. Conclude that

$$\Phi(x) = \sum_{k=1}^{n} x \cdot \varepsilon_k \Phi(\varepsilon_k).$$

Now prove that $\Phi(x) = Tx$ for an orthogonal matrix T.

D. The General Matrix

Now we are going to discuss the relation between the measure of A and the measure of TA, where T is an arbitrary $n \times n$ matrix.

Theorem: *Let T be an $n \times n$ matrix and $A \subset \mathbb{R}^n$. Then*

$$\lambda^*(TA) = \mid \det T \mid \lambda^*(A),$$
$$\lambda_*(TA) = \mid \det T \mid \lambda_*(A).$$

If A is measurable, then TA is measurable and

$$\lambda(TA) = \mid \det T \mid \lambda(A).$$

Proof: We first handle the case in which T is invertible. Notice that if the theorem is valid for two invertible matrices, then it is automatically valid for the product of these matrices. This is because $\det(T_1 T_2) = \det T_1 \det T_2$. Therefore, Section A implies that we can assume T is an *elementary* matrix. And most of the proof we shall give is independent of the type of elementary matrix T is. Therefore, we shall first state and prove a general lemma, and only after the lemma shall we investigate elementary matrices in detail.

Lemma: *Let T be an elementary matrix. Let J be the (nonspecial) rectangle*

$$J = [0,1) \times \cdots \times [0,1).$$

Let ρ be equal to the ratio

$$\rho = \frac{\lambda(TJ)}{\lambda(J)}.$$

Then if $A \subset \mathbb{R}^n$,

$$\lambda^*(TA) = \rho\lambda^*(A),$$
$$\lambda_*(TA) = \rho\lambda_*(A).$$

If A is measurable, then TA is measurable and

$$\lambda(TA) = \rho\lambda(A).$$

Proof: The linear function $x \to Tx$ determined by T is continuous, as is its inverse. Therefore, any topological property of a set A is also a property of TA. In particular, if A is compact then TA is compact, and if A is open then TA is open. Moreover, since J is a countable union of compact sets,

$$J = \bigcup_{k=1}^{\infty} [0, 1 - k^{-1}] \times \cdots \times [0, 1 - k^{-1}],$$

TJ is also a countable union of compact sets. In particular, TJ is measurable, so the definition of ρ makes sense.

Thanks to these observations, an examination of the proof presented in Section B shows that we have only to establish these results for an arbitrary open set G. Then they follow in the generality stated by working through Stages 4, 5, 6 in the construction of Lebesgue measure in Chapter 2.

Now let $G \subset \mathbb{R}^n$ be an arbitrary nonempty open set. As in Problem 2.9, we are going to "pave" G with a countable disjoint collection of translations of dilations of J. (This disjointness is possible because we used the intervals $[0,1)$ in the definition of J.) The procedure is straightforward: First pave $\mathbb{R}^n$ with the rectangles: $[\alpha_1, \alpha_1 + 1) \times [\alpha_2, \alpha_2 + 1) \times \cdots \times [\alpha_n, \alpha_n + 1)$, where each $\alpha_k \in \mathbb{Z}$. "Select" those rectangles which are contained in G. Then pave each unselected rectangle with the 2^n rectangles obtained by bisecting the edges of the original rectangle. These rectangles all have the form $[\alpha_1/2, \alpha_1/2 + 1/2) \times \cdots \times [\alpha_n/2, \alpha_n/2 + 1/2)$ with $\alpha_k \in \mathbb{Z}$. Now select those new rectangles which are contained in G. By continuing this process it follows that an expression is obtained of the form

$$G = \bigcup_{k=1}^{\infty} J_k,$$

where the J_k's are disjoint, and each J_k is a translation of a dilation of J:

$$J_k = z_k + t_k J.$$

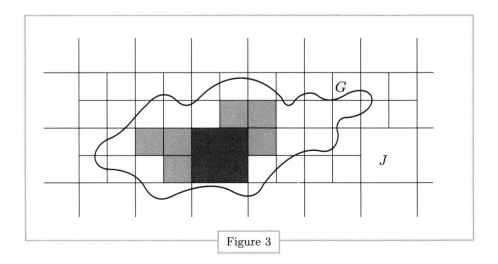

Figure 3

Now we easily compute:

$$\lambda(J_k) = t_k^n \lambda(J) \qquad \text{(by Section B)};$$
$$T J_k = T z_k + t_k T J \quad \text{(by linear algebra)};$$
$$\lambda(T J_k) = t_k^n \lambda(T J) \qquad \text{(by Section B)};$$

and thus

$$\lambda(T J_k) = \rho \lambda(J_k) \qquad \text{(by definition of } \rho\text{)}.$$

Therefore, by the countable additivity of Lebesgue measure, and the disjointness of the $T J_k$'s,

$$\lambda(TG) = \lambda \left(\bigcup_{k=1}^{\infty} T J_k \right)$$
$$= \sum_{k=1}^{\infty} \lambda(T J_k)$$
$$= \sum_{k=1}^{\infty} \rho \lambda(J_k)$$
$$= \rho \lambda(G).$$

(QED for the lemma)

Now we prove that $\rho = |\det T|$. This will complete the proof of the theorem. Remember that we are assuming that T is an elementary matrix and that we know there is an equation

$$\lambda(TA) = \rho \lambda(A)$$

for all measurable sets A. So all that is left is to choose a set A for which we can actually calculate the ratio $\lambda(TA)/\lambda(A)$. We treat the two types of elementary matrices separately.

1. T is a *multiplying* matrix. We may as well assume $T = (t_{ij})$ with $t_{11} = c$ and $t_{ii} = 1$ for $i \neq 1$. Thus, $\det T = c$. Choose $A = [0,1] \times \cdots \times [0,1]$. If $c > 0$, then $TA = [0,c] \times [0,1] \times \cdots \times [0,1]$; if $c < 0$, then $TA = [c,0] \times [0,1] \times \cdots \times [0,1]$. In either case, $\lambda(TA) = |c|$ and $\lambda(A) = 1$, so the result follows.

2. T is an *adding* matrix. This case is a little more subtle. We may as well assume that T has the form

$$T = \begin{pmatrix} 1 & c & 0 & \cdots & 0 \\ 0 & 1 & 0 & \cdots & 0 \\ \vdots & \vdots & \vdots & & \vdots \\ 0 & 0 & 0 & \cdots & 1 \end{pmatrix}.$$

For the sake of definiteness assume $c > 0$. Now choose

$$A = \{x \mid -cx_2 \le x_1 \le 0,\ 0 \le x_2 \le 1, \dots, 0 \le x_n \le 1\}.$$

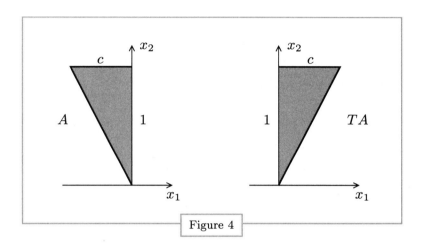

Figure 4

It is a simple matter to calculate

$$TA = \{x \mid 0 \le x_1 \le cx_2,\ 0 \le x_2 \le 1, \dots, 0 \le x_n \le 1\}.$$

(See Figure 4.) If M is the multiplication matrix

$$M = \begin{pmatrix} -1 & 0 & \cdots & 0 \\ 0 & 1 & \cdots & 0 \\ \vdots & \vdots & & \vdots \\ 0 & 0 & \cdots & 1 \end{pmatrix},$$

there follows for this particular A

$$TA = MA.$$

The previous case therefore implies $\lambda(TA) = \lambda(MA) = \lambda(A)$. Thus, in this case $\rho = 1$ and $\det T = 1$.

Both cases have now been successfully dealt with. Finally, we must treat the degenerate case in which $\det T = 0$. This is quite simple, as we can show that $T\mathbb{R}^n$ itself has zero measure, so that the assertions of the theorem are trivial.

Since $\det T = 0$, the vectors in $\mathbb{R}^n$ which constitute the *columns* of the matrix T are linearly dependent. They span a subspace Σ of $\mathbb{R}^n$ of some dimension $m < n$. Choose an orthonormal basis $\{\varepsilon_1, \ldots, \varepsilon_n\}$ of $\mathbb{R}^n$, where the vectors $\varepsilon_1, \ldots, \varepsilon_m$ form a basis for Σ. Then let S be the matrix whose columns are the vectors $\varepsilon_1, \ldots, \varepsilon_n$, in that order.

The matrix S is orthogonal, and it is easy to calculate

$$S(\mathbb{R}^m \times \{0\}) = \Sigma.$$

(Here 0 stands for the origin in $\mathbb{R}^{n-m}$.) Therefore,

$$
\begin{aligned}
\lambda(T\mathbb{R}^n) &= \lambda(\Sigma) \\
&= \lambda\Big(S(\mathbb{R}^m \times \{0\}) \Big) \\
&= |\det S| \lambda(\mathbb{R}^m \times \{0\}) \quad \text{(by the non-degenerate case)} \\
&= \lambda(\mathbb{R}^m \times \{0\}) \\
&= 0 \quad\quad\quad\quad\quad\quad\quad \text{(by Problem 2.32).}
\end{aligned}
$$

QED

Remark: It is instructive to notice the special case of an orthogonal matrix T. As the lemma really only requires T to be invertible, not elementary, it follows that $\lambda(TA) = \rho\lambda(A)$ for all measurable A. Then we can simply choose $A = B(0,1)$. Since T is orthogonal, $|Tx| = |x|$ for all $x \in \mathbb{R}^n$ by Problem 6. Therefore, $TA = A$ and we conclude $\rho = 1$.

Problem 19. Let $a_1, a_2, \ldots, a_n \in \mathbb{R}^n$ and write $a_j = (a_{1j}, a_{2j}, \ldots, a_{nj})$. Let A be the "parallelogram"

$$A = \{t_1 a_1 + \cdots + t_n a_n \mid 0 \leq t_k \leq 1 \quad \text{for all } k\}.$$

Prove that $\lambda(A)$ is the absolute value of the determinant of (a_{ij}).

Some Interesting Sets

A. A Nonmeasurable Set

Now we establish the existence of nonmeasurable sets. As you will see, the proof is highly nonconstructive.

> **Theorem:** *There exists a set $E \subset \mathbb{R}^n$ such that E is not measurable.*

Proof: We shall be using the set $\mathbb{Q}^n$ of points $x \in \mathbb{R}^n$ all of whose coordinates are rational numbers. For any $x \in \mathbb{R}^n$ consider the translate $x + \mathbb{Q}^n$ of the set $\mathbb{Q}^n$. Of course, $y \in x + \mathbb{Q}^n \iff y - x \in \mathbb{Q}^n$.

The crucial property we require is that if $x, x' \in \mathbb{R}^n$, then either

$$x + \mathbb{Q}^n = x' + \mathbb{Q}^n$$

or

$$(x + \mathbb{Q}^n) \cap (x' + \mathbb{Q}^n) = \emptyset.$$

(Prove this yourself.) Thus, every point of $\mathbb{R}^n$ belongs to one and only one of the sets $x + \mathbb{Q}^n$, though the choice of x is not unique. This means that $\mathbb{R}^n$ is covered disjointly by the translates of $\mathbb{Q}^n$. Now we invoke the AXIOM OF CHOICE to "choose" one and only one point from each translate of $\mathbb{Q}^n$. Precisely, the axiom implies that there exists a set $E \subset \mathbb{R}^n$ such that every point of $\mathbb{R}^n$ belongs to one and only one of the sets $x + \mathbb{Q}^n$ for $x \in E$:

$$\mathbb{R}^n = \bigcup_{x \in E} (x + \mathbb{Q}^n) \qquad \text{(disjoint union)}.$$

Another way of expressing the property of E is this: For any $x \in \mathbb{R}^n$ there exist a unique $y \in E$ and a unique $z \in \mathbb{Q}^n$ such that $x = y + z$. Thus, if we enumerate $\mathbb{Q}^n = \{r_1, r_2, r_3, \ldots\}$, then

$$\mathbb{R}^n = \bigcup_{k=1}^{\infty} (r_k + E) \qquad \text{(disjoint union)}.$$

We conclude that $\lambda^*(E) > 0$. Otherwise, we should have $\lambda(E) = 0$ and thus $\lambda(r_k + E) = 0$. This would imply $\lambda(\mathbb{R}^n) = 0$.

On the other hand, $\lambda_*(E) = 0$. This can be seen as follows. Let K be an arbitrary compact set such that $K \subset E$. Let $D = B(0,1) \cap \mathbb{Q}^n$. Thus, D is a bounded infinite countable set. Now the choice of E implies

$$\bigcup_{r \in D} (r + K)$$

is an infinite countable disjoint union. Since this union is contained in $D + K$ and both D and K are bounded, the union has finite measure. By the countable additivity of λ,

$$\infty > \lambda \left(\bigcup_{r \in D} (r + K) \right)$$
$$= \sum_{r \in D} \lambda(r + K)$$
$$= \sum_{r \in D} \lambda(K).$$

Since the latter sum is an infinite series, $\lambda(K) = 0$. Since K is arbitrary, therefore $\lambda_*(E) = 0$. Thus, $0 = \lambda_*(E) < \lambda^*(E)$, and we conclude that $E \notin \mathcal{L}$. **QED**

The existence of the nonmeasurable set E easily implies the existence of many others, as we now show.

> **Corollary:** *If $A \subset \mathbb{R}^n$ is measurable and $\lambda(A) > 0$, then there exists $B \subset A$ such that B is not measurable.*

Proof: Using the notation of the proof of the theorem,

$$A = \bigcup_{k=1}^{\infty} (r_k + E) \cap A.$$

Since $\lambda(A) > 0$, the countable additivity of λ implies that at least one of the sets $(r_k + E) \cap A$ fails to have zero (outer) measure. Thus, we set $B = (r_k + E) \cap A$ with $\lambda^*(B) > 0$. Then we also have

$$\lambda_*(B) = \lambda_*((r_k + E) \cap A)$$
$$\leq \lambda_*(r_k + E)$$
$$= \lambda_*(E)$$
$$= 0.$$

Thus, $B \notin \mathcal{L}$.   **QED**

Remark: The use of the axiom of choice in the construction of non-measurable sets is very interesting. A very striking application of this axiom is discussed in an article by Karl Stromberg, "The Banach-Tarski Paradox," *Amer. Math. Monthly 86* (1979), 151–161,and in a book by Stan Wagon, *The Banach-Tarski Paradox*, Cambridge University Press, 1985. Here is one version of the Banach-Tarski paradox, found on p. 29 of Wagon's book:

Let A and B be any two bounded subsets of $\mathbb{R}^3$, each having nonempty interior. Then each can be expressed as a disjoint finite union

$$A = \bigcup_{k=1}^{n} A_k, \quad B = \bigcup_{k=1}^{n} B_k,$$

and there exist rigid motions Φ_k such that $\Phi_k(A_k) = B_k$ for $k = 1$, 2, ..., n.

Problem 1. Prove that there exist disjoint subsets A and B of $\mathbb{R}^n$ such that
$$\lambda^*(A \cup B) < \lambda^*(A) + \lambda^*(B)$$
and
$$\lambda_*(A \cup B) > \lambda_*(A) + \lambda_*(B).$$

Problem 2. Prove that if A and B are subsets of $\mathbb{R}^n$ which are "separated" in the sense that there exists a measurable set C such that
$$A \subset C \quad \text{and} \quad \lambda(B \cap C) = 0,$$
then
$$\lambda^*(A \cup B) = \lambda^*(A) + \lambda^*(B).$$
(**HINT:** Use the Carathéodory criterion M12.)

B. A Bevy of Cantor Sets

As in the construction of the Cantor ternary set in Section 2.A, we start with the closed interval $[0, 1] \subset \mathbb{R}$. Choose any positive numbers l_k such that
$$1 = l_0 > 2l_1 > 4l_2 > \cdots > 2^k l_k > \dots .$$

Now remove from $[0, 1]$ the open interval with center $1/2$ and length $1 - 2l_1$; thus, the two remaining closed intervals each have length l_1. For reasons to be explained later, we choose to designate the deleted open interval as $J_{1/2}$:

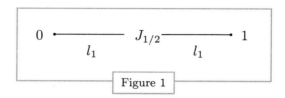

Figure 1

Now remove from the two remaining closed intervals the two concentric open intervals with length $l_1 - 2l_2$, leaving four closed intervals each having length l_2. Designate these deleted open intervals $J_{1/4}$ and $J_{3/4}$:

$$0 \xrightarrow{\qquad} J_{1/4} \xrightarrow{\qquad} J_{1/2} \xrightarrow{\qquad} J_{3/4} \xrightarrow{\qquad} 1$$
$$\quad l_2 \qquad\qquad l_2 \qquad\qquad l_2 \qquad\qquad l_2$$

Figure 2

Repeat this process indefinitely. The Cantor set we finally achieve is the intersection of all these unions of closed intervals, or, what is the same thing, the complement in $[0, 1]$ of all the open intervals which have been discarded. At the kth stage of the construction there remain 2^k closed disjoint intervals each of length l_k. We choose to call these "*black*" intervals.

Call this set A. Thus, A is compact and

$$\lambda(A) = \lim_{k \to \infty} 2^k l_k.$$

Notice that the Cantor ternary set is obtained if $l_k = 3^{-k}$.

The closed set A is *nowhere dense* (in general, a set is said to be *nowhere dense* if its closure contains no interior points). For, if $A^\circ \neq \emptyset$, then A must contain an interval I with positive length. Choose k such that $2^{-k} \leq \lambda(I)$. Since A is contained in a union of 2^k disjoint closed black intervals of length l_k, I must be contained in one such interval. Thus, $\lambda(I) \leq l_k$, but then $2^{-k} \leq \lambda(I) \leq l_k < 2^{-k}$, a contradiction.

In spite of this property, $\lambda(A)$ can be as close to 1 as we please. For example, suppose $0 \le \theta < 1$, and choose

$$2^k l_k = \frac{\theta k + 1}{k + 1}.$$

With this choice, $\lambda(A) = \theta$.

In case the Cantor set A has positive measure, it is sometimes called a "fat" Cantor set.

The set A is also *perfect* (a set which is closed is said to be *perfect* if none of its points is isolated, i.e., if each point of the set is a limit point of the set). In fact, more generally we have

Problem 3. Let $F \subset \mathbb{R}$ be closed. Then F^c has a unique representation as a countable disjoint union of open intervals: $F^c = \bigcup_{k=1}^{\infty} (a_k, b_k)$. This follows from Problem 2.6. Prove that F is perfect $\iff$ no pair of the constituent open intervals in F^c abut (have a common endpoint).

Problem 4. Let A be a Cantor set constructed as above, but with an additional restriction. Let $0 < \rho < 1$ be fixed. At a certain stage of the construction there are a certain number 2^{k-1} of black intervals of length l_{k-1} which remain. From each of them an open interval of length $l_{k-1} - 2l_k$ is deleted. We suppose that we remove at least the fraction ρ of what was present:

$$\frac{l_{k-1} - 2l_k}{l_{k-1}} \ge \rho \quad \text{for all } k.$$

Prove that if $I \subset \mathbb{R}$ is any interval having finite positive measure, then there exists an open interval $J \subset I \cap A^c$ such that

$$\frac{\lambda(J)}{\lambda(I)} \ge \frac{\rho}{1 + 2\rho}.$$

(**HINT:** You can surely assume I contains points of A. Suppose $I = [a, b]$. If $a \in A^c$, let a' be the largest number such that $(a, a') \subset A^c$. Choose $b' < b$ in a similar way. Choose k such that $l_k < b' - a' \le l_{k-1}$. Then a' and b' must belong to two different of the 2^k black intervals of the common length l_k. Let J' be one of the open intervals between a' and b' which have length $l_{j-1} - 2l_j$ with $j \le k$ and which are part of A^c. Now prove that at least one of the intervals (a, a'), (b', b), and J' satisfies the required inequality.)

Problem 5. Suppose further that

$$\frac{l_{k-1} - 2l_k}{l_{k-1}} = \rho \quad \text{for all } k.$$

(This means that $l_k = ((1 - \rho)/2)^k$.) Prove that the number $\rho/(1 + 2\rho)$ in the preceding problem is sharp.

Problem 6. Let C be the Cantor ternary set. Let $I \subset \mathbb{R}$ be an interval having finite positive measure. Prove that there exists an open interval $J \subset I \cap C^c$ such that

$$\frac{\lambda(J)}{\lambda(I)} \geq \frac{1}{5}.$$

C. The Lebesgue Function Associated with a Cantor Set

We continue with the discussion of the Cantor set A constructed in the preceding section, keeping the notation of that section. We now fix attention on the excluded open intervals $J_{1/2}$; $J_{1/4}$, $J_{3/4}$; $J_{1/8}$, $J_{3/8}$, etc. The situation will appear even more logical if we adjoin two other open intervals at the outset: $J_0 = (-\infty, 0)$ and $J_1 = (1, \infty)$.

Let D denote the *dyadic* rationals in $[0, 1]$, i.e., the rational numbers of the form $m/2^n$ for integers m and n such that $0 \leq m \leq 2^n$, $0 \leq n$. Then our construction produces for each $r \in D$ an open interval J_r. These disjoint open intervals are positioned in $\mathbb{R}$ with an order corresponding to the natural ordering of D. That is, $r < r' \implies J_r$ is entirely to the left of $J_{r'}$.

The function we are going to construct will be denoted f, and will eventually be defined for all real numbers. For the moment, however, we define f only on the union of the open intervals J_r by the equation

$$f(x) = r \quad \text{for all } x \in J_r, r \in D.$$

Since $A = \mathbb{R} \sim \bigcup_{r \in D} J_r$ by definition, f is now defined on A^c. Clearly, f

is an increasing function which is constant on all the intervals J_r. It is very instructive to consider a portion of its graph:

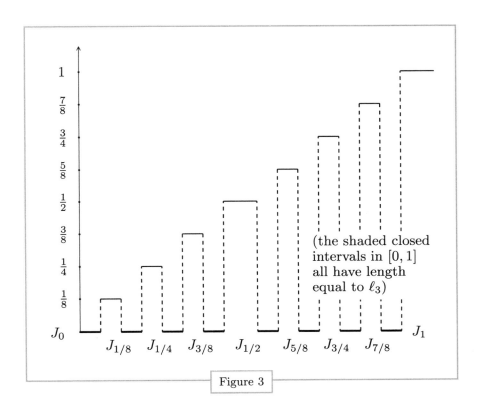

Figure 3

Now we discuss the continuity of f on A^c. From Figure 3 it is quite evident that if x, $y \in A^c$ and $|x - y| \leq l_3$ (for example), then x and y cannot belong to two different J_r for dyadic rationals r with denominators less than or equal to 8. Therefore, $|f(x) - f(y)| \leq \frac{1}{8}$. This argument is quite general. Indeed, suppose x, $y \in A^c$ and $|x - y| \leq l_k$. At one stage of the construction A is contained in the union of 2^k disjoint black intervals of length l_k. No such interval can be contained in the interval from x to y since $|x - y| \leq l_k$. Thus, if neither x nor y belongs to one of these black intervals, then x and y must belong to the same excluded open interval, so that $f(x) = f(y)$. We therefore assume that either x or y (or both) belongs to one of these black intervals. Figure 4 depicts the situation involving two consecutive black intervals I and I' each having length l_k.

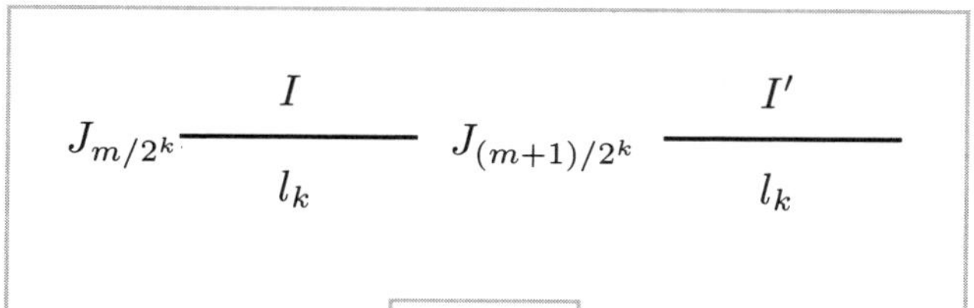

Figure 4

There are three types of possible situations for the location of x and y:

$x \in I, y \in I$. In this case $|f(x) - f(y)| < (m+1)/2^k - m/2^k = 1/2^k$.

$x \in I, y \in J_{(m+1)/2^k}$. In this case

$$|f(x) - f(y)| = (m+1)/2^k - f(x) < (m+1)/2^k - m/2^k = 1/2^k.$$

$x \in I, y \in I'$. Since f is increasing,

$$|\, f(x) - f(y) \,| = f(y) - f(x) < \frac{m+2}{2^k} - \frac{m}{2^k} = \frac{2}{2^k}.$$

But a more delicate analysis is interesting: since the procedure for constructing f looks the same in both I and I', and since the values of f in I' are precisely $1/2^k$ larger than the corresponding values in I, it follows that

$$|\, f(x) - f(y) \,| = f(y) - f(x) < \frac{1}{2^k}.$$

For the inequality $|x - y| \le l_k$ implies that y is further left relative to I' than x is relative to I.

So we have proved that

$$x, y \in A^c \quad \text{and} \quad |\, x - y \,| \le l_k \Rightarrow |\, f(x) - f(y) \,| < 2^{-k}.$$

This establishes the *uniform* continuity (Section 1.E) of f as a function from A^c into $[0,1]$. The following problem shows that there is a unique function on the closure of A^c which is continuous and which agrees with f on A^c.

Problem 7. Let $E \subset \mathbb{R}^n$ be an arbitrary set and let $E \xrightarrow{\ f\ } \mathbb{R}$ be *uniformly* continuous. That is, for all $\epsilon > 0$ there exists $\delta > 0$ such that

$$x, y \in E \quad \text{and} \quad \mid x - y \mid < \delta \Rightarrow \mid f(x) - f(y) \mid < \epsilon.$$

Prove that there exists a unique function $E^- \xrightarrow{\ F\ } \mathbb{R}$ such that F is continuous and $F = f$ on E.

(**HINT**: Try defining F in the following way: For $x \in E^-$ let x_k be a sequence such that $x_k \in E$ and $\lim\limits_{k \to \infty} x_k = x$. Then let $F(x) = \lim\limits_{k \to \infty} f(x_k)$.)

In the present case A is nowhere dense, so $\overline{A^c} = \mathbb{R}$. Thus, there exists a unique continuous function on $\mathbb{R}$ which agrees with f on A^c. Let us continue to denote this extended function by the letter f. This function is called the *Lebesgue function* for the Cantor set A. It has the following properties:

$f = r$ on each open interval J_r for any $r \in D$,

f is nondecreasing,

$f : \mathbb{R} \to [0, 1]$,

f is continuous — in fact, $\mid x - y \mid \le l_k \Rightarrow \mid f(x) - f(y) \mid \le 2^{-k}$.

One further property is of special interest: Suppose $x < y$ and $x, y \in A$. Then $f(x) < f(y)$ unless $(x, y) = J_r$ for some $r \in D$. The reason is clear: If the interval (x, y) is not equal to one of the J_r's, then there must exist infinitely many J_r's between x and y, proving that f is not constant on (x, y). Thus, f *almost* establishes a one-to-one correspondence between A and the interval $[0, 1]$. Namely, if we denote by B the set consisting of all the left end points of the J_r's, together with the origin, then f *is* a bijection of $A \sim B$ onto $(0, 1)$. Since B is countable, this shows that A and $(0, 1)$ can be placed in one-to-one correspondence. The proof of this is a simple exercise in elementary cardinal arithmetic, as we now show.

Lemma: *Suppose that A and X are infinite sets and B is a countable subset of A such that $A \sim B$ and X are in one-to-one correspondence. Then A and X are also in one-to-one correspondence.*

Proof: Two sets which are in one-to-one correspondence are said to be *equipotent*. Thus, $A \sim B$ and X are equipotent. This means that there exists a bijection $A \sim B \xrightarrow{\ F\ } X$. Since $A \sim B$ is infinite, Problem 1.7 implies that there exists a countable infinite set $B_1 \subset A \sim B$. Then

$F(B_1)$ is also countable and infinite, and

$$A \sim B \sim B_1 \quad \text{and} \quad X \sim F(B_1) \text{ are equipotent.}$$

Now $B \cup B_1$ is also countable and infinite, so we conclude

$$B \cup B_1 \quad \text{and} \quad F(B_1) \text{ are equipotent.}$$

These two equipotencies imply that A and X are equipotent.   **QED**

We conclude that any of our Cantor sets A is equipotent with the interval $(0, 1)$. Thus, they are also equipotent with $\mathbb{R}$, since $(0, 1)$ and $\mathbb{R}$ are equipotent. Here is an example of a bijection from $(0, 1)$ to $\mathbb{R}$:

$$F(x) = \frac{1}{1 - x} - \frac{1}{x}.$$

Perhaps it has occurred to you that there was really nothing to worry about in proving that A is equipotent with $\mathbb{R}$. Perhaps your reasoning goes something like this: Since $A \sim \{\text{countable set}\}$ is equipotent with $(0, 1)$, A is not countable. Since $A \subset \mathbb{R}$, however, the only remaining possibility is that A is equipotent with $\mathbb{R}$. Simple as that sounds, it is not obvious. In fact, it is frequently taken as an *axiom* of set theory, and is called the CONTINUUM HYPOTHESIS: Any noncountable subset of $\mathbb{R}$ is equipotent with $\mathbb{R}$. But of course we needed no such axiom in dealing with the Cantor sets — we were able to prove directly that they are equipotent with $\mathbb{R}$.

Problem 8. Prove that all of the Lebesgue functions satisfy $f(1 - x) + f(x) = 1$.

Now we are going to give an explicit analysis of the Cantor set A which generalizes the use of ternary expansions for the Cantor ternary set. We continue using the notation of Section B. Then we have the following result.

Lemma: *Let r be a dyadic rational in $[0, 1)$ and suppose r is given by*

$$r = \sum_{j=1}^{k} \epsilon_j 2^{-j},$$

where $\epsilon_j = 0$ or 1. Then the corresponding deleted open interval $J_r = (a, b)$ has a right end point given by

$$b = \sum_{j=1}^{k} \epsilon_j (l_{j-1} - l_j).$$

Proof: We argue by induction. For $k = 1$ we have $r = \epsilon_1 2^{-1}$. If $\epsilon_1 = 0$, then $J_0 = (-\infty, 0)$ and the formula gives $b = 0$, which is correct; if $\epsilon_1 = 1$, then $J_{1/2} = (l_1, l_0 - l_1)$, and the formula gives $b = l_0 - l_1$, which is also correct. Now we assume its validity for $k - 1$, and prove it for k. Thus, we assume $r = \sum_{j=1}^{k} \epsilon_j 2^{-j}$ and $J_r = (a, b)$. Note that we can assume $\epsilon_k = 1$, otherwise the result would follow from its validity for $k - 1$. Therefore, the interval J_r is deleted from a certain black interval of length l_{k-1} as shown in the figure:

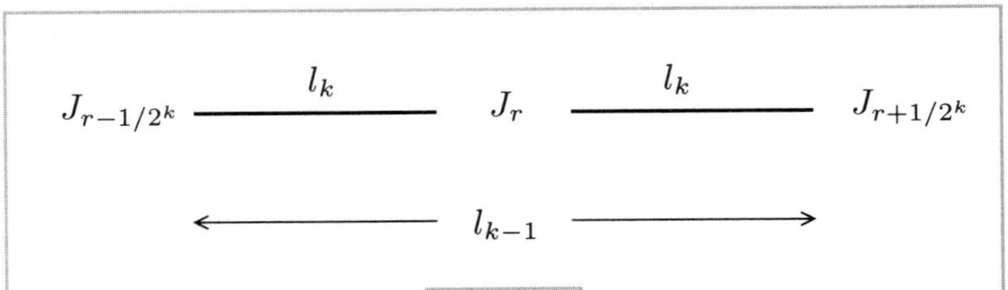

Figure 5

Since $r - 1/2^k = \sum_{j=1}^{k-1} \epsilon_j 2^{-j}$, the induction hypothesis implies that the right end point of $J_{r-1/2^k}$ is $\sum_{j=1}^{k-1} \epsilon_j (l_{j-1} - l_j)$. Therefore we see immediately that

$$b = \sum_{j=1}^{k-1} \epsilon_j (l_{j-1} - l_j) + (l_{k-1} - l_k).$$

QED

Theorem: *Let A be the Cantor set constructed in Section B. Let $0 \leq x \leq 1$. Then $x \in A \Longleftrightarrow$*

$$x = \sum_{j=1}^{\infty} \epsilon_j (l_{j-1} - l_j),$$

where $\epsilon_j = 0$ or 1. This representation of x is unique. Furthermore, if f is the Lebesgue function for A, then

$$f(x) = \sum_{j=1}^{\infty} \epsilon_j 2^{-j}.$$

Proof: First assume that x has such a representation. Then define

$$x_k = \sum_{j=1}^{k} \epsilon_j (l_{j-1} - l_j).$$

By the lemma, x_k is the right end point of a deleted interval J_{r_k}, and thus $x_k \in A$. Since $x_k \to x$ and A is closed, $x \in A$. Furthermore,

$$f(x_k) = r_k = \sum_{j=1}^{k} \epsilon_j 2^{-j}.$$

Since f is continuous, we obtain the required formula for $f(x)$ by letting $k \to \infty$.

Conversely, assume $x \in A$. Then for any k we know that x belongs to one of the black intervals of length l_k:

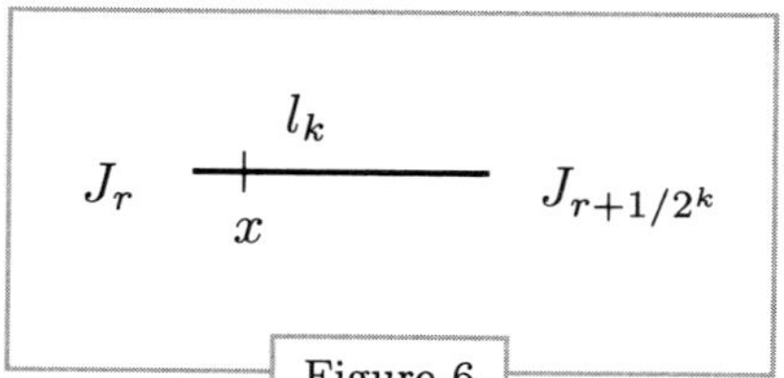

Figure 6

Now r has the form

$$r = \sum_{j=1}^{k} \epsilon_j 2^{-j},$$

and the lemma gives the right end point of J_r. Therefore,

$$\sum_{j=1}^{k} \epsilon_j (l_{j-1} - l_j) \leq x \leq \sum_{j=1}^{k} \epsilon_j (l_{j-1} - l_j) + l_k,$$

for a unique determination of $\epsilon_1, \ldots, \epsilon_k$. At the next stage in the construction we obtain an inequality of the sort

$$\sum_{j=1}^{k+1} \delta_j (l_{j-1} - l_j) \leq x \leq \sum_{j=1}^{k+1} \delta_j (l_{j-1} - l_j) + l_{k+1}.$$

But we easily see that $\delta_j = \epsilon_j$ for $1 \leq j \leq k$. Indeed, the second inequality implies

$$\sum_{j=1}^{k} \delta_j (l_{j-1} - l_j) \leq x \leq \sum_{j=1}^{k} \delta_j (l_{j-1} - l_j) + l_k,$$

where we have used $\delta_{k+1} \geq 0$ to get the left inequality and $\delta_{k+1} \leq 1$ to get the right. But the uniqueness of the kth stage implies that $\delta_j = \epsilon_j$ for $1 \leq j \leq k$. Since $l_k \to 0$ as $k \to \infty$, we now conclude that

$$x = \sum_{j=1}^{\infty} \epsilon_j (l_{j-1} - l_j).$$

Finally, we must prove the representation is unique. Suppose that the contrary were true. Then we would have

$$\sum_{j=1}^{\infty} \epsilon_j (l_{j-1} - l_j) = \sum_{j=1}^{\infty} \delta_j (l_{j-1} - l_j),$$

and there would be a smallest $k \geq 1$ such that $\epsilon_k \neq \delta_k$. We may assume

$\epsilon_k = 1$, $\delta_k = 0$. Then

$$l_{k-1} - l_k \leq \sum_{j=k}^{\infty} \epsilon_j (l_{j-1} - l_j)$$

$$= \sum_{j=k}^{\infty} \delta_j (l_{j-1} - l_j)$$

$$\leq \sum_{j=k+1}^{\infty} (l_{j-1} - l_j)$$

$$= l_k.$$

Therefore, $l_{k-1} \leq 2l_k$, which is a contradiction.   **QED**

Problem 9. Let f be the Lebesgue function for the Cantor ternary set. Use the preceding theorem to conclude that for every x in the Cantor ternary set, if

$$x = .\alpha_1 \alpha_2 \alpha_3 \ldots \qquad \text{(a ternary expansion without 1's)},$$

then

$$f(x) = .\frac{\alpha_1}{2} \frac{\alpha_2}{2} \frac{\alpha_3}{2} \ldots \qquad \text{(binary expansion)}.$$

Problem 10. Prove that if f is the Lebesgue function for the Cantor ternary set, then

$$f\left(\frac{x}{3}\right) = \frac{1}{2} f(x) \qquad \text{for } 0 \leq x \leq 1.$$

Problem 11. At the kth stage in the construction of A there remain 2^k black intervals each of length l_k. Suppose that I and I' are two consecutive such intervals and suppose that $\alpha > 0$ and $I' = \alpha + I$. If f is the associated Lebesgue function, prove that $f(\alpha + x) = f(x) + 2^{-k}$ for all $x \in I$.

Problem 12. Let r be a dyadic rational in $(0, 1)$, and suppose the corresponding deleted open interval is $J_r = (a, b)$. Prove that corresponding to the dyadic rational $1 - r$ is the interval $J_{1-r} = (1 - b, 1 - a)$.

D. Appendix: The Modulus of Continuity of the Lebesgue Functions

Again, consider the Cantor ternary set first. We shall subsequently generalize. From the properties listed in Section C, we conclude that

$$| \, x - y \, | \le 3^{-k} \Rightarrow | \, f(x) - f(y) \, | \le 2^{-k}.$$

If x and y are arbitrary, $x \ne y$, choose the largest k such that $| \, x - y \, | \le 3^{-k}$. Therefore, $3^{-k-1} < | \, x - y \, | \le 3^{-k}$, so that

$$-k - 1 < \frac{\log | \, x - y \, |}{\log 3} \le -k.$$

Thus,

$$| \, f(x) - f(y) \, | \le 2^{-k} < 2^{1 + \log|x-y| / \log 3} = 2 \, | \, x - y \, |^{\log 2 / \log 3} \, .$$

Let $\theta = \log 2 / \log 3$. We have shown for all x and y that

$$| \, f(x) - f(y) \, | \le 2 \, | \, x - y \, |^{\theta} \, .$$

We would now like to generalize this estimate for the continuity properties of f to more general Cantor sets, and at the same time prove a better estimate, one in which the "2" does not appear. This is not because we really care about the factor "2," but because a more careful analysis brings out some of the finer structure of the Cantor sets.

First we must introduce a function to take the place of t^{θ}. So let h be a function on $[0, 1]$ which satisfies the properties:

> h is continuous and increasing,
> $h(0) = 0$, $h(1) = 1$, and
> h is *strictly concave*.

The latter condition means that if any chord is inscribed in the graph $y = h(t)$, then the graph lies strictly above the chord, i.e., if $0 \le a < b < c \le 1$, then

$$h(b) > \frac{c - b}{c - a} h(a) + \frac{b - a}{c - a} h(c).$$

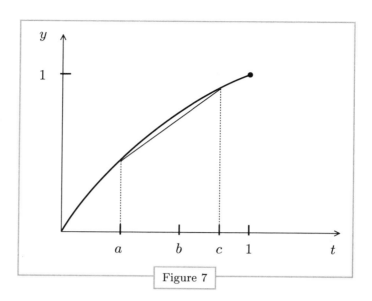

Figure 7

A sufficient condition for h to be concave is that h be of class C^2 and $h'' \le 0$. This condition becomes sufficient for *strict* concavity if $h'' < 0$. Thus, if $0 < \theta < 1$, then $h(t) = t^\theta$ is strictly concave. Other examples of acceptable functions are (for any $m > 1$)

$$h(t) = mt - (m-1)t^2.$$

Problem 13. Verify that $h(t) = \dfrac{1}{1 + \frac{1}{2}\log t^{-1}}$ is acceptable; i.e., prove it satisfies the conditions we are placing on h.

We note an important property of these concave functions by choosing $a = 0$, $b = t$, $c = 2t$ above. Then we see that

$$2h(t) > h(2t) \quad \text{if} \quad 0 < t \le \frac{1}{2}.$$

In the construction of the Cantor sets which has been described in Section B, we now choose the intervals by a method which uses a fixed concave function h as a guideline. Namely, we choose l_k such that

$$h(l_k) = 2^{-k}, \quad k = 0, 1, 2, \dots .$$

Note that the previous inequality then implies

$$
\begin{aligned}
h(l_{k-1}) &= 2^{1-k} \\
&= 2h(l_k) \\
&> h(2l_k).
\end{aligned}
$$

Since h is increasing, $l_{k-1} > 2l_k$. Since $h(l_0) = 1$, so that $l_0 = 1$, we see that the sequence l_k does satisfy the basic requirement given in Section B. Thus, a Cantor set A can be constructed depending only on the function h. We can also explicitly calculate its measure, using the formula for $\lambda(A)$ obtained earlier:

$$\lambda(A) = \lim_{k \to \infty} 2^k l_k = \lim_{k \to \infty} \frac{l_k}{h(l_k)}.$$

Since h is concave, $h'(0)$ exists. And since $l_k \to 0$, we conclude that

$$\lambda(A) = \frac{1}{h'(0)},$$

where of course this is interpreted to be zero if $h'(0) = \infty$. Note that if $h(t) = t^\theta$ for some $\theta \in (0,1)$, then $\lambda(A) = 0$. If $h(t) = mt - (m-1)t^2$ for some $m \in (1,\infty)$, then $\lambda(A) = 1/m$.

In Section C we have associated with the Cantor set A a certain function f, the Lebesgue function for A. The result we wish to prove can be stated in the form:

Theorem: *In the above situation*

$$\mid f(x) - f(y) \mid \le h(\mid x - y \mid) \qquad \textit{for all } \ x, y \in [0,1].$$

The rest of this section is devoted to proving this theorem. As you will see, the proof is quite long. Therefore, we present the proof in the form of a discussion.

1. First, we note that since the union of the excluded intervals J_r for dyadic rationals $r \in (0,1)$ is dense in $[0,1]$ and since f and h are continuous, it suffices to prove the inequality for x and y belonging to this union of J_r's. And since f is constant $(= r)$ on J_r, we can assume x and y belong to two different J_r's. We can also by symmetry assume that $x < y$. Thus, we assume

$$x \in J_{r_1}, y \in J_{r_2}, 0 < r_1 < r_2 < 1.$$

Then we must prove
$$r_2 - r_1 \le h(y - x).$$

Using the generic notation
$$J_r = (a, b),$$

note that $a_1 < x < b_1$ and $a_2 < y < b_2$. Therefore, $y - x > a_2 - b_1$ (and $a_2 - b_1 > 0$). Since h is increasing, it suffices to prove

$$r_2 - r_1 \leq h(a_2 - b_1).$$

A pictorial representation of this situation appears as below:

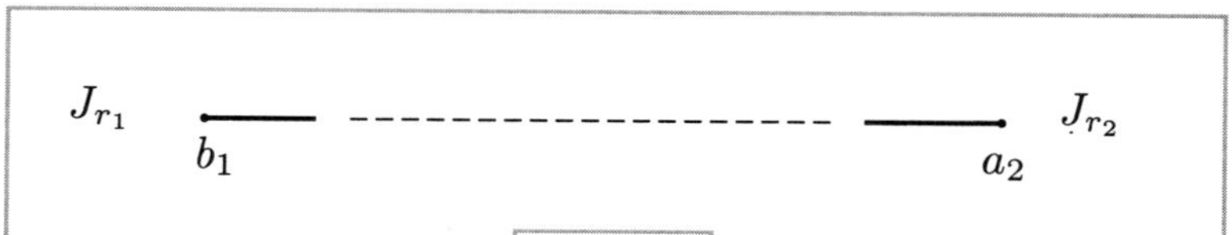

Figure 8

2. By Problem 12 we discover that $J_{1-r_2} = (1 - b_2, 1 - a_2)$. The second lemma in Section C shows that if

$$r_1 = \sum_{j=1}^{k} \epsilon_j 2^{-j} \quad \text{and} \quad 1 - r_2 = \sum_{j=1}^{k} \delta_j 2^{-j},$$

then

$$b_1 = \sum_{j=1}^{k} \epsilon_j (l_{j-1} - l_j) \quad \text{and} \quad 1 - a_2 = \sum_{j=1}^{k} \delta_j (l_{j-1} - l_j).$$

Here each ϵ_j and each δ_j is 0 or 1. Therefore, we have to prove that

$$1 - \sum_{j=1}^{k} (\epsilon_j + \delta_j) 2^{-j} \leq h\left(1 - \sum_{j=1}^{k} (\epsilon_j + \delta_j)(l_{j-1} - l_j) \right),$$

provided that the left side is positive. Since ϵ_j and δ_j are 0 or 1, we can write $\epsilon_j + \delta_j = \alpha_j$, and $\alpha_j = 0$, 1, or 2. Thus, we have to prove

$$(*) \qquad 1 - \sum_{1}^{k} \alpha_j 2^{-j} \leq h\left(1 - \sum_{1}^{k} \alpha_j (l_{j-1} - l_j) \right),$$

provided that the left side is positive, and $\alpha_j = 0$, 1, or 2.

3. **Lemma:** *If each $\alpha_j = 0$, 1, or 2, and*

$$\sum_1^k \alpha_j 2^{-j} < 1,$$

then

$$\sum_1^k \alpha_j(l_{j-1} - l_j) \leq 1 - l_k.$$

Proof: Use induction on k, the case $k = 1$ being trivial. To handle the inductive step, assume $k > 1$ and

$$\sum_1^k \alpha_j 2^{-j} < 1.$$

This inequality requires α_1 to be 0 or 1. If $\alpha_1 = 0$, then

$$\begin{aligned}
\sum_1^k \alpha_j(l_{j-1} - l_j) &\leq \sum_2^k 2(l_{j-1} - l_j) \\
&= 2(l_1 - l_k) \\
&< 2l_1 - l_k \\
&< 1 - l_k,
\end{aligned}$$

so the conclusion is valid. If $\alpha_1 = 1$, then we rewrite the hypothesis in the form

$$\sum_2^k \alpha_j 2^{-j} < \frac{1}{2};$$

multiplying by 2 yields

$$\sum_1^{k-1} \alpha_{j+1} 2^{-j} < 1.$$

Now consider the new function

$$h^*(x) = \frac{h(l_1 x)}{h(l_1)} = 2h(l_1 x), \qquad 0 \leq x \leq 1.$$

This function is acceptable according to our stipulations, and the corresponding numbers l_j^* are defined by

$$h^*(l_j^*) = 2^{-j}.$$

Therefore,

$$l_1 l_j^* = l_{j+1},$$

and we obtain by the inductive hypothesis

$$\sum_{1}^{k-1} \alpha_{j+1}(l_{j-1}^* - l_j^*) \leq 1 - l_{k-1}^*.$$

That is,

$$\sum_{1}^{k-1} \alpha_{j+1}(l_j - l_{j+1}) \leq l_1 - l_k.$$

Since $\alpha_1 = 1$, this implies

$$\sum_{1}^{k} \alpha_j(l_{j-1} - l_j) \leq 1 - l_1 + l_1 - l_k$$

$$= 1 - l_k,$$

so the lemma's conclusion follows.

(QED for the lemma)

4. We now prove (∗) by induction on the number $\sum_{1}^{k} \alpha_j$. If this sum is 0, then all $\alpha_j = 0$ and (∗) is trivial. To perform the inductive step, we may assume $\alpha_k \neq 0$. Then we obtain by the inductive hypothesis

$$1 - \sum_{1}^{k} \alpha_j 2^{-j} = \left(1 - \sum_{1}^{k-1} \alpha_j 2^{-j} - (\alpha_k - 1)2^{-k}\right) - 2^{-k}$$

$$\leq h(x) - 2^{-k},$$

where

$$x = 1 - \sum_{1}^{k-1} \alpha_j(l_{j-1} - l_j) - (\alpha_k - 1)(l_{k-1} - l_k).$$

The desired inequality then follows from

$$h(x) - 2^{-k} \leq h(x - l_{k-1} + l_k).$$

In other words, it suffices to prove that

$$h(x) - h(x - l_{k-1} + l_k) \leq h(l_{k-1}) - h(l_k).$$

Since h is concave, its difference quotients *decrease* as the chords move to the right (see Section 16.I). Thus, it suffices to prove that $x \geq l_{k-1}$. By definition of x, this means

$$\sum_{1}^{k} \alpha_j (l_{j-1} - l_j) \leq 1 - l_k,$$

but this inequality is precisely the conclusion of our lemma. The hypothesis of the lemma is just that the left side of $(*)$ is positive.   **QED**

Algebras of Sets and Measurable Functions

The primary purpose of this chapter is to finish the necessary background material for the discussion of the integral in Chapter 6.

A. Algebras and σ-Algebras

Let X be any set. It is best to think purely abstractly for the time being, so we say nothing more about X. The *power set* of X is the collection of all subsets of X (including $\emptyset$ and X). We shall use a standard notation for the power set of X, namely, 2^X.

(The reason for this strange notation is that in abstract set theory the set consisting of all functions from X to Y is denoted Y^X. This is done because the definition of the cardinal number process of raising to a power leads to such notation. Now if Y consists of exactly two points, say $Y = \{0, 1\}$, then there is a natural bijection of Y^X and the power set of X. Namely, if $A \subset X$ we define the *characteristic function* (also known as the *indicator function*) of A to be the function χ_A given by

$$\chi_A(x) = \begin{cases} 1 & \text{if } x \in A, \\ 0 & \text{if } x \in A^c. \end{cases}$$

Then clearly the correspondence $A \to \chi_A$ is a bijection from the power set of X to Y^X. Finally, since Y consists of 2 points, the notation Y^X is replaced by 2^X.)

Definition: An *algebra* of subsets of X is a collection of sets $\mathcal{M} \subset 2^X$ which satisfies

(a) $\emptyset \in \mathcal{M}$,

(b) $A, B \in \mathcal{M} \Longrightarrow A \cup B \in \mathcal{M}$,

(c) $A \in \mathcal{M} \Longrightarrow A^c \in \mathcal{M}$. (Here A^c means $X \sim A$.)

Of course, de Morgan's laws immediately show that an algebra must satisfy other properties: $X \in \mathcal{M}$; if $A, B \in \mathcal{M}$, then $A \cap B \in \mathcal{M}$ and $A \sim B \in \mathcal{M}$. These properties are the reason that $\mathcal{M}$ is termed an "algebra": The standard set operations (complement, union, intersection, difference) performed finitely many times on sets in $\mathcal{M}$ always produce sets which are also in $\mathcal{M}$.

Definition: Let $\mathcal{M} \subset 2^X$ be an algebra. Then $\mathcal{M}$ is a *σ-algebra* if also

$$\textbf{(b')} \qquad\qquad A_1, A_2, A_3, \ldots \in \mathcal{M} \Longrightarrow \bigcup_{k=1}^{\infty} A_k \in \mathcal{M}.$$

Again, it follows immediately from de Morgan's laws that $\bigcap_{k=1}^{\infty} A_k \in \mathcal{M}$ as well. The prefix σ is used to signify that "countable sums" of sets in $\mathcal{M}$ are also in $\mathcal{M}$. Thus, in a σ-algebra all the standard set operations performed countably many times on sets in $\mathcal{M}$ result in sets which also are in $\mathcal{M}$.

EXAMPLES.

1. The power set itself 2^X is a σ-algebra.

2. The collection $\{\emptyset, X\}$ is a σ-algebra.

3. If $\mathcal{M}$ is any algebra of sets in X, then $\{\emptyset, X\} \subset \mathcal{M} \subset 2^X$.

4. If $X = \mathbb{R}^n$, the measurable sets $\mathcal{L}$ are a σ-algebra. (This follows immediately from Properties M1 and M2 in Chapter 2.)

5. Let X be any set. Let $A \in \mathcal{M}_0 \Longleftrightarrow$ either A is finite or A^c is finite. Note that if X is a finite set, then $\mathcal{M}_0 = 2^X$. Therefore assume X is infinite. Then $\mathcal{M}_0$ is an algebra but not a σ-algebra.

6. Let X be any set. Let $A \in \mathcal{M}_1 \Longleftrightarrow$ either A is countable or A^c is countable. Then $\mathcal{M}_1$ is a σ-algebra.

7. Let $X = \mathbb{R}$. Let $A \in \mathcal{M} \Longleftrightarrow A = \emptyset$ or A is a finite union of intervals of the form $[a, b)$ or of the form $(-\infty, b)$, where $-\infty < a < b \leq \infty$. Then $\mathcal{M}$ is an algebra but not a σ-algebra.

8. If $\mathcal{M}$ is an algebra and is finite (i.e., contains only a finite number of sets), then $\mathcal{M}$ is a σ-algebra.

Problem 1. Prove all the assertions made in Examples 5–8.

The σ-algebra generated by a collection of sets. This is undoubtedly the most important idea in this abstract setting. It is based on the following simple observation: If $\mathcal{M}_i \subset 2^X$ is a σ-algebra for each

i belonging to an index set $\mathcal{I}$ (which is not required to be countable), then also

$$\mathcal{M} = \bigcap_{i \in \mathcal{I}} \mathcal{M}_i$$

is a σ-algebra. Be sure you understand the logical significance of this intersection. It has nothing to do with taking intersections of subsets of X. Instead, it merely means that if A is a subset of X, then $A \in \mathcal{M} \iff A \in \mathcal{M}_i$ for every $i \in \mathcal{I}$.

Problem 2. Prove that $\mathcal{M}$ is a σ-algebra.

Problem 3. If it is known only that each $\mathcal{M}_i$ is an algebra, prove that $\mathcal{M}$ is an algebra.

Problem 4. Give an example of two σ-algebras in a set X whose *union* is not an algebra.

Problem 5. Prove that if the union of two σ-algebras in X is an algebra, then it is a σ-algebra.

Now we apply this idea to the following situation. Suppose that $\mathcal{N}$ is *any* collection of subsets of X. Now consider *all* the σ-algebras which contain $\mathcal{N}$. There are clearly such σ-algebras; namely, 2^X is itself a σ-algebra which contains $\mathcal{N}$ (and it might be the only one). Then according to our previous remarks, the *intersection* of all σ-algebras which contain $\mathcal{N}$ is also a σ-algebra. And it clearly contains $\mathcal{N}$. Further, since it is defined in this way, it is contained in every σ-algebra which contains $\mathcal{N}$. Thus, it is the *smallest* σ-algebra which contains $\mathcal{N}$.

SUMMARY. If $\mathcal{N} \subset 2^X$, then there exists a smallest σ-algebra which contains $\mathcal{N}$. It is called the σ-algebra *generated* by $\mathcal{N}$.

Great care is needed when working with this concept. The reason is that the definition is completely nonconstructive. To convince you of this, suppose we denote by Σ the collection of all σ-algebras which contain $\mathcal{N}$. Let $\mathcal{M}$ be the σ-algebra generated by $\mathcal{N}$. Then the definition is exactly

$$\mathcal{M} = \bigcap_{\mathcal{P} \in \Sigma} \mathcal{P}.$$

This is surely a strange definition of $\mathcal{M}$, as $\mathcal{M}$ itself appears on the right side of this equation! For $\mathcal{M}$ itself belongs to Σ.

Because students frequently are uncomfortable with such a nonconstructive definition, they are sometimes apt to work with an attempted constructive defintion, which goes something like this: For any sets A_1,

A_2, A_3, ... such that either $A_k \in \mathcal{N}$ or $A_k^c \in \mathcal{N}$, define new sets of the form

$$A_1 * A_2 * A_3 * \dots \; ,$$

where each $*$ is either $\bigcup$ or $\bigcap$. Then the collection of all such sets is a σ-algebra (they say), and obviously is also the smallest σ-algebra containing $\mathcal{N}$. *This is not the case.* In fact, there *is* a way to construct the generated σ-algebra, but it requires transfinite induction applied to constructions similar to the one we have just discussed. We do not choose to use this construction, as it requires heavy use of the arithmetic of ordinal numbers, and the effort required to exploit the construction is still considerable in most applications.

Problem 6. If $\mathcal{N}_1 \subset \mathcal{N}_2 \subset 2^X$ and $\mathcal{M}_i$ is the σ-algebra generated by $\mathcal{N}_i$, prove that $\mathcal{M}_1 \subset \mathcal{M}_2$.

Problem 7. If $\mathcal{N} \subset 2^X$, prove that there exists a smallest *algebra* which contains $\mathcal{N}$.

Problem 8. Let $\mathcal{N} \subset 2^X$. Let $\mathcal{M}$ be the σ-algebra generated by $\mathcal{N}$ and let $\mathcal{M}'$ be the algebra generated by $\mathcal{N}$. What relation must hold between $\mathcal{M}$ and $\mathcal{M}'$?

Problem 9. Let X be any set and let $\mathcal{M}_0$ and $\mathcal{M}_1$ be the algebras described in Examples 5 and 6, respectively. Prove that $\mathcal{M}_1$ is the σ-algebra generated by $\mathcal{M}_0$.

Problem 10. As preparation for the next problem, prove that the set consisting of all sequences $e = (e_1, e_2, e_3, \ldots)$ of 0's and 1's (that is, $e_k = 0$ or 1 for all k) is in one-to-one correspondence with $\mathbb{R}$.

(**HINT:** This is an immediate consequence of some of the results in Section 4.C.)

Problem 11. Prove that there does not exist a countable infinite σ-algebra.

(**HINT:** Suppose that $\mathcal{M} = \{B_1, B_2, B_3, \ldots\}$ is a countable infinite σ-algebra of subsets of X.

(a) For all $x \in X$ define the "atom" $B_x = \bigcap \{B_k \mid x \in B_k, \; k = 1, 2, \ldots\}$. Prove that if $x, y \in X$, then either $B_x \cap B_y = \emptyset$ or $B_x = B_y$.

(b) Conclude that there exist sets C_1, C_2, $C_3, \ldots \in \mathcal{M}$ such that $\bigcup_{k=1}^{\infty} C_k = X$ and the C_k's are disjoint and nonempty.

(c) For every sequence $e = (e_1, e_2, e_3, \ldots)$ of 0's and 1's let

$$D_e = \bigcup \{C_k \mid e_k = 1, k = 1, 2, \ldots\}.$$

Prove that $e \neq e' \Rightarrow D_e \neq D_{e'}$.)

B. Borel Sets

Now we shall restrict attention to $\mathbb{R}^n$ and shall combine topological notions with the discussion of σ-algebras.

Definition: The class of *Borel sets* in $\mathbb{R}^n$ is the σ-algebra generated by the collection of open sets. We denote by $\mathcal{B}$ the Borel sets in $\mathbb{R}^n$. In cases in which we need to indicate the dimension, we shall use the notation $\mathcal{B}_n$. Thus, $\mathcal{B}$ contains all the open sets and also all the closed sets. Furthermore, $\mathcal{B} \subset \mathcal{L}$ because $\mathcal{L}$ is itself a σ-algebra which contains the open sets.

Problem 12. Let $\mathcal{N}$ be the collection of all special rectangles in $\mathbb{R}^n$ (Section 2.A, Stage 1). Prove that the σ-algebra generated by $\mathcal{N}$ is equal to $\mathcal{B}$, using the following steps (only Step (a) has any actual mathematics):

(a) Let $\mathcal{M} =$ the σ-algebra generated by $\mathcal{N}$, and let $\mathcal{T}$ be the collection of open sets in $\mathbb{R}^n$. Prove that $\mathcal{T} \subset \mathcal{M}$.

(b) Prove that $\mathcal{B} \subset \mathcal{M}$.

(c) Prove that $\mathcal{N} \subset \mathcal{B}$.

(d) Prove that $\mathcal{M} \subset \mathcal{B}$.

This problem is a good example of how you must approach the Borel sets. The remarks at the end of Section A continue to be valid for Borel sets. Do not think that every Borel set can be constructed from the open sets by countably many of the standard set operations. Instead, proofs involving Borel sets in this book will rely on the basic definition of the Borel sets as the smallest σ-algebra containing the open sets. For this reason, proofs which involve Borel sets are usually easy, though perhaps the methods may at first appear strange.

Definition: If $A \subset \mathbb{R}^n$ is measurable and $\lambda(A) = 0$, then A is a *null* set. Observe that A is a null set $\Longleftrightarrow \lambda^*(A) = 0$. For if $\lambda^*(A) = 0$, then $A \in \mathcal{L}$.

Notice that countable unions of null sets are again null sets.

Theorem: *Suppose A is a measurable set in $\mathbb{R}^n$. Then A can be decomposed in the following manner:*

$$A = E \cup N,$$
$$E \text{ and } N \text{ are disjoint,}$$
$$E \text{ is a Borel set,}$$
$$N \text{ is a null set.}$$

Proof: By the approximation property M9 of Section 2.B, for every $k \in \mathbb{N}$ there exists a closed set $F_k \subset A$ such that $\lambda(A \sim F_k) < k^{-1}$. Let $E = \bigcup_{k=1}^{\infty} F_k$. Then $E \subset A$ and $E \in \mathcal{B}$ (since each $F_k \in \mathcal{B}$ and $\mathcal{B}$ is a σ-algebra). For any k

$$\lambda(A \sim E) \leq \lambda(A \sim F_k)$$
$$< k^{-1},$$

and thus $\lambda(A \sim E) = 0$. Thus, $N = A \sim E$ is a null set.   **QED**

The preceding theorem and proof are of course extremely simple, yet the theorem asserts a remarkable fact: Measurable sets are close to being Borel sets — they differ from Borel sets only by null sets. Notice also that null sets do not in general enjoy the nice topological property of being Borel sets (in the next section we shall exhibit measurable sets which are not Borel sets). The assertion of the theorem that $E \in \mathcal{B}$ is actually much less than was proved. The proof actually constructs a set E which is an "F_σ," a countable union of closed sets.

Problem 13. Prove that if N is a null set in $\mathbb{R}^n$, then there exists a *Borel* null set N' such that $N \subset N'$. In fact, prove that N' may be chosen to be a "G_δ," a countable intersection of open sets.

Problem 14. Prove that a set $A \subset \mathbb{R}^n$ is measurable $\Longleftrightarrow$ there exist a set B which is an F_σ and a set C which is a G_δ such that $B \subset A \subset C$ and $C \sim B$ is a null set.

Since the Borel sets are defined with reference to the topology of $\mathbb{R}^n$, it should come as no surprise that there is an easy theorem about the action of continuous functions on Borel sets.

> **Theorem:** *Let E be a Borel set in $\mathbb{R}^n$. Let $E \xrightarrow{f} \mathbb{R}^m$ be a continuous function. If A is a Borel set in $\mathbb{R}^m$, then $f^{-1}(A)$ is a Borel set in $\mathbb{R}^n$.*

Proof: Remember! We don't know how to *construct* Borel sets, so we are unable to provide a proof which begins by analyzing the structure of A and then progresses to a statement about the structure of $f^{-1}(A)$. Instead, we must give a cleverer (and easier!) proof based on the definition of the Borel sets. In fact, our proof will ignore the set A entirely, and will instead prove the desired conclusion for all Borel sets in $\mathbb{R}^m$.

Thus, *define*

$$\mathcal{M} = \{A \mid A \subset \mathbb{R}^m \quad \text{and} \quad f^{-1}(A) \in \mathcal{B}_n\}.$$

What we have to prove is precisely that $\mathcal{B}_m \subset \mathcal{M}$. Since $\mathcal{B}_m$ is the smallest σ-algebra containing all open sets in $\mathbb{R}^m$, the proof will be complete if we prove that $\mathcal{M}$ contains all open sets and $\mathcal{M}$ is a σ-algebra.

$\underline{\mathcal{M} \text{ is a } \sigma\text{-algebra}}$: This is automatic.

(a) $f^{-1}(\emptyset) = \emptyset$ and $\emptyset \in \mathcal{B}_n$. Therefore, $\emptyset \in \mathcal{M}$.

(b') Suppose $A_k \in \mathcal{M}$ for all $k \in \mathbb{N}$. Then $f^{-1}(A_k) \in \mathcal{B}_n$. But

$$f^{-1}\left(\bigcup_{k=1}^{\infty} A_k\right) = \bigcup_{k=1}^{\infty} f^{-1}(A_k)$$

then also belongs to $\mathcal{B}_n$. Therefore, $\bigcup_{k=1}^{\infty} A_k \in \mathcal{M}$.

(c) Suppose $A \in \mathcal{M}$. Then $f^{-1}(A) \in \mathcal{B}_n$ and we see

$$\begin{aligned}
f^{-1}(A^c) &= \{x \in E \mid f(x) \notin A\} \\
&= E \sim \{x \in E \mid f(x) \in A\} \\
&= E \sim f^{-1}(A)
\end{aligned}$$

is also in $\mathcal{B}_n$ (since $E \in \mathcal{B}_n$). Therefore, $A^c \in \mathcal{M}$.

$\underline{\mathcal{M} \text{ contains the open sets}}$: until now we have not used the hypothesis of continuity of f. Assume $G \subset \mathbb{R}^m$ is open. Then the theorem on p.16

implies that $f^{-1}(G) = E \cap H$, where $H \subset \mathbb{R}^n$ is open. Since H is open, $H \in \mathcal{B}_n$, and thus $f^{-1}(G) \in \mathcal{B}_n$. Therefore, $G \in \mathcal{M}$.   **QED**

Remark: Observe how abstract this proof really is. In particular, we have no idea whatsoever what $\mathcal{M}$ is. It may be much larger than the class of Borel sets. Indeed, if f is a constant function, then $\mathcal{M} = 2^{\mathbb{R}^m}$.

Corollary: *Let $E \subset \mathbb{R}^n$ and $F \subset \mathbb{R}^m$ be Borel sets. Let $E \xrightarrow{f} F$ be a homeomorphism of E onto F. If $B \subset E$, then $B \in \mathcal{B}_n \iff f(B) \in \mathcal{B}_m$.*

Proof: Since f^{-1} is also a continuous function, the corollary follows immediately.   **QED**

C. A Measurable Set which Is Not a Borel Set

Theorem: $\mathcal{B} \neq \mathcal{L}$.

Proof: We give an example in dimension 1 only, as our later results on product spaces show the result is much simpler in $\mathbb{R}^n$ than $\mathbb{R}$ if $n > 1$.

Let $C \subset [0, 1]$ be the Cantor ternary set, and let f be the associated Lebesgue function. See Section 4.C. We need to modify f to obtain a strictly increasing function. This can be done very easily by defining

$$g(x) = x + f(x), \quad 0 \leq x \leq 1.$$

The function g is continuous and strictly increasing, and $g(0) = 0$, $g(1) = 2$. Thus, g is a homeomorphism of $[0, 1]$ onto $[0, 2]$.

Using the notation of Sections 4.B and C, the open set $[0, 1] \sim C$ is the union of the open intervals J_r for dyadic rationals $r \in (0, 1)$. On each J_r the Lebesgue function is the constant r. Thus, on each J_r the function $g(x) = x + r$, so that g transforms J_r into another open interval with the same length as J_r. Thus, $\lambda(g(J_r)) = \lambda(J_r)$. Therefore, we calculate as follows:

$$\lambda(g(C)) = \lambda([0,2] \sim \bigcup_r g(J_r))$$

$$= \lambda([0,2]) - \lambda\left(\bigcup_r g(J_r)\right)$$

$$= 2 - \sum_r \lambda(g(J_r))$$

$$= 2 - \sum_r \lambda(J_r)$$

$$= 2 - \lambda\left(\bigcup_r J_r\right)$$

$$= 2 - 1$$

$$= 1$$

since $\lambda(C) = 0$.

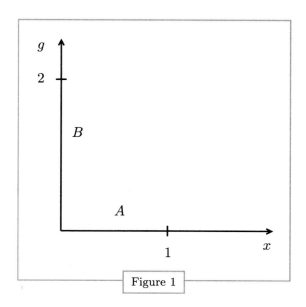

Figure 1

Since $g(C)$ has positive measure, the corollary on p.82 implies the existence of a set $B \subset g(C)$ such that $B \notin \mathcal{L}$.
    Let
$$A = g^{-1}(B).$$

Then we see that $A \subset C$ and thus $\lambda^*(A) \le \lambda(C) = 0$. Therefore, $A \in \mathcal{L}$. But $A \notin \mathcal{B}$. For g is a homeomorphism, and if $A \in \mathcal{B}$, then the corollary on p.110 implies $g(A) = B \in \mathcal{B}$. However, B does not even belong to $\mathcal{L}$, so we conclude that $A \in \mathcal{L}$ but $A \notin \mathcal{B}$.   **QED**

Remark: For later reference we note the equation

$$\chi_B = \chi_A \circ g^{-1}.$$

In this expression g is a homeomorphism, and $A \in \mathcal{L}$, $B \notin \mathcal{L}$. In particular, observe that the corollary in the preceding section becomes false if $\mathcal{B}$ is replaced by $\mathcal{L}$: Homeomorphisms do not necessarily preserve measurable sets.

D. Measurable Functions

In the following chapter, when we begin to think about integrating a real function defined on $\mathbb{R}^n$, it will be natural to examine the sets in $\mathbb{R}^n$ on which f is "nearly constant." That is, for an arbitrary $a \in \mathbb{R}$ and a small $\epsilon > 0$, we shall need to consider sets like

$$E = \{x \in \mathbb{R}^n \mid a \le f(x) < a + \epsilon\}.$$

We shall then be led to say that the integral of f over the set E is approximately equal to a times $\lambda(E)$. In order that this make sense, the set E is required to be *measurable*. And if this property holds for all $a \in \mathbb{R}$ and all $\epsilon > 0$, then we shall say that the function f is *measurable*.

It will prove to be useful to allow f to take the extended real values $\pm\infty$ at various points. Thus, we shall use the extended real number system $[-\infty, \infty]$ with the usual order relations. We shall also use the natural algebraic conventions

$$
\begin{aligned}
x + \infty &= \infty && \text{if } x \in \mathbb{R},\\
\infty + \infty &= \infty,\\
a \cdot \infty &= \infty && \text{if } 0 < a \le \infty,\\
a \cdot \infty &= -\infty && \text{if } -\infty \le a < 0.
\end{aligned}
$$

However,

$$
\begin{aligned}
-\infty + \infty \quad &\text{is always undefined,}\\
0 \cdot \infty \quad &\text{is usually undefined, but frequently is } 0.
\end{aligned}
$$

In this section there is some advantage to be gained by dealing with a general case right from the start, and there are no additional difficulties in the general situation. Therefore, we assume that X is any set and $\mathcal{M}$ is any σ-algebra of subsets of X.

Definition: Suppose $f : X \to [-\infty, \infty]$. Then f is $\mathcal{M}$-*measurable* if for all $t \in [-\infty, \infty]$ the set $f^{-1}([-\infty, t])$ belongs to $\mathcal{M}$. In other words,

$$\{x \in X \mid f(x) \leq t\} \in \mathcal{M}.$$

We have chosen the form of the inequality $f(x) \leq t$ for no good reason. The choice is completely arbitrary, as the proposition below will demonstrate.

SPECIAL CASES. In case $X = \mathbb{R}^n$ and $\mathcal{M} = \mathcal{L}$, we say that an $\mathcal{L}$-measurable function is *Lebesgue measurable function* measurable. Likewise, a $\mathcal{B}$-measurable function is said to be *Borel* measurable.

Thus, every Borel measurable function is Lebesgue measurable.

Note that *any continuous function is Borel measurable*; this follows because the continuity of f implies $f^{-1}([-\infty, t])$ is a closed set for any t.

Problem 15. For $A \subset X$, prove that the characteristic function χ_A is $\mathcal{M}$-measurable $\iff A \in \mathcal{M}$.

Problem 16. Describe explicitly the $\mathcal{M}$-measurable functions in case $\mathcal{M}$ is one of the following σ-algebras:

(a) $\mathcal{M} = \{\emptyset, X\}$.

(b) $\mathcal{M} = 2^X$.

(c) For certain disjoint sets $E_1, \ldots, E_N$, $X = \bigcup_{k=1}^{N} E_k$, and $\mathcal{M}$ is the algebra (in fact, σ-algebra) generated by the collection of sets $\{E_1, \ldots, E_N\}$.

Proposition: Suppose $\mathcal{M}$ is any σ-algebra of subsets of X and suppose $f : X \to [-\infty, \infty]$. Then f is $\mathcal{M}$-measurable if and only if any one of the following conditions is satisfied:

1. $f^{-1}([-\infty, t]) \in \mathcal{M}$ for every $t \in [-\infty, \infty]$.

2. $f^{-1}([-\infty, t)) \in \mathcal{M}$ for every $t \in (-\infty, \infty]$.

3. $f^{-1}([t, \infty]) \in \mathcal{M}$ for every $t \in [-\infty, \infty]$.

4. $f^{-1}((t, \infty]) \in \mathcal{M}$ *for every* $t \in [-\infty, \infty)$.

5. $f^{-1}(\{-\infty\})$ *and* $f^{-1}(\{\infty\})$ *belong to* $\mathcal{M}$, *and* $f^{-1}(E) \in \mathcal{M}$ *for every Borel set* $E \subset \mathbb{R}$.

Proof: $1 \Leftrightarrow 4$ and $2 \Leftrightarrow 3$ are proved simply by taking complements. Next, note that $f(x) < t \Leftrightarrow$ there exists $r \in \mathbb{Q}$ such that $f(x) \leq r < t$; i.e.,

$$f^{-1}([-\infty, t)) = \bigcup_{r \in \mathbb{Q}, r < t} f^{-1}([-\infty, r]).$$

Therefore, $1 \Rightarrow 2$. Likewise,

$$f^{-1}([-\infty, t]) = \bigcap_{r \in \mathbb{Q}, r > t} f^{-1}([-\infty, r)),$$

and this proves that $2 \Rightarrow 1$. Thus, 1, 2, 3, and 4 are all equivalent. Obviously, $5 \Rightarrow 1$ is proved by choosing the Borel set $E = (-\infty, t]$.

Finally, we prove that if Conditions 1–4 are valid, then also 5 is valid. Obviously, taking $t = -\infty$ in 1 implies $f^{-1}(\{-\infty\}) \in \mathcal{M}$. Likewise, 3 implies $f^{-1}(\{\infty\}) \in \mathcal{M}$. To establish the remaining assertion about Borel sets, we must of course give an argument using the definition of the Borel sets as the σ-algebra generated by the open subsets of $\mathbb{R}$. Define the class $\mathcal{S}$ of subsets of $\mathbb{R}$ as follows:

$$\mathcal{S} = \{E \subset \mathbb{R} \mid f^{-1}(E) \in \mathcal{M}\}.$$

It is easy to verify that $\mathcal{S}$ is a σ-algebra; the proof is like that given on p.109, so we shall not write it out. If we now prove that $\mathcal{S}$ contains all the open sets in $\mathbb{R}$, then Condition 5 will follow. Recall that Problem 2.6 shows that every open subset of $\mathbb{R}$ is a countable union of open intervals; since $\mathcal{S}$ is a σ-algebra, we need only prove that every open interval (a, b) belongs to $\mathcal{S}$. But

$$f^{-1}((a, b)) = f^{-1}([-\infty, b)) \cap f^{-1}((a, \infty])$$

is an intersection of two sets known to be in $\mathcal{M}$, and thus $f^{-1}((a, b)) \in \mathcal{M}$. Therefore, $(a, b) \in \mathcal{S}$.   **QED**

Properties

Assume that $f : X \to \mathbb{R}$ and $g : X \to \mathbb{R}$ are $\mathcal{M}$-measurable. Then

MF1 If $\phi : \mathbb{R} \to \mathbb{R}$ is Borel measurable, then $\phi \circ f$ is $\mathcal{M}$-measurable.

MF2 If $f \neq 0$, then $\frac{1}{f}$ is $\mathcal{M}$-measurable.

MF3 Let $0 < p < \infty$. Then $|f|^p$ is $\mathcal{M}$-measurable.

MF4 $f + g$ is $\mathcal{M}$-measurable.

MF5 fg is $\mathcal{M}$-measurable.

MF6 Assume $f_k : X \to [-\infty, \infty]$ is $\mathcal{M}$-measurable for all $k \in \mathbb{N}$. Then all the following functions are $\mathcal{M}$-measurable:

$$\sup_k f_k, \quad \inf_k f_k,$$

$$\limsup_{k \to \infty} f_k, \quad \liminf_{k \to \infty} f_k,$$

$$\lim_{k \to \infty} f_k, \quad (\text{if it exists}).$$

Proof: All of these except perhaps MF4 and MF5 are quite easy.

MF1 If $E \subset \mathbb{R}$ is a Borel set, then $\phi^{-1}(E)$ is a Borel set. Thus, Part 5 of the preceding theorem implies

$$(\phi \circ f)^{-1}(E) = f^{-1}(\phi^{-1}(E))$$

belongs to $\mathcal{M}$.

MF2 See Problem 17 below.

MF3 Since the function $\phi(t) = |t|^p$ is continuous, it is Borel measurable. Since $|f|^p = \phi \circ f$, the result follows from MF1.

MF4 Note that $f(x) + g(x) < t \Leftrightarrow f(x) < t - g(x) \Leftrightarrow$ there exists $r \in \mathbb{Q}$ such that $f(x) < r < t - g(x)$. Therefore,

$$\{x \mid f(x) + g(x) < t\} = \bigcup_{r \in \mathbb{Q}} f^{-1}((-\infty, r)) \cap g^{-1}((-\infty, t - r)),$$

and we see that the set on the left side therefore belongs to $\mathcal{M}$.

MF5 By a standard trick (sometimes called *polarization*) we can pass from the case $f = g$ to the general case, using MF4. The identity is

$$fg = \frac{1}{4}(f + g)^2 - \frac{1}{4}(f - g)^2.$$

MF6 Clearly,

$$\{x \mid \sup_k f_k(x) \leq t\} = \bigcap_k \{x \mid f_k(x) \leq t\}.$$

Thus, $\sup f_k$ is $\mathcal{M}$-measurable. Likewise, so is $\inf f_k$. But then $\limsup f_k$ is measurable since by definition

$$\limsup f_k = \inf_{j \geq 1} \left(\sup_{k \geq j} f_k \right).$$

Likewise, $\liminf f_k$ is measurable. Finally, if the limit exists, then $\lim f_k = \limsup f_k = \liminf f_k$.

QED

Problem 17. Prove that the function $\phi(t) = t^{-1}$ is Borel measurable (thus, MF2 is proved by applying MF1).

Problem 18. Suppose that for any $s \in \mathbb{R}$ there is given an $\mathcal{M}$-measurable function $f_s : X \to [-\infty, \infty]$. Suppose that $\lim_{s \to \infty} f_s(x)$ exists for all $x \in X$. Prove that $\lim f_s$ is also $\mathcal{M}$-measurable.

Problem 19. If f is $\mathcal{M}$-measurable, then of course the proposition implies that for every t, the set $f^{-1}(\{t\}) \in \mathcal{M}$. But this condition does not imply that f is $\mathcal{M}$-measurable. To see this let $E \subset \mathbb{R}$ be a set which is not in $\mathcal{L}$. Define $f : \mathbb{R} \to \mathbb{R}$ by

$$f(x) = \begin{cases} e^x & \text{if } x \in E, \\ -e^x & \text{if } x \in E^c. \end{cases}$$

(a) Prove that f is not Lebesgue measurable.

(b) Prove that for all t, $f^{-1}(\{t\}) \in \mathcal{L}$.

Problem 20. Let $f : \mathbb{R} \to \mathbb{R}$ be *differentiable*. Prove that the derivative f' is Borel measurable. (Be careful: f' might not be continuous.)

Remark: Note that Property MF1 allows composition of functions in a *certain* order: a Borel measurable function of an $\mathcal{M}$-measurable function is $\mathcal{M}$-measurable. But one cannot say that in general an $\mathcal{M}$-measurable function of even a homeomorphism is $\mathcal{M}$-measurable. In fact, we have given a counterexample already at the end of Section C. In that example χ_A is $\mathcal{L}$-measurable, g^{-1} is a homeomorphism, but $\chi_A \circ g^{-1}$ fails to be $\mathcal{L}$-measurable. The same example shows that in Property MF1 we cannot generalize to say that a Lebesgue measurable function of an $\mathcal{M}$-measurable function is $\mathcal{M}$-measurable.

E. Simple Functions

Definition: A *simple* function from X to $[-\infty, \infty]$ is any function which assumes only a finite number of distinct values. Thus, if s is a simple function, it can be represented in the form

$$s = \sum_{k=1}^{m} \alpha_k \chi_{A_k},$$

where the sets A_k are disjoint and the numbers $\alpha_k \in [-\infty, \infty]$ are distinct.

Problem 21. Prove that a simple function expressed in the above form is $\mathcal{M}$-measurable $\iff$ each set $A_k \in \mathcal{M}$.

Problem 22. Suppose that s_1 and s_2 are simple functions. Prove that the following are also simple functions (if they are defined): $1/s_1$, $|s_1|^p$, $s_1 + s_2$, $s_1 s_2$.

Before proving the next theorem, we need a very important but elementary *definition*:
if $a \in [-\infty, \infty]$, then

$$a_+ = \begin{cases} a & \text{if } a \geq 0, \\ 0 & \text{if } a < 0; \end{cases}$$

$$a_- = \begin{cases} 0 & \text{if } a \geq 0, \\ -a & \text{if } a < 0. \end{cases}$$

The number a_+ is called the *positive part* of a and a_- is called the *negative part* of a. Note that

$$a_+ \geq 0, \; a_- \geq 0,$$
$$a = a_+ - a_-,$$
$$|a| = a_+ + a_-, \text{ and}$$
$$a_+ a_- = 0.$$

Also, if $f : X \to [-\infty, \infty]$ is any function, f_+ and f_- are the functions $f_+(x) = (f(x))_+$ and $f_-(x) = (f(x))_-$.

Problem 23. Prove that if f is $\mathcal{M}$-measurable, then f_+ and f_- are also $\mathcal{M}$-measurable.

We shall be particularly interested in $\mathcal{M}$-measurable simple function-s. Of course, Property MF6 implies that the limit of any convergent sequence of such functions is also $\mathcal{M}$-measurable. Remarkably, the converse of this statement is also valid, and is easy to prove:

Theorem: *Suppose $f : X \to [-\infty, \infty]$ is $\mathcal{M}$-measurable. Then there exists a sequence s_1, s_2, ... of $\mathcal{M}$-measurable simple functions such that*

$$\lim_{k \to \infty} s_k = f \ \ on \ X.$$

If $f \geq 0$, then the sequence may be chosen to satisfy $0 \leq s_1 \leq s_2 \leq s_3 \leq \ldots$. In general, the sequence may be chosen such that $|s_1| \leq |s_2| \leq |s_3| \leq \ldots$.

Proof: Suppose first that $f \geq 0$. Then s_k is defined as follows:

$$s_k(x) = \begin{cases} (i-1)/2^k & \text{if } (i-1)/2^k \leq f(x) < i/2^k, \\ & \text{where } i = 1, 2, \ldots, 2^k k, \\ k & \text{if } k \leq f(x). \end{cases}$$

Since f is $\mathcal{M}$-measurable, the sets $f^{-1}\left(\left[(i-1)/2^k, \ i/2^k\right)\right)$ and $f^{-1}([k, \infty])$ are in $\mathcal{M}$. It therefore follows that the simple function s_k is also $\mathcal{M}$-measurable. All the other properties are easily checked, so we omit the proofs.

In the general case, choose a sequence $0 \leq s_1' \leq s_2' \ldots$ converging to f_+ and a sequence $0 \leq s_1'' \leq s_2'' \ldots$ converging to f_-. Then define $s_k = s_k' - s_k''$. The observation that for any x all of $s_k'(x) = 0$ or else all of $s_k''(x) = 0$ easily completes the proof. **QED**

Problem 24. Prove that if the measurable function $f : X \to \mathbb{R}$ is bounded, then the sequence of simple functions constructed above converges to f *uniformly.*

Theorem: *Suppose $f : \mathbb{R}^n \to [-\infty, \infty]$ is Lebesgue measurable. Then there exists a Borel measurable function g such that the set*

$$\{x \in \mathbb{R}^n \mid f(x) \neq g(x)\}$$

is a null set.

Proof: This result is a generalization of the first theorem in Section B. That theorem is also a major tool in the proof we now give. First, assume $f \geq 0$. By the preceding theorem there exists a sequence $0 \leq s_1 \leq s_1 \leq \ldots$ of Lebesgue measurable simple functions s_k such that $\lim_{k \to \infty} s_k = f$. Each individual s_k has the form

$$s_k = \sum_{j=1}^{m} \alpha_j \chi_{A_j},$$

where the A_j's are disjoint and $A_j \in \mathcal{L}$. By the aforementioned theorem in Section B, each A_j is the disjoint union of a null set and a Borel set E_j. Let

$$\sigma_k = \sum_{j=1}^{m} \alpha_j \chi_{E_j}.$$

Then σ_k is a Borel measurable simple function with the properties

$$0 \leq \sigma_k \leq s_k,$$
$$\sigma_k = s_k \text{ except on a null set } N_k.$$

Now define

$$N = \bigcup_{k=1}^{\infty} N_k,$$
$$g = \sup_k \sigma_k.$$

Then N is a null set, $0 \leq g \leq f$, and $g = f$ except on N. Moreover, Property MF6 implies that g is Borel measurable.

In the general case we now know there exist a Borel measurable g_1 such that $0 \leq g_1 \leq f_+$ and $g_1 = f_+$ except on a null set, and a Borel measurable g_2 such that $0 \leq g_2 \leq f_-$ and $g_2 = f_-$ except on a null set. Then $g = g_1 - g_2$ satisfies the requirements of the theorem. (Note that we are not in danger of committing the subtraction $\infty - \infty$ in the definition of g; for $g_1 \leq f_+$ and $g_2 \leq f_-$ imply that for every $x \in \mathbb{R}^n$, either $g_1(x) = 0$ or $g_2(x) = 0$.)   **QED**

Integration

In the first four sections we shall discuss the Lebesgue integral on $\mathbb{R}^n$, and therefore we shall need to speak exclusively of the σ-algebra $\mathcal{L}$ of Lebesgue measurable subsets of $\mathbb{R}^n$. Therefore, instead of saying that a function is Lebesgue measurable, or $\mathcal{L}$-measurable, we shall simply say that the function is measurable.

There is great advantage in restricting attention to nonnegative functions at first.

A. Nonnegative Functions

Notation: We shall denote by S the class of measurable simple functions s on $\mathbb{R}^n$ such that $0 \le s(x) < \infty$ for all $x \in \mathbb{R}^n$.

Definition: If $s \in S$, then the *integral* of s, denoted $\int s d\lambda$, is the number given as follows:

If s is presented in the form

$$s = \sum_{k=1}^{m} \alpha_k \chi_{A_k},$$

where $0 \le \alpha_k < \infty$ and the sets A_k are measurable and disjoint, then

$$\int s d\lambda = \sum_{k=1}^{m} \alpha_k \lambda(A_k).$$

In this definition we use the convention $0 \cdot \infty = 0$.

Of course, we have to check for consistency. This will be part of the basic properties of this integral, as we now show.

Properties

S1 $\int s d\lambda$ is well defined.

S2 $0 \le \int s d\lambda \le \infty$.

S3 If $0 \le c < \infty$ is a constant, $\int cs d\lambda = c \int s d\lambda$.

S4 If s, $t \in S$, then $\int (s + t)d\lambda = \int s d\lambda + \int t d\lambda$.

S5 If s, $t \in S$ and $s \leq t$, then $\int s d\lambda \leq \int t d\lambda$.

Proof:

S2 and S3   These are obvious (once we know S1 is true).

S1 and S5   Suppose that s, $t \in S$ and $s \leq t$. Then s and t have representations of the form

$$s = \sum_{k=1}^{m} \alpha_k \chi_{A_k},$$

$$t = \sum_{j=1}^{l} \beta_j \chi_{B_j}.$$

In the representation of s, the A_k's are disjoint and measurable. We can further assume that $\bigcup_{k=1}^{m} A_k = \mathbb{R}^n$. For, if this is not already the case, we can adjoin another term to the representation of s of the form $\alpha_{m+1} \chi_{A_{m+1}}$, where $\alpha_{m+1} = 0$ and $A_{m+1} = \left(\bigcup_{k=1}^{m} A_k \right)^c$. This does not affect the definition of $\int s d\lambda$, since $\alpha_{m+1} \lambda(A_{m+1}) = 0$. Likewise, we assume without loss of generality that the B_j's are disjoint and measurable and $\bigcup_{j=1}^{l} B_j = \mathbb{R}^n$.

By definition,

$$\int s d\lambda = \sum_{k=1}^{m} \alpha_k \lambda(A_k) = \sum_{k=1}^{m} \sum_{j=1}^{l} \alpha_k \lambda(A_k \cap B_j),$$

$$\int t d\lambda = \sum_{j=1}^{l} \beta_j \lambda(B_j) = \sum_{j=1}^{l} \sum_{k=1}^{m} \beta_j \lambda(A_k \cap B_j).$$

We are assuming $s \leq t$. If $\lambda(A_k \cap B_j) \neq 0$, then in particular $A_k \cap B_j \neq \emptyset$, so there exists $x \in A_k \cap B_j$. But then

$$\alpha_k = s(x) \leq t(x) = \beta_j,$$

and we conclude

$(*)$ $$\alpha_k \lambda(A_k \cap B_j) \leq \beta_j \lambda(A_k \cap B_j).$$

If $\lambda(A_k \cap B_j) = 0$, then the inequality $(*)$ is trivially valid. Thus $(*)$ is valid for all k, j. Therefore, $\int s d\lambda \leq \int t d\lambda$. This proves S5. Moreover, it actually proves S1 as well. For if we assume $s = t$, then we are just dealing with two presentations of the one simple function s. The proof then shows that

$$\sum_{k=1}^{m} \alpha_k \lambda(A_k) \leq \sum_{j=1}^{l} \beta_j \lambda(B_j) \qquad \text{(since } s \leq t\text{)}.$$

In this case symmetry considerations imply that the reverse inequality also holds.

S4   We retain the above notation. Then

$$s + t = \sum_{k=1}^{m} \sum_{j=1}^{l} (\alpha_k + \beta_j) \chi_{A_k \cap B_j},$$

so that

$$\int (s + t) d\lambda = \sum_{k=1}^{m} \sum_{j=1}^{l} (\alpha_k + \beta_j) \lambda(A_k \cap B_j)$$
$$= \int s d\lambda + \int t d\lambda.$$

QED

Definition: Suppose $f : \mathbb{R}^n \to [0, \infty]$ is measurable. Then the *integral* of f is

$$\int f d\lambda = \sup \left\{ \int s d\lambda \mid s \leq f, \ s \in S \right\}.$$

This number is also called the *Lebesgue integral* of f. Incidentally, we are using this brief notation for the integral only for the present time.

Other notations which we shall employ from time to time are

$$\int_{\mathbb{R}^n} f\, d\lambda,$$

$$\int f\, dx,$$

$$\int_{\mathbb{R}^n} f\, dx,$$

$$\int_{\mathbb{R}^n} f(x)\, dx,$$

$$\int_{-\infty}^{\infty} \cdots \int_{-\infty}^{\infty} f(x_1, \ldots, x_n)\, dx_1 \ldots dx_n, \qquad \text{etc.}$$

We shall also be required to integrate over subsets of $\mathbb{R}^n$ as well. This will be handled very easily later, so we do not worry about it now.

The analogs of four of the properties S1–S5 are quite obvious. Namely,

1 $\int f\, d\lambda$ is well defined,

2 $0 \leq \int f\, d\lambda \leq \infty$,

3 $\int cf\, d\lambda = c\int f\, d\lambda$,

5 if $f \leq g$, then $\int f\, d\lambda \leq \int g\, d\lambda$.

However, it surely is not obvious that

4 $\int (f+g)\, d\lambda = \int f\, d\lambda + \int g\, d\lambda$.

This equation is indeed true, but all that follows directly from the definition is the inequality

$$\int (f+g)\, d\lambda \geq \int f\, d\lambda + \int g\, d\lambda.$$

The "proof" that the fourth property is not obvious is quite straightforward. It stems from the fact that our definition of the integral is highly nonsymmetric. What we have defined is in reality only a *lower* integral, since the definition employs only those $s \in S$ which satisfy $s \leq f$. For the lower integral of a sum $f + g$ we can obtain only the inequality. This is analogous to the situation in Section 2.A concerning outer and inner measure. Property *4 showed that $\lambda_*(A \cup B) \geq \lambda_*(A) + \lambda_*(B)$ if $A \cap B = \emptyset$; and this is all that can be said without assuming that A and B are measurable. The analogy is not perfect, because we *are* assuming f and g are measurable functions. We have not yet, however, made use of that assumption.

One way to obtain Property 4 is to define also an upper integral and prove the reverse inequality for the upper integral of $f + g$. Then we could say that f is *integrable* if its upper and lower integrals are equal (and finite). From this the desired additivity of the integral would be an immediate consequence. Then we should prove a difficult theorem, stating that f is integrable if and only if f is measurable (and $\int f d\lambda < \infty$).

Instead of such a procedure, we prefer to use the definition of $\int f d\lambda$ we have already given. We shall then obtain the missing Property 4 by immediately proving a BIG theorem, virtually the most important theorem of the book. Consequences of this theorem include not only Property 4 but also almost all the classical important convergence theorems in integration theory.

Problem 1. *"The vanishing property."*
Assume that $f \geq 0$ and f is measurable. Prove that $\int f d\lambda = 0 \iff \{x \mid f(x) > 0\}$ is a null set.

Problem 2. *"The finiteness property."*
Assume that $f \geq 0$ and f is measurable. Prove that $\int f d\lambda < \infty \implies \{x \mid f(x) = \infty\}$ is a null set.

Problem 3. Assume $f : \mathbb{R}^n \to [0, \infty]$ is a measurable simple function, presented in the form

$$f = \sum_{k=1}^{m} \alpha_k \chi_{A_k},$$

where $0 \leq \alpha_k \leq \infty$ and the sets A_k are measurable and disjoint. Prove that

$$\int f d\lambda = \sum_{k=1}^{m} \alpha_k \lambda(A_k),$$

where we assume $\infty \cdot 0 = 0$. (This differs only from the definition of the integral of a function in S in that α_k is now allowed to equal ∞.) In particular, if $s \in S$ then the two definitions we have for $\int s d\lambda$ produce the same number for the integral.

Problem 4. Prove that if $f \geq 0$ and f is measurable, then Property 3 is valid also with $c = \infty$:

$$\int \infty f d\lambda = \infty \int f d\lambda,$$

where we interpret $\infty \cdot 0 = 0$.

LICT

Lebesgue's Increasing Convergence Theorem: Assume that f_1, f_2, ... *are measurable functions on* $\mathbb{R}^n$ *such that*

$$0 \leq f_1 \leq f_2 \leq f_3 \leq \dots .$$

Then

$$\lim_{k \to \infty} \int f_k d\lambda = \int \left(\lim_{k \to \infty} f_k \right) d\lambda.$$

Proof: Use the notation $f = \lim_{k \to \infty} f_k$. Note that $0 \leq f \leq \infty$ and f is measurable. Also, the inequalities $f_k \leq f_{k+1} \leq f$ imply that $\int f_k d\lambda \leq \int f_{k+1} d\lambda \leq \int f d\lambda$. Therefore, the limit

$$I = \lim_{k \to \infty} \int f_k d\lambda$$

does exist and satisfies $I \leq \int f d\lambda$. Thus, we have to prove the opposite inequality $I \geq \int f d\lambda$. If c is an arbitrary real number such that $c < \int f d\lambda$, it suffices to prove $I \geq c$. By definition of $\int f d\lambda$, there exists $s \in S$ such that $0 \leq s \leq f$ and $c < \int s d\lambda$. The simple function s has a representation of the form

$$s = \sum_{i=1}^{N} \alpha_i \chi_{A_i},$$

where $0 < \alpha_i < \infty$ and the sets A_i are disjoint and measurable. By replacing each α_i by $\alpha_i - \epsilon$, where ϵ is small, we obtain a new simple function $s' \in S$ such that $c < \int s' d\lambda$ and $0 \leq s' \leq f$ and, furthermore, if $f(x) > 0$ then $s'(x) < f(x)$. Let us now change the notation and assume that the original simple function s has this additional property.

Summarizing,

$$0 \leq s \leq f,$$
$$\text{if } f(x) > 0 \text{ then } s(x) < f(x),$$
$$\int s d\lambda > c.$$

The beauty of this situation is that we have to deal with only one simple function s.

Now define the set

$$E_k = \{x \mid f_k(x) \geq s(x)\}.$$

This set is measurable since the function $f_k - s$ is measurable. Since the sequence f_k is increasing, $E_1 \subset E_2 \subset E_3 \subset \ldots$. Moreover,

$$\bigcup_{k=1}^{\infty} E_k = \mathbb{R}^n.$$

To verify this equation, consider any $x \in \mathbb{R}^n$. If $f(x) = 0$, then $s(x) = 0$ and all $f_k(x) = 0$, so $x \in E_k$ for all k; if $f(x) > 0$, then $f(x) > s(x)$ and thus $f_k(x) > s(x)$ for all sufficiently large k, proving that $x \in E_k$.

For any fixed k we have

$$f_k \geq f_k \chi_{E_k}$$
$$\geq s \chi_{E_k}$$
$$= \sum_{i=1}^{N} \alpha_i \chi_{A_i \cap E_k}.$$

Therefore,

$$\int f_k d\lambda \geq \sum_{i=1}^{N} \alpha_i \lambda(A_i \cap E_k).$$

Now we shall make crucial use of the properties of λ: This measure is *countably additive*. The particular use we make of this property is the application of Property M5 on p.50 to conclude that

$$\lim_{k \to \infty} \lambda(A_i \cap E_k) = \lambda(A_i).$$

Therefore,

$$I = \lim_{k \to \infty} \int f_k d\lambda \geq \sum_{i=1}^{N} \alpha_i \lambda(A_i) = \int s d\lambda > c.$$

QED

Now we are able to derive the additivity of the integral:

4
$$\int (f+g)d\lambda = \int f d\lambda + \int g d\lambda.$$

The proof begins by using the theorem on p.118 to obtain sequences in S with the properties:

$$0 \le s_1 \le s_2 \le \dots \quad \text{and} \quad \lim_{k \to \infty} s_k = f,$$

$$0 \le t_1 \le t_2 \le \dots \quad \text{and} \quad \lim_{k \to \infty} t_k = g.$$

But then $s_k + t_k$ is an increasing sequence of measurable functions whose limit is $f + g$. Thus, the additivity Property S4 implies

$$\int (f+g)d\lambda = \lim_{k \to \infty} \int (s_k + t_k)d\lambda \qquad \text{(LICT)}$$

$$= \lim_{k \to \infty} \left[\int s_k d\lambda + \int t_k d\lambda \right]$$

$$= \int f d\lambda + \int g d\lambda \qquad \text{(LICT)}.$$

We can now give a tremendous generalization of this additivity:

Theorem: *Assume $f_1, f_2, \dots$ are nonnegative measurable functions on $\mathbb{R}^n$. Then*

$$\int \left(\sum_{k=1}^{\infty} f_k \right) d\lambda = \sum_{k=1}^{\infty} \int f_k d\lambda.$$

Proof: Let

$$F_j = \sum_{k=1}^{j} f_k \quad \text{and} \quad F = \sum_{k=1}^{\infty} f_k.$$

Then the sequence F_j increases to F and we can apply LICT:

$$\int F d\lambda = \lim_{j \to \infty} \int F_j d\lambda$$

$$= \lim_{j \to \infty} \sum_{k=1}^{j} \int f_k d\lambda \quad \text{(using the finite additivity)}$$

$$= \sum_{k=1}^{\infty} \int f_k d\lambda.$$

QED

We shall now establish a slight generalization of LICT which for historical reasons is called

---

Fatou's Lemma: *Assume* f_1, f_2, ... *are nonnegative measurable functions. Then*

$$\int \left(\liminf_{k \to \infty} f_k \right) d\lambda \leq \liminf_{k \to \infty} \int f_k d\lambda.$$

Proof: Define
$$g_k = \inf\{f_k, f_{k+1}, f_{k+2}, \dots\}.$$

Then $g_k \geq 0$, g_k is measurable, $g_k \leq f_k$, the sequence g_k is increasing, and $\lim g_k = \liminf f_k$. Therefore, LICT implies

$$\int (\liminf f_k) \, d\lambda = \int (\lim g_k) d\lambda$$

$$= \lim \int g_k d\lambda$$

$$= \liminf \int g_k d\lambda$$

$$\leq \liminf \int f_k d\lambda \quad (\text{since } g_k \leq f_k).$$

QED

Problem 5. Give an example which shows that the conclusion of Fatou's lemma cannot be strengthened to an equality. Do this by constructing a sequence of simple functions s_k on $\mathbb{R}$ such that $s_k = 0$ outside of $[0, 1]$, $\lim s_k = 0$, and $\lim \int s_k d\lambda = \infty$.

Problem 6. Show that Fatou's lemma implies that for any measurable sets A_k
$$\lambda(\liminf A_k) \leq \liminf \lambda(A_k)$$

(cf. Problem 2.46). Give an example in $\mathbb{R}$ of a sequence of measurable sets A_k such that $A_k \subset [0, 1]$, $\lim \lambda(A_k) = 1$, but $\liminf A_k = \emptyset$.

Problem 7. If "lim inf" is replaced by "lim sup" in Fatou's lemma, show that neither inequality is valid in general. The invalidity of "$\geq$" follows from Problem 5. To prove that "$\leq$" is invalid, construct a sequence of measurable sets $A_k \subset \mathbb{R}$ such that $\limsup A_k = \mathbb{R}$ but $\lambda(A_k) = 1$ for all k (cf. Problem 2.46).

Problem 8. Here is a result very similar to Fatou's lemma, except that integration is replaced by summation. For every $k \in \mathbb{N}$ let f_k be a nonnegative *sequence* $f_k(1), f_k(2), f_k(3), \ldots$. Prove that

$$\sum_{n=1}^{\infty} \liminf_{k \to \infty} f_k(n) \leq \liminf_{k \to \infty} \sum_{n=1}^{\infty} f_k(n).$$

(**HINT:** This is very simple. Take the $\liminf$ of each side of the inequality $\sum_{n=1}^{N} f_k(n) \leq \sum_{n=1}^{\infty} f_k(n)$. What can you say about the $\liminf$ of a finite sum? Then let $N \to \infty$.)

We shall later see in Problem 39 that this result is actually nothing more than a special case of Fatou's lemma.

B. General Measurable Functions

We are going to generalize the integral to functions which are not necessarily nonnegative.

Definition: Let $f : \mathbb{R}^n \to [-\infty, \infty]$ be measurable. Therefore, Section 5.E shows that f_+ and f_- are also measurable. As these functions are nonnegative, both integrals $\int f_+ d\lambda$ and $\int f_- d\lambda$ exist. In case both these integrals are *finite*, then f is said to be *integrable* and its *integral* is the real number

$$\int f d\lambda = \int f_+ d\lambda - \int f_- d\lambda.$$

Notation: The collection of all integrable functions will be denoted L^1, or sometimes $L^1(\mathbb{R}^n)$ or $L^1(\mathbb{R}^n, \mathcal{L}, \lambda)$.

Problem 9. Assume f is measurable. Prove that $f \in L^1 \iff |f| \in L^1$.

Also prove that

$$\left| \int f d\lambda \right| \le \int |f| \, d\lambda.$$

Problem 10. Assume f and g are measurable, $g \in L^1$, and $|f| \le |g|$. Prove that $f \in L^1$.

Proposition: *Suppose* $f, g \in L^1$ *and* $a, b \in \mathbb{R}$. *Then* $af + bg \in L^1$ *and*

$$\int (af + bg) d\lambda = a \int f d\lambda + b \int g d\lambda.$$

(There is a minor problem with the statement of this result. Namely, it could happen that $af + bg$ is undefined at some points of $\mathbb{R}^n$ because calculating $af(x) + bg(x)$ might require an addition such as $-\infty + \infty$. However, Problem 2 shows that f or g can be infinite only on a null set, and we shall discuss in Section C the fact that for integration purposes we can ignore null sets. Therefore, we are content to assume for the present that f and g are finite on all of $\mathbb{R}^n$.)

Proof: It suffices to show that

$$\int af d\lambda = a \int f d\lambda,$$

$$\int (f + g) d\lambda = \int f d\lambda + \int g d\lambda.$$

First, suppose $a \ge 0$. Then $(af)_+ = af_+$ and $(af)_- = af_-$, so we obtain

$$\int af d\lambda = \int af_+ d\lambda - \int af_- d\lambda$$

$$= a \int f_+ d\lambda - a \int f_- d\lambda \quad \text{(by Section A)}$$

$$= a \left[\int f_+ d\lambda - \int f_- d\lambda \right]$$

$$= a \int f d\lambda.$$

If $a < 0$, then $(af)_+ = -af_-$ and $(af)_- = -af_+$, so we obtain

$$\int af d\lambda = \int -af_- d\lambda - \int -af_+ d\lambda$$

$$= -a \int f_- d\lambda + a \int f_+ d\lambda$$

$$= a \int f d\lambda.$$

Finally, let $h = f + g$. Then

$$h_+ - h_- = h = f + g = (f_+ - f_-) + (g_+ - g_-).$$

Rearranging this equation yields

$$h_+ + f_- + g_- = h_- + f_+ + g_+.$$

But then the additivity which was proved in Section A implies

$$\int h_+ d\lambda + \int f_- d\lambda + \int g_- d\lambda = \int h_- d\lambda + \int f_+ d\lambda + \int g_+ d\lambda.$$

Rearranging this equation yields

$$\int h d\lambda = \int f d\lambda + \int g d\lambda.$$

This last step has one problem involved in it. Namely, we do not yet know that $\int h d\lambda$ exists. We must prove that $\int h_+ d\lambda$ and $\int h_- d\lambda$ are both *finite*. But it is easy to check, e.g., that $h_+ \leq f_+ + g_+$, and therefore

$$\int h_+ d\lambda \leq \int f_+ d\lambda + \int g_+ d\lambda < \infty.$$

QED

Now we are ready to state and prove the principal convergence theorem in the theory of integration.

> ### *Lebesgue's Dominated Convergence Theorem:* *Assume f_1, f_2, ... are measurable functions on $\mathbb{R}^n$. Assume $g \geq 0$, $g \in L^1$. Assume*
>
> $$\lim_{k \to \infty} f_k(x) \quad \text{exists for all} \quad x \in \mathbb{R}^n$$
>
> *and*
>
> $$\mid f_k(x) \mid \leq g(x) \quad \text{for all} \quad x \in \mathbb{R}^n.$$
>
> *Then $\lim_{k \to \infty} f_k \in L^1$ and*
>
> $$\int \left(\lim_{k \to \infty} f_k \right) d\lambda = \lim_{k \to \infty} \int f_k d\lambda.$$

LDCT

(This is termed the *dominated* convergence theorem because all the functions f_k are dominated by a single integrable function g.)

Proof: Let $f = \lim f_k$. Since $|f| \leq g$, we conclude that f, together with all the functions f_k, is integrable. This is a consequence of Problem 10.

Now we apply Fatou's lemma to the *nonnegative* functions $g + f_k$, and we obtain

$$\int (g+f)d\lambda \leq \liminf \int (g+f_k)d\lambda.$$

That is,

$$\int g d\lambda + \int f d\lambda \leq \int g d\lambda + \liminf \int f_k d\lambda.$$

Now subtract the (finite!) number $\int g d\lambda$ from both sides of this inequality, obtaining

$$\int f d\lambda \leq \liminf \int f_k d\lambda.$$

We could have performed the same steps with $g - f_k$ rather than $g + f_k$. Thus, we also obtain

$$\int (-f)d\lambda \leq \liminf \int (-f_k)d\lambda$$

$$= \liminf - \int f_k d\lambda$$

$$= -\limsup \int f_k d\lambda.$$

That is,

$$\limsup \int f_k d\lambda \le \int f d\lambda.$$

The combination of the two inequalities we have obtained is:

$$\limsup \int f_k d\lambda \le \int f d\lambda \le \liminf \int f_k d\lambda.$$

Therefore, we conclude that $\lim \int f_k d\lambda$ exists and equals $\int f d\lambda$.   **QED**

Problem 11. Assume $f \in L^1(\mathbb{R}^n)$. Define

$$f_k(x) = \begin{cases} f(x) & \text{if } |f(x)| \le k \text{ and } |x| \le k, \\ 0 & \text{otherwise.} \end{cases}$$

Prove that

$$\lim_{k \to \infty} \int f_k d\lambda = \int f d\lambda.$$

Problem 12. Assume $f \in L^1(\mathbb{R}^n)$. Prove that

$$\lim_{k \to \infty} \int f(x) e^{-|x|^2/k} dx = \int f(x) dx.$$

Problem 13. Give another proof of Problem 2.42, based upon the inequality

$$\sum_{k=1}^{\infty} \chi_{A_k} \le d\chi_{\bigcup\limits_{k=1}^{\infty} A_k}.$$

Problem 14. Assume $A_1, A_2, \ldots$ are measurable sets. Let $m \in \mathbb{N}$, and let E_m be the set defined as follows: $x \in E_m \iff x$ is a member of at least m of the sets A_k. Prove that E_m is measurable and that

$$m\lambda(E_m) \le \sum_{k=1}^{\infty} \lambda(A_k).$$

Problem 15. Give another proof of Problem 2.41, based upon the result in Problem 14.

C. Almost Everywhere

If some property is valid except on a null set (a set $A \in \mathcal{L}$ satisfying $\lambda(A) = 0$), we shall say that the property is valid *almost everywhere*, abbreviated *a.e.* Also we shall use variants of this terminology without giving an explicit definition. For instance, for the rational numbers $\mathbb{Q} \subset \mathbb{R}$ we say that $\chi_{\mathbb{Q}} = 0$ a.e., and we also say that almost all real numbers are irrational.

If f and g are two measurable functions, then we shall be very interested in the situation $f(x) = g(x)$ for a.e. x. We shall also say that $f = g$ a.e. Of course, this means that $\{x \mid f(x) \neq g(x)\}$ is a null set. In case $f = g$ a.e., then we *usually* shall not distinguish f from g. That is, we shall just regard them as equal. We could be very formal and proper by introducing the equivalence relation

$$f \sim g \Longleftrightarrow f = g \quad \text{a.e.},$$

but the properties are so elementary that this hardly seems necessary. Indeed, it is easy to see that for purposes of integration we *cannot* distinguish f from g if these functions are equal a.e. In fact,

  1. if $f = g$ a.e. and both are nonnegative, then $\int f d\lambda = \int g d\lambda$.

  2. if $f = g$ a.e., then $f \in L^1 \Longleftrightarrow g \in L^1$; and then $\int f d\lambda = \int g d\lambda$.

These facts are immediate consequences of a generalization of part of Problem 1. Problem 1 asserts that if $f \geq 0$ and f is measurable, then $\int f d\lambda = 0 \Leftrightarrow f = 0$ a.e. Here is the generalization:

Problem 16. If f is measurable and $f = 0$ a.e., prove that $f \in L^1$ and $\int f d\lambda = 0$.

Another situation which frequently arises is that a function f is *defined* only a.e. Then we say that f is measurable if and only if its extension to $\mathbb{R}^n$ obtained by defining it to be 0 where it was undefined is measurable. The choice "0" is unimportant, as the following problem shows.

Problem 17. Suppose f is defined a.e., and suppose g and h are defined on all of $\mathbb{R}^n$, and $g = f$ a.e. and $h = f$ a.e. Prove that g is measurable $\Longleftrightarrow h$ is measurable.

Thus, if f is defined a.e. and g is defined on all of $\mathbb{R}^n$ and is equal to f a.e. and is measurable, we say without ambiguity that $f \in L^1$ if $g \in L^1$, and we define $\int f d\lambda = \int g d\lambda$.

We shall usually use these conventions without even mentioning them at all. And all the theorems concerning convergence of integrals immediately generalize. For example, LDCT becomes

<table>
<tr><td>LDCT (bis)</td><td>

Assume f_1, f_2, ... are measurable functions defined a.e. on $\mathbb{R}^n$. Assume g is defined a.e., $g \geq 0$, $g \in L^1$. Assume

$$\lim_{k \to \infty} f_k(x) \quad \text{exists for a.e.} \quad x \in \mathbb{R}^n$$

and

$$\mid f_k(x) \mid \leq g(x) \quad \text{for a.e.} \quad x \in \mathbb{R}^n.$$

Then

$$\int \left(\lim_{k \to \infty} f_k \right) d\lambda = \lim_{k \to \infty} \int f_k d\lambda.$$

</td></tr>
</table>

It is really not necessary to write out a proof. There is just one key observation to be made. Namely, each statement in the hypothesis occurs except on an associated null set, and there are only countably many of them. Thus, there is one "giant" null set outside of which all the statements are valid. Now redefine all the functions to be zero on this giant null set and apply the original version of LDCT in Section B.

> **Theorem:** *Assume f_1, f_2, ... are in L^1 and assume*
>
> $$\sum_{k=1}^{\infty} \int \mid f_k \mid d\lambda < \infty.$$
>
> *Then*
>
> $$\sum_{k=1}^{\infty} f_k(x) \quad \text{exists for a.e.} \quad x \in \mathbb{R}^n$$
>
> *and*
>
> $$\int \left(\sum_{k=1}^{\infty} f_k \right) d\lambda = \sum_{k=1}^{\infty} \int f_k d\lambda.$$

Proof: Let $g = \sum\limits_{k=1}^{\infty} \mid f_k \mid$. Then $g \in L^1$ because of the theorem on p.128:

$$\int g d\lambda = \sum_{k=1}^{\infty} \int \mid f_k \mid d\lambda < \infty.$$

Thus the finiteness property of Problem 2 implies $g(x) < \infty$ for a.e. x. Therefore $\sum\limits_{k=1}^{\infty} \mid f_k(x) \mid < \infty$ for a.e x, so that the series $\sum\limits_{k=1}^{\infty} f_k(x)$ converges absolutely for such x. Moreover, if $F_j = \sum\limits_{k=1}^{j} f_k$, then $\mid F_j \mid \leq g$ for all j, so that LDCT implies $\int \left(\lim\limits_{j\to\infty} F_j \right) d\lambda = \lim\limits_{j\to\infty} \int F_j d\lambda$.   **QED**

Problem 18. Suppose that for any $s \in \mathbb{R}$ there is given a measurable function f_s defined a.e. Suppose that $\lim\limits_{s\to\infty} f_s$ exists a.e., and notice that this statement requires that for a.e. $x \in \mathbb{R}^n$, *all* the functions $f_s(x)$ are defined. Suppose $g \geq 0$, $g \in L^1$, and $|f_s| \leq g$ a.e. (the null set may depend on s). Prove that $\lim\limits_{s\to\infty} f_s$ is measurable, and integrable, and

$$\int \left(\lim_{s\to\infty} f_s \right) d\lambda = \lim_{s\to\infty} \int f_s d\lambda.$$

(**HINT**: Consider Problem 5.18.)

Before going on to the next section, let us investigate a couple of typical applications of the ideas we have discussed thus far.

Example: If f_k is a sequence of nonnegative measurable functions on $\mathbb{R}^n$ such that $\int f_k d\lambda \leq 1$ for all k, and if $\lim\limits_{k\to\infty} f_k = f$ exists a.e., then $\int f d\lambda \leq 1$, and thus f is integrable. This is an immediate consequence of Fatou's lemma. Note that even if $\int f_k d\lambda = 1$ for all k, still all that can be said is that $\int f d\lambda \leq 1$. (See Problem 5.)

Example: Let ϕ be the function on $\mathbb{R}$:

$$\phi(x) = \begin{cases} \mid x \mid^{-1/2} & \text{if } \mid x \mid \leq 1, \\ 0 & \text{if } \mid x \mid > 1. \end{cases}$$

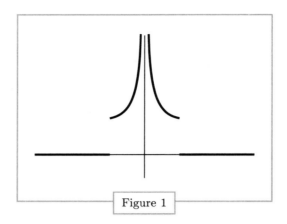

Figure 1

This function is measurable, and we shall soon learn that the integral of ϕ is the same as its (improper) Riemann integral and can thus be computed by the use of the fundamental theorem of calculus. Thus, $\int \phi d\lambda = 4$. Now define

$$f(x) = \sum_{j=1}^{\infty} \sum_{k=-\infty}^{\infty} 2^{-j-|k|} \phi\left(x - \frac{k}{j}\right)$$

It then follows immediately from Section A that

$$\int f d\lambda = \sum_{j=1}^{\infty} \sum_{k=-\infty}^{\infty} 2^{-j-|k|} \cdot 4$$

(assuming the translation invariance of the integral, which will be proved later). Thus, $\int f d\lambda = 12$. There are some interesting facts to note about this function. First, for *any* rational number r it is true that $\lim\limits_{x \to r} f(x) = \infty$; yet the function is integrable. Second, since $\int f d\lambda < \infty$, Problem 2 shows that $f < \infty$ a.e. Therefore, for almost every $x \in \mathbb{R}$ the series

$$\sum_{j=1}^{\infty} \sum_{k=-\infty}^{\infty} 2^{-j-|k|} \phi\left(x - \frac{k}{j}\right)$$

converges. Just try giving a direct proof of that fact! This is a typical method of proving the almost everywhere convergence of a series.

Problem 19. Here is a useful generalization of LDCT. Assume f_1, f_2, ... are measurable functions defined a.e. on $\mathbb{R}^n$, and

$$\lim_{k \to \infty} f_k(x) = f(x) \text{ exists for a.e. } x \in \mathbb{R}^n.$$

Also assume g_1, g_2, ... are nonnegative functions in L^1, that

$$| f_k(x) | \le g_k(x) \text{ for a.e. } x \in \mathbb{R}^n,$$

that

$$\lim_{k \to \infty} g_k(x) = g(x) \text{ exists for a.e. } x \in \mathbb{R}^n,$$

that $g \in L^1$, and that

$$\int g d\lambda = \lim_{k \to \infty} \int g_k d\lambda.$$

Prove that

$$\int f d\lambda = \lim_{k \to \infty} \int f_k d\lambda.$$

(**HINT:** Imitate the proof of LDCT.)

D. Integration Over Subsets of $\mathbb{R}^n$

Given a measurable function f and a measurable set $E \subset \mathbb{R}^n$, we define whenever possible the *integral of f over the set E* by the formula

$$\int_E f d\lambda = \int f \chi_E d\lambda.$$

"Whenever possible" signifies that if $f \ge 0$ a.e. on E, then $\int_E f d\lambda$ is defined (and may be ∞), and otherwise $\int_E f d\lambda$ is defined if $f\chi_E$ is integrable.

Moreover, if it is the case that a function f is defined only on E, then f is said to be *measurable* if the function

$$g(x) = \begin{cases} f(x) & \text{if } x \in E, \\ 0 & \text{if } x \in E^c, \end{cases}$$

is measurable. Equivalently, this means that for all $t \in [-\infty, \infty]$ the set

$$\{x \in E \mid f(x) \le t\} \in \mathcal{L}.$$

(We are assuming $E \in \mathcal{L}$.) It then makes sense to say that $f \in L^1(E)$ if $g \in L^1(\mathbb{R}^n)$, and to *define*

$$\int_E f d\lambda = \int g d\lambda.$$

Problem 20. Assume $\lambda(E) = 0$. Prove that every function defined on E is measurable and that $\int_E f d\lambda = 0$ for all f.

Now we give a couple of theorems which treat these ideas.

Countable Additivity of the Integral: *Assume that E_1, E_2, ... are disjoint measurable sets, and let $E = \bigcup_{k=1}^{\infty} E_k$. Let f be a measurable function on E and assume that either $f \ge 0$ or $f \in L^1(E)$. Then*

$$\int_E f d\lambda = \sum_{k=1}^{\infty} \int_{E_k} f d\lambda.$$

Proof: In case $f \ge 0$ the result is an immediate consequence of the theorem on p.128:

$$\int_E f d\lambda = \int f \chi_E d\lambda$$

$$= \int \sum_{k=1}^{\infty} f \chi_{E_k} d\lambda$$

$$= \sum_{k=1}^{\infty} \int f \chi_{E_k} d\lambda$$

$$= \sum_{k=1}^{\infty} \int_{E_k} f d\lambda.$$

Now suppose $f \in L^1(E)$. In this case we apply the last theorem of Section B, using the sequence $f\chi_{E_k}$. The only hypothesis that requires checking is the convergence of the series of integrals of $| f\chi_{E_k} |$. This follows, however, by the case we have just treated:

$$\sum_{k=1}^{\infty} \int | f\chi_{E_k} | \, d\lambda = \sum_{k=1}^{\infty} \int_{E_k} | f | \, d\lambda$$

$$= \int_E | f | \, d\lambda$$

$$< \infty.$$

QED

The next theorem is about "absolute continuity," a concept we shall treat in great detail later. The idea is that not only is it true that $\lambda(E) = 0 \Rightarrow \int_E f d\lambda = 0$ (Problem 20) but that something more precise is true.

Theorem on Absolute Continuity: *Let $f \in L^1(\mathbb{R}^n)$. Let $\epsilon > 0$. Then there exists $\delta > 0$ such that if E is measurable and $\lambda(E) < \delta$, then*

$$\left| \int_E f d\lambda \right| < \epsilon.$$

Proof: Clearly, we can assume $f \geq 0$, thanks to Problem 9. By the definition of $\int f d\lambda$, there exists a simple function $s \in S$ such that $0 \leq s \leq f$ and

$$\int s d\lambda > \int f d\lambda - \frac{\epsilon}{2}.$$

Since s assumes only a finite number of distinct values, which are all real, there exists a positive constant C such that $s(x) \leq C$ for all $x \in \mathbb{R}^n$.

Therefore,

$$\int_E f d\lambda = \int_E s d\lambda + \int_E (f - s) d\lambda$$

$$\leq \int_E C d\lambda + \int_{\mathbb{R}^n} (f - s) d\lambda$$

$$= C\lambda(E) + \int f d\lambda - \int s d\lambda$$

$$< C\lambda(E) + \frac{\epsilon}{2}.$$

Thus, the choice $\delta = \epsilon/2C$ satisfies the requirements of the theorem.

                                                                              QED

Problem 21. Assume f_1, f_2, ... are nonnegative functions in L^1, that

$$\lim_{k \to \infty} f_k(x) = f(x) \text{ exists a.e. in } \mathbb{R}^n,$$

that $f \in L^1$, and that

$$\int f d\lambda = \lim_{k \to \infty} \int f_k d\lambda.$$

Prove that

$$\lim_{k \to \infty} \int | f_k - f | \, d\lambda = 0.$$

(**HINT**: Use Problem 19.)

Show that this implies that for every measurable set E

$$\int_E f d\lambda = \lim_{k \to \infty} \int_E f_k d\lambda.$$

E. Generalization: Measure Spaces

Everything we have discussed so far in this chapter can be *instantly* generalized, simply by introducing one new definition and changing the notation on the theorems. We merely assume as axioms the essential properties of the measure λ which have been needed.

Definition: A *measure space* consists of the following three things:

    1. a nonempty *set X*;

    2. a *σ-algebra $\mathcal{M} \subset 2^X$*;

    3. a *function μ* defined on $\mathcal{M}$ satisfying

        a. $0 \leq \mu(A) \leq \infty$ for all $A \in \mathcal{M}$,

        b. $\mu(\emptyset) = 0$, and

        c. if A_1, A_2, ... are disjoint sets in $\mathcal{M}$,

$$\mu \left(\bigcup_{k=1}^{\infty} A_k \right) = \sum_{k=1}^{\infty} \mu(A_k).$$

This function μ is called a *measure*.

Problem 22. Prove that if A, $B \in \mathcal{M}$ and $A \subset B$, then $\mu(A) \leq \mu(B)$.

Problem 23. Prove that if $A \in \mathcal{M}$ and $\mu(A) = 0$, and if $E \subset A$ and $E \in \mathcal{M}$, then $\mu(E) = 0$. (It cannot be proved that $E \subset A$ implies $E \in \mathcal{M}$ in this situation, as examples below will demonstrate.)

Problem 24. Prove that if A_1, A_2, ... are in $\mathcal{M}$, then

$$\mu \left(\bigcup_{k=1}^{\infty} A_k \right) \leq \sum_{k=1}^{\infty} \mu(A_k).$$

Problem 25. Prove that if $A_1 \subset A_2 \subset \ldots$ are in $\mathcal{M}$, then

$$\mu \left(\bigcup_{k=1}^{\infty} A_k \right) = \lim_{k \to \infty} \mu(A_k).$$

Problem 26. Conversely, prove that if μ is a function on $\mathcal{M}$ which satisfies a, b, and c for *finite* disjoint unions, and the condition of Problem 25, then μ is a measure.

    Example 1: $X = \mathbb{R}^n$, $\mathcal{M} = \mathcal{L}$, $\mu = \lambda$. This is of course our primary example, the one which we have been discussing all along.

Example 2: $X = \mathbb{R}^n$, $\mathcal{M} = \mathcal{B}$ (Borel sets), $\mu = \lambda$. Same set, same function, but a smaller σ-algebra.

Example 3: $X =$ any nonempty set, $\mathcal{M} = 2^X$, $\mu(A) = \infty$ if $A \neq \emptyset$. This is of course a rather silly example, but it is nevertheless a measure space.

Example 4: $X =$ any nonempty set, $\mathcal{M} = 2^X$, and μ is *counting measure*:

$$\mu(A) = \begin{cases} \text{number of points in } A \text{ if } A \text{ is finite,} \\ \infty \text{ if } A \text{ is infinite.} \end{cases}$$

Problem 27. Verify that counting measure satisfies Property c.

Example 5: $X =$ any nonempty set, $\mathcal{M} = 2^X$. Let $x_0 \in X$ and define

$$\mu(A) = \chi_A(x_0).$$

This measure is called the *Dirac measure* at x_0, and is usually denoted δ_{x_0}. Thus,

$$\delta_{x_0}(A) = \begin{cases} 1 & \text{if } x_0 \in A, \\ 0 & \text{if } x_0 \notin A. \end{cases}$$

The measure δ_{x_0} is also frequently called the *Dirac delta "function."*

Example 6: $X =$ any uncountable set. The σ-algebra $\mathcal{M}$ is the one described in Section 5.A, Example 6: $A \in \mathcal{M} \iff$ either A or A^c is countable. Then define the measure

$$\mu(A) = \begin{cases} 0 & \text{if } A \text{ is countable,} \\ 1 & \text{if } A^c \text{ is countable.} \end{cases}$$

We shall describe other examples later.

Here is the important point of all this: ALL THE DEFINITIONS AND THEOREMS IN SECTIONS A–D OF THE PRESENT CHAPTER ARE VALID FOR GENERAL MEASURE SPACES. The reason for this is that none of the theorems or proofs actually used any property of $\mathbb{R}^n$, $\mathcal{L}$, λ that is not true also for X, $\mathcal{M}$, μ. Here are a few of the details. Let X, $\mathcal{M}$, μ be a measure space, and assume all functions we discuss are $\mathcal{M}$-measurable. As regards the definition of the integral, we now say that if

$$s = \sum_{k=1}^{m} \alpha_k \chi_{A_k},$$

then

$$\int s d\mu = \int_X s d\mu = \sum_{k=1}^m \alpha_k \mu(A_k).$$

All the properties are the same. And if $f : X \to [0, \infty]$ is $\mathcal{M}$-measurable, then we define as in Section A:

$$\int f d\lambda = \sup \left\{ \int s d\mu \mid 0 \le s \le f \right\},$$

where the functions s are $\mathcal{M}$-measurable simple functions satisfying $0 \le s < \infty$. All the proofs go through without change, except for replacing $\mathbb{R}^n$ by X, $\mathcal{L}$ by $\mathcal{M}$, and λ by μ. When we wish to speak of "null" sets, we should be careful to specify that they are μ-*null sets*. We shall also use the terminology μ-*a.e.*, that is, almost everywhere with respect to the measure μ.

In order to illustrate the fact that the results of this chapter are valid in the context of an arbitrary measure space, we shall now pause to work out the solutions to Problems 1 and 2.

"THE VANISHING PROPERTY." *Assume that* $f : X \to [0, \infty]$ *is* $\mathcal{M}$-*measurable. Then* $\int f d\mu = 0 \iff f = 0$ μ-*a.e.* Assume first that $\int f d\mu = 0$. Let $A_k = \{x \in X \mid f(x) \ge k^{-1}\}$ for $k \in \mathbb{N}$. Then $k^{-1} \chi_{A_k}$ is an $\mathcal{M}$-measurable simple function which satisfies $0 \le k^{-1} \chi_{A_k} \le f$. By definition, $\int k^{-1} \chi_{A_k} d\mu \le \int f d\mu$; that is, $k^{-1} \mu(A_k) \le 0$. Thus, A_k is a μ-null set. But then $\{x \in X \mid f(x) > 0\} = \bigcup_{k=1}^{\infty} A_k$ is also a μ-null set.

Conversely, assume $A = \{x \in X \mid f(x) > 0\}$ is a μ-null set. Suppose $s = \sum_{k=1}^m \alpha_k \chi_{A_k}$ is any $\mathcal{M}$-measurable simple function such that $0 \le s \le f$. If $\alpha_k > 0$, then $s > 0$ on A_k. Therefore, $f \ge s > 0$ on A_k, proving that $A_k \subset A$, and thus that $\mu(A_k) = 0$. Therefore, if $\alpha_k > 0$, then $\alpha_k \mu(A_k) = 0$. Also $\alpha_k \mu(A_k) = 0$ if $\alpha_k = 0$. Thus, $\int s d\mu = \sum_{k=1}^m \alpha_k \mu(A_k) = 0$. By definition of the integral, $\int f d\mu = 0$.

"THE FINITENESS PROPERTY." *Assume that* $f : X \to [0, \infty]$ *is* $\mathcal{M}$-*measurable and that* $\int f d\mu < \infty$. *Then* $f < \infty$ μ-*a.e.* Let $B = \{x \in X \mid f(x) = \infty\}$. Then we must prove that $\mu(B) = 0$. For any $k \in \mathbb{N}$ the $\mathcal{M}$-measurable simple function $k\chi_B$ satisfies $0 \le k\chi_B \le f$. Therefore, $\int k\chi_B d\mu \le \int f d\mu$. That is,

$$\mu(B) \le \frac{\int f d\mu}{k}.$$

Since k is arbitrary, we conclude that $\mu(B) = 0$.

Knowing how to integrate on the measure space X, $\mathcal{M}$, μ, we can now give another class of examples of measure spaces.

Example 7: Let X, $\mathcal{M}$, μ, be a given measure space and let h be a fixed $\mathcal{M}$-measurable function from X to $[0, \infty]$. Define another measure ν by the formula

$$\nu(A) = \int_A h\,d\mu \qquad \text{for all}\ \ A \in \mathcal{M}.$$

The theorem in Section D on the countable additivity of the integral shows that ν satisfies Property c in the definition of a measure. Therefore, X, $\mathcal{M}$, ν is also a measure space. Note that $\mu(A) = 0 \Longrightarrow \nu(A) = 0$. This is a very important property; because of it the measure ν is said to be *absolutely continuous* with respect to μ.

Example 8: This is a special case of Example 7, obtained by taking $h = \chi_Y$, where $Y \in \mathcal{M}$ is fixed. Thus,

$$\nu(A) = \mu(A \cap Y) \qquad \text{for all}\ \ A \in \mathcal{M}.$$

The next example will introduce the important concept of the *completion* of a measure space.

Example 9: Let X, $\mathcal{M}$, μ be a given measure space. We can then define a new σ-algebra $\overline{\mathcal{M}}$ which contains $\mathcal{M}$ and a new measure $\overline{\mu}$ as follows:

$$A \in \overline{\mathcal{M}} \Longleftrightarrow \text{there exist } B, C \in \mathcal{M} \text{ such that}$$
$$B \subset A \subset C \quad \text{and} \quad \mu(C \sim B) = 0.$$

In this situation $\mu(B) = \mu(C)$, so we can define
$$\overline{\mu}(A) = \mu(B) = \mu(C).$$

The simple construction of this example is quite important in certain applications. It also affords an opportunity for you to work out some elementary properties of the construction.

Problem 28. Prove that $\overline{\mathcal{M}}$ is a σ-algebra.

Problem 29. Prove that $\overline{\mu}$ is well defined and is a measure.

Problem 30. Prove that $\overline{\mu}(A) = 0 \iff A$ is contained in a set in $\mathcal{M}$ which is a μ-null set.

Problem 31. Prove that if $E \subset A \in \overline{\mathcal{M}}$ and $\overline{\mu}(A) = 0$, then $E \in \overline{\mathcal{M}}$ (and therefore $\overline{\mu}(E) = 0$).

Definition: A measure space X, $\mathcal{M}$, μ is *complete* if whenever $E \subset A \in \mathcal{M}$ and $\mu(A) = 0$, then $E \in \mathcal{M}$ (and therefore $\mu(E) = 0$).

Thus, Problem 31 states that X, $\overline{\mathcal{M}}$, $\overline{\mu}$ is a complete measure space; it is called the *completion* of the measure space X, $\mathcal{M}$, μ.

Problem 32. Prove that $\overline{\mathcal{M}}$ can also be expressed as the collection of all sets of the form $A \cup N$, where $A \in \mathcal{M}$ and N is contained in a set in $\mathcal{M}$ which is a μ-null set.

Problem 33. Prove that $\overline{\mathcal{M}}$ is the σ-algebra generated by the collection of sets which either belong to $\mathcal{M}$ or are subsets of μ-null sets.

Problem 34. Prove that $\overline{\mathcal{M}} = \mathcal{M} \iff X$, $\mathcal{M}$, μ is complete.

Problem 35. Prove that the completion of $\mathbb{R}^n$, $\mathcal{B}$, λ is $\mathbb{R}^n$, $\mathcal{L}$, λ.

(**HINT:** Refer to Section 5.B.)

F. Some Calculations

It is instructive to take each of the examples given in the preceding section, determine precisely which functions are measurable, and calculate the corresponding integral.

Examples 1 and 2: We have nothing more to say about Lebesgue integration at this time. See Sections A–D.

Example 3 is trivial. All functions are measurable. If $f \geq 0$, then $\int f d\mu = \infty$ unless $f = 0$. If $f : X \to [-\infty, \infty]$, then $f \in L^1 \iff f = 0$.

Example 4 is simple, but rather useful. To treat integration with respect to counting measure we first have to discuss summing the values of a function. Suppose $f : X \to [0, \infty]$. Then we *define*

$$\sum_{x \in X} f(x) = \sup \left\{ \sum_{x \in F} f(x) \mid F \text{ is any finite subset of } X \right\}.$$

Problem 36. Assume $f : X \to [0, \infty]$. Prove that if $\sum\limits_{x \in X} f(x) < \infty$, then $\{x \in X \mid f(x) > 0\}$ is a countable set.

(**HINT**: Show that for every $k \in \mathbb{N}$ the set $\{x \in X \mid f(x) > k^{-1}\}$ is finite.)

Problem 37. In the special case $X = \mathbb{N}$, prove that

$$\sum_{x \in \mathbb{N}} f(x) = \lim_{n \to \infty} \sum_{k=1}^{n} f(k).$$

In the situation of Example 4, μ is counting measure. All functions are measurable. We then have the following result:

Proposition: Assume $f : X \to [0, \infty]$. Then

$$\int_X f \, d\mu = \sum_{x \in X} f(x).$$

Proof: Obviously, this formula is valid in case f is a simple function which vanishes except on a finite subset of X. Now if F is any finite subset of X, then $f\chi_F$ is such a simple function, and $f\chi_F \leq f$. Therefore,

$$\int f \, d\mu \geq \int f\chi_F \, d\mu$$
$$= \sum_{x \in X} f(x)\chi_F(x)$$
$$= \sum_{x \in F} f(x).$$

Since F is arbitrary,

$$\int f \, d\mu \geq \sum_{x \in X} f(x).$$

To prove the reverse inequality, it suffices to deal with the case that $\sum\limits_{x \in X} f(x) < \infty$. If s is any simple function satisfying $0 \leq s \leq f$, then

$$\sum_{x \in X} s(x) \leq \sum_{x \in X} f(x) < \infty,$$

so that s can assume a positive value only on a finite set. Thus, there exists a finite set $F \subset X$ such that $s = 0$ on F^c. Therefore,

$$\int s d\mu = \sum_{x \in X} s(x)$$

$$= \sum_{x \in F} s(x)$$

$$\leq \sum_{x \in F} f(x)$$

$$\leq \sum_{x \in X} f(x).$$

Since s is arbitrary, the definition of the integral implies that

$$\int f d\mu \leq \sum_{x \in X} f(x).$$

QED

Problem 38. This still concerns counting measure and Example 4. If $f : X \to [-\infty, \infty]$, prove that $f \in L^1 \iff \sum_{x \in X} |f(x)| < \infty$.

Here is an illustration of how the convergence theorems of Sections A and B appear in particular cases. Consider counting measure on the set $\mathbb{N}$. Then LDCT asserts:

If $g(1), g(2), \ldots$ is a convergent series of nonnegative numbers,

$$\sum_{n=1}^{\infty} g(n) < \infty,$$

and if $f_k(1), f_k(2), \ldots$ is a series such that

$$| f_k(n) | \leq g(n),$$
$$\lim_{k \to \infty} f_k(n) = f(n) \text{ exists for all } n,$$

then

$$\lim_{k \to \infty} \sum_{n=1}^{\infty} f_k(n) = \sum_{n=1}^{\infty} f(n).$$

For example,

$$\lim_{x \to 1-} \sum_{n=1}^{\infty} \frac{x^n}{n^2} = \sum_{n=1}^{\infty} \frac{1}{n^2}.$$

(The notation $x \to 1-$ signifies that $x < 1$ as the limit is taken.) These results can be proved directly in this case, without recourse to LDCT. However, the illustration might be helpful to some.

Problem 39. Show that the result in Problem 8 is precisely the statement of Fatou's lemma for the case of counting measure on $\mathbb{N}$.

Example 5: This is the example of Dirac measure at a point $x_0 \in X$. All functions are measurable. Here is a problem containing the results:

Problem 40. If $f : X \to [0, \infty]$, prove that $\int f d\delta_{x_0} = f(x_0)$. In general, prove that if $f : X \to [-\infty, \infty]$, then $f \in L^1 \iff f(x_0) \in \mathbb{R}$. In that case,

$$\int f d\delta_{x_0} = f(x_0).$$

Example 6: This is perhaps a rather unnatural example, but the class of measurable functions turns out to be quite interesting. Suppose that $f : X \to [-\infty, \infty]$ is $\mathcal{M}$-measurable. Then let $E \subset [-\infty, \infty]$ be defined as follows: $t \in E \iff \{x \mid f(x) < t\}$ is countable. Note that $E \neq \emptyset$ since $-\infty \in E$. The set E is clearly an interval. Let c be the least upper bound of E; thus, $-\infty \leq c \leq \infty$. Consider a sequence $t_1 \leq t_2 \leq t_3 \leq \ldots$ of points in E converging to c, with all $t_k < c$ (unless $c = -\infty$). Then we see that $\{x \mid f(x) < c\}$ is also countable, so that $c \in E$ (even true if $c = -\infty$). Then if $c < c'$, the set $\{x \mid f(x) < c'\}$ is uncountable. Now, *since f is measurable*, this set is measurable and hence has a countable complement: $\{x \mid f(x) \geq c'\}$ is countable. By again considering a sequence decreasing to c, we conclude that $\{x \mid f(x) > c\}$ is countable.

Therefore, we conclude that if f is measurable, then there exists a (unique) $c \in [-\infty, \infty]$ such that $\{x \mid f(x) \neq c\}$ is countable. Since this measure space assigns measure 0 to every countable set, another way to express the derived property of f is that $f = c$ a.e. As the converse is obvious, we have found that f is measurable $\iff f = c$ a.e. This makes the integral extremely easy to calculate:

$$\int f d\mu = c \quad \text{since} \quad f = c \ \ a.e.$$

Example 7: This example is concerned with a measure space X, $\mathcal{M}$, μ, a function $h : X \to [0, \infty]$ which is $\mathcal{M}$-measurable, and the measure

$$\nu(A) = \int_A h d\mu, \quad A \in \mathcal{M}.$$

If s is a nonnegative $\mathcal{M}$-measurable simple function, then s has a representation

$$s = \sum_{k=1}^{m} \alpha_k \chi_{A_k},$$

and we calculate

$$\int s d\nu = \sum_{k=1}^{m} \alpha_k \nu(A_k)$$

$$= \sum_{k=1}^{m} \alpha_k \int_{A_k} h d\mu$$

$$= \sum_{k=1}^{m} \alpha_k \int \chi_{A_k} h d\mu$$

$$= \int \sum_{k=1}^{m} \alpha_k \chi_{A_k} h d\mu$$

$$= \int s h d\mu.$$

Then it is an easy matter to prove the following result:

Proposition: *If* $f : X \to [0, \infty]$ *is* $\mathcal{M}$*-measurable, then*

$$\int f d\nu = \int f h d\mu.$$

Proof: By Section 5.E there exists a sequence of $\mathcal{M}$-measurable simple functions $0 \le s_1 \le s_2 \le \ldots$ such that $\lim_{k \to \infty} s_k = f$. Therefore, it is also true that $0 \le s_1 h \le s_2 h \le \ldots$ and $\lim_{k \to \infty} s_k h = fh$. Therefore, two applications of LICT produce

$$\int f d\nu = \lim_{k \to \infty} \int s_k d\nu$$

$$= \lim_{k \to \infty} \int s_k h d\mu$$

$$= \int f h d\mu.$$

$$\textbf{QED}$$

The equation obtained in this proposition is written *symbolically* as

$$d\nu = hd\mu \quad \text{or even} \quad \frac{d\nu}{d\mu} = h.$$

Example 8:   This is the special case of Example 7 with $h = \chi_Y$ for some $Y \in \mathcal{M}$. Thus, $\nu(A) = \mu(A \cap Y)$ and

$$\int_X f d\nu = \int_Y f d\mu.$$

Example 9:   This is quite simple. The example treats the completion of a measure space. The proof of the theorem in Section 5.E relating Lebesgue measurable functions and Borel measurable functions is quite general. The proof shows that if f is an $\overline{\mathcal{M}}$-measurable function, then there exists an $\mathcal{M}$-measurable function g such that $f = g$ except on a $\overline{\mu}$-null set. But then we have

$$\int f d\overline{\mu} = \int g d\mu,$$

so the "new" $\overline{\mu}$ integral is merely calculated from the original μ integral on the measure space X, $\mathcal{M}$, μ.

Problem 41. This calculation we have just finished assumes that if g is $\mathcal{M}$-measurable, then $\int g d\overline{\mu} = \int g d\mu$. Prove this.

Problem 42. Generalize the result of Problem 2.42: Suppose X, $\mathcal{M}$, μ is a measure space and A_1, A_2, A_3, ... are sets in $\mathcal{M}$ such that each point of X belongs to no more than d of the A_k's. Then

$$\sum_{k=1}^{\infty} \mu(A_k) \le d\mu \left(\bigcup_{k=1}^{\infty} A_k \right).$$

(See Problem 13.)

G. Miscellany

In this section we merely collect some facts about integration which will be needed later on.

Problem 43. Let f be an integrable function on a measure space X, $\mathcal{M}$, μ such that

$$\int_E f d\mu = 0$$

for all sets $E \in \mathcal{M}$. Prove that $f = 0$ μ-a.e.

Problem 44. Let f be an integrable function on the measure space $\mathbb{R}$, $\mathcal{L}$, λ such that

$$\int_a^b f d\lambda = 0$$

for all $-\infty < a < b < \infty$. Prove that $f = 0$ a.e.

Problem 45. Prove that there does not exist a set $E \subset \mathbb{R}$ such that $\lambda(E \cap [a,b]) = \frac{1}{2}(b - a)$ for all $-\infty < a < b < \infty$.

The next result has to do with *integrals depending on a parameter*. Suppose that X, $\mathcal{M}$, μ is a measure space, and suppose that $J \subset \mathbb{R}$ is an interval. Suppose that for every $t \in J$ there corresponds an integrable function on X. Thus, we are given

$$f : X \times J \to [-\infty, \infty],$$

and we write the functional dependence as $f(x,t)$ for $x \in X$, $t \in J$. For any fixed $t \in J$, this function can be integrated over X. Let $F(t)$ denote the integral:

$$F(t) = \int_X f(x,t) d\mu(x).$$

Then we want to discuss the way $F(t)$ varies with t. Specifically, we want to know if F is continuous, differentiable, etc. The continuity will be discussed first.

> ***Theorem:*** *Use the preceding notation. Assume that for each $t \in J$, $f(x,t)$ is an integrable function of x on X. Assume that there exists $g \in L^1(X)$ such that*
>
> $$|f(x,t)| \le g(x) \qquad for\ all\ \ (x,t) \in X \times J.$$
>
> *Assume that $t_0 \in J$ and that for μ-a.e. $x \in X$, $f(x,t)$ is a continuous function at $t = t_0$. Then F is also continuous at t_0.*

Proof: The proof is an immediate application of LDCT, the function g serving as a dominating function to insure that

$$\lim_{t \to t_0} \int_X f(x,t) d\mu(x) = \int_X \lim_{t \to t_0} f(x,t) d\mu(x)$$

$$= \int_X f(x,t_0) d\mu(x).$$

QED

Corollary:*Assume that for each $t \in J$, $f(x,t)$ is an integrable function of x on X. Assume that for μ-a.e. $x \in X$, $f(x,t)$ is differentiable at all $t \in J$. Moreover, assume that there exists $h \in L^1(X)$ such that the derivative satisfies for μ-a.e. $x \in X$ and all $t \in J$,*

$$\left| \frac{df(x,t)}{dt} \right| \le h(x).$$

Then F is also differentiable on J, and

$$\frac{dF}{dt}(t) = \int_X \frac{df(x,t)}{dt} d\mu(x).$$

(We call this result "differentiating under the integral sign.")

Proof: Let $t \in J$ be fixed. For small $|\delta|$ consider

$$\frac{F(t+\delta) - F(t)}{\delta} = \int_X \frac{f(x,t+\delta) - f(x,t)}{\delta} d\mu(x).$$

This equation is set up so that the theorem applies to it, with δ now being the parameter and $\delta = 0$ being the point of interest. Just two things must be noted. First, the integrand is continuous at $\delta = 0$:

$$\lim_{\delta \to 0} \frac{f(x,t+\delta) - f(x,t)}{\delta} = \frac{df}{dt}(x,t)$$

exists, by hypothesis. Second, the mean value theorem of differential calculus implies the estimate required in the hypothesis of the theorem:

$$\left| \frac{f(x,t+\delta) - f(x,t)}{\delta} \right| = \left| \frac{df}{dt}(x,t') \right|$$

$$\le h(x),$$

where t' is some number between t and $t + \delta$. Thus, the theorem implies

$$\lim_{\delta \to 0} \frac{F(t+\delta) - F(t)}{\delta} = \int_X \frac{df}{dt}(x,t)d\mu(x).$$

QED

We now give an example to show that the hypothesis in the corollary cannot be neglected. We make use of an integral identity that will not actually be proved until the next chapter. Namely,

$$\int_0^\infty e^{-x}d\lambda = 1.$$

(This is a consequence of the fundamental theorem of calculus.) It also follows that if $t \neq 0$,

$$\int_0^\infty t^2 e^{-t^2 x}d\lambda = 1.$$

Now let

$$f(x,t) = t^3 e^{-t^2 x} \qquad \text{for } x > 0, \ -\infty < t < \infty.$$

Then

$$F(t) = \int_0^\infty f(x,t)d\lambda(x)$$

$$= t \quad \text{for } -\infty < t < \infty.$$

Therefore, $F'(0) = 1$. But $df/dt(x,t)\,|_{t=0} = 0$, so the equation

$$F'(0) = \int_0^\infty \frac{df}{dt}(x,0)d\lambda(x)$$

is false.

Lebesgue Integral on $\mathbb{R}^n$

Although Chapter 6 contains most of the important theorems about integration and especially about convergence of integrals, there is nevertheless something lacking. As we observed in Section 6.E, the treatment of the integral had been quite general up to that stage. This presented a definite advantage — namely, it was easy to detect the specific things about the measure space $\mathbb{R}^n$, $\mathcal{L}$, λ which were needed to develop the integral, so we were able immediately to generalize the definitions and theorems to an arbitrary measure space.

The easy generality also contains a disadvantage, however. We have used so little information about $\mathbb{R}^n$, $\mathcal{L}$, λ that we know correspondingly little about specific properties of the integral $\int f d\lambda$. We shall begin to rectify this situation in the present chapter by working exclusively with Lebesgue measure and deriving very useful results which are particular to Lebesgue integration.

A. Riemann Integral

Before discussing Riemann's definition of the integral, we find it convenient to give some simple background information about semicontinuity.

1. Semicontinuity

Definition: Let $f : \mathbb{R}^n \to [-\infty, \infty]$ and let $x \in \mathbb{R}^n$. Then f is *lower semicontinuous* at x if for any $t < f(x)$ there exists $\delta > 0$ such that for all $y \in B(x, \delta)$, $t < f(y)$.

In other words, f is lower semicontinuous at x if and only if for any t such that $t < f(x)$, it follows that $t < f$ on some neighborhood of x.

We shall abbreviate by saying that f is LSC at x. If the function f is LSC at x for every $x \in \mathbb{R}^n$, we say that f is LSC.

In the same way we say that f is *upper semicontinuous* at x if for any $t > f(x)$, it follows that $t > f$ on some neighborhood of x. Of course, f is USC at x if and only if $-f$ is LSC at x.

Problem 1. Let $A \subset \mathbb{R}^n$. Prove that χ_A is LSC $\iff$ A is open.

Definition: Let $f : \mathbb{R}^n \to [-\infty, \infty]$. Then define the function $\underline{f}$ as follows:

$$\underline{f}(x) = \liminf_{y \to x} f(y)$$

$$= \sup_{\delta > 0} \inf\{f(y) \mid y \in B(x, \delta)\}.$$

Note that $\inf\{f(y) \mid y \in B(x, \delta)\}$ is a decreasing function of δ, so that we could also write

$$\underline{f}(x) = \lim_{\delta \to 0} \inf\{f(y) \mid y \in B(x, \delta)\}.$$

Likewise, we define $\overline{f}(x) = \limsup_{y \to x} f(y)$. Obviously,

$$\underline{f} \le f \le \overline{f}.$$

Problem 2. Let $A \subset \mathbb{R}^n$. Prove that $\underline{\chi_A} = \chi_{A^\circ}$, $\overline{\chi_A} = \chi_{A^-}$.

Properties

SC1 If $f(x) = -\infty$, then f is LSC at x.

SC2 If $f(x) = \infty$, then f is LSC at $x \iff \lim_{y \to x} f(y) = \infty$.

SC3 f is continuous at $x \iff f$ is LSC and USC at x.

SC4 f is LSC at $x \iff \underline{f}(x) = f(x)$.

SC5 f is continuous at $x \iff \underline{f}(x) = f(x) = \overline{f}(x)$.

SC6 $\underline{f}$ is LSC and $\overline{f}$ is USC.

SC7 $\underline{f}$ is the largest LSC function which is $\le f$.

SC8 If f is LSC, then f is Borel measurable.

SC9 If f_i is LSC for each $i \in \mathcal{I}$, then $\sup_i f_i$ is LSC.

Proof:

SC1 and SC2 are trivial.

SC3   In this and SC5 we allow the values $\pm\infty$ for a continuous function. If $t < f(x) < s$ and f is continuous at x, then $t < f(y) < s$ for all y in some neighborhood of x. Thus,

f is LSC and USC at x. If $t < f(x) < s$ and f is LSC and USC at x, then there exist $\delta_1 > 0$ and $\delta_2 > 0$ such that $t < f$ on $B(x, \delta_1)$ and $f < s$ on $B(x, \delta_2)$. Let $\delta = \min(\delta_1, \delta_2)$, so $t < f < s$ on $B(x, \delta)$. Thus, f is continuous at x.

SC4   Assume f is LSC at x. If $t < f(x)$, then there exists $\delta > 0$ such that $t < f(y)$ for all $y \in B(x, \delta)$. Thus, $t \leq \inf\{f(y) \mid y \in B(x, \delta)\}$ and we conclude that $t \leq \underline{f}(x)$. Since t is arbitrary, $f(x) \leq \underline{f}(x)$. Therefore, $f(x) = \underline{f}(x)$. Conversely, assume $\underline{f}(x) = f(x)$. Then if $t < f(x)$, also $t < \underline{f}(x)$ so that there exists $\delta > 0$ such that $t < \inf\{f(y) \mid y \in B(x, \delta)\}$. Therefore, $t < f(y)$ for all $y \in B(x, \delta)$. Therefore, f is LSC at x.

SC5   By SC4, it is also true that f is USC at $x \Leftrightarrow \overline{f}(x) = f(x)$. Therefore, SC5 follows from this and SC3.

SC6   Suppose $t < \underline{f}(x)$. Then there exists $\delta_0 > 0$ such that $t < \inf\{f(y) \mid y \in B(x, \delta_0)\}$. For any $y_0 \in B(x, \delta_0)$ let $\delta = \delta_0 - d(y_0, x)$. Then $\delta > 0$ and $B(y_0, \delta) \subset B(x, \delta_0)$, as indicated in Figure 1. Therefore, $t < \inf\{f(y) \mid y \in B(y_0, \delta)\}$. But this inequality implies that $t < \underline{f}(y_0)$. Thus, we have proved that if $t < \underline{f}(x)$, then $t < \underline{f}$ on $B(x, \delta_0)$, showing $\underline{f}$ to be LSC at x.

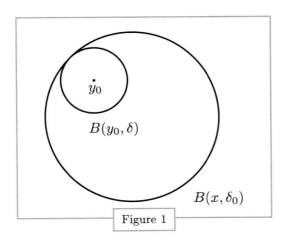

Figure 1

SC7   Suppose g is LSC and $g \leq f$. Then $g = \underline{g} \leq \underline{f}$.

SC8   If f is LSC, then by definition $f^{-1}((t,\infty])$ is an open set, and thus a Borel set. By the proposition on p.113, f is Borel measurable.

SC9   Let $f = \sup_i f_i$. If $t < f(x)$, then there exists $i \in \mathcal{I}$ such that $t < f_i(x)$. Since f_i is LSC, there exists $\delta > 0$ such that $t < f_i$ on $B(x,\delta)$. Therefore, $t < f$ on $B(x,\delta)$, proving that f is LSC at x.

                                                                                   QED

Properties SC8 and 9 are frequently used in conjunction in the following manner. Suppose f_i is a *continuous* function for each $i \in \mathcal{I}$. If $\mathcal{I}$ is infinite, it might not be true that $\sup_i f_i$ is continuous. Yet $\sup_i f_i$ is LSC and therefore Borel measurable. Thus, even an uncountable supremum of continuous functions is Borel measurable.

Problem 3. If $\mathcal{I}$ is finite and f_i is LSC for each $i \in \mathcal{I}$, prove that $\min_i f_i$ is LSC. Give an example to show that this result does not extend to infinite $\mathcal{I}$.

2. Step Functions

For Riemann integration we shall deal with a fixed special rectangle I. A *partition* of I is a collection of non-overlapping special rectangles $I_1, I_2, \ldots, I_N$ whose union is I.

(Recall that special rectangles are closed, so we cannot require the I_j's to be disjoint.)

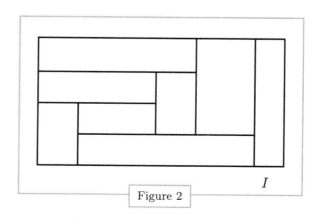

I

Figure 2

Definition: A *step function* on I is a function $\sigma : I \to \mathbb{R}$ such that there exists a partition $I_1, I_2, \ldots, I_N$ of I for which σ is constant on each of the *open* rectangles I_j°.

Do not worry about the fact that we have allowed σ to be unspecified on the boundaries of the I_j's. These boundaries have zero measure in $\mathbb{R}^n$, so each step function is Lebesgue measurable. If we so desire, we can modify σ (for instance, redefine σ to be 0 on each of the boundaries of the I_j's) on a null set so that it becomes a *simple* function, and, indeed, a Borel measurable simple function. Of course, none of this has to be mentioned in case we are in dimension $n = 1$, as the boundaries of the I_j's consist of just two points each.

3.   Riemann Integration

Bernhard Riemann was not the first to define the concept of a definite integral. However, he was the first to apply a definition of integration to any function, without first specifying what properties the function has. He then singled out those functions to which the integration process assigned a well defined number. These functions are called "integrable." He then derived a necessary and sufficient condition for a function to be integrable. This is contained in his *Habilitationsschrift* at Göttingen, 1854, entitled "Üeber die Darstellbarkeit einer Function durch eine trigonometrische Reihe." We shall actually present an equivalent version which is a little more appropriate for our discussion. This version was first published by Darboux in 1875.

Definition: Suppose f is a *bounded* function on a special rectangle I. Then f is *Riemann integrable* if for every $\epsilon > 0$ there exist step functions σ and τ defined on I such that

$$\sigma \le f \le \tau$$

and

$$\int_I (\tau - \sigma) d\lambda < \epsilon.$$

In case f is Riemann integrable, its *Riemann integral* is the common value

$$r\int_I f d\lambda = \sup\left\{\int_I \sigma d\lambda \mid \sigma \leq f\right\}$$

$$= \inf\left\{\int_I \tau d\lambda \mid \tau \geq f\right\}.$$

Of course, σ and τ stand for step functions on I.

Remark: Notice that for step functions we are using the integral which was defined in Chapter 6. This is really nothing but a notational convenience. If σ is a step function on I and $\sigma = c_j$ on I_j°, where I_1, I_2, ..., I_N is a suitable partition of I, then

$$\int \sigma d\lambda = \sum_{j=1}^{N} c_j \lambda(I_j).$$

Thus, we require only knowledge of the measure of special rectangles for the definition of the Riemann integral.

Notice also that f must be assumed to be bounded for the definition to make sense, inasmuch as both σ and τ are bounded.

Even in case f is not Riemann integrable, Darboux defined a *lower* and an *upper* integral of f as follows:

$$r\underline{\int} f d\lambda = \sup\left\{\int_I \sigma d\lambda \mid \sigma \leq f\right\},$$

$$r\overline{\int} f d\lambda = \inf\left\{\int_I \tau d\lambda \mid \tau \geq f\right\}.$$

(The boundedness of f insures that the indicated sets are not empty.) Clearly, f is Riemann integrable if and only if $r\underline{\int} f d\lambda = r\overline{\int} f d\lambda$.

Problem 4. If f and g are bounded functions on I, prove that

$$r\overline{\int}(f+g)d\lambda \leq r\overline{\int} f d\lambda + r\overline{\int} g d\lambda;$$

$$r\underline{\int}(f+g)d\lambda \geq r\underline{\int} f d\lambda + r\underline{\int} g d\lambda.$$

Problem 5. Suppose f_1, f_2, ... are Riemann integrable functions on I, and suppose $f = \lim\limits_{k \to \infty} f_k$ exists *uniformly*. Prove that f is Riemann integrable and that

$$r \int_I f d\lambda = \lim_{k \to \infty} r \int_I f_k d\lambda.$$

The following remarkable theorem characterizes Riemann integrable functions. It is due to Lebesgue (who lived 1875–1941). However, Riemann actually gave a very similar condition in his 1854 paper.

Theorem: *Let f be a bounded function on a special rectangle I. Then*

(a) f is Riemann integrable $\Longleftrightarrow$ f is continuous a.e.

(b) If f is Riemann integrable, then f is measurable and its Riemann and Lebesgue integrals on I are equal:

$$r \int_I f d\lambda = \int_I f d\lambda.$$

Proof: Assume first that f is Riemann integrable. By definition there exist step functions σ_k and τ_k on I such that

$$\sigma_k \le f \le \tau_k,$$

$$\int_I (\tau_k - \sigma_k) d\lambda < k^{-1},$$

for any $k \in \mathbb{N}$. Since step functions are continuous a.e., the results derived in Part 1 show that

$$\sigma_k \le \underline{f} \le \overline{f} \le \tau_k \quad \text{a.e.}$$

Now define

$$g = \sup_k \sigma_k \quad \text{and} \quad h = \inf_k \tau_k.$$

Then g and h are measurable functions and satisfy

$$g \le \underline{f} \le \overline{f} \le h \quad \text{a.e.}$$

Moreover, since $h - g \leq \tau_k - \sigma_k$ for any k,

$$\int_I (h - g)d\lambda \leq \int_I (\tau_k - \sigma_k)d\lambda < k^{-1}.$$

Therefore, $\int_I (h - g)d\lambda = 0$. Since $h - g \geq 0$, Problem 6.1 implies that $h - g = 0$ a.e. Therefore,

$$g = \underline{f} = \overline{f} = h \quad \text{a.e.}$$

Therefore, Property SC5 shows that f is continuous a.e.

Before proving the converse, we can now prove easily the second statement of the theorem. Since $f = g = h$ a.e., it follows that f is measurable (and thus Lebesgue integrable over I, as it is bounded). Moreover,

$$r \int_I f d\lambda \leq \int_I \tau_k d\lambda$$

$$< \int_I \sigma_k d\lambda + k^{-1}$$

$$\leq \int_I f d\lambda + k^{-1}.$$

Since k is arbitrary,

$$r \int_I f d\lambda \leq \int_I f d\lambda.$$

The reverse inequality can be proved by the same method, so we conclude that $r \int_I f d\lambda = \int_I f d\lambda$. Therefore, (b) is proved.

Now we shall prove the converse, so we assume that f is continuous a.e. We must prove that f is Riemann integrable, so we must construct some appropriate step functions on I. Since f is bounded, there exist numbers α and β such that $\alpha \leq f \leq \beta$. We now define a sequence σ_1, σ_2, σ_3, ... of step functions as follows. Partition I into 2^{nk} congruent rectangles. If J is one of these special rectangles, σ_k will be constant on its interior J° and its value on J° will be the number $\inf_J f$.

On the boundary of J we simply let $\sigma_k = \alpha$.

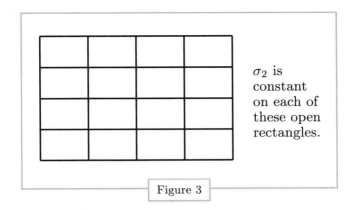

σ_2 is
constant
on each of
these open
rectangles.

Figure 3

Since each rectangle used in the construction of σ_{k+1} is contained in a rectangle used for σ_k, it follows that $\sigma_k \leq \sigma_{k+1}$ except on the boundaries of the rectangles involved. Therefore, we surely have $\sigma_k \leq \sigma_{k+1}$ a.e. We therefore have constructed a sequence of step functions such that

$$\sigma_1 \leq \sigma_2 \leq \sigma_3 \leq \ldots \quad \text{a.e.,}$$
$$\sigma_k \leq f \quad \text{on} \ I.$$

The way these step functions have been constructed implies

$$\lim_{k\to\infty} \sigma_k \geq \underline{f} \quad \text{a.e.}$$

To see that this is so, suppose x is any point in I which is not a boundary point of any rectangle which appears in any of the partitions. Suppose $\underline{f}(x) > t$. By definition of $\underline{f}(x)$ it follows that $f > t$ in some neighborhood of x. But it is the case that for all sufficiently large k, the rectangle which contains x and which is used in the partition for σ_k is contained in this neighborhood where $f > t$. Therefore, $\sigma_k(x) \geq t$ for such k. Thus, $\lim_{k\to\infty} \sigma_k(x) \geq t$. Since t is arbitrary, $\lim_{k\to\infty} \sigma_k(x) \geq \underline{f}(x)$.

Now repeat the entire construction, but with the inequalities reversed. This produces step functions τ_k which satisfy

$$\tau_1 \geq \tau_2 \geq \tau_3 \geq \ldots \quad \text{a.e.,}$$
$$\tau_k \geq f \quad \text{on} \ I,$$
$$\lim_{k\to\infty} \tau_k \leq \overline{f} \quad \text{a.e.}$$

Now we use the hypothesis that f is continuous a.e. By Property SC5, $\underline{f} = \overline{f} = f$ a.e. Thus,

$$\lim_{k\to\infty} \sigma_k = \lim_{k\to\infty} \tau_k = f \quad \text{a.e.}$$

Since all these functions have values between α and β, and since constants are integrable on I, LDCT implies

$$\lim_{k \to \infty} \int_I \sigma_k d\lambda = \lim_{k \to \infty} \int_I \tau_k d\lambda = \int_I f d\lambda.$$

Therefore, $\lim_{k \to \infty} \int_I (\tau_k - \sigma_k) d\lambda = 0$, and we conclude that f is Riemann integrable.

Note that we have just given another proof of (b).   **QED**

Warning: Be careful that you read the preceding theorem correctly. Students sometimes confound the condition "f is continuous a.e." and the condition "f equals a continuous function a.e." These conditions are very different, as the next problem shows.

Problem 6. Provide examples on the interval $[0, 1] \subset \mathbb{R}$ as follows:

(a) a function f and a continuous function g such that $f = g$ a.e. and f is not continuous a.e. (in fact, make f nowhere continuous);

(b) a function f continuous a.e. such that there exists no continuous function g with $f = g$ a.e.

Problem 7. In the original paper of Riemann, he provided an interesting example of a function which is (Riemann) integrable and discontinuous on a dense set.

Riemann defined (x) to be x minus the integer nearest x unless $x \in \frac{1}{2} + \mathbb{Z}$ and to be 0 if $x \in \frac{1}{2} + \mathbb{Z}$. See the graph of (x) in Figure 4. Then he defined

$$f(x) = \sum_{n=1}^{\infty} \frac{(nx)}{n^2}.$$

Prove that f is Riemann integrable on any interval $[a, b]$.

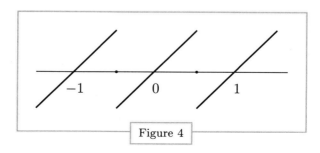

Figure 4

Problem 8. Continue with the notation of Problem 7. Prove that f is discontinuous at every rational x of the form $x = p/2m$, where $m \in \mathbb{N}$ and p is an odd integer relatively prime to m. Also prove that these are the only points of discontinuity of f. If x has the above form and if

$$f(x+) = \lim_{\substack{y \to x \\ y > x}} f(y), \quad f(x-) = \lim_{\substack{y \to x \\ y < x}} f(y),$$

show that

$$f(x+) = f(x) - \frac{\pi^2}{16m^2},$$

$$f(x-) = f(x) + \frac{\pi^2}{16m^2}.$$

In doing this you may assume the fact $\frac{1}{1} + \frac{1}{9} + \frac{1}{25} + \frac{1}{49} + \cdots = \frac{\pi^2}{8}$. (This will be proved in Problem 14.45.)

Problem 9. Let $f : [a,b] \to \mathbb{R}$ be increasing or decreasing. ("Increasing" means that $x \leq y \Rightarrow f(x) \leq f(y)$.) Prove that f is Riemann integrable by constructing appropriate step functions. Also prove directly that f is continuous a.e. by proving that f has only a countable number of discontinuities.

Problem 10. Construct a Riemann integrable function on $[0,1] \subset \mathbb{R}$ which has an uncountable set of discontinuities.

A standard example of a function on an interval $[a,b] \subset \mathbb{R}$ which is Lebesgue integrable but not Riemann integrable is the function $\chi_{\mathbb{Q}}$. It is not Riemann integrable since it is continuous nowhere. It is Lebesgue integrable since it vanishes a.e. However, this example is not very convincing, as this function is equal to a Riemann integrable function a.e. If it were the case that every bounded Lebesgue integrable function were equal a.e. to a Riemann integrable function, one could calculate a Lebesgue integral simply by Riemann integrating the equivalent Riemann integrable function. But this is not the case:

Problem 11. Let $A \subset [0,1]$ be a fat Cantor set. That is, $\lambda(A) > 0$ and A is constructed as in Section 4.B. Prove that there exists no Riemann integrable function f on $[0,1]$ such that $f = \chi_A$ a.e.

We conclude this part of the discussion of Riemann integration with two observations. First, we can perform various simple operations on

Riemann integrable functions and still have Riemann integrable functions. Namely, suppose f and g are Riemann integrable on the special rectangle I, and a, $b \in \mathbb{R}$. Then all the following functions are also Riemann integrable:

$$af + bg,$$

$$fg,$$

$$|f|, \quad f_+, f_-.$$

The proofs follow easily from the definition, or trivially from the theorem in this section. (For instance, f and g are continuous a.e.; therefore, fg is continuous a.e.; therefore, fg is Riemann integrable.)

Problem 12. Prove directly from the definition that if f and g are Riemann integrable, then fg is Riemann integrable.

(**HINT**: By adding constants to the functions, show that you may assume $f \geq 0$, $g \geq 0$.)

The second observation is more important. The theorem we have proved has some very pleasant consequences. Of course, primarily it shows that the Riemann and Lebesgue integrals are consistent and that the Lebesgue integral is more extensive. A secondary effect is that whatever theorems and properties concerning the Riemann integral you have ever learned, these theorems and properties are still valid for the *Lebesgue* integral of Riemann integrable functions. In particular, the fundamental theorem of calculus is true. So we can use such results as

$$\int_0^1 \frac{1}{1 + x^2} dx = \frac{\pi}{4},$$

where this integral is the Lebesgue integral constructed in Chapter 4. It will be convenient to use such known results from time to time. However, logically speaking it is not necessary to do this. For example, if you will examine a proof of the fundamental theorem of calculus, you will immediately realize that the proof has nothing to do with Riemann integration *per se*.

4.   Jordan Content

This discussion is given primarily for historical interest. The problem arises because we frequently must integrate over more complicated sets than the special rectangle I. If it is Riemann integration we are interested in, then for a set $A \subset I$ we should like to define

$$r \int_A f d\lambda = r \int_I f\chi_A d\lambda.$$

Therefore, we need to know what sort of set A has the property that $f\chi_A$ is Riemann integrable whenever f is. So we merely have to give a criterion for χ_A to be Riemann integrable. The criterion we have is that χ_A be continuous a.e. If $\chi_A(x) = 1$, then $x \in A$, and χ_A is continuous at $x \iff \chi_A = 1$ near $x \iff x$ is an interior point of A. Likewise, if $\chi_A(x) = 0$, then χ_A is continuous at $x \iff x$ is an interior point of A^c. Thus, χ_A is *not* continuous at $x \iff x \notin A^\circ \cup (A^c)^\circ$.

Definition: If $A \subset \mathbb{R}^n$, the *boundary* of A is the set

$$\partial A = [A^\circ \cup (A^c)^\circ]^c.$$

Problem 13. Prove that ∂A is closed and that $\mathbb{R}^n = A^\circ \cup (A^c)^\circ \cup \partial A$ is a disjoint union. Prove also that $\partial A = A^- \cap (A^c)^-$.

Problem 14. Prove that $\partial A = A^- \sim A^\circ$.

Problem 15. Prove that if A is not $\emptyset$ and is not $\mathbb{R}^n$, then $\partial A \neq \emptyset$. (Compare with Problem 1.31.)

Problem 16. Prove that

$$\partial(A \cup B) \subset \partial A \cup \partial B,$$
$$\partial(A \cap B) \subset \partial A \cup \partial B,$$
$$\partial(A^c) = \partial A,$$
$$\partial(A \sim B) \subset \partial A \cup \partial B.$$

Our discussion above has already proved the following result.

Proposition: Let $A \subset \mathbb{R}^n$ be a bounded set. Then χ_A is Riemann integrable $\iff \partial A$ is a null set.

Problem 17. Give an example of an open set whose boundary is not a null set.

Definition: A bounded set $A \subset \mathbb{R}^n$ is *Jordan measurable* if χ_A is Riemann integrable. For historical reasons, the number $\lambda(A)$ is called the *Jordan content* of A.

Problem 18. Consider sets which are contained in a fixed special rectangle I. Thus, in this problem we write $A^c = I \sim A$ for sets $A \subset I$. Prove that the collection of Jordan measurable sets contained in I forms an algebra, but not a σ-algebra.

Problem 19. Prove that there exists a Jordan measurable set contained in $\mathbb{R}$ which is not a Borel set.

(**HINT:** Consider the set A defined in Section 5.C.)

B. Linear Change of Variables

We now turn to *Lebesgue* integration on $\mathbb{R}^n$. We shall generalize the results of Chapter 3 to corresponding properties of the integral. The only reason this was not done back in Chapter 3 is that we had not yet defined the integral.

Theorem: Let T be an invertible $n \times n$ matrix. For any function f on $\mathbb{R}^n$ let $f \circ T$ be the function $f \circ T(x) = f(Tx)$.

(a) If f is measurable, then $f \circ T$ is measurable.

(b) If $f \geq 0$ and f is measurable, then

$$\int f(x)dx =\mid \det T \mid \int f(Tx)dx.$$

(c) If $f \in L^1$, then $f \circ T \in L^1$ and the same integration formula holds.

Proof: First, let A be a measurable set and consider χ_A. Then $\chi_A \circ T = \chi_{T^{-1}A}$. Therefore, $\chi_A \circ T$ is a measurable function and

$$\int \chi_A \circ T dx = \lambda(T^{-1}A)$$

$$=\mid \det T^{-1} \mid \lambda(A)$$

$$=\mid \det T \mid^{-1} \int \chi_A dx.$$

This follows from the theorem on p.76. By taking linear combinations, we conclude that the theorem is valid for measurable simple functions. The proof in general now follows from the fact that measurable functions can be approximated by measurable simple functions, as shown in Section 5.E. Thus, (a) follows. The truth of (b) is seen to be a result of the definition of $\int f(x)dx$ as the least upper bound of $\int s(x)dx$ for measurable simple functions satisfying $0 \le s \le f$. And (c) follows easily from (b) and the definition of L^1.   **QED**

We particularly shall require in the next section the special case of this theorem for which $T = a$ id. We also need the corresponding result for translations, proved in the same way:

$$|a|^n \int f(ax)dx = \int f(x)dx \quad \text{for any } a \ne 0;$$

$$\int f(x+y)dx = \int f(x)dx \quad \text{for any } y \in \mathbb{R}^n.$$

You will notice that we have now begun to prefer the notation dx to the notation $d\lambda$, as the notation we are now using displays which parameters are to be regarded as constants in the integration process.

C. Approximation of Functions in L^1

1. The Norm

If $f \in L^1(\mathbb{R}^n)$, we define the L^1-*norm* of f to be the number

$$\|f\|_1 = \int_{\mathbb{R}^n} | f(x) | \, dx.$$

This has the usual properties which justify the name "norm":

(a) $0 \le \|f\|_1 < \infty.$

(b) $\|f\|_1 = 0 \iff f = 0$ (a.e.).

(c) $\|cf\|_1 = |c|\|f\|_1$ if $c \in \mathbb{R}.$

(d) $\|f + g\|_1 \le \|f\|_1 + \|g\|_1.$

The last property follows from the inequality $\mid f(x)+g(x) \mid \leq \mid f(x) \mid +$ $\mid g(x) \mid$. The others are straightforward consequences of the properties of integration known to us.

We must comment on (b). A norm is always required to satisfy the condition that if the norm of an element is zero, then the element must be zero. Back in Section 6.C we discussed the fact that for our purposes, to say that $f = 0$ a.e. is the same as saying f is zero. We did not then and do not now distinguish two functions from one another if they are equal a.e.

When we discuss L^p spaces in Chapter 10 we shall then discuss in detail what is meant by a norm. It is essentially the very properties listed above. The important thing for us is that when we speak of approximation in the present context, we shall use the L^1-norm as the measure of the approximation.

2.   Approximation by Continuous Functions

First, let us agree on the following notation:

Definition: If $\mathcal{F}$ is any collection of functions defined on $\mathbb{R}^n$, then $\mathcal{F}_c$ denotes the collection of those functions which belong to $\mathcal{F}$ and which are zero outside of some compact set. (Other notations you may come across include $\mathcal{F}_0$ and $\mathcal{F}_{00}$.)

Definition: Let $m \in \{0, 1, 2, \ldots\}$. Then C^m is the collection of functions $f : \mathbb{R}^n \to \mathbb{R}$ such that f is continuous and f has continuous partial derivatives of all orders $\leq m$. In case $m = 0$ we shall usually write C instead of C^0.

Definition: C^∞ is the collection of functions which have continuous partial derivatives of all orders. That is,

$$C^\infty = \bigcap_{m=0}^{\infty} C^m.$$

We obviously have the inclusions $C^\infty \subset \cdots \subset C^3 \subset C^2 \subset C^1 \subset C$.

The space C_c then consists of all functions $f : \mathbb{R}^n \to \mathbb{R}$ such that f is continuous and f vanishes outside some compact set. We emphasize that f must be continuous on *all* of $\mathbb{R}^n$: e.g., $\chi_{B(x_0,r)}$ is not in C_c, although it vanishes outside some compact set and is continuous on the set where it does not vanish.

Definition: If $f \in C$, the *support* of f is

$$\mathrm{supp}f = \{x \in \mathbb{R}^n \mid f(x) \neq 0\}^-.$$

Problem 20. Prove that $\mathrm{supp}f$ is the complement of the largest open set where $f = 0$:

$$\mathrm{supp}f = \{x \mid f(x) = 0\}^{oc}.$$

Thus, $C_c = \{f \in C \mid f \text{ has compact support}\}$.

Likewise, C_c^∞ consists of all functions in C^∞ which have compact support. It may be not known to you whether C_c^∞ contains any function at all besides 0, but we shall show in Part 3 that there are many such functions indeed. In fact, the theorem of Section C is that C_c^∞ is *dense* in L^1. That is, for any $f \in L^1$ and any $\epsilon > 0$, there exists $g \in C_c^\infty$ such that $\|g - f\|_1 < \epsilon$. In order to prove this we first prove a weaker version:

Lemma: C_c *is dense in* L^1.

Proof: We prove this in several stages, really working backwards from the desired conclusion.

1. LDCT implies that $\lim\limits_{k \to \infty} \|f\chi_{B(0,k)} - f\|_1 = 0$ for any $f \in L^1$. Therefore, $(L^1)_c$ is dense in L^1. We use this fact by saying that if we want to approximate f, it suffices to restrict attention to the case that f vanishes outside a bounded set.

2. Since $f = f_+ - f_-$, it follows that if we successfully approximate f_+ and f_-, then we can approximate f also. Thus, we can assume $f \geq 0$ and f vanishes outside a bounded set.

3. By the results in Section 5.E there exists a sequence of measurable simple functions $0 \leq s_1 \leq s_2 \leq \cdots \leq f$ such that $\lim\limits_{k \to \infty} s_k = f$. By LDCT $\|s_k - f\|_1 \to 0$. Thus, we can assume we are trying to approximate a measurable simple function which is nonnegative and vanishes outside a bounded set.

4. Such a function has a representation of the form

$$\sum_{k=1}^m \alpha_k \chi_{A_k},$$

where each $A_k \in \mathcal{L}$ and $\alpha_k \in [0, \infty)$. If we approximate each χ_{A_k} by a function in C_c, then the corresponding linear combination will approximate the simple function. Thus, we only must prove that we can approximate functions of the form χ_A, where $A \in \mathcal{L}$ and A is bounded.

5. Finally, we shall actually accomplish this approximation. Given any $\epsilon > 0$, the approximation theorem on p.45 implies the existence of a compact set K and an open set G such that

$$K \subset A \subset G$$

and

$$\lambda(G \sim K) < \epsilon.$$

Now we apply the theorem on p.22 to obtain an Urysohn function g which is continuous on $\mathbb{R}^n$, $0 \le g \le 1$, $g = 1$ on K and $g = 0$ outside of G. Of course, we can assume the open set G is bounded, and thus $g \in C_c$. Now we observe

$$x \in K \Rightarrow g(x) - \chi_A(x) = 1 - 1 = 0,$$

$$x \in G^c \Rightarrow g(x) - \chi_A(x) = 0 - 0 = 0.$$

Thus, $\mid g(x) - \chi_A(x) \mid \le 1$ for all $x \in \mathbb{R}^n$ and $g(x) - \chi_A(x)$ vanishes except for $x \in G \sim K$. Thus,

$$\|g - \chi_A\|_1 \le \int_{G \sim K} 1 dx = \lambda(G \sim K) < \epsilon.$$

QED

Problem 21. Suppose $f : \mathbb{R}^n \to [-\infty, \infty]$ is $\mathcal{L}$-measurable. Define a subset of $\mathbb{R}^n$, called supp f, by the statement

$$x \in (\mathrm{supp} f)^c \iff f = 0 \text{ a.e. in some neighborhood of } x.$$

Prove that supp$f$ is closed. Prove that if $f \in C$, then this definition agrees with the one given just before Problem 20.

3. Approximation by Infinitely Differentiable Functions

The remainder of the discussion rests on the fact that C_c^∞ does indeed contain nontrivial functions. This in turn hinges on the construction of just one such function on $\mathbb{R}$. Here is one specific example: First define $h : \mathbb{R} \to \mathbb{R}$ by

$$h(t) = \begin{cases} 0 & \text{if } t \leq 0, \\ \exp(-1/t) & \text{if } t > 0. \end{cases}$$

Here is a sketch of its graph:

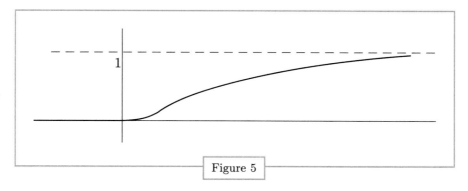

Figure 5

Problem 22. Prove that $h \in C^\infty$.

(**HINT**: Prove by induction that $h^{(n)}(t) = P_n(1/t)\exp(-1/t)$ for $t > 0$, where P_n is a polynomial (of degree $2n$). Then prove by induction that $h^{(n)}(0) = 0$.)

Next, we define by composition a function on $\mathbb{R}^n$ whose value at $x \in \mathbb{R}^n$ is

$$h(1 - |x|^2) = h(1 - x_1^2 - \cdots - x_n^2).$$

This function is of class C^∞ on $\mathbb{R}^n$. Moreover, $|x| \geq 1 \Rightarrow 1 - |x|^2 \leq 0 \Rightarrow h(1 - |x|^2) = 0$. Therefore, this function belongs to C_c^∞. Moreover, it is positive if $|x| < 1$. Thus, it has a positive integral

$$c = \int h(1 - |x|^2)dx = \int_{B(0,1)} h(1 - |x|^2)dx.$$

Finally, we define

$$\phi(x) = c^{-1}h(1 - |x|^2).$$

Here is a summary of the properties of ϕ:

$$\phi \in C_c^\infty(\mathbb{R}^n),$$

$$\phi \geq 0,$$

$$\phi(x) > 0 \iff |x| < 1,$$

$$\int_{\mathbb{R}^n} \phi(x)dx = 1.$$

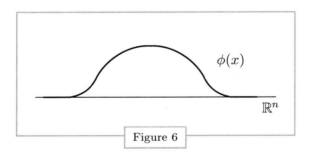

$$\phi(x)$$

$$\mathbb{R}^n$$

Figure 6

This function has another property which is often useful in applications, but will not be needed in this chapter: ϕ is *radially symmetric* in the sense that it is a function of $|x|$ only.

We shall also require this function to be rescaled. Thus, for any $a \in (0, \infty)$ define

$$\phi_a(x) = a^{-n}\phi\left(\tfrac{x}{a}\right).$$

Then

$$\phi_a \in C_c^\infty(\mathbb{R}^n),$$

$$\phi_a \geq 0,$$

$$\phi_a(x) > 0 \iff |x| < a,$$

$$\int_{\mathbb{R}^n} \phi_a(x)dx = 1.$$

In Figure 7 we have superimposed the graphs of $\phi = \phi_1$ and $\phi_{1/3}$.

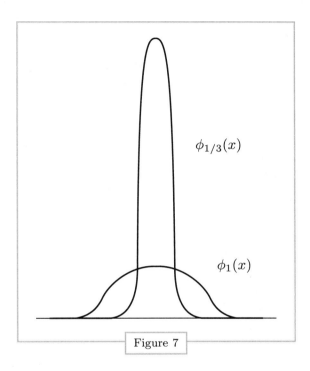

$\phi_{1/3}(x)$

$\phi_1(x)$

Figure 7

The calculation of the integral of ϕ_a follows from Section B.

We are particularly interested in small values of the parameter a, for which $\phi_a > 0$ only in a small ball centered at 0, but ϕ_a is so large near the origin that its integral is equal to 1.

The process that we are going to use to approximate by infinitely differentiable functions is so important that we want to discuss it thoroughly. It is called

MOLLIFYING. Suppose that $f \in L^1(\mathbb{R}^n)$. For any $a > 0$ define a new function g by the expression

$$g(x) = \int_{\mathbb{R}^n} f(y)\phi_a(x - y)dy.$$

Observe that this integral makes good sense: Since ϕ_a is bounded (and measurable), the product $f(y)\phi_a(x - y)$ is integrable as a function of

y. Moreover, $g \in C^\infty(\mathbb{R}^n)$. This is just a result of elementary calculus, called "differentiating under the integral sign." This has been thoroughly discussed in the theorem and corollary of Section 6.G. We see immediately that g is continuous on $\mathbb{R}^n$. Moreover, if we wish to calculate a derivative $\partial g/\partial x_k$, we obtain

$$\frac{\partial g}{\partial x_k}(x) = \int\limits_{\mathbb{R}^n} f(y)\frac{\partial \phi_a}{\partial x_k}(x - y)dy.$$

Since this derivative is given by an expression similar to the one which defines g itself, we see that $\partial g/\partial x_k$ is continuous. By induction it follows that g possesses continuous partial derivatives of all orders.

Next, we note that if f has compact support, then so does g. Indeed, suppose that $f = 0$ on $B(0, r)^c$. If $g(x) \neq 0$, then the definition of $g(x)$ shows that there surely exists $y \in \mathbb{R}^n$ such that $f(y)\phi_a(x-y) \neq 0$. Thus, $f(y) \neq 0 \Rightarrow y \in B(0, r)$ and $\phi_a(x - y) \neq 0 \Rightarrow x - y \in B(0, a)$. But then $|x| \leq |y| + |x - y| < r + a$. Thus, $g(x) = 0$ if $|x| \geq r + a$. Hence we conclude that $g \in C_c^\infty$.

Notation: Based upon notation to be used and discussed in detail in Chapter 12, we write

$$g = f * \phi_a.$$

The function g is called the *convolution* of f and ϕ_a. Note that we have proved

$$\frac{\partial(f * \phi_a)}{\partial x_k} = f * \frac{\partial \phi_a}{\partial x_k}.$$

Theorem: C_c^∞ *is dense in* L^1.

Proof: The lemma of Part 2 shows that C_c is dense in L^1. Therefore, we need only prove that C_c^∞ is dense in C_c. Thus, assume $f \in C_c$. Then there exists $r > 0$ such that $f = 0$ on $B(0, r)^c$. Let $\epsilon > 0$. Since f has compact support, f is uniformly continuous (see p.19). Therefore, there exists $a > 0$ such that

$$|y - x| \leq a \Rightarrow |f(y) - f(x)| \leq \frac{\epsilon}{\lambda(B(0, r + 1))};$$

we can require $0 < a \leq 1$ without loss of generality. Since $\int \phi_a(x)dx = 1$, we also conclude from Section B that for any $x \in \mathbb{R}^n$

$$\int \phi_a(x - y)dy = 1.$$

Therefore,

$$f * \phi_a(x) = \int f(y)\phi_a(x - y)dy,$$

$$f(x) = \int f(x)\phi_a(x - y)dy.$$

The latter equation is valid because $f(x)$ is just a constant in that integration. Subtract these two equations to obtain

$$\mid f * \phi_a(x) - f(x) \mid = \mid \int [f(y) - f(x)]\phi_a(x - y)dy \mid$$

$$\leq \int \mid f(y) - f(x) \mid \phi_a(x - y)dy$$

$$= \int_{|x-y| \leq a} \mid f(y) - f(x) \mid \phi_a(x - y)dy$$

$$\leq \frac{\epsilon}{\lambda(B(0, r + 1))} \int_{|x-y| \leq a} \phi_a(x - y)dy$$

$$= \frac{\epsilon}{\lambda(B(0, r + 1))}.$$

Since $f = 0$ on $B(0, r)^c$ and $f * \phi_a = 0$ on $B(0, r + a)^c$ and $a \leq 1$, both f and $f * \phi_a$ vanish on $B(0, r + 1)^c$. Thus,

$$\|f * \phi_a - f\|_1 = \int_{B(0,r+1)} \mid f * \phi_a(x) - f(x) \mid dx$$

$$\leq \frac{\epsilon}{\lambda(B(0, r + 1))} \int_{B(0,r+1)} dx$$

$$= \epsilon.$$

QED

Remark: The above proof shows in fact that every function in C_c can be uniformly approximated by functions in C_c^∞.

D. Continuity of Translation in L^1

Theorem: *Assume $f \in L^1(\mathbb{R}^n)$. Then*

$$\lim_{y \to 0} \int_{\mathbb{R}^n} \mid f(x+y) - f(x) \mid dx = 0.$$

Proof: We shall use the notation τ_y for the operation of translating the independent variable by $y \in \mathbb{R}^n$. Thus,

$$(\tau_y f)(x) = f(x+y),$$

and we must prove that $\lim_{y \to 0} \|\tau_y f - f\|_1 = 0$. This of course signifies that when this norm is used for measurement, the translated function $\tau_y f$ depends continuously on y at $y = 0$.

Let $\epsilon > 0$. Then the theorem or even the lemma of Section C shows that there exists $g \in C_c$ such that

$$\|g - f\|_1 < \epsilon/3.$$

Then also

$$\|\tau_y g - \tau_y f\|_1 = \|g - f\|_1 < \epsilon/3.$$

Since $g = 0$ on $B(0, r)^c$ for some r, it follows that g is uniformly continuous on $\mathbb{R}^n$. Therefore there exists $0 < \delta \leq 1$ such that if $|y| \leq \delta$, then

$$\mid g(x+y) - g(x) \mid < \frac{\epsilon}{3\lambda(B(0, r+1))} \qquad \text{for all} \quad x \in \mathbb{R}^n.$$

Since $\tau_y g - g = 0$ on $B(0, r+1)^c$, we conclude that

$$\|\tau_y g - g\|_1 < \epsilon/3.$$

Therefore, $|y| \leq \delta \Rightarrow$

$$\|\tau_y f - f\|_1 \leq \|\tau_y f - \tau_y g\|_1 + \|\tau_y g - g\|_1 + \|g - f\|_1$$
$$< \epsilon/3 + \epsilon/3 + \epsilon/3$$
$$= \epsilon.$$

QED

Fubini's Theorem for $\mathbb{R}^n$

The material presented in this chapter will actually be greatly generalized later, in Chapter 11. However, it seems worthwhile to treat the concrete case of Euclidean space first. For we do not require any further techniques, and we shall immediately apply these results in the following chapters.

Fubini's theorem is a very important result, for many reasons. An outstanding example is its role in calculations of certain explicit integrals. Fubini's theorem allows the Lebesgue integral to be expressed as an "iterated integral." Frequently the iterated integral can be calculated by using standard techniques of calculus, whereas there are few techniques which apply directly to the calculation of "multiple integrals." In particular, at the present time we do not know how to calculate $\lambda(B(x,r))$, but we shall do this easily in Chapter 9.

Before we carry out the actual analysis, we need to introduce some notation which will prevent the bookkeeping problems from getting out of hand.

Notation: Let l and m be positive integers, and $n = l + m$. We then express $\mathbb{R}^n$ as a Cartesian product,

$$\mathbb{R}^n = \mathbb{R}^l \times \mathbb{R}^m,$$

and we shall strive to designate points in $\mathbb{R}^n$ consistently in the following manner:

$$z \in \mathbb{R}^n;\ x \in \mathbb{R}^l,\ y \in \mathbb{R}^m,$$
$$z = (x, y).$$

Of course, we mean by this notation that

$$z_i = x_i \quad \text{for } 1 \le i \le l,$$
$$z_i = y_{i-l} \quad \text{for } l+1 \le i \le n.$$

If f is a function on $\mathbb{R}^n$ and $y \in \mathbb{R}^m$ is fixed, then f_y is the function on $\mathbb{R}^l$ defined by

$$f_y(x) = f(x, y).$$

The function f_y is called the *section* of f determined by y. In particular, suppose $A \subset \mathbb{R}^n$ and $f = \chi_A$. Then by definition

$$f_y(x) = \begin{cases} 1 & \text{if } (x,y) \in A, \\ 0 & \text{if } (x,y) \in A^c. \end{cases}$$

Therefore, f_y is the characteristic function of a subset of $\mathbb{R}^l$, and a point $x \in \mathbb{R}^l$ belongs to this set $\Longleftrightarrow (x, y) \in A$. We denote this set by A_y:

$$A_y = \{x \in \mathbb{R}^l \mid (x, y) \in A\}.$$

The set A_y is called the *section* of A determined by y. Thus, we have shown

$$(\chi_A)_y = \chi_{A_y}.$$

Here is a sketch of a set $A \subset \mathbb{R}^2$ and a corresponding section:

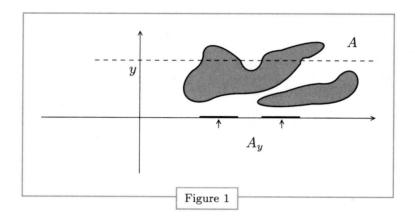

Figure 1

Now we are going to describe the situation to be discussed in this chapter. We assume that f is a given function on $\mathbb{R}^n$. If $y \in \mathbb{R}^m$, then it may occur that the function f_y on $\mathbb{R}^l$ can be integrated. If this does happen, then we shall perform the integration and shall denote the resulting number as

$$F(y) = \int_{\mathbb{R}^l} f_y(x)dx.$$

We certainly must know that f_y is $\mathcal{L}$-measurable in order for this to happen. And then there are two ways that $F(y)$ could exist. One is that $f_y \geq 0$, in which case $F(y)$ exists and satisfies $0 \leq F(y) \leq \infty$. The other is that $f_y \in L^1(\mathbb{R}^l)$, and then $F(y)$ exists and satisfies $-\infty < F(y) < \infty$.

We then ultimately want to write an equation

$$\int_{\mathbb{R}^m} F(y)dy = \int_{\mathbb{R}^n} f(z)dz.$$

Thus, we must assume f is $\mathcal{L}$-measurable and has an integral, and we shall have to prove that $F(y)$ exists for a.e. $y \in \mathbb{R}^m$ and that F is $\mathcal{L}$-measurable on $\mathbb{R}^m$ and has an integral.

The following simple example shows that we cannot expect that f_y is an $\mathcal{L}$-measurable function for every $y \in \mathbb{R}^m$. Let $E \subset \mathbb{R}^l$ be any nonmeasurable set, let $y_0 \in \mathbb{R}^m$ be fixed, and let $A = E \times \{y_0\}$. Then $A_y = \emptyset$ if $y \neq y_0$, but $A_{y_0} = E$. The set A is measurable, since it is contained in an affine subspace of $\mathbb{R}^n$ of dimension $l < n$. In fact, $\lambda(A) = 0$. But the section A_{y_0} is not a measurable subset of $\mathbb{R}^l$. Notice that A_y is measurable for a.e. $y \in \mathbb{R}^m$, and that $\lambda(A_y) = 0$ for $y \neq y_0$.

Now we state the first theorem of this chapter.

> **Fubini's Theorem for Nonnegative Functions:** *Assume that $f : \mathbb{R}^n \to [0, \infty]$ is $\mathcal{L}$-measurable. Then for a.e. $y \in \mathbb{R}^m$ the function $f_y : \mathbb{R}^l \to [0, \infty]$ is $\mathcal{L}$-measurable, and thus $F(y)$ exists:*
>
> $$F(y) = \int_{\mathbb{R}^l} f_y(x)dx.$$
>
> *Furthermore, F is $\mathcal{L}$-measurable on $\mathbb{R}^m$, and*
>
> $$\int_{\mathbb{R}^m} F(y)dy = \int_{\mathbb{R}^n} f(z)dz.$$

Notation: Instead of having to repeat all the statements made in this theorem, we shall express Fubini's theorem symbolically as follows: replace the symbol dz by $dxdy$ and then write

$$\int_{\mathbb{R}^m} \left[\int_{\mathbb{R}^l} f(x,y)dx \right] dy = \int_{\mathbb{R}^n} f(x,y)dxdy.$$

We can also write the left side of this equation without brackets as

$$\int_{\mathbb{R}^m} \int_{\mathbb{R}^l} f(x,y)dxdy \quad \text{or} \quad \int_{\mathbb{R}^m} dy \int_{\mathbb{R}^l} f(x,y)dx.$$

Any time we choose to write an equation like this we must realize it is just shorthand for the complete statement of one of the versions of

Fubini's theorem. Thus, we realize that the integral $\int_{\mathbb{R}^l} f(x,y)dx$ makes sense for a.e. $y \in \mathbb{R}^m$, and that the resulting function of y which is defined a.e. on $\mathbb{R}^m$ is $\mathcal{L}$-measurable.

Remark: The theorem we have just stated is frequently called *Tonelli's* theorem, with some justification. The second theorem of this chapter is then called *Fubini's* theorem.

Proof: The proof is rather long, but can be broken up into short pieces. In the first six steps the function will be the characteristic function of a set in $\mathbb{R}^n$; we then have to prove for $A \subset \mathbb{R}^n$ (a measurable set),

$$\int_{\mathbb{R}^m} \lambda(A_y)dy = \lambda(A).$$

This special case of the theorem is sometimes called "Cavalieri's principle."

1. If $J \subset \mathbb{R}^n$ is a rectangle with sides parallel to the coordinate axes, the result is trivial for J. Indeed, $J = J' \times J''$, where J' and J'' are rectangles in $\mathbb{R}^l$ and $\mathbb{R}^m$, respectively. Then for any $y \in \mathbb{R}^m$

$$J_y = \begin{cases} J' & \text{if } y \in J'', \\ \emptyset & \text{if } y \notin J''. \end{cases}$$

Therefore,

$$\lambda(J_y) = \begin{cases} \lambda(J') & \text{if } y \in J'', \\ 0 & \text{if } y \notin J'', \end{cases}$$

which is to say that $\lambda(J_y) = \lambda(J')\chi_{J''}(y)$. Therefore,

$$\int_{\mathbb{R}^m} \lambda(J_y)dy = \lambda(J')\lambda(J'')$$

$$= \lambda(J).$$

2. Let $G \subset \mathbb{R}^n$ be an open set. Then G can be expressed as a countable disjoint union of rectangles, as on p.77:

$$G = \bigcup_{k=1}^{\infty} J_k.$$

Therefore it follows that for all $y \in \mathbb{R}^m$

$$G_y = \bigcup_{k=1}^{\infty} J_{k,y},$$

also a countable disjoint union. Therefore $\lambda(G_y) = \sum_{k=1}^{\infty} \lambda(J_{k,y})$, and we conclude from the theorem on p.128 that

$$\int_{\mathbb{R}^m} \lambda(G_y) dy = \sum_{k=1}^{\infty} \int_{\mathbb{R}^m} \lambda(J_{k,y}) dy$$

$$= \sum_{k=1}^{\infty} \lambda(J_k) \quad \text{(by Step 1)}$$

$$= \lambda(G).$$

3. Let $K \subset \mathbb{R}^n$ be compact. Choose any bounded open set $G \supset K$, and apply Step 2 to $G \sim K$:

$$\int_{\mathbb{R}^m} \lambda(G_y \sim K_y) dy = \lambda(G \sim K);$$

$$\int_{\mathbb{R}^m} \lambda(G_y) dy - \int_{\mathbb{R}^m} \lambda(K_y) dy = \lambda(G) - \lambda(K);$$

therefore the application of Step 2 to G yields

$$\int_{\mathbb{R}^m} \lambda(K_y) dy = \lambda(K).$$

4. Assume $K_1 \subset K_2 \subset \ldots$ are compact subsets of $\mathbb{R}^n$. Then the result is valid for their union $B = \bigcup_{j=1}^{\infty} K_j$. First note that for all $y \in \mathbb{R}^m$

$$B_y = \bigcup_{j=1}^{\infty} K_{j,y}.$$

Therefore, B_y is measurable and $\lambda(B_y) = \lim_{j\to\infty} \lambda(K_{j,y})$, and this is an increasing limit. Thus, LICT implies

$$\int_{\mathbb{R}^m} \lambda(B_y)dy = \lim_{j\to\infty} \int_{\mathbb{R}^m} \lambda(K_{j,y})dy$$
$$= \lim_{j\to\infty} \lambda(K_j) \quad \text{(by Step 3)}$$
$$= \lambda(B).$$

5. Likewise, if $G_1 \supset G_2 \supset \ldots$ are *bounded* open subsets of $\mathbb{R}^n$, the result is valid for their intersection $C = \bigcap_{j=1}^{\infty} G_j$. To see this, choose any compact $K \supset G_1$ and apply Step 4 to

$$K \sim C = \bigcup_{j=1}^{\infty}(K \sim G_j).$$

Thus,

$$\int_{\mathbb{R}^m} \lambda(K_y \sim C_y)dy = \lambda(K \sim C).$$

Since also

$$\int_{\mathbb{R}^m} \lambda(K_y)dy = \lambda(K),$$

the result follows by subtraction.

6. THE CRUCIAL STEP: Let $A \subset \mathbb{R}^n$ be any bounded measurable set. By the theorem on approximation on p.45, there exist compact sets K_j and bounded open sets G_j such that

$$K_1 \subset K_2 \subset \cdots \subset A \subset \cdots \subset G_2 \subset G_1$$

and

$$\lim_{j\to\infty} \lambda(K_j) = \lambda(A) = \lim_{j\to\infty} \lambda(G_j).$$

Define

$$B = \bigcup_{j=1}^{\infty} K_j \quad \text{and} \quad C = \bigcap_{j=1}^{\infty} G_j.$$

Then $B \subset A \subset C$ and $\lambda(B) = \lambda(A) = \lambda(C)$. By Steps 4 and 5,

$$\int_{\mathbb{R}^m} \lambda(B_y)dy = \lambda(B),$$

$$\int_{\mathbb{R}^m} \lambda(C_y)dy = \lambda(C).$$

Subtract these equations to obtain

$$\int_{\mathbb{R}^m} [\lambda(C_y) - \lambda(B_y)]\, dy = 0.$$

Since the integrand is nonnegative, the vanishing principle of Problem 6.1 implies that

$$\lambda(C_y) - \lambda(B_y) = 0 \qquad \text{for a.e.} \quad y \in \mathbb{R}^m.$$

Therefore, $C_y \sim B_y$ is a null set in $\mathbb{R}^l$ for a.e. $y \in \mathbb{R}^m$. For such y, the inclusion $B_y \subset A_y \subset C_y$ implies that A_y is the union of B_y and a null set. Therefore, A_y is measurable for such y and $\lambda(A_y) = \lambda(B_y) = \lambda(C_y)$. Thus, $\lambda(A_y)$ itself is a measurable function of y, and

$$\int_{\mathbb{R}^m} \lambda(A_y)dy = \int_{\mathbb{R}^m} \lambda(B_y)dy$$

$$= \lambda(B)$$

$$= \lambda(A).$$

Notice that not until this step have we seen the situation in which A_y is not necessarily measurable for all $y \in \mathbb{R}^m$.

7. The remainder of the proof is quite straightforward and depends primarily on the following observation: If the theorem is valid for each function in an increasing sequence $0 \leq f_1 \leq f_2 \leq \ldots$, then it is also valid for the limit $f = \lim_j f_j$. This is an easy argument which employs LICT, as in Steps 2 and 4. For, $f_{j,y}$ increases to f_y

as $j \to \infty$. Since $f_{j,y}$ is measurable for a.e. y, it follows that f_y is $\mathcal{L}$-measurable also for a.e. y. Thus, for a.e. $y \in \mathbb{R}^m$

$$F(y) = \int_{\mathbb{R}^l} f_y(x)dx$$

$$= \lim_{j \to \infty} \int_{\mathbb{R}^l} f_{j,y}(x)dx \quad \text{(by LICT)}$$

$$= \lim_{j \to \infty} F_j(y).$$

This is also an increasing limit. Since each F_j is measurable, so is F, and LICT implies

$$\int_{\mathbb{R}^m} F(y)dy = \lim_{j \to \infty} \int_{\mathbb{R}^m} F_j(y)dy$$

$$= \lim_{j \to \infty} \int_{\mathbb{R}^n} f_j(z)dz$$

$$= \int_{\mathbb{R}^n} f(z)dz.$$

8. We now conclude that the theorem is valid for $f = \chi_A$, where $A \subset \mathbb{R}^n$ is any measurable set (not necessarily bounded). To see this, let f_j be the characteristic function of the *bounded* set $A \cap B(0,j)$ and apply Step 6 and the observation in Step 7.

9. The theorem is valid for any nonnegative measurable simple function, since such a function is a finite linear combination of functions considered in Step 8.

10. Finally, assume f is any nonnegative $\mathcal{L}$-measurable function. From p.118 we know that there exists a sequence of $\mathcal{L}$-measurable simple functions satisfying

$$0 \leq s_1 \leq s_2 \leq \dots ,$$
$$\lim_{j \to \infty} s_j = f.$$

By Step 9 the theorem is valid for each s_j. By Step 7 the theorem is valid for f.

QED

The next theorem is an immediate consequence of the preceding.

Fubini's Theorem for Integrable Functions: *Assume that $f \in L^1(\mathbb{R}^n)$. Then for a.e. $y \in \mathbb{R}^m$ the function $f_y \in L^1(\mathbb{R}^l)$, and thus there exists*

$$F(y) = \int_{\mathbb{R}^l} f_y(x)dx.$$

Furthermore, $F \in L^1(\mathbb{R}^m)$, and

$$\int_{\mathbb{R}^m} F(y)dy = \int_{\mathbb{R}^n} f(z)dz.$$

Proof: Of course, we write $f = f_+ - f_-$ and apply the preceding theorem to f_+ and f_-. Thus, for a.e. $y \in \mathbb{R}^m$ the sections $f_{+,y}$ and $f_{-,y}$ are $\mathcal{L}$-measurable, and we can define

$$G(y) = \int_{\mathbb{R}^l} f_{-,y}dx,$$

$$H(y) = \int_{\mathbb{R}^l} f_{+,y}dx.$$

Moreover,

$$\int_{\mathbb{R}^m} G\,dy = \int_{\mathbb{R}^n} f_-dz,$$

$$\int_{\mathbb{R}^m} H\,dy = \int_{\mathbb{R}^n} f_+dz.$$

As these integrals are finite, the finiteness principle of Problem 6.2 shows that $G(y) < \infty$ and $H(y) < \infty$ for a.e. y. That is, for a.e. y it is true that

$$\int_{\mathbb{R}^l} f_{-,y}dx < \infty \quad \text{and} \quad \int_{\mathbb{R}^l} f_{+,y}dx < \infty,$$

and these inequalities say exactly that $f_y \in L^1(\mathbb{R}^l)$. Moreover, for a.e.

y we also have $F(y) = H(y) - G(y)$. Therefore, $F \in L^1(\mathbb{R}^m)$ and

$$\int_{\mathbb{R}^m} F dy = \int_{\mathbb{R}^m} H dy - \int_{\mathbb{R}^m} G dy$$

$$= \int_{\mathbb{R}^n} f_+ dz - \int_{\mathbb{R}^n} f_- dz$$

$$= \int_{\mathbb{R}^n} f dz.$$

QED

Remark: The two Fubini theorems of this chapter are often used in conjunction, in the following manner. Assume f is known to be measurable, but not known to be integrable. It is then sometimes possible either to calculate or to estimate

$$\int_{\mathbb{R}^m} dy \int_{\mathbb{R}^l} |f(x,y)| \, dx$$

and to see that this iterated integral is finite. The first theorem then shows that also $\int_{\mathbb{R}^n} |f(z)| dz < \infty$, and we conclude that $f \in L^1(\mathbb{R}^n)$. Then the second theorem can be applied to prove that

$$\int_{\mathbb{R}^m} dy \int_{\mathbb{R}^l} f(x,y) dx = \int_{\mathbb{R}^n} f dz.$$

EQUALITY OF ITERATED INTEGRALS. There is another use of Fubini's theorem we need to mention. It depends on the fact that frequently we may be in a situation in which we do not actually care about the value of the integral $\int_{\mathbb{R}^n} f(z) dz$, but do care about one or another iterated integral. Fubini's theorem may be applied, as follows. Suppose that f satisfies the hypothesis of one of the Fubini theorems. Then any iterated integral of f exists and is independent of the way the iterated integral is formed. Thus, for example,

$$\int_{\mathbb{R}^m} dy \int_{\mathbb{R}^l} f(x,y) dx = \int_{\mathbb{R}^l} dx \int_{\mathbb{R}^m} f(x,y) dy$$

$$= \int_{\mathbb{R}} dz_1 \int_{\mathbb{R}} dz_2 \ldots \int_{\mathbb{R}} f(z) dz_n$$

$$= \text{etc.}$$

These results hold because all the integrals in question are actually equal to $\int\limits_{\mathbb{R}^n} f(z)dz$.

Example: Suppose we wish to calculate the integral in $\mathbb{R}^2$

$$\int\limits_E y \sin x e^{-xy} dxdy,$$

where E is the set $\{(x,y)|0 < x < \infty, 0 < y < 1\}$. Since the function $f(x,y) = y \sin x e^{-xy}$ is continuous, it is $\mathcal{L}$-measurable. If we perform an iterated integration, doing the x integration first, we find

$$F(y) = \int\limits_0^\infty y \sin x e^{-xy} dx$$

$$= \frac{y}{y^2 + 1}.$$

(This result may be found by integrating by parts, using an integral table, etc.) Therefore, we conclude

$$\int\limits_0^1 F(y)dy = \frac{1}{2} \log 2.$$

But the question is this: Can we assert that $\int\limits_E f(x,y)dxdy = \frac{1}{2}\log 2$? If we knew the function f to be integrable, this would be a valid consequence of Fubini's theorem for integrable functions. To show that f is actually integrable, we can use Fubini's theorem for nonnegative functions. For $|f(x,y)| \le ye^{-xy}$, so we conclude

$$\int\limits_E |f(x,y)|\, dxdy \le \int\limits_E ye^{-xy} dxdy$$

$$= \int\limits_0^1 dy \int\limits_0^\infty ye^{-xy} dx$$

$$= \int\limits_0^1 dy$$

$$= 1.$$

Incidentally, doing the y integration first yields

$$\int_0^1 y \sin x e^{-xy} dy = \frac{\sin x}{x} \left(\frac{1 - e^{-x}}{x} - e^{-x} \right).$$

Thus, Fubini's theorem gives us the evaluation of a rather strange integral:

$$\int_0^\infty \frac{\sin x}{x} \left(\frac{1 - e^{-x}}{x} - e^{-x} \right) dx = \frac{1}{2} \log 2.$$

In working the problems in this chapter, you may find it helpful to apply elementary integration techniques of basic calculus. This is of course legitimate.

Problem 1. Integrate the (nonnegative) function $xe^{-x^2(1+y^2)}$ over the set $(0, \infty) \times (0, \infty)$ in two different ways. Conclude from your calculations that

$$\int_0^\infty e^{-t^2} dt = \frac{\sqrt{\pi}}{2}.$$

This is one of the most important integrals in all of mathematics.

Problem 2. Integrate the function $\sin x e^{-xy}$ over the set $(0, a) \times (0, \infty)$. Show that

$$\int_0^a \frac{\sin x}{x} dx = \frac{\pi}{2} - \cos a \int_0^\infty \frac{e^{-ay}}{1 + y^2} dy - \sin a \int_0^\infty \frac{y e^{-ay}}{1 + y^2} dy.$$

Problem 3. Using Problem 2, show that

$$\lim_{a \to \infty} \int_0^a \frac{\sin x}{x} dx = \frac{\pi}{2}.$$

Do this by demonstrating *carefully* that both integrals on the right side of Problem 2 tend to zero as $a \to \infty$. (You should not require LDCT to do this.)

Problem 4. Prove that $\dfrac{\sin x}{x}$ is *not* integrable on $(0, \infty)$. (Nevertheless, we feel comfortable writing the result of Problem 3 in shorthand:

$$\int_0^\infty \frac{\sin x}{x} dx = \frac{\pi}{2}.)$$

Problem 5. In the shorthand notation of Problem 4, show that

$$\int_0^\infty \frac{\sin ax}{x} dx = \begin{cases} \frac{\pi}{2} & \text{if } a > 0, \\ 0 & \text{if } a = 0, \\ -\frac{\pi}{2} & \text{if } a < 0. \end{cases}$$

Problem 6. By an integration by parts applied to the result of Problem 5, show that

$$\int_0^\infty \frac{1 - \cos ax}{x^2} dx = \frac{\pi}{2}|a|.$$

Show that $\dfrac{1 - \cos ax}{x^2}$ *is an integrable function on* $(0, \infty)$.

Problem 7. By integrating e^{-xy} over an appropriate region, show that

$$\int_0^\infty \frac{e^{-ax} - e^{-bx}}{x} dx = \log \frac{b}{a} \quad \text{if } a > 0, \ b > 0.$$

Problem 8. Let $a_i > 0$ for $1 \le i \le n$, and let $J = (0,1) \times \cdots \times (0,1)$. Prove that

$$\int_J \frac{1}{x_1^{a_1} + x_2^{a_2} + \cdots + x_n^{a_n}} dx < \infty \iff \sum_{i=1}^n \frac{1}{a_i} > 1.$$

(**HINT:** Let $G_i = \{x \in J | x_j^{a_j} \le x_i^{a_i} \text{ for all } j\}$. Note that for $x \in G_i$,

$x_i^{a_i} \le x_1^{a_1} + \cdots + x_n^{a_n} \le n x_i^{a_i}$. Note that $J = \bigcup_{i=1}^{n} G_i$. Calculate

$$\int_{G_i} \frac{dx}{x_i^{a_i}} = \int_0^1 x_i^{a_i(\sum_{j=1}^{n} \frac{1}{a_j} - 1) - 1} \, dx_i$$

and use the fact that $\int_0^1 t^{s-1} dt < \infty \iff s > 0$.)

Problem 9. Using the same notation as in Problem 8, let

$$J' = (0, \infty) \times \cdots \times (0, \infty) \sim J.$$

Prove that

$$\int_{J'} \frac{1}{x_1^{a_1} + x_2^{a_2} + \cdots + x_n^{a_n}} dx < \infty \iff \sum_{i=1}^{n} \frac{1}{a_i} < 1.$$

Problem 10. Recall that $|x|$ is the Euclidean norm of $x \in \mathbb{R}^n$. If $a > 0$, prove there exists $c > 0$ depending only on n and a such that

$$c^{-1} \left(|x_1|^a + \cdots + |x_n|^a \right) \le |x|^a \le c \left(|x_1|^a + \cdots + |x_n|^a \right).$$

Problem 11. Prove that the integrals on $\mathbb{R}^n$ satisfy:

$$\int_{B(0,1)} \frac{dx}{|x|^a} < \infty \iff a < n;$$

$$\int_{B(0,1)^c} \frac{dx}{|x|^a} < \infty \iff a > n.$$

Problem 12. This example and the three following problems show what can go wrong if $f \notin L^1$ and f changes signs. Even if the iterated integrals exist, they might not be equal. On $(0,1) \times (0,1)$ let

$$f(x,y) = \begin{cases} x^{-2} & \text{if } y < x < 1, \\ -y^{-2} & \text{if } x < y < 1. \end{cases}$$

Show that $\int\limits_0^1 dx \int\limits_0^1 f(x,y)dy = 1$ and $\int\limits_0^1 dy \int\limits_0^1 f(x,y)dx = -1$.

Problem 13. Let $f(x,y) = \dfrac{x^2 - y^2}{(x^2 + y^2)^2}$. Show that

$$\int\limits_0^1 dx \int\limits_0^1 f(x,y)dy = \frac{\pi}{4} \quad \text{and} \quad \int\limits_0^1 dy \int\limits_0^1 f(x,y)dx = -\frac{\pi}{4}.$$

Problem 14. Show that

$$\int\limits_0^1 dx \int\limits_0^1 \frac{x-y}{(x+y)^3}dy = \frac{1}{2} \quad \text{and} \quad \int\limits_0^1 dy \int\limits_0^1 \frac{x-y}{(x+y)^3}dx = -\frac{1}{2}.$$

Problem 15. Let $f(x,y) = \text{sgn}(x-y)e^{-|x-y|}$, where by definition

$$\text{sgn } t = \begin{cases} 1 & \text{if } t > 0, \\ 0 & \text{if } t = 0, \\ -1 & \text{if } t < 0. \end{cases}$$

Show that

$$\int\limits_0^\infty dx \int\limits_0^\infty f(x,y)dy = -\int\limits_0^\infty dy \int\limits_0^\infty f(x,y)dx = -1.$$

Before stating the next four problems we need to take care of an important but rather elementary result, which we state as

Proposition: *In the general case of $\mathbb{R}^n = \mathbb{R}^l \times \mathbb{R}^m$, suppose X is an $\mathcal{L}$-measurable subset of $\mathbb{R}^l$ and Y is an $\mathcal{L}$-measurable subset of $\mathbb{R}^m$. Then*

the Cartesian product $X \times Y$ is an $\mathcal{L}$-measurable subset of $\mathbb{R}^n$. Moreover,

$$\lambda(X \times Y) = \lambda(X)\lambda(Y).$$

Proof: Of course once we know $X \times Y$ is measurable, the equation is an immediate consequence of Fubini's theorem. First, since X and Y are both countable unions of sets with finite measure,

$$X = \bigcup_{k=1}^{\infty} X_k,$$

$$Y = \bigcup_{k=1}^{\infty} Y_k,$$

we also have

$$X \times Y = \bigcup_{j,k=1}^{\infty} X_j \times Y_k.$$

Thus, if we prove $X_j \times Y_k$ is measurable, the result will follow.

Thus we may as well assume from the outset that X and Y each have finite measure. Given $\epsilon > 0$, we use the approximation property M9 of Chapter 2 to conclude the existence of

$$\text{closed } F_1 \subset X \subset \text{ open } G_1 \subset \mathbb{R}^l,$$
$$\text{closed } F_2 \subset Y \subset \text{ open } G_2 \subset \mathbb{R}^m,$$

such that

$$\lambda(G_1 \sim F_1) < \epsilon,$$
$$\lambda(G_2 \sim F_2) < \epsilon.$$

Then $F_1 \times F_2$ is closed, $G_1 \times G_2$ is open, and

$$F_1 \times F_2 \subset X \times Y \subset G_1 \times G_2.$$

Now we just notice that

$$G_1 \times G_2 \sim F_1 \times F_2 = [(G_1 \sim F_1) \times G_2] \cup [F_1 \times (G_2 \sim F_2)]$$
$$\subset [(G_1 \sim F_1) \times G_2] \cup [G_1 \times (G_2 \sim F_2)].$$

The set on the right side of this inclusion is open, and has measure less than or equal to

$$\lambda([(G_1 \sim F_1) \times G_2]) + \lambda([G_1 \times (G_2 \sim F_2)])$$
$$= \lambda(G_1 \sim F_1)\lambda(G_2) + \lambda(G_1)\lambda(G_2 \sim F_2)$$
$$\leq \epsilon\lambda(G_2) + \epsilon\lambda(G_1)$$
$$< \epsilon(\lambda(F_2) + \epsilon) + \epsilon(\lambda(F_1) + \epsilon)$$
$$\leq \epsilon(\lambda(Y) + \lambda(X) + 2\epsilon).$$

Thus $\lambda(G_1 \times G_2 \sim F_1 \times F_2)$ is as small as we please, so that the approximation property implies $X \times Y$ is measurable. **QED**

The next four problems deal with the familiar interpretation of integrals as areas or volumes. Thus, if $f \geq 0$ on $[a, b]$, then we frequently think of $\int_a^b f(x)dx$ as the area under the graph of f and above the x-axis. In these problems assume that $f : E \to [0, \infty]$, where $E \subset \mathbb{R}^n$ is a measurable set, and assume that f is $\mathcal{L}$-measurable. We shall also consider $\mathbb{R}^{n+1} = \mathbb{R}^n \times \mathbb{R}$ and shall use coordinates $x \in \mathbb{R}^n$ and $y \in \mathbb{R}$.

Problem 16. In this context prove that the function f, *regarded as a function on $\mathbb{R}^{n+1}$ which is independent of y*, is an $\mathcal{L}$-measurable function on $\mathbb{R}^{n+1}$.

(**HINT**: Use the proposition.)

As a result of this problem, the sets

$$A = \{(x, y) \in \mathbb{R}^{n+1} \mid 0 \leq y < f(x), \quad x \in E\},$$
$$B = \{(x, y) \in \mathbb{R}^{n+1} \mid 0 \leq y \leq f(x), \quad x \in E\},$$

are measurable subsets of $\mathbb{R}^{n+1}$.

Problem 17. Prove that

$$\lambda(A) = \lambda(B) = \int_E f(x)dx.$$

Problem 18. Prove that

$$\int_E f(x)dx = \int_0^\infty \lambda(\{x \in E \mid f(x) > y\})dy$$

$$= \int_0^\infty \lambda(\{x \in E \mid f(x) \geq y\})dy.$$

Problem 19. Problem 17 shows that if $f \in L^1$ and $f \geq 0$, then $\lambda(B \sim A) = 0$. Of course, $B \sim A = \{(x, y) \in \mathbb{R}^{n+1} | y = f(x),\ x \in E\}$ is the *graph* of f. Extend this result: if $f : E \to \mathbb{R}$ is $\mathcal{L}$-measurable, prove that the graph of f is a null set in $\mathbb{R}^{n+1}$.

The Gamma Function

This chapter is included primarily to give additional useful yet simple applications of Fubini's theorem. After discussing the gamma function, we shall apply the results to the problem of calculating the measure of balls in $\mathbb{R}^n$.

A. Definition and Simple Properties

If $0 < a < \infty$, the function x^{a-1} is integrable on the interval $(0, 1) \subset \mathbb{R}$. This is an easy consequence of LICT and the fundamental theorem of calculus:

$$\int_0^1 x^{a-1}dx = \lim_{\epsilon \to 0} \int_\epsilon^1 x^{a-1}dx \qquad \text{(LICT)}$$
$$= \lim_{\epsilon \to 0} \frac{1 - \epsilon^a}{a}$$
$$= \frac{1}{a}.$$

And since exponential decay overpowers any power, $x^{a-1}e^{-x}$ is an integrable function on $(1, \infty)$, for there exists a constant C depending only on a such that $x^{a-1}e^{-x} \le Ce^{-x/2}$ for $1 \le x < \infty$. Thus, we conclude that $x^{a-1}e^{-x}$ is integrable on $(0, \infty)$, and we are able to define the *gamma function* by

$$\Gamma(a) = \int_0^\infty x^{a-1}e^{-x}dx, \qquad 0 < a < \infty.$$

Note that $\Gamma(1) = 1$.

A closely associated function is the *beta function*:

$$B(a, b) = \int_0^1 x^{a-1}(1 - x)^{b-1}dx, \qquad 0 < a < \infty, \ 0 < b < \infty.$$

(That is an upper case *beta*. I don't think you'll be in danger of confusing this with similar notation for a ball with center a and radius b.) Note that the integrand is integrable near 0 because $a > 0$ and near 1 because $b > 0$. The change of variable $x = 1 - y$ shows that $B(a, b) = B(b, a)$. A more interesting formula is obtained by the change of variable $x = \sin^2 \theta$ for $0 < \theta < \frac{\pi}{2}$. Then $dx = 2 \sin \theta \cos \theta d\theta$, and we find

$$B(a, b) = 2 \int_0^{\pi/2} \sin^{2a-1} \theta \cos^{2b-1} \theta d\theta.$$

Notice that we are exploiting the elementary substitution techniques of calculus. It is an easy matter to justify their applicability to these so-called improper integrals. We omit the details. (Better results will be obtained in Section 15.J.)

Note the two formulas

$$B\left(\tfrac{1}{2}, \tfrac{1}{2}\right) = \pi,$$

$$B(a, 1) = \frac{1}{a}.$$

The relation between Γ and B is given by the next result.

Theorem:

$$B(a, b) = \frac{\Gamma(a)\Gamma(b)}{\Gamma(a + b)}.$$

Proof: We employ the device of using two different "dummy" variables in the formulas for $\Gamma(a)$ and $\Gamma(b)$:

$$\Gamma(a)\Gamma(b) = \int_0^\infty x^{a-1} e^{-x} dx \cdot \int_0^\infty y^{b-1} e^{-y} dy$$

$$= \int_0^\infty dx \int_0^\infty x^{a-1} y^{b-1} e^{-x} e^{-y} dy.$$

Nothing has actually happened in writing $\Gamma(a)\Gamma(b)$ as the iterated integral. Now for each x make the substitution $y = \eta - x$:

$$\Gamma(a)\Gamma(b) = \int_0^\infty dx \int_x^\infty x^{a-1} (\eta - x)^{b-1} e^{-\eta} d\eta.$$

This is an iterated integral in the x, η space over the region of integration $\{(x, \eta) | 0 < x < \eta < \infty\}$. Because the integrand is nonnegative, Fubini's theorem implies that the integral coincides with the iterated integral taken in the other order:

$$\Gamma(a)\Gamma(b) = \int_0^\infty d\eta \int_0^\eta x^{a-1}(\eta - x)^{b-1}e^{-\eta}dx$$

$$= \int_0^\infty e^{-\eta}d\eta \int_0^\eta x^{a-1}(\eta - x)^{b-1}dx.$$

The inner integral looks very much like $B(a, b)$, and can be recognized by making the substitution $x = \eta\xi$ (with η fixed):

$$\Gamma(a)\Gamma(b) = \int_0^\infty e^{-\eta}d\eta \int_0^1 \eta^{a-1}\xi^{a-1}(\eta - \eta\xi)^{b-1}\eta d\xi$$

$$= \int_0^\infty \eta^{a-1+b-1+1}e^{-\eta}d\eta \int_0^1 \xi^{a-1}(1 - \xi)^{b-1}d\xi$$

$$= \int_0^\infty \eta^{a+b-1}e^{-\eta}d\eta B(a, b)$$

$$= \Gamma(a + b)B(a, b).$$

QED

Now we present some of the repercussions of this formula. First, if $b = 1$ we obtain $1/a = B(a, 1) = \Gamma(a)/\Gamma(a + 1)$, or

$$\Gamma(a + 1) = a\Gamma(a).$$

In particular, if n is a nonnegative integer,

$$\Gamma(n + 1) = n!.$$

Problem 1. Establish the relation $\Gamma(a + 1) = a\Gamma(a)$ directly from the definition of Γ by integrating by parts.

By setting $a = b = \frac{1}{2}$, it follows that $\pi = B\left(\frac{1}{2}, \frac{1}{2}\right) = \Gamma\left(\frac{1}{2}\right)^2$. Since $\Gamma\left(\frac{1}{2}\right) > 0$, we obtain

$$\Gamma\left(\tfrac{1}{2}\right) = \sqrt{\pi}.$$

Notice that the substitution $x = y^2$ in the definition of $\Gamma(a)$ yields

$$\Gamma(a) = 2 \int_0^\infty y^{2a-1} e^{-y^2} \, dy.$$

In particular, the choice $a = \frac{1}{2}$ yields

$$\int_0^\infty e^{-y^2} \, dy = \frac{\sqrt{\pi}}{2},$$

a result also obtained in Problem 8.1 by another method.

B. Generalization

The calculation of $\Gamma(a)\Gamma(b)$ given in the preceding section can be greatly generalized. This generalization will then lead directly to a formula for the volume of balls in $\mathbb{R}^n$. As in Section A, the key ingredient in the calculation is Fubini's theorem.

In order not to clutter the statement of the theorem, let us discuss the hypothesis here. We assume f is a nonnegative measurable function defined on the interval $(0, \infty)$ of positive real numbers. Use the notation $\mathbb{R}_+^n = (0, \infty) \times \cdots \times (0, \infty)$. Define the function f_1 on $\mathbb{R}^n$ by

$$f_1(x) = \begin{cases} f(x_1) & \text{if } x_1 > 0, \\ 0 & \text{if } x_1 \le 0. \end{cases}$$

Then f_1 is Lebesgue measurable, thanks to the proposition on p.195. If T is the matrix

$$T = \begin{pmatrix} 1 & 1 & 1 & \cdots & 1 \\ 0 & 1 & 0 & \cdots & 0 \\ 0 & 0 & 1 & \cdots & 0, \\ \vdots & \vdots & \vdots & & \vdots \\ 0 & 0 & 0 & \cdots & 1 \end{pmatrix},$$

then $f_1(Tx)$ is also a measurable function of x, thanks to the theorem on p.170. But of course $f_1(Tx) = f(x_1 + x_2 + \cdots + x_n)$, so we conclude that the function defined on $\mathbb{R}_+^n$ by

$$x \to f(x_1 + x_2 + \cdots + x_n)$$

is itself measurable. Therefore, it is possible to integrate it, as we have assumed it to be nonnegative. The point of the following calculation is that certain integrals over $\mathbb{R}^n_+$ involving this function should somehow be reducible to integrals over $(0, \infty)$ of f itself. Indeed, we have

---

Theorem: *In addition to the above hypothesis on f, assume $0 < a_k < \infty$ for $k = 1, \ldots, n$. Then*

$$\int_{\mathbb{R}^n_+} f(x_1 + \cdots + x_n) x_1^{a_1-1} \ldots x_n^{a_n-1} dx$$

$$= \frac{\Gamma(a_1) \ldots \Gamma(a_n)}{\Gamma(a_1 + \cdots + a_n)} \int_0^\infty f(t) t^{a_1 + \cdots + a_n - 1} dt.$$

Proof: Denote by L the left side of the desired equation. Starting with the integral L, apply Fubini's theorem in order to perform the x_n integration first, and then change variables by setting $x_n = t - x_1 - \cdots - x_{n-1}$ for each fixed $(x_1, \ldots, x_{n-1})$:

$$L = \int_{\mathbb{R}^{n-1}_+} x_1^{a_1-1} \ldots x_{n-1}^{a_{n-1}-1} dx_1 \ldots dx_{n-1} \int_0^\infty f(x_1 + \cdots + x_n) x_n^{a_n-1} dx_n$$

$$= \int_{\mathbb{R}^{n-1}_+} x_1^{a_1-1} \ldots x_{n-1}^{a_{n-1}-1} dx_1 \ldots dx_{n-1} \int_{x_1 + \cdots + x_{n-1}}^\infty f(t) \cdot$$

$$(t - x_1 - \cdots - x_{n-1})^{a_n-1} dt.$$

This can be regarded as an integral extended over the set

$$\{(x_1, \ldots, x_{n-1}, t) \mid \text{ all } x_k > 0, x_1 + \cdots + x_{n-1} < t < \infty\}.$$

We apply Fubini's theorem once again in order to do the t integration last:

$$L = \int_0^\infty f(t) dt \int_{\substack{x_1 + \cdots + x_{n-1} < t \\ \text{all } x_k > 0}} x_1^{a_1-1} \ldots x_{n-1}^{a_{n-1}-1} (t - x_1 - \cdots - x_{n-1})^{a_n-1}$$

$$dx_1 \ldots dx_{n-1}.$$

Now in the $(n-1)$-dimensional integral make the substitutions $x_k = t\xi_k$ (with t fixed). The resulting equation has the form

$$L = C \int_0^\infty f(t) t^{a_1 + \cdots + a_n - 1} dt,$$

where the constant C is given by

$$C = \int_{\substack{\xi_1 + \cdots + \xi_{n-1} < 1 \\ \text{all } \xi_k > 0}} \xi_1^{a_1 - 1} \cdots \xi_{n-1}^{a_{n-1} - 1} (1 - \xi_1 - \cdots - \xi_{n-1})^{a_n - 1} d\xi_1 \ldots d\xi_{n-1}.$$

This equation for L gives the theorem, once we evaluate the constant. The evaluation can be done inductively, but there is a more elegant way. Namely, apply what has been proved to the special case $f(t) = e^{-t}$. Because of Fubini's theorem and the special properties of the exponential, we obtain in this particular case

$$L = \int_0^\infty e^{-x_1} x_1^{a_1 - 1} dx_1 \ldots \int_0^\infty e^{-x_n} x_n^{a_n - 1} dx_n$$

$$= \Gamma(a_1) \ldots \Gamma(a_n).$$

Likewise,

$$\int_0^\infty e^{-t} t^{a_1 + \cdots + a_n - 1} dt = \Gamma(a_1 + \cdots + a_n).$$

Therefore, since C is independent of f,

$$C = \frac{\Gamma(a_1) \ldots \Gamma(a_n)}{\Gamma(a_1 + \cdots + a_n)}.$$

QED

Remark: As a corollary of the proof we obtain again the theorem of Section A about the beta function, for if $n = 2$, then

$$C = \int_0^1 \xi_1^{a_1 - 1} (1 - \xi_1)^{a_2 - 1} d\xi_1$$

$$= B(a_1, a_2).$$

Thus,

$$B(a_1, a_2) = \frac{\Gamma(a_1)\Gamma(a_2)}{\Gamma(a_1 + a_2)}.$$

Problem 2. In addition to the hypothesis of the theorem suppose that $0 < b_k < \infty$ for $k = 1, \ldots, n$. Use the variable transformations $x_k = y_k^{b_k}$ to prove that

$$\int_{\mathbb{R}_+^n} f(x_1^{b_1} + \cdots + x_n^{b_n})x_1^{a_1-1} \ldots x_n^{a_n-1}dx$$

$$= \frac{\Gamma\left(\frac{a_1}{b_1}\right) \ldots \Gamma\left(\frac{a_n}{b_n}\right)}{b_1 \ldots b_n \Gamma\left(\frac{a_1}{b_1} + \cdots + \frac{a_n}{b_n}\right)} \int_0^\infty f(t)t^{a_1/b_1 + \cdots + a_n/b_n - 1}dt.$$

Don't worry about measurability questions, as they will be taken care of in Chapter 15.

C. The Measure of Balls

We are now able to calculate for any dimension n the Lebesgue measure of the ball $B(x, r) = \{y \in \mathbb{R}^n \,|\, d(x, y) < r\}$. The result is

$$\lambda(B(x, r)) = \frac{\pi^{n/2}}{\Gamma\left(\frac{n}{2} + 1\right)}r^n.$$

Thus, for $n = 1, 2, 3, 4$ we obtain respectively $2r$, πr^2, $\frac{4}{3}\pi r^3$, $\frac{1}{2}\pi^2 r^4$. In fact, we can just as easily prove something more general. Suppose there is given a function on $\mathbb{R}^n$ which is nonnegative and measurable and *rotationally symmetric*. This function thus depends only on the Euclidean norm $|x|$, and so can be expressed as $f(|x|)$, where f is a function defined on $[0, \infty)$. Then we shall prove

$$\int_{\mathbb{R}^n} f(|x|)dx = \omega_n \int_0^\infty f(r)r^{n-1}dr,$$

where the number ω_n is

$$\omega_n = \frac{2\pi^{n/2}}{\Gamma(n/2)}.$$

Before proving this formula, we show how it is used to find the measure of a ball. The ball $B(x, a)$ has the same measure as $B(0, a)$. Thus, by choosing $f(r) = \chi_{(0,a)}(r)$ we obtain

$$\lambda(B(x, a)) = \lambda(B(0, a))$$

$$= \int_{\mathbb{R}^n} \chi_{(0,a)}(|x|)dx$$

$$= \omega_n \int_0^a r^{n-1}dr$$

$$= \frac{2\pi^{n/2}}{\Gamma(n/2)} \cdot \frac{a^n}{n}$$

$$= \frac{\pi^{n/2}}{\Gamma\left(\frac{n}{2} + 1\right)}a^n.$$

The integration formula is an easy special case of Problem 2 in Section B. Just choose each $a_k = 1$ and each $b_k = 2$ in that problem to obtain

$$\int_{\mathbb{R}^n_+} f(|x|^2)dx = \frac{\Gamma(1/2)^n}{2^n\Gamma(n/2)} \int_0^\infty f(t)t^{n/2-1}dt.$$

Now replace the function $f(t)$ by $f(\sqrt{t})$, and the dummy variable t by r^2:

$$\int_{\mathbb{R}^n_+} f(|x|)dx = \frac{\pi^{n/2}}{2^n\Gamma(n/2)} \int_0^\infty f(r)r^{n-2}2rdr$$

$$= \frac{\omega_n}{2^n} \int_0^\infty f(r)r^{n-1}dr.$$

Finally, the integral over all of $\mathbb{R}^n$ is 2^n times the integral over just $\mathbb{R}^n_+$. This is because the integral of the symmetric function $f(|x|)$ over each of the 2^n "quadrants" is the same.

Problem 3. Let $a_1 > 0, \ldots, a_n > 0$, and let E be the *ellipsoid* in $\mathbb{R}^n$ defined by

$$x \in E \iff \frac{x_1^2}{a_1^2} + \cdots + \frac{x_n^2}{a_n^2} < 1.$$

Prove that $\lambda(E) = \frac{\pi^{n/2}}{\Gamma\left(\frac{n}{2}+1\right)} a_1 a_2 \ldots a_n$.

Problem 4. The ratio of the volume of the unit ball in $\mathbb{R}^n$ to the volume of the "circumscribed" cube $[-1, 1]^n$ is

$$\frac{\pi^{n/2}}{2^n \Gamma\left(\frac{n}{2} + 1\right)}.$$

Prove that this ratio *decreases* to 0 as $n \to \infty$.

Problem 5. Use the formula for integrating rotationally symmetric functions to provide a quick solution to Problem 8.11: For integrals on $\mathbb{R}^n$,

$$\int_{B(0,1)} \frac{dx}{|x|^a} < \infty \iff a < n;$$

$$\int_{B(0,1)^c} \frac{dx}{|x|^a} < \infty \iff a > n.$$

Problem 6. If $a < n$, calculate the integrals

$$\int_{\mathbb{R}^n} |x|^{-a} e^{-|x|} dx;$$

$$\int_{\mathbb{R}^n} |x|^{-a} e^{-|x|^2} dx.$$

Problem 7. Show that

$$\int_{\mathbb{R}^n} e^{-|x|^2} dx = \pi^{n/2}.$$

Problem 8. Let $r > 0$ and let

$$E = \left\{ x \in \mathbb{R}^n_+ \mid x_1^{b_1} + \cdots + x_n^{b_n} < r \right\}.$$

Prove that

$$\lambda(E) = \frac{\Gamma\left(\frac{1}{b_1} + 1\right) \cdots \Gamma\left(\frac{1}{b_n} + 1\right)}{\Gamma\left(\frac{1}{b_1} + \cdots + \frac{1}{b_n} + 1\right)} r^{1/b_1 + \cdots + 1/b_n}.$$

This result provides a generalization of the measure of balls. For if $b_1 = \cdots = b_n = 2$ and r is replaced by r^2, it states that

$$\lambda(B(0,r) \cap \mathbb{R}^n_+) = \frac{\Gamma\left(\frac{3}{2}\right)^n}{\Gamma\left(\frac{n}{2} + 1\right)} r^n$$

$$= \frac{1}{2^n} \frac{\pi^{n/2}}{\Gamma\left(\frac{n}{2} + 1\right)} r^n.$$

The factor 2^{-n} appears because we have restricted attention to only one of the 2^n "quadrants" of $\mathbb{R}^n$, the one in which all $x_i > 0$.

Problem 9. A typical freshman calculus problem asks for the area of the region in $\mathbb{R}^2$ described as the interior of the curve $x^{2/3} + y^{2/3} = a^{2/3}$. Show that the answer is $3\pi a^2/8$.

Problem 10. Here is another solution to Problem 8.8. Prove that result and *calculate* the related integral

$$\int_{\substack{x \in \mathbb{R}^n_+ \\ x_1^{a_1} + \cdots + x_n^{a_n} < 1}} \frac{1}{x_1^{a_1} + \cdots + x_n^{a_n}} dx$$

if $\frac{1}{a_1} + \cdots + \frac{1}{a_n} > 1$.

D. Further Properties of the Gamma Function

Problem 11. By making an appropriate substitution prove that if a, b, c are all positive numbers, then

$$\int_0^1 \frac{x^{a-1}(1-x)^{b-1}}{(x+c)^{a+b}}\,dx = \frac{B(a,b)}{(1+c)^a c^b}.$$

Problem 12. Let $a > 0$. By the obvious substitution show that for any $n > 0$

$$\int_0^n t^{a-1}\left(1-\frac{t}{n}\right)^n dt = n^a B(a, n+1).$$

In case $n \in \mathbb{N}$ show that

$$\int_0^n t^{a-1}\left(1-\frac{t}{n}\right)^n dt = \frac{n^a n!}{a(a+1)\ldots(a+n)}.$$

Problem 13. *Carefully* justify the result obtained by letting $n \to \infty$ in Problem 12:

$$\Gamma(a) = \lim_{n\to\infty}\frac{n^a n!}{a(a+1)\ldots(a+n)}.$$

(**HINT:** Apply LDCT, proving first that $\left(1-\frac{t}{n}\right)^n < e^{-t}$ for $0 < t < n$.)

Problem 14. Using Problem 13, derive *Wallis' formula:*

$$\frac{\pi}{2} = \frac{2}{1}\cdot\frac{2}{3}\cdot\frac{4}{3}\cdot\frac{4}{5}\cdot\frac{6}{5}\cdot\frac{6}{7}\cdots$$

$$= \text{(by definition)} \lim_{n\to\infty}\frac{2^2 4^2 \ldots (2n)^2}{1\cdot 3^2 \ldots (2n-1)^2(2n+1)}.$$

Before proceeding with further problems, we want to obtain formulas for the derivatives of the gamma function. Of course, we expect the result to be

$$\Gamma^{(k)}(a) = \int_0^\infty x^{a-1}(\log x)^k e^{-x} dx.$$

This is obtained by formal differentiation of the expression defining $\Gamma(a)$. To justify the formula, we can appeal to the analysis in Section 6.G concerning differentiation with respect to a parameter. To use the corollary on p.154, we need to show that for any $0 < a_0 < a_1 < \infty$, the function

$$h(x) = \sup_{a_0 \le a \le a_1} x^{a-1}(\log x)^k e^{-x}$$

is integrable on $(0, \infty)$. But $\log x$ has such weak infinities as $x \to 0$ or $x \to \infty$ that $x^{a_0-1}(\log x)^k e^{-x}$ is integrable on $(0,1)$ and $x^{a_1-1}(\log x)^k e^{-x}$ is integrable on $(1, \infty)$.

Problem 15. Show that

$$\Gamma'(1) = \int_0^\infty e^{-x} \log x\, dx$$

$$= \int_0^1 \frac{e^{-x} - 1}{x} dx + \int_1^\infty \frac{e^{-x}}{x} dx.$$

Problem 16. The *Euler constant* is the number

$$\gamma = \lim_{n \to \infty} \left(\sum_{k=1}^n \frac{1}{k} - \log n \right).$$

It is not difficult to establish the existence of this limit. We omit a standard proof, as this problem will contain a proof as a side benefit. Prove that

$$\Gamma'(1) = -\gamma.$$

(**HINT:** Prove first that $\Gamma'(1) = \lim_{n\to\infty} \int_0^n \log x \left(1 - \frac{x}{n}\right)^n dx$. In the integral substitute $1 - \frac{x}{n} = t$, obtaining the expression

$$\frac{n}{n+1} \log n + n \int_0^1 \log(1-t) t^n dt.$$

Integrate by parts to convert the integral into $-\frac{n}{n+1}\int\limits_{0}^{1}\frac{1-t^{n+1}}{1-t}dt$.)

Problem 17. Prove that for any $n \in \mathbb{N}$

$$\Gamma'(n+1) = n!\left(1 + \frac{1}{2} + \cdots + \frac{1}{n} - \gamma\right).$$

(**HINT**: Use the relation $\Gamma(a+1) = a\Gamma(a)$ and prove the formula by induction.)

Problem 18. Prove that

$$\frac{1}{\Gamma(a)} = \lim_{n\to\infty} ae^{\gamma a}\prod_{k=1}^{n}\left(1+\frac{a}{k}\right)e^{-a/k}.$$

This is also expressed as

$$\frac{1}{\Gamma(a)} = ae^{\gamma a}\prod_{k=1}^{\infty}\left(1+\frac{a}{k}\right)e^{-a/k}.$$

(**HINT**: In the result of Problem 13 write

$$n^a = e^{a\log n} = \prod_{k=1}^{n} e^{a/k} \cdot e^{a[\log n - 1 - 1/2 - \cdots - 1/n]}.)$$

Problem 19. Justify the following calculations:

$$\log\Gamma(a) = -\log a - \gamma a - \sum_{k=1}^{\infty}\left[\log\left(1+\frac{a}{k}\right) - \frac{a}{k}\right];$$

$$\frac{\Gamma'(a)}{\Gamma(a)} = -\frac{1}{a} - \gamma - \sum_{k=1}^{\infty}\left(\frac{1}{k+a} - \frac{1}{k}\right);$$

$$\frac{d}{da}\frac{\Gamma'(a)}{\Gamma(a)} = \sum_{k=0}^{\infty}\frac{1}{(k+a)^2}.$$

Problem 20. Show that

$$\frac{d^2}{da^2}\left[\log\Gamma(a) + \log\Gamma\left(a + \frac{1}{2}\right) - \log\Gamma(2a)\right] = 0.$$

By integrating and evaluating at certain values of a, prove the *duplication formula*

$$\Gamma(2a)\sqrt{\pi} = 2^{2a-1}\Gamma(a)\Gamma\left(a + \frac{1}{2}\right).$$

Problem 21. By the same method prove that for any $n \in \mathbb{N}$ there exists a constant c such that

$$\Gamma(na) = cn^{na}\Gamma(a)\Gamma\left(a + \frac{1}{n}\right)\dots\Gamma\left(a + \frac{n-1}{n}\right).$$

(For the evaluation of c, see Problem 25.)

Problem 22. Here is another way to obtain the duplication formula. First prove that

$$\frac{\Gamma(a)^2}{\Gamma(2a)} = 2\int_0^{1/2} x^{a-1}(1-x)^{a-1}dx.$$

Then make the substitution $x = \frac{1}{2} - \frac{1}{2}\sqrt{t}$ and juggle terms.

Problem 23. Show that $\Gamma\left(\frac{1}{4}\right)\Gamma\left(\frac{3}{4}\right) = \pi\sqrt{2}$.

E. Stirling's Formula

We are now going to give a proof of the remarkable formula of Stirling, which states that as $a \to \infty$, $\Gamma(a+1)$ is *asymptotic* to $\sqrt{2\pi}a^{a+1/2}e^{-a}$:

$$\Gamma(a+1) \sim \sqrt{2\pi}a^{a+1/2}e^{-a},$$

where this notation means that

$$\lim_{a\to\infty}\frac{\Gamma(a+1)}{\sqrt{2\pi}a^{a+1/2}e^{-a}} = 1.$$

To prove this, substitute $x = at$ in the formula for $\Gamma(a+1)$:

$$\Gamma(a+1) = \int_0^\infty x^a e^{-x} dx$$

$$= a^{a+1} \int_0^\infty t^a e^{-at} dt$$

$$= a^{a+1} \int_0^\infty e^{a(\log t - t)} dt.$$

Thus,

$$\frac{\Gamma(a+1)}{a^{a+1/2} e^{-a}} = \sqrt{a} \int_0^\infty e^{a(\log t + 1 - t)} dt.$$

Now define

$$\phi(t) = -\log t - 1 + t.$$

Then we have to prove that

$$\lim_{a \to \infty} \sqrt{a} \int_0^\infty e^{-a\phi(t)} dt = \sqrt{2\pi}.$$

Note that $\phi'(t) = 1 - t^{-1}$ and $\phi''(t) = t^{-2}$, so the graph of $\phi(t)$ appears as in the figure:

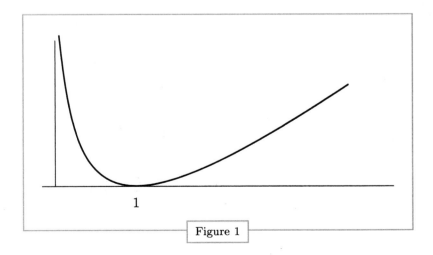

1

Figure 1

Since $\phi'' > 0$, there is a constant $c > 0$ such that

$$\phi(t) \geq c(t-1)^2 \qquad \text{for } 0 < t < 2,$$
$$\phi(t) \geq c(t-1) \qquad \text{for } 2 \leq t < \infty.$$

Now make the substitution $t = 1 + a^{-1/2}s$:

$$\sqrt{a} \int_0^\infty e^{-a\phi(t)}\,dt = \int_{-\sqrt{a}}^\infty e^{-a\phi(1+s/\sqrt{a})}\,ds.$$

If we now let $a \to \infty$, the result will be a consequence of LDCT. First,

$$\lim_{a\to\infty} a\phi\left(1 + \frac{s}{\sqrt{a}}\right) = \frac{1}{2}\phi''(1)s^2 = \frac{1}{2}s^2,$$

as can be seen by using Taylor series, for example. Second, we can estimate as follows: If $-\sqrt{a} < s < \sqrt{a}$, then

$$a\phi\left(1 + \frac{s}{\sqrt{a}}\right) \geq ac\frac{s^2}{a} = cs^2 \geq c|s| - c;$$

if $\sqrt{a} \leq s$, then

$$a\phi\left(1 + \frac{s}{\sqrt{a}}\right) \geq ac\frac{s}{\sqrt{a}} = c\sqrt{a}s \geq cs > c|s| - c,$$

assuming $a \geq 1$. Thus,

$$e^{-a\phi\left(1+s/\sqrt{a}\right)} \leq e^{-c|s|+c},$$

and the right side belongs to $L^1(\mathbb{R})$. Therefore, LDCT implies

$$\lim_{a\to\infty} \int_{-\sqrt{a}}^\infty e^{-a\phi(1+s/\sqrt{a})}\,ds = \int_{-\infty}^\infty e^{-s^2/2}\,ds$$

$$= \sqrt{2} \int_{-\infty}^\infty e^{-r^2}\,dr$$

$$= \sqrt{2\pi}.$$

Thus, Stirling's formula is proved.

Problem 24. Prove that for any fixed $b \in \mathbb{R}$

$$\Gamma(a+b) \sim \sqrt{2\pi} a^{a+b-1/2} e^{-a} \quad \text{as} \quad a \to \infty.$$

Problem 25. Evaluate the constant c which appears in the conclusion of Problem 21, by letting $a \to \infty$. Thus prove that

$$\Gamma(na) = (2\pi)^{(1-n)/2} n^{na-1/2} \Gamma(a) \Gamma\left(a + \frac{1}{n}\right) \ldots \Gamma\left(a + \frac{n-1}{n}\right).$$

Problem 26. Use Stirling's formula to give another proof of Wallis' formula (which is stated in Problem 14).

Problem 27. In this problem you will derive a quantitative version of Stirling's formula, namely,

$$\sqrt{2\pi} a^{a+1/2} e^{-a} < \Gamma(a+1) < \sqrt{2\pi} a^{a+1/2} e^{-a+1/12a}.$$

(a) Let

$$f(a) = \frac{\Gamma(a+1)}{\sqrt{2\pi} a^{a+1/2} e^{-a}},$$

and show that

$$\log f(a) = \log f(a+1) + \left(a + \frac{1}{2}\right) \log\left(1 + \frac{1}{a}\right) - 1.$$

(b) Let $g(a) = \left(a + \frac{1}{2}\right) \log\left(1 + \frac{1}{a}\right) - 1$. Use (a) to prove that

$$\log f(a) = \sum_{k=0}^{\infty} g(a+k).$$

(c) Show that

$$g(a) = \frac{1}{2b} \log \frac{1+b}{1-b} - 1,$$

where $b = \frac{1}{2a+1}$.

(d) Write the Taylor expansion for $g(a)$ in powers of b in the form

$$g(a) = \frac{b^2}{3} + \frac{b^4}{5} + \frac{b^6}{7} + \cdots .$$

Conclude that

$$0 < g(a) < \frac{1}{12a(a+1)}.$$

(e) Use (b) to prove the required inequalities.

F. The Gamma Function on $\mathbb{R}$

The integral we used in the definition of $\Gamma(a)$ makes sense (for real a) only if $a > 0$. But it is easy to extend the definition of Γ to all of $\mathbb{R}$ by using the relation

$$\Gamma(a+1) = a\Gamma(a)$$

as a means of definition. Thus, for example, if $-1 < a < 0$, *define*

$$\Gamma(a) = \frac{\Gamma(a+1)}{a}.$$

Then $\Gamma(a)$ can be defined by the same relation for $-2 < a < -1$. Proceeding by induction, $\Gamma(a)$ becomes a function defined on all of $\mathbb{R}$ except for the nonpositive integers. A slightly different way of expressing this is to say that we define

$$\Gamma(a) = \frac{\Gamma(a+k+1)}{a(a+1)\ldots(a+k)}$$

if k is sufficiently large that $a + k + 1 > 0$.

Problem 28. Prove that Γ is well defined on $\mathbb{R} \sim \{\text{nonpositive integers}\}$, such that $\Gamma(a+1) = a\Gamma(a)$ for all such a, and that for any integer $m \geq 0$

$$\lim_{a \to -m} (a+m)\Gamma(a) = \frac{(-1)^m}{m!}.$$

Problem 29. Prove that if the function $1/\Gamma(a)$ is defined to have the value 0 whenever a is a nonpositive integer, then $1/\Gamma(a)$ is an infinitely differentiable function of $a \in \mathbb{R}$.

Therefore, we might think that $1/\Gamma(a)$ is somehow a more natural function to consider than $\Gamma(a)$. It is indeed not difficult to show that Problem 13 and Problem 18 can be extended to yield formulas

$$\frac{1}{\Gamma(a)} = \lim_{n\to\infty} \frac{a(a+1)\dots(a+n)}{n^a n!}$$

and

$$\frac{1}{\Gamma(a)} = ae^{\gamma a} \prod_{k=1}^{\infty} \left(1 + \frac{a}{k}\right) e^{-a/k},$$

respectively, which are valid for real a. (Not only this, but both of these formulas have right hand sides which exist for all *complex* numbers a. In this way, $1/\Gamma(a)$ is well defined for all $a \in \mathbb{C}$.)

Problem 30. Prove that the duplication formula

$$\Gamma(2a)\sqrt{\pi} = 2^{2a-1}\Gamma(a)\Gamma\left(a + \frac{1}{2}\right)$$

is valid for all $a \in \mathbb{R}$ (excluding a such that $2a$ is a nonpositive integer).

Now we shall obtain a beautiful formula connecting Γ and the sine function. The derivation of this formula is taken from the interesting book of Emil Artin, *The Gamma Function*, Holt, Rinehart, and Winston, 1964.

Problem 31. Define

$$\phi(a) = \Gamma(a)\Gamma(1-a)\sin\pi a.$$

Prove that ϕ can be regarded as an infinitely differentiable function on all of $\mathbb{R}$, that $\phi(a+1) = \phi(a)$ for all a, that $\phi(0) = \pi$, and that $\phi(a) > 0$ for all a.

Problem 32. Prove that

$$\phi(2a)\pi = \phi(a)\phi\left(a + \frac{1}{2}\right).$$

Problem 33. Prove that for all $a \in \mathbb{R}$

$$\Gamma(a)\Gamma(1 - a) = \frac{\pi}{\sin \pi a}.$$

(HINT: You have to prove the above function ϕ is constant. Use Problems 31 and 32 to show that if ψ is the second derivative of $\log \phi$, then $4\psi(2a) = \psi(a) + \psi(a + \frac{1}{2})$. If C is the maximum value of $|\psi|$, why does this imply $C = 0$? Knowing $C = 0$, derive the conclusion that $\log \phi$ is constant.)

Problem 34. Combine Problems 13 and 33 to show that

$$\sin \pi a = \pi a \prod_{n=1}^{\infty} \left(1 - \frac{a^2}{n^2} \right).$$

Problem 35. Combine Problems 25 and 33 to show that

$$\sin nx = 2^{n-1} \prod_{k=0}^{n-1} \sin \left(x + \frac{k\pi}{n} \right).$$

Problem 36. Show that

$$\prod_{k=1}^{n-1} \sin \frac{k\pi}{n} = n/2^{n-1}.$$

Problem 37. Use Problem 34 to show that

$$\cos \pi a = \prod_{n=0}^{\infty} \left(1 - \frac{a^2}{(n + \frac{1}{2})^2} \right).$$

(HINT: $\sin 2\pi a = 2 \sin \pi a \cos \pi a$.)

Problem 38. Prove that for $0 < a < 1$

$$\int_0^1 \left(\frac{t}{1 - t} \right)^a \frac{dt}{t} = \frac{\pi}{\sin \pi a}.$$

Problem 39. Prove that for $0 < a < 1$

$$\int_0^\infty \frac{1}{(1+x)x^a}\,dx = \frac{\pi}{\sin \pi a}.$$

Problem 40. Prove that for $-1 < a < 1$

$$\int_0^{\pi/2} \tan^a \theta\, d\theta = \frac{\pi}{2} \sec \frac{\pi a}{2}.$$

L^p Spaces

This chapter will once again treat general measure spaces, as discussed in Chapter 6, Sections E, F, G. The reason is simply that the results are quite general and are no easier to prove in the special case of Lebesgue measure on $\mathbb{R}^n$.

A. Definition and Basic Inequalities

Let X, $\mathcal{M}$, μ be a measure space and let $1 \le p < \infty$ (in Section D we shall consider the correct definition for the case $p = \infty$).

Definition: Let $f : X \to [-\infty, \infty]$ be $\mathcal{M}$-measurable. It follows that $|f|^p$ is also measurable, so its integral over X exists. Then we say that $f \in L^p$ or, more precisely, $f \in L^p(X, \mathcal{M}, \mu)$ if

$$\int_X |f|^p d\mu < \infty.$$

As we carefully discussed in Section 6.C, we are really thinking of f as the equivalence class of all functions which are equal to f almost everywhere. Thus, L^p actually consists of equivalence classes of functions rather than functions. As usual, we shall hardly ever mention the distinction.

If $f \in L^p$, the *norm* of f is the number

$$\|f\|_p = \left(\int_X |f|^p d\mu \right)^{1/p}.$$

In case $p = 1$, we have already discussed the space L^1 and have used the norm in Sections C and D of Chapter 7. As in that case, we see immediately that the first three of the following properties are valid:

(a) $0 \le \|f\|_p < \infty$.

(b) $\|f\|_p = 0 \iff f = 0$ (μ-a.e.).

(c) $\|cf\|_p = |c| \, \|f\|_p$ if $c \in \mathbb{R}$.

(d) $\|f + g\|_p \leq \|f\|_p + \|g\|_p$.

The last of these is not trivial if $p \neq 1$, and even bears a name, Minkowski's inequality. We shall prove it later in this section.

Complex-Valued Functions

It will be very important later to be able to integrate complex-valued functions. This is basically due to the fact that the Fourier transform is most natural in the context of complex exponentials: It will prove simpler to use $e^{i\theta}$ rather than $\cos\theta$ and $\sin\theta$. We shall denote by $\mathbb{C}$ the complex number field and shall use the standard notations: If $z = x + iy$, where $x,\, y \in \mathbb{R}$, then $\mathrm{Re}\, z = x$, $\mathrm{Im}\, z = y$, modulus of $z = |z| = (x^2 + y^2)^{1/2}$. We shall treat functions $f : X \to \mathbb{C}$ (actually, we require only that f be defined μ-a.e.). Such a function is said to be $\mathcal{M}$-measurable if and only if $\mathrm{Re}\, f$ and $\mathrm{Im}\, f$ are $\mathcal{M}$-measurable. If f is $\mathcal{M}$-measurable, we say that $f \in L^1$ if and only if $\mathrm{Re}\, f$ and $\mathrm{Im}\, f$ are integrable, and we define the integral

$$\int_X f d\mu = \int_X \mathrm{Re}\, f d\mu + i \int_X \mathrm{Im}\, f d\mu.$$

This integral satisfies the usual linearity properties, and we shall use these without further mention. It also satisfies the important inequality

$$\left| \int_X f d\mu \right| \leq \int_X |f| d\mu.$$

The proof is easy if approached in the right way: Choose the argument $\theta \in \mathbb{R}$:

$$\int_X f d\mu = \left| \int_X f d\mu \right| e^{i\theta}.$$

Then

$$\left| \int_X f d\mu \right| = e^{-i\theta} \int_X f d\mu$$

$$= \int_X e^{-i\theta} f d\mu$$

$$= \mathrm{Re} \int_X e^{-i\theta} f d\mu \quad \text{(since the preceding integral is } \textit{real}\text{)}$$

$$= \int_X \mathrm{Re}(e^{-i\theta} f) d\mu \quad \text{(definition of the integral)}$$

$$\leq \int_X | e^{-i\theta} f | d\mu$$

$$= \int_X | f | d\mu.$$

In this connection, notice also that if $f : X \to \mathbb{C}$ is $\mathcal{M}$-measurable, then $f \in L^1 \iff |f| \in L^1$. We also shall usually consider L^p to consist of complex-valued functions. The definition and the norm are given in the same way and the properties will be the same. Note that property (c) now should read that $\|cf\|_p = |c| \, \|f\|_p$ for all $c \in \mathbb{C}$. Unless explicit mention of the contrary is given, all functions are allowed to be complex-valued from this moment on.

Definition: If $1 < p < \infty$, the *Hölder conjugate* of p is the number p' which satisfies

$$\frac{1}{p} + \frac{1}{p'} = 1.$$

If $p = 1$, then we define $p' = \infty$. If $p = \infty$, then $p' = 1$. Note that the symmetry of this relationship shows that $(p')' = p$. Also note that

$$p' = \frac{p}{p-1}.$$

Problem 1. If $1 < p < \infty$ and $a \geq 0$, $b \geq 0$, prove that

$$ab \leq \frac{a^p}{p} + \frac{b^{p'}}{p'},$$

with equality if and only if $a^p = b^{p'}$.

(**HINT:** This follows from elementary calculus: Let b be fixed and maximize the function $ab - \dfrac{a^p}{p}$. This shows *where* the number p' comes from.)

Hölder's Inequality: *Let* $1 < p < \infty$ *and assume* $f \in L^p$ *and* $g \in L^{p'}$. *Then* $fg \in L^1$ *and*

$$\left| \int_X fg d\mu \right| \leq \|f\|_p \|g\|_{p'}.$$

Proof: If $f = 0$ or $g = 0$, the result is trivial. We can therefore assume $\|f\|_p > 0$ and $\|g\|_{p'} > 0$. In fact, by multiplying f and g by suitable constants, we see there is no loss of generality in assuming $\|f\|_p = \|g\|_{p'} = 1$. By Problem 1,

$$| f(x)g(x) | \leq \frac{1}{p} | f(x) |^p + \frac{1}{p'} | g(x) |^{p'} .$$

Integrate this inequality:

$$\int_X | f(x)g(x) | \, d\mu \leq \frac{1}{p}\|f\|_p^p + \frac{1}{p'}\|g\|_{p'}^{p'}$$

$$= \frac{1}{p} + \frac{1}{p'}$$

$$= 1.$$

QED

Problem 2. Assume $1 < p_k < \infty$ for $k = 1, \ldots, N$, and $\displaystyle\sum_{k=1}^{N} 1/p_k = 1$.

Prove that

$$\left| \int_X f_1 f_2 \ldots f_N d\mu \right| \leq \|f_1\|_{p_1} \|f_2\|_{p_2} \ldots \|f_N\|_{p_N}.$$

Problem 3. Assume in Hölder's inequality $f \geq 0$, $g \geq 0$, and

$$\int_X fg d\mu = \|f\|_p \|g\|_{p'}.$$

Prove that $f(x)^p = g(x)^{p'}$ μ-a.e., to within a multiplicative constant.

Problem 4. This gives the "reverse" of Hölder's inequality. For a given $f \in L^p$, Hölder's inequality states that for all $g \in L^{p'}$ such that $\|g\|_{p'} = 1$,

$$\left| \int_X fg d\mu \right| \leq \|f\|_p.$$

Prove that there exists $g \in L^{p'}$ such that $\|g\|_{p'} = 1$ and

$$\int_X fg d\mu = \|f\|_p.$$

Problem 5. If $0 < a < \infty$, prove that $\| |f|^a \|_p = \|f\|_{ap}^a$.

We are now prepared to settle the *triangle inequality* for the L^p norm, Property (d).

Minkowski's Inequality: Assume $1 \leq p < \infty$ and assume f, $g \in L^p$. Then $f + g \in L^p$ and

$$\|f + g\|_p \leq \|f\|_p + \|g\|_p.$$

Proof: We first must prove the qualitative statement that $f + g \in L^p$.

By the trivial inequalities,

$$|f + g|^p \leq (|f| + |g|)^p$$
$$\leq (2 \max (|f|, |g|))^p$$
$$= 2^p \max (|f|^p, |g|^p)$$
$$\leq 2^p (|f|^p + |g|^p),$$

we see that $|f + g|^p$ is dominated by an integrable function, and is thus integrable. Thus, $f + g \in L^p$. (By the way, we may assume that $1 < p < \infty$ since the result is known if $p = 1$.) Now we establish the inequality. If $\|f + g\|_p = 0$, there is nothing to prove. Otherwise, we normalize to make $\|f + g\|_p = 1$. Then we apply Hölder's inequality:

$$1 = \int |f + g|^p \, d\mu$$

$$= \int |f + g| \, |f + g|^{p-1} \, d\mu$$

$$\leq \int |f| \, |f + g|^{p-1} \, d\mu + \int |g| \, |f + g|^{p-1} \, d\mu$$

$$\leq \|f\|_p \, \| \, |f + g|^{p-1} \, \|_{p'} + \|g\|_p \, \| \, |f + g|^{p-1} \, \|_{p'}$$

$$= \|f\|_p + \|g\|_p.$$

The last equality follows because Problem 5 shows that

$$\| \, |f + g|^{p-1} \, \|_{p'} = \|f + g\|_{(p-1)p'}^{p-1}$$
$$= \|f + g\|_p^{p-1}$$
$$= 1.$$

QED

Problem 6. Suppose $p, q, r \in [1, \infty)$ and $\frac{1}{r} = \frac{1}{p} + \frac{1}{q}$. Prove that

$$\|fg\|_r \leq \|f\|_p \, \|g\|_q.$$

Problem 7. Suppose $1 \leq p < r < q < \infty$. Prove that $L^p \cap L^q \subset L^r$.

Before stating the main theorem of this chapter, we need some abstract concepts.

B. Metric Spaces and Normed Spaces

Definition: A *metric space* is a set M together with a "distance function" or "metric" d which satisfies for all f, g, $h \in M$

(a) $0 \leq d(f, g) < \infty$.

(b) $d(f, f) = 0$.

(c) $d(f, g) > 0$ if $f \neq g$.

(d) $d(f, g) = d(g, f)$.

(e) $d(f, g) \leq d(f, h) + d(h, g)$ *(triangle inequality)*.

A given metric space admits discussions of a topological nature. These discussions are based on the properties of balls. An open ball, by definition, is a set of the form $\{g \in M | d(f, g) < r\}$ for any $f \in M$ and any $r \in (0, \infty)$. In particular, a sequence f_1, f_2, $\ldots$ in M is said to *converge* to $f \in M$ if

$$\lim_{k \to \infty} d(f_k, f) = 0.$$

We then write $f_k \to f$ or $\lim_{k \to \infty} f_k = f$.

For our purposes, we will be more interested in another property of a sequence, which is not exactly a topological property but which actually depends on the metric d itself. Namely, a sequence f_1, $f_2 \ldots$ is said to be a *Cauchy sequence* if for every $\epsilon > 0$ there exists a positive integer $N(\epsilon)$ such that

$$d(f_j, f_k) \leq \epsilon \qquad \text{if} \quad j, \, k \geq N(\epsilon).$$

Note that the triangle inequality immediately implies that if a sequence $\{f_k\}$ converges, then it is necessarily a Cauchy sequence. But the converse of this statement is not true. For an obvious example, let $M = \mathbb{R} \sim \{0\}$ with the metric $d(x, y) = |x - y|$. The sequence $\{k^{-1}\}$ is a Cauchy sequence, but does not converge. Of course, a fundamental property of $\mathbb{R}$ itself is that every Cauchy sequence does converge. (This is the *completeness* axiom which $\mathbb{R}$ satisfies.)

Definition: A metric space is *complete* if every Cauchy sequence converges.

(Do not confuse this notion with that of complete measure spaces.)

Definition: A *normed space* is a vector space V together with a function $\| \; \|$ defined on it, called a *norm*, satisfying for all $f, g \in V$:

(a) $0 \leq \|f\| < \infty$.

(b) $\|f\| = 0 \iff f = 0$.

(c) $\|cf\| = |c|\,\|f\|$ for c any scalar (*homogeneity*).

(d) $\|f + g\| \leq \|f\| + \|g\|$ (*triangle inequality*).

Note that any normed space becomes a metric space by a natural definition of a metric:
$$d(f, g) = \|f - g\|.$$

Problem 8. Prove that $\big|\, \|f\| - \|g\| \,\big| \leq \|f - g\|$.

Definition: Let V be a normed space. Then V is a metric space under the above definition of the metric d. If this metric space is complete, then V is a *Banach space*.

Example 1: $\mathbb{R}^n$ is a Banach space if we use the Euclidean norm
$$\|x\| = |x| = \sqrt{x_1^2 + \cdots + x_n^2}.$$

Example 2: $\mathbb{R}^n$ is also a Banach space if we use the norm
$$\|x\| = |x_1| + \cdots + |x_n|;$$

also if we use the norm
$$\|x\| = \max\{|x_k| \mid k = 1, \ldots, n\}.$$

Example 3:   Given any metric space M (or really any topological space M) let
$$C_b(M) = \{f \mid f : M \to \mathbb{R} \text{ is continuous and bounded}\};$$
$$\|f\| = \sup_{t \in M} |f(t)|.$$

Then $C_b(M)$ is a Banach space.

Proof: Suppose $\{f_k\}$ is a Cauchy sequence. Then for any $\epsilon > 0$ we have
$$\|f_j - f_k\| \leq \epsilon \qquad \text{if } j, k \geq N(\epsilon).$$

Thus,
$$| f_j(t) - f_k(t) | \le \epsilon \quad \text{if} \quad j, \, k \ge N(\epsilon) \quad \text{and} \quad t \in M.$$

Since $\mathbb{R}$ is complete and for each t the sequence $\{f_k(t)\}$ is a Cauchy sequence in $\mathbb{R}$, there exists $f(t) \in \mathbb{R}$ such that $\lim\limits_{k \to \infty} f_k(t) = f(t)$. Therefore, if we let $k \to \infty$ in the previous inequality,

$$| f_j(t) - f(t) | \le \epsilon \quad \text{if} \quad j \ge N(\epsilon) \quad \text{and} \quad t \in M.$$

Now we can prove $f \in C_b(M)$. Evidently f is a bounded function, so we need only prove its continuity. Let $t_0 \in M$ and $\epsilon > 0$. Choose $j = N(\epsilon/3)$, so that

$$| f_j(t) - f(t) | \le \frac{\epsilon}{3} \qquad \text{for all} \ \ t \in M.$$

Since f_j is continuous, there exists an open set G containing t_0 such that

$$| f_j(t) - f_j(t_0) | \le \frac{\epsilon}{3} \qquad \text{for all} \ \ t \in G.$$

Therefore, for all $t \in G$ it follows that

$$| f(t) - f(t_0) | \le | f(t) - f_j(t) | + | f_j(t) - f_j(t_0) | + | f_j(t_0) - f(t_0) |$$
$$\le \frac{\epsilon}{3} + \frac{\epsilon}{3} + \frac{\epsilon}{3} = \epsilon.$$

Thus, we see that f is continuous at t_0. Finally, we have

$$\|f_j - f\| \le \epsilon \qquad \text{if} \ \ j \ge N(\epsilon),$$

and we have proved that the sequence $\{f_k\}$ converges to f.   **QED**

Example 4:   On $\mathbb{R}^n$ the space of continuous functions $f : \mathbb{R}^n \to \mathbb{R}$ satisfying
$$\lim_{|x| \to \infty} f(x) = 0$$

is denoted $C_0(\mathbb{R}^n)$. Let $\|f\| = \sup\{|f(x)| \mid x \in \mathbb{R}^n\}$. Then C_0 is a Banach space. Note that $C_0 \subset C_b$. In order to prove that C_0 is complete, we start with a Cauchy sequence $\{f_k\}$ in C_0. We realize from Example 3 that there is a limit $f \in C_b$. Therefore, we need only show that C_0 is a *closed* subset of C_b: i.e., if $f_k \in C_0$ and $f \in C_b$ and $\|f_k - f\| \to 0$, then $f \in C_0$. To prove this, let $\epsilon > 0$. Then there exists $k \in \mathbb{N}$ such that

$\|f_k - f\| \le \epsilon/2$. Since $f_k \in C_0$, there exists $r > 0$ such that $|f_k(x)| \le \epsilon/2$ if $|x| \ge r$. But then if $|x| \ge r$,

$$|f(x)| \le |f_k(x)| + \|f_k - f\|$$
$$\le \frac{\epsilon}{2} + \frac{\epsilon}{2} = \epsilon.$$

Thus, $f \in C_0$.

Example 5: Add to the above example the space C_c (as discussed in Section 7.C) of continuous functions on $\mathbb{R}^n$ which vanish outside some bounded subset of $\mathbb{R}^n$. Then $C_c \subset C_0 \subset C_b$. But C_c is *not* a Banach space. In fact, it is not difficult to prove that C_c is dense in C_0.

Example 6: Similarly, $C_c \subset L^1$, and we can define a norm on C_c by the equation

$$\|f\| = \|f\|_1.$$

Then C_c is a normed space, but not a Banach space. In fact, C_c is dense in L^1, as we know from Section 7.C.

Example 7: We know that $L^p(X, M, \mu)$ is a normed space. The only difficult matter is the triangle inequality, and Minkowski's inequality takes care of that. We do not yet know this is a Banach space. In fact, the major theorem of this chapter asserts exactly that. To prepare for the proof we need a couple of lemmas.

Lemma: *Given a metric space M, suppose $\{f_k\}$ is a Cauchy sequence which has a subsequence which converges. Then the sequence $\{f_k\}$ converges.*

Proof: Suppose the subsequence $\{f_{n_k}\}$ converges to f. Thus, there exist $N_1(\epsilon)$ and $N_2(\epsilon)$ such that

$$d(f_j, f_k) \le \epsilon \qquad \text{if } j, \, k \ge N_1(\epsilon);$$
$$d(f_{n_k}, f) \le \epsilon \qquad \text{if } k \ge N_2(\epsilon).$$

Choose k such that

$$n_k \ge N_1(\epsilon) \quad \text{and} \quad k \ge N_2(\epsilon).$$

Then if $j \ge N_1(\epsilon)$,

$$d(f_j, f) \le d(f_j, f_{n_k}) + d(f_{n_k}, f)$$
$$\le \epsilon + \epsilon = 2\epsilon,$$

proving that $\lim_{j \to \infty} d(f_j, f) = 0$.

QED

Lemma: *Suppose $\{f_k\}$ is a Cauchy sequence. Then there exists a subsequence $\{f_{n_k}\}$ such that*

$$d\left(f_{n_{k+1}}, f_{n_k}\right) \leq 2^{-k}.$$

Proof: For any $\epsilon > 0$ there exists $N(\epsilon)$ such that $d(f_j, f_k) \leq \epsilon$ if $j, k \geq N(\epsilon)$. Choose the sequence $\{n_k\}$ in the following manner:

$$n_1 \geq N(2^{-1});$$
$$n_k \geq N(2^{-k}) \quad \text{and} \quad n_k > n_{k-1} \quad \text{for} \quad k = 2, 3, \ldots .$$

Then since $n_{k+1} > n_k \geq N(2^{-k})$, it follows that $d(f_{n_{k+1}}, f_{n_k}) \leq 2^{-k}$.

$$\textbf{QED}$$

C. Completeness of L^p

Now we come to a famous theorem which not only is extremely important in integration theory, but is of great historical interest as well. The theorem was discovered independently by F. Riesz and E. Fischer, primarily because of investigations in the theory of Fourier series. But the crux of their results was the proof of the completeness of L^2.

First we establish a lemma.

Lemma: *Assume f_1, f_2, f_3, ... are in L^p and each $f_k \geq 0$. Then*

$$\left\| \sum_{k=1}^{\infty} f_k \right\|_p \leq \sum_{k=1}^{\infty} \|f_k\|_p.$$

Proof: This result looks like Minkowski's inequality for a countable sum rather than a finite sum. To prove it let $F_N = \sum_{k=1}^{N} f_k$. Then Minkowski's inequality implies

$$\|F_N\|_p \leq \sum_{k=1}^{N} \|f_k\|_p \leq \sum_{k=1}^{\infty} \|f_k\|_p.$$

Since F_N^p increases as N increases, LICT implies

$$\Big\| \sum_{k=1}^{\infty} f_k \Big\|_p = \big\| \lim_{N \to \infty} F_N \big\|_p$$

$$= \lim_{N \to \infty} \| F_N \|_p$$

$$\leq \sum_{k=1}^{\infty} \| f_k \|_p .$$

QED

> ***Riesz-Fischer Theorem:*** *For $1 \leq p < \infty$, $L^p(X, M, \mu)$ is a Banach space.*

Proof: Since Minkowski's inequality shows that L^p is a normed space, all we are required to prove is the completeness property. Consider an arbitrary Cauchy sequence in L^p. The first lemma in Section B shows that it will suffice to prove that a subsequence converges; and the second lemma shows how to select a subsequence with a particularly convenient property. Let us name this subsequence $\{f_k\}$. We shall prove that it converges.

We have thus arrived at the following situation: Each $f_k \in L^p$ and

$$\| f_{k+1} - f_k \|_p \leq 2^{-k}, \quad k = 1, 2, \ldots .$$

Now define the function F as follows:

$$F = |f_1| + \sum_{j=1}^{\infty} |f_{j+1} - f_j|.$$

Then F is $\mathcal{M}$-measurable, and the lemma preceding this theorem implies that

$$\| F \|_p \leq \| f_1 \|_p + \sum_{j=1}^{\infty} \| f_{j+1} - f_j \|_p$$

$$\leq \| f_1 \|_p + \sum_{j=1}^{\infty} 2^{-j}$$

$$= \| f_1 \|_p + 1 < \infty.$$

Since $\int_X F^p d\mu < \infty$, the finiteness principle on p.145 shows that $F < \infty$ μ-a.e. That is, there exists a μ-null set $N \subset X$ such that $F(x) < \infty$

for all $x \in N^c$. Thus, if $x \in N^c$, we can make the following sequence of assertions:

$$|f_1(x)| + \sum_{j=1}^{\infty} |f_{j+1}(x) - f_j(x)| \quad \text{converges;}$$

$$f_1(x) + \sum_{j=1}^{\infty} [f_{j+1}(x) - f_j(x)] \quad \text{converges (absolutely);}$$

$$\lim_{k \to \infty} \left\{ f_1(x) + \sum_{j=1}^{k-1} [f_{j+1}(x) - f_j(x)] \right\} \quad \text{exists;}$$

$$\lim_{k \to \infty} f_k(x) \quad \text{exists.}$$

Therefore, we are able to define

$$f(x) = \begin{cases} \lim_{k \to \infty} f_k(x) & \text{if } x \in N^c, \\ 0 & \text{if } x \in N. \end{cases}$$

Then f is $\mathcal{M}$-measurable, and for $x \in N^c$ we have the formula

$$f(x) = f_1(x) + \sum_{j=1}^{\infty} [f_{j+1}(x) - f_j(x)].$$

Therefore,

$$f(x) - f_k(x) = \sum_{j=k}^{\infty} [f_{j+1}(x) - f_j(x)] \quad \text{for } x \in N^c.$$

Therefore,

$$|f - f_k| \leq \sum_{j=k}^{\infty} |f_{j+1} - f_j| \qquad \mu\text{-a.e. in } X.$$

Now the lemma of this section once again implies:

$$\|f - f_k\|_p \leq \sum_{j=k}^{\infty} \|f_{j+1} - f_j\|_p$$

$$\leq \sum_{j=k}^{\infty} 2^{-j}$$

$$= 2^{1-k}.$$

We therefore conclude first that $f \in L^p$ (since $f - f_k \in L^p$) and second that $\lim\limits_{k \to \infty} \|f - f_k\|_p = 0$.   **QED**

Not only is the Riesz-Fischer theorem of great importance, but also the proof is useful. In fact, it is often necessary to use a particular portion of the proof, which we now state.

Corollary (of the proof): If a sequence $f_k \to f$ in $L^p(X, M, \mu)$ then there exists a subsequence $\{f_{n_k}\}$ such that

$$\lim_{k \to \infty} f_{n_k}(x) = f(x) \qquad \text{for } \mu\text{-a.e. } x \in X.$$

Proof: We have shown that a subsequence $\{f_{n_k}\}$ can be found with the property that it converges to a function, say g, in *two* senses: $f_{n_k} \to g$ in L^p and also $f_{n_k} \to g$ μ-a.e. But since f_{n_k} also converges to f in L^p, we conclude that $f = g$ (μ-a.e.).   **QED**

Examples: It is tempting to read more into convergence in L^p than is true. Therefore, we want to list some easy examples which you should keep in mind. All these examples will be for the measure space $\mathbb{R}$, $\mathcal{L}$, λ.

1. *A sequence in L^p can converge a.e. without converging in L^p.*

   This has already been indicated in Problem 6.5. For instance, let $f_k = k^2 \chi_{(0,k^{-1})}$. Then $f_k \in L^p$ for every p and $f_k \to 0$ everywhere on $\mathbb{R}$. But for all p

$$\|f_k\|_p = k^{2 - p^{-1}} \geq k \to \infty.$$

2. *A sequence can converge in L^p without converging a.e.*

   For simplicity replace the measure space by the Lebesgue measure space on the interval $[0, 1]$. Here is an example. The sequence will be $f_1;\ f_2, f_3;\ f_4, f_5, f_6, f_7;$ etc., where

$$f_{2^k + j} = k \chi_{[j/2^k, (j+1)/2^k]}, \qquad j = 0, 1, \ldots, 2^k - 1.$$

   Then for all $p \in [1, \infty)$,

$$\|f_{2^k + j}\|_p = k 2^{-k/p} \to 0$$

as $k \to \infty$. Thus, this sequence converges to 0 in every L^p space, $1 \le p < \infty$. But for *all* $x \in [0,1]$ the sequence $f_m(x)$ fails to converge. In fact, for all $x \in [0,1]$ we have

$$\limsup_{m \to \infty} f_m(x) = \infty,$$

$$\liminf_{m \to \infty} f_m(x) = 0.$$

This is an excellent illustration of the corollary. Indeed,

$$\lim_{k \to \infty} f_{2^k+1}(x) = 0 \qquad \text{for all} \ \ x \in [0,1].$$

3. *A sequence can belong to $L^{p_1} \cap L^{p_2}$ and converge in L^{p_1} without converging in L^{p_2}.*

To see this, consider $f_k = k^{-1} \chi_{(k,2k)}$. Then

$$\|f_k\|_p = k^{-1+1/p}.$$

Thus, $f_k \to 0$ in L^p if $1 < p < \infty$, but $\|f_k\|_1 = 1$ does not converge to 0.

Problem 9. Let $1 < p_0 < \infty$. Find an example of a sequence $\{f_k\}$ such that $f_k \in L^p$ for $1 \le p < \infty$, $f_k \to 0$ in L^p for $1 \le p < p_0$, but f_k does not converge in L^{p_0}.

Problem 10. Suppose $\{f_k\}$ is a sequence of $\mathcal{M}$-measurable functions on X. Let p_1 and $p_2 \in [1,\infty)$, and suppose $f_k \in L^{p_1} \cap L^{p_2}$. Also suppose there exist $g \in L^{p_1}$ and $h \in L^{p_2}$ such that $f_k \to g$ in L^{p_1}, $f_k \to h$ in L^{p_2}. Prove that $g = h$ (μ-a.e.).

D.   The Case $p = \infty$

Still we consider an arbitrary measure space X, $\mathcal{M}$, μ. We now want to define L^∞. This will differ substantially from L^p for $p < \infty$, as integration is *not* involved in the definition of L^∞. The only role played by the measure μ is the definition of the almost everywhere concept. The class L^∞ is going to consist of the bounded measurable functions. Actually, that is not quite true, as we still want to neglect the behavior of a function on a μ-null set. This consideration causes our definition to be a little complicated.

Definition: Let f be an $\mathcal{M}$-measurable function on X (it can be defined only μ-a.e., and it is allowed to be either real- or complex-valued). Then f is *essentially bounded* if there exists a number M such that $0 \le M < \infty$ and

$$|f(x)| \le M \qquad \text{for} \quad \mu\text{-a.e.} \quad x \in X.$$

Definition: $L^\infty(X, \mathcal{M}, \mu)$ or L^∞ is the collection of all essentially bounded $\mathcal{M}$-measurable functions on X. Moreover, the *norm* of a function $f \in L^\infty$ is the number

$$\|f\|_\infty = \inf\{M \mid |f(x)| \le M \qquad \text{for} \quad \mu\text{-a.e.} \quad x \in X\}.$$

Although we have taken care to define $\|f\|_\infty$ as a greatest lower bound, the next result shows that $\|f\|_\infty$ is actually the minimum M.

Proposition: *If $f \in L^\infty$, then $|f(x)| \le \|f\|_\infty$ for μ-a.e. $x \in X$.*

Proof: By the definition of inf, there exists a sequence M_k such that $|f(x)| \le M_k$ for μ-a.e. x and $M_k \to \|f\|_\infty$. That is, there exist μ-null sets $N_k \subset X$ such that $|f(x)| \le M_k$ for $x \in N_k^c$. Define $N = \bigcup_{k=1}^\infty N_k$. Then N is also a μ-null set, and if $x \in N^c$ then $|f(x)| \le M_k$ for all k. Thus, $x \in N^c$ implies $|f(x)| \le \|f\|_\infty$.   **QED**

We repeat: If $f \in L^\infty$, then there exists a smallest number M such that $|f(x)| \le M$ for μ-a.e. x. This smallest number is called $\|f\|_\infty$.

Problem 11. Prove that $\|f\|_\infty$ is the smallest of all numbers of the form $\sup\{|g(x)| \mid x \in X\}$, where $f = g$ μ-a.e.

We now observe very easily that L^∞ together with the norm $\| \ \|_\infty$ satisfies all the requirements to be a normed space. Note that the triangle inequality is trivial in this case: Since $|f(x)| \le \|f\|_\infty$ μ-a.e. and $|g(x)| \le \|g\|_\infty$ μ-a.e., then $|f(x)+g(x)| \le \|f\|_\infty + \|g\|_\infty$ μ-a.e. Therefore, $\|f + g\|_\infty \le \|f\|_\infty + \|g\|_\infty$.

Problem 12. Let f be a *continuous* function on the measure space $\mathbb{R}^n$, $\mathcal{L}$, λ. Prove that $\|f\|_\infty = \sup\{|f(x)| \mid x \in \mathbb{R}^n\}$.

Proposition: *L^∞ is a Banach space.*

Proof: This is not labeled "Riesz-Fischer theorem" because it is elementary, unlike the completeness of L^p for $p < \infty$. Suppose that $\{f_k\}$ is a Cauchy sequence in L^∞. Then for any $m \in \mathbb{N}$ there exists a positive integer $J(m)$ such that $\|f_j - f_k\|_\infty \le m^{-1}$ if $j,\, k \ge J(m)$. Thus, there exists a μ-null set $N_{j,k,m}$ such that

$$|f_j(x) - f_k(x)| \le m^{-1} \quad \text{if} \quad j, k \ge J(m) \quad \text{and} \quad x \in N^c_{j,k,m}.$$

This follows from the preceding proposition. Now let N be the union of all the sets $N_{j,k,m}$ for $m \in \mathbb{N}$ and $j,\, k \ge J(m)$. Then N is also a μ-null set. And if $x \in N^c$, then

$$|f_j(x) - f_k(x)| \le m^{-1} \qquad \text{if} \quad j, k \ge J(m).$$

Thus, $x \in N^c$ implies that the sequence $\{f_k(x)\}$ is a Cauchy sequence of numbers. As $\mathbb{R}$ (or $\mathbb{C}$) is complete, there exists

$$f(x) = \lim_{k \to \infty} f_k(x) \qquad \text{if} \ x \in N^c.$$

Then f is $\mathcal{M}$-measurable, and letting $k \to \infty$ in the preceding inequality yields for all $x \in N^c$

$$|f_j(x) - f(x)| \le m^{-1} \qquad \text{if} \ j \ge J(m).$$

This inequality implies that $f_j - f$ is essentially bounded, and thus that $f \in L^\infty$. Moreover, it implies $\|f_j - f\|_\infty \le m^{-1}$ if $j \ge J(m)$. Thus, $f_j \to f$ in L^∞, and this proves L^∞ is complete.   **QED**

Remark: We can now go back through the chapter and remove the restriction $p < \infty$ in various places. For instance, in Hölder's inequality we can now allow $1 \le p \le \infty$. This is because it is trivial that

$$\left| \int_X f g \, d\mu \right| \le \|f\|_1 \, \|g\|_\infty.$$

(No one would bother giving a name to such an inequality.) The same remarks are relevant to Minkowski's inequality. In Problem 6 we need only assume $p,\, q,\, r \in [1, \infty]$ and $\frac{1}{r} = \frac{1}{p} + \frac{1}{q}$, but the result is trivial if any of these indices is ∞. If $q = \infty$ in Problem 7, the following is obtained:

Problem 13. Suppose $1 \le p < r < \infty$. Prove that $L^p \cap L^\infty \subset L^r$. Moreover, show that if $f \in L^p \cap L^\infty$, then

$$\|f\|_r \le \|f\|_p^{p/r} \ \|f\|_\infty^{1-p/r}.$$

E.   Relations between L^p Spaces

First we consider the case of Lebesgue measure on $(0, \infty) \subset \mathbb{R}$. Remember that x^a is integrable on $(0,1) \iff a > -1$, and is integrable on $(1, \infty) \iff a < -1$. Now suppose $1 \le p < q \le \infty$. Choose any number b such that $q^{-1} < b < p^{-1}$. Then $x^{-b}\chi_{(0,1)}$ belongs to L^p but not to L^q, showing that $L^p \not\subset L^q$. On the other hand, $x^{-b}\chi_{(1,\infty)}$ belongs to L^q but not to L^p, so $L^q \not\subset L^p$. We conclude that *in general there is no inclusion relation between two of the L^p spaces.*

Problem 14. Suppose $\mu(X) = \infty$ and there exist sets $A_1, A_2, A_3, \ldots$ in $\mathcal{M}$ such that $\mu(A_k) < \infty$ for every k and $X = \bigcup_{k=1}^\infty A_k$. (Then X is said to be *σ-finite*; cf. p.261.)

(a) Prove that there exist *disjoint* sets $B_1, B_2, B_3, \ldots$ in $\mathcal{M}$ such that
$$1 \le \mu(B_k) < \infty \text{ for every } k \text{ and } X = \bigcup_{k=1}^\infty B_k.$$

(b) Prove that there exists $f \notin L^1(X)$ such that for all $1 < p \le \infty$, $f \in L^p(X)$.

(**HINT:** Take f to be constant on each B_k.)

Problem 15. Give an example of a measure space such that $\mu(X) = \infty$ and $f \in L^p(X)$ for some $1 < p < \infty \implies f \in L^1(X)$.

1.   The Limit of $\|f\|_p$ as $p \to \infty$

Here we derive a result which serves to justify the notation $\|f\|_\infty$. It will be convenient to define $\|f\|_p = \infty$ in case f is $\mathcal{M}$-measurable but $f \notin L^p$.

Theorem: *Assume $f \in L^r$ for some $r < \infty$. Then*

$$\lim_{p \to \infty} \|f\|_p = \|f\|_\infty.$$

Proof: First, suppose $0 \leq t < \|f\|_\infty$. By definition of the L^∞ norm, the set

$$A = \{x \in X \mid |f(x)| \geq t\}$$

is not a μ-null set; that is, $\mu(A) > 0$. Now we note the trivial inequality

$$\|f\|_p \geq \left(\int_A |f|^p d\mu \right)^{1/p}$$
$$\geq (t^p \mu(A))^{1/p}$$
$$= t\mu(A)^{1/p}.$$

If $0 < \mu(A) < \infty$, then $\mu(A)^{1/p} \to 1$ as $p \to \infty$; if $\mu(A) = \infty$, then $\mu(A)^{1/p} = \infty$. In either case,

$$\liminf_{p \to \infty} \|f\|_p \geq t.$$

Since t is arbitrary,

$$\liminf_{p \to \infty} \|f\|_p \geq \|f\|_\infty.$$

Now we prove a reverse inequality, for which we shall require the hypothesis that $f \in L^r$. For $r < p < \infty$, Problem 13 implies

$$\|f\|_p \leq \|f\|_r^{r/p} \|f\|_\infty^{1-r/p}.$$

Since $\|f\|_r < \infty$, this implies

$$\limsup_{p \to \infty} \|f\|_p \leq \|f\|_\infty.$$

Since we have now proved that $\limsup_{p \to \infty} \|f\|_p \leq \|f\|_\infty \leq \liminf_{p \to \infty} \|f\|_p$, the theorem is proved. **QED**

Problem 16. Suppose that $\mu(X) = \infty$. Give an example of $f \in L^\infty$ such that $\|f\|_p = \infty$ for all $p < \infty$. On the other hand, prove that if $\mu(X) < \infty$, then every $\mathcal{M}$-measurable function f satisfies

$$\lim_{p \to \infty} \|f\|_p = \|f\|_\infty.$$

Remark: The "trivial inequality" used in the above proof can be expressed in the form:

$$\mu\left(\{x \in X \mid |f(x)| \geq t\}\right) \leq \left(\frac{\|f\|_p}{t}\right)^p.$$

This is called *Chebyshev's inequality.*

2.   Finite Measure Spaces

In this part we assume $\mu(X) < \infty$. To exclude trivial cases we also assume $\mu(X) > 0$.

Theorem: *If* $1 \leq p < q < \infty$*, then* $L^q \subset L^p$*.*

Proof: Apply Hölder's inequality to the functions $|f|^p$ and 1 to obtain

$$\int |f|^p d\mu = \int |f|^p \cdot 1 \, d\mu$$

$$\leq \left(\int |f|^{pq/p} d\mu\right)^{p/q} \left(\int d\mu\right)^{1-p/q}$$

$$= \left(\int |f|^q d\mu\right)^{p/q} \mu(X)^{1-p/q}.$$

QED

Remark: This inequality can also be expressed in the form

$$\left[\frac{1}{\mu(X)} \int_X |f|^p d\mu\right]^{1/p} \leq \left[\frac{1}{\mu(X)} \int_X |f|^q d\mu\right]^{1/q},$$

which states that the *normalized L^p* norm of the function f is an increasing function of p. In particular, if $\mu(X) = 1$, then we have for $1 \leq p < q \leq \infty$,

$$\|f\|_1 \leq \|f\|_p \leq \|f\|_q \leq \|f\|_\infty.$$

3.   Counting Measure and the l^p Spaces

In this part the measure space will be any set X, the σ-algebra 2^X of all subsets of X, and $\mu =$ counting measure. This is discussed in Chapter 6, Sections E and F, Example 4. Recall that $\mu(A)$ is the number of points in A if A is finite; otherwise, $\mu(A) = \infty$. "Integration" is described in Section 6.F, where we introduced the notation

$$\int_X f\,d\mu = \sum_{x \in X} f(x)$$

for nonnegative functions on X. In this case L^p is usually denoted l^p or $l^p(X)$.

Theorem: *If $1 \leq p < q \leq \infty$, then $l^p \subset l^q$. Moreover,*

$$\|f\|_\infty \leq \|f\|_q \leq \|f\|_p \leq \|f\|_1.$$

Proof: This is extremely easy. If $q = \infty$, we simply note that for any $x_0 \in X$, $|f(x_0)| \leq \left(\sum_{x \in X} |f(x)|^p \right)^{1/p}$. Thus, assume $q < \infty$. Then we have to prove

$$\left(\sum_{x \in X} |f(x)|^q \right)^{1/q} \leq \left(\sum_{x \in X} |f(x)|^p \right)^{1/p}.$$

Multiply by a normalizing constant to make the right side equal to 1. Thus, assuming $\sum |f(x)|^p = 1$, we must prove $\sum |f(x)|^q \leq 1$. But this is trivial: $|f(x)| \leq 1$ for all x, and thus $|f(x)|^q \leq |f(x)|^p$ since $q > p$.

QED

We see therefore that in a certain sense counting measure and a finite measure act in reverse ways for the L^p spaces.

4. Local L^p Spaces

Because there is no general relationship between L^p spaces for different p, there is frequently a need to introduce other spaces related to L^p which do exhibit satisfactory inclusion relations. In this part we restrict attention to the Lebesgue measure space on $\mathbb{R}^n$.

Definition: Let G be an open set in $\mathbb{R}^n$. The *local L^p* space on G consists of all $\mathcal{L}$-measurable functions f defined a.e. on G such that for every compact set $K \subset G$ the function $f\chi_K$ has a finite L^p norm. That is,

$$\int\limits_K |f(x)|^p dx < \infty \qquad \text{if } 1 \le p < \infty;$$

f is essentially bounded on K if $p = \infty$.

The collection of all such functions f is denoted $L^p_{\text{loc}}(G)$.

Because of the results of Part 2 we see immediately that for $1 \le p < q \le \infty$

$$L^\infty_{\text{loc}}(G) \subset L^q_{\text{loc}}(G) \subset L^p_{\text{loc}}(G) \subset L^1_{\text{loc}}(G).$$

5. Convexity Relations

We shall now generalize Problem 13 and at the same time make the result of Problem 7 more precise. We are now back in the case of an arbitrary measure space X, $\mathcal{M}$, μ.

Theorem: *Let $1 \le p < r < q < \infty$ and suppose $f \in L^p \cap L^q$. Then $f \in L^r$ and*

$$\log \|f\|_r \le \frac{\frac{1}{r} - \frac{1}{q}}{\frac{1}{p} - \frac{1}{q}} \log \|f\|_p + \frac{\frac{1}{p} - \frac{1}{r}}{\frac{1}{p} - \frac{1}{q}} \log \|f\|_q.$$

Proof: This looks stranger than it is — the inequality is merely a simple application of Hölder's inequality. What makes the proof work is the fact that since $q^{-1} < r^{-1} < p^{-1}$, there is a unique θ such that

$$\frac{1}{r} = \frac{\theta}{p} + \frac{1 - \theta}{q}.$$

This number satisfies $0 < \theta < 1$ and is given explicitly as

$$\theta = \frac{\frac{1}{r} - \frac{1}{q}}{\frac{1}{p} - \frac{1}{q}}, \quad 1 - \theta = \frac{\frac{1}{p} - \frac{1}{r}}{\frac{1}{p} - \frac{1}{q}}.$$

We must prove $\log \|f\|_r \le \theta \log \|f\|_p + (1 - \theta) \log \|f\|_q$. Note that

$$1 = \frac{r\theta}{p} + \frac{r(1 - \theta)}{q},$$

so that the numbers $p/r\theta$ and $q/r(1 - \theta)$ are Hölder conjugates. Therefore, Hölder's inequality implies (assuming $f \ge 0$, as we may)

$$\begin{aligned}
\|f\|_r &= \|f^\theta f^{1-\theta}\|_r \\
&= \|f^{r\theta} f^{r(1-\theta)}\|_1^{1/r} \\
&\le \left\{ \|f^{r\theta}\|_{p/r\theta} \, \|f^{r(1-\theta)}\|_{q/r(1-\theta)} \right\}^{1/r} \\
&= \left\{ \|f\|_p^{r\theta} \, \|f\|_q^{r(1-\theta)} \right\}^{1/r} \\
&= \|f\|_p^\theta \, \|f\|_q^{1-\theta}.
\end{aligned}$$

QED

The inequality we have just proved is termed a *convexity* relation because a real function $h(t)$ defined for t in an interval of real numbers is said to be *convex* if for all $t_1 < t_2 < t_3$ in the interval

$$h(t_2) \le \frac{t_3 - t_2}{t_3 - t_1} h(t_1) + \frac{t_2 - t_1}{t_3 - t_1} h(t_3).$$

This means precisely that the graph of h lies below any of its chords:

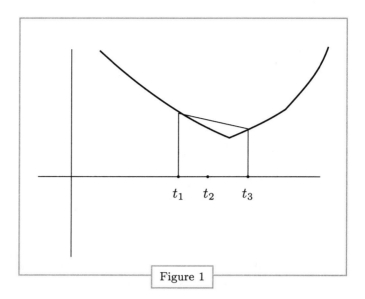

Figure 1

Thus, the theorem asserts the following: Assume f is an $\mathcal{M}$-measurable function on X such that f is not the zero function. Then the set of indices p such that $f \in L^p$ is an *interval* $\subset [1, \infty]$. Furthermore, on this interval $\log \|f\|_p$ is a convex function of $1/p$.

Problem 17. Suppose h is a real function defined on a subinterval of $(0, \infty)$. Prove that $h(t)$ is a convex function of $1/t \iff th(t)$ is a convex function of t. Conclude that $\log \|f\|_p^p$ is a convex function of p.

Problem 18. Let $1 \leq p_0 \leq \infty$. Construct a function $f \in L^{p_0}(\mathbb{R})$ such that for all $p \neq p_0$, $f \notin L^p(\mathbb{R})$.

F. Approximation by $C_c^\infty(\mathbb{R}^n)$

In this section we work with Lebesgue measure on $\mathbb{R}^n$. We are going to establish the analog for L^p of the approximation theorem for L^1 proved in Section 7.C. First note that if $C_c^\infty(\mathbb{R}^n)$ is to be dense in $L^p(\mathbb{R}^n)$, then necessarily $p < \infty$. This is simply because the uniform limit of a sequence of continuous functions must itself be continuous, as was shown in Example 3 of Section B. Thus, if $f_k \in C_c^\infty(\mathbb{R}^n)$ and $\|f_k - f\|_\infty \to 0$, the limit f must be continuous on $\mathbb{R}^n$. (But of course $L^\infty(\mathbb{R}^n)$ contains (plenty of) discontinuous functions.) In fact, Example 4 of Section B shows that the closure of $C_c^\infty(\mathbb{R}^n)$ in $L^\infty(\mathbb{R}^n)$ is contained in $C_0(\mathbb{R}^n)$ (actually, it is easy to see that it is *equal* to $C_0(\mathbb{R}^n)$).

> **Theorem:** *Assume* $1 \le p < \infty$. *Then* $C_c^\infty(\mathbb{R}^n)$ *is dense in* $L^p(\mathbb{R}^n)$.

Proof: There is no need to give a detailed proof, as we need only to make minor modifications in the proof given in Section 7.C for the case $p = 1$. Just as in that proof, we first establish the denseness of C_c. The proof of the corresponding lemma in Section 7.C consisted of five steps. The first four are unchanged, and the fifth is virtually the same. The only difference is that in the present case the final inequality in the proof reads

$$\|g - \chi_A\|_p \le \left(\int_{G \sim K} 1 \, dx \right)^{1/p} = \lambda(G \sim K)^{1/p} < \epsilon^{1/p}.$$

The rest of the proof uses the mollifying technique on functions in C_c, and the proof in the case of general p is virtually identical to that in the case $p = 1$. That is because the proof produces functions in C_c^∞ which approximate the continuous function uniformly and whose supports are contained in a fixed bounded subset of $\mathbb{R}^n$.   **QED**

Just as in the case $p = 1$, we obtain an immediate corollary.

Corollary: *Assume* $1 \le p < \infty$. *Let* τ_y *denote the translation operator:*

$$(\tau_y f)(x) = f(x + y).$$

If $f \in L^p(\mathbb{R}^n)$, *then*

$$\lim_{y \to 0} \|\tau_y f - f\|_p = 0.$$

Proof: The proof is so similar to that used for $p = 1$ at the end of Chapter 7 that it will be omitted.   **QED**

Problem 19. Let $1 \le p < \infty$ and assume $f \in L^p(\mathbb{R}^n)$. Prove that

$$\lim_{|y| \to \infty} \|\tau_y f + f\|_p = 2^{1/p} \|f\|_p.$$

G.   Miscellaneous Problems

Problem 20. Let $1 \le p < \infty$ and assume $f \in L^p(\mathbb{R})$. Prove that

$$\lim_{x \to \infty} \int_x^{x+1} f(t)dt = 0.$$

Problem 21. Assume that f is a measurable function on the interval $[0,1]$ such that $0 < f(x) < \infty$ for $x \in [0,1]$. Prove that

$$\int_0^1 f(x)dx \cdot \int_0^1 \frac{1}{f(x)}dx \ge 1.$$

Problem 22. Suppose that $\{f_k\}$ is a sequence in $L^p(X, \mathcal{M}, \mu)$ such that the limit

$$f(x) = \lim_{k \to \infty} f_k(x)$$

exists for μ-a.e. $x \in X$. Assume $1 \le p < \infty$. Assume that

$$\liminf_{k \to \infty} \|f_k\|_p = a$$

is finite. Prove that $f \in L^p$ and $\|f\|_p \le a$.

Problem 23. Let $1 \le p < \infty$.

(a) Prove that for $a, b \in [0, \infty)$, $(a + b)^p \le 2^{p-1}(a^p + b^p)$.

(b) Assume the hypotheses of Problem 22. In addition assume that

$$\|f\|_p = \lim_{k \to \infty} \|f_k\|_p.$$

Prove that $\lim_{k \to \infty} \|f - f_k\|_p = 0$.

(**HINT:** Apply Problem 6.19 to the situation described by

$$|f - f_k|^p \le 2^{p-1}(|f|^p + |f_k|^p)$$

and see what happens.)

Problem 24. Let $1 \leq p < \infty$. Suppose that $\{f_k\}$ is a sequence in $L^p(X, \mathcal{M}, \mu)$ such that the limit

$$f(x) = \lim_{k \to \infty} f_k(x)$$

exists μ-a.e., and $f \in L^p$. Prove that $f_k \to f$ in L^p $\Longleftrightarrow$

$$\|f\|_p = \lim_{k \to \infty} \|f_k\|_p.$$

Problem 25. Let X, $\mathcal{M}$, μ be a measure space for which $\mu(X) < \infty$. Let $1 < p < \infty$. Suppose $\{f_k\}$ is a sequence in L^p such that

$$\|f_k\|_p \leq a \quad \text{for} \quad k = 1, 2, \dots,$$

$$\lim_{k \to \infty} f_k(x) = f(x) \quad \text{exists for} \quad \mu\text{-a.e.} \ x.$$

Prove that $f_k \to f$ in L^1.

(**HINT:** First show that it is sufficient to handle the case $f = 0$. Use Problem 22 for that. Let M be a large number and let $f_k = g_k + h_k$, where $g_k(x) = f_k(x)$ if $|f_k(x)| \leq M$, $g_k(x) = 0$ if $|f_k(x)| > M$. Show that $\|g_k\|_1 \to 0$. Show that $\|h_k\|_1 \leq a^p M^{1-p}$.)

Problem 26. ("Reverse" of Hölder's inequality again — see Problem 4.) Assume X is σ-finite, as defined in Problem 14. (It is also allowed that $\mu(X) < \infty$.) Assume f is an $\mathcal{M}$-measurable function, $1 \leq p \leq \infty$, and there exists a constant C such that for every $g \in L^{p'}$

$$\left| \int_X fg \, d\mu \right| \leq C\|g\|_{p'},$$

Prove that $f \in L^p$ and $\|f\|_p \leq C$.

(**HINT:** Prove that there exist sets $E_1 \subset E_2 \subset E_3 \subset \cdots$ in $\mathcal{M}$ such that $\mu(E_k) < \infty$ and $X = \bigcup_{k=1}^{\infty} E_k$. Let $a > 0$ and take

$$g(x) = \begin{cases} \overline{f(x)}|f(x)|^{p-2} & \text{if } 0 < |f(x)| < a \text{ and } x \in E_k, \\ 0 & \text{otherwise.} \end{cases}$$

Let $a \to \infty$ and $k \to \infty$. You will also need to show that f is finite almost everywhere. A separate proof is required in case $p = \infty$.)

Problem 27. Give an example of a measure space (which is not σ-finite) and a measurable function $f \notin L^\infty$ such that for every $g \in L^1$

$$\left| \int_X fg \, d\mu \right| \le \|g\|_1.$$

Problem 28. ("Reverse" of Hölder one more time.) Assume X is σ-finite. Assume f is an $\mathcal{M}$-measurable function, $1 \le p \le \infty$, and

$$g \in L^{p'} \Rightarrow fg \in L^1.$$

Prove that $f \in L^p$.

(**HINT:** Assume $f \notin L^p$ and define ν as in Example 7 on p.146 by

$$\nu(A) = \int_A |f|^p \, d\mu.$$

Show that X, $\mathcal{M}$, ν is σ-finite. Apply Problem 14 to obtain $h \in L^{p'}(X, \mathcal{M}, \nu)$ such that $h \notin L^1(X, \mathcal{M}, \nu)$. Let $g = h|f|^{p-1}$. In case $p = \infty$, a separate proof is required.)

Problem 29. Suppose $1 < p < \infty$ and $f, g \in L^p(X, \mathcal{M}, \mu)$. Suppose $\|f\|_p$ and $\|g\|_p$ are nonzero, and

$$\|f + g\|_p = \|f\|_p + \|g\|_p.$$

Prove that

$$\frac{f}{\|f\|_p} = \frac{g}{\|g\|_p} \qquad \mu - \text{a.e.}$$

Problem 30. Suppose X, $\mathcal{M}$, μ is a measure space for which

$$\mu(A) > 0 \Rightarrow \mu(A) \ge 1.$$

Prove that if $1 \le p < q \le \infty$, then $L^p \subset L^q$, and

$$\|f\|_\infty \le \|f\|_q \le \|f\|_p \le \|f\|_1.$$

The next four problems have nothing to do with L^p. However, they concern the integration of complex-valued functions, and that is why they are placed here.

Problem 31. Let $1 < a < \infty$ be a fixed number, and define

$$f(x, \theta) = e^{-e^{ia\theta}x^a} \quad \text{for } 0 \le x < \infty, \theta \in \mathbb{R}.$$

Then define

$$F(\theta) = \int_0^\infty f(x, \theta)dx \quad \text{for } -\frac{\pi}{2a} < \theta < \frac{\pi}{2a}.$$

The following steps are designed to provide a calculation of this interesting integral.

(a) Prove that $F(\theta)$ exists.

(b) Show that $\partial f / \partial \theta = ix \partial f / \partial x$.

(c) Show that $F'(\theta) = -iF(\theta)$.

(d) Conclude that $F(\theta) = \Gamma\left(\frac{1}{a} + 1\right)e^{-i\theta}$.

Problem 32. Integrate by parts in the above expression for $F(\theta)$ to show that for $-\pi/2a < \theta < \pi/2a$

$$F(\theta) = \int_0^\infty \frac{1 - a}{ax^a e^{ia\theta}} \left[f(x, \theta) - 1\right] dx.$$

Conclude that the limit as $\theta \to \frac{\pi}{2a}-$ yields

$$\int_0^\infty \frac{1 - a}{iax^a} \left[e^{-ix^a} - 1\right] dx = \Gamma\left(\frac{1}{a} + 1\right)e^{-i\pi/2a}.$$

Problem 33. Integrate by parts once again in the above expression to conclude that the *improper* integral

$$\int_0^\infty e^{-ix^a}dx = \lim_{b\to\infty} \int_0^b e^{-ix^a}dx$$

$$= \Gamma\left(\frac{1}{a}+1\right)e^{-i\pi/2a}, \quad 1 < a < \infty.$$

(The special case $a = 2$ yields the famous *Fresnel* integrals

$$\int_0^\infty \cos x^2 dx = \sqrt{\frac{\pi}{8}},$$

$$\int_0^\infty \sin x^2 dx = \sqrt{\frac{\pi}{8}}.)$$

Problem 34. Demonstrate the improper integral for $0 < \alpha < \beta$

$$\int_0^\infty x^{\alpha-1}e^{ix^\beta}dx = \frac{1}{\beta}\Gamma\left(\frac{\alpha}{\beta}\right)e^{i\pi\alpha/2\beta}.$$

In particular, show that

$$\int_0^\infty x^{\alpha-1}e^{-ix\xi}dx = \frac{\Gamma(\alpha)e^{-i\pi\alpha/2\,\mathrm{sgn}\xi}}{|\xi|^\alpha}$$

for $0 < \alpha < 1$ and $\xi \in \mathbb{R} \sim \{0\}$.

H.   The Case $0 < p < 1$

It is sometimes important to discuss L^p spaces when $p < 1$, although the present section will not be needed in the rest of the book. We shall retain the notation we have been using. That is, a measurable function

f on X belongs to $L^p(X, \mathcal{M}, \mu)$ if $|f|^p$ is integrable, and we also then define

$$\|f\|_p = \left(\int_X |f|^p d\mu \right)^{1/p}.$$

Here we allow $0 < p < \infty$. We shall see, however, that $\|f\|_p$ is *not* a norm if $0 < p < 1$. The triangle inequality breaks down, but in its place we have the following result.

Proposition: If f, $g \in L^p(X, \mathcal{M}, \mu)$ and $0 < p < 1$, then $f + g \in L^p(X, \mathcal{M}, \mu)$, and

$$\|f + g\|_p^p \leq \|f\|_p^p + \|g\|_p^p.$$

Proof: We are supposed to prove the inequality

$$\int_X |f + g|^p d\mu \leq \int_X |f|^p d\mu + \int_X |g|^p d\mu.$$

We shall actually prove more: We shall prove that for all $x \in X$,

$$|f(x) + g(x)|^p \leq |f(x)|^p + |g(x)|^p.$$

The proof of this reduces to the proof that for $0 < a < \infty$, $0 < b < \infty$,

$$(a + b)^p \leq a^p + b^p.$$

This is finally a simple exercise in calculus, obtained by showing $(a + b)^p - a^p$ is a decreasing function of a. This uses $0 < p < 1$.   **QED**

From now on we assume $0 < p < 1$. We know that $L^p(X, \mathcal{M}, \mu)$ is a vector space. Furthermore, we have a *metric* defined on L^p:

$$d(f, g) = \|f - g\|_p^p.$$

This metric does not arise from a norm, since $\|f\|_p^p$ does not satisfy the homogeneity required of a norm. On the other hand, $\|f\|_p$ satisfies the homogeneity but not the triangle inequality.

Problem 35. Prove that the triangle inequality does not hold for $\|f\|_p$.

You might wonder whether another function on L^p might exist which does provide a norm giving the same topology on L^p as the above metric.

This does happen in simple cases, such as the case in which X is finite and μ is counting measure. The next result gives a counterexample.

Proposition: *In the case of $L^p([0,1], \mathcal{L}, \lambda)$ there exists no norm $\|\ \|$ such that $f_k \to 0$ in L^p implies $\|f_k\| \to 0$.*

Proof: We argue by contradiction. If there is such a norm, then there exists a constant C such that $\|f\| \leq C\|f\|_p$ for all $f \in L^p$. (To see this, argue by contradiction to obtain a sequence $\|f_k\| > k\|f_k\|_p$ and then normalize to obtain $\|f_k\| = 1$ and $\|f_k\|_p < k^{-1}$. This contradicts the hypothesis.) Knowing that C exists, we choose the *minimum* such C. Now let $f \in L^p$ be arbitrary. Then choose $0 < c < 1$ such that

$$\int\limits_0^c |f|^p d\lambda = \int\limits_c^1 |f|^p d\lambda = \frac{1}{2} \int\limits_0^1 |f|^p d\lambda.$$

Next, define

$$g = f\chi_{[0,c]} \quad \text{and} \quad h = f\chi_{[c,1]}.$$

Then $f = g + h$ and $\|g\|_p = \|h\|_p = 2^{-1/p}\|f\|_p$. Thus,

$$\begin{aligned}
\|f\| &\leq \|g\| + \|h\| \\
&\leq C\|g\|_p + C\|h\|_p \\
&= C2^{-1/p}\|f\|_p + C2^{-1/p}\|f\|_p \\
&= C2^{1-1/p}\|f\|_p.
\end{aligned}$$

Since $1 - 1/p < 0$, $2^{1-1/p} < 1$. Since C is minimal, then $C \leq C2^{1-1/p}$. The conclusion is $C = 0$. This implies $\|f\| = 0$ for all f, contradicting the fact that $\|\ \|$ is a norm.   **QED**

The next result is a kind of Hölder inequality. We still define p' by the equation

$$\frac{1}{p} + \frac{1}{p'} = 1.$$

Notice now that $p' < 0$.

Proposition: *Let f and g be nonnegative $\mathcal{M}$-measurable functions. Then*

$$\int\limits_X fg\, d\mu \geq \left(\int\limits_X f^p d\mu \right)^{1/p} \left(\int\limits_X g^{p'} d\mu \right)^{1/p'}.$$

Proof: Notice that if $g = 0$ on a set of positive measure, the second factor on the right side must be interpreted to be 0. Thus, we may assume in the proof that $g > 0$. Likewise, we may assume that $fg < \infty$ everywhere. We shall apply Hölder's inequality with exponents $1/p$ and

$$\left(\frac{1}{p}\right)' = \frac{1}{1-p}.$$

Then

$$\int f^p d\mu = \int (fg)^p g^{-p} d\mu$$

$$\leq \left(\int fg \, d\mu\right)^p \left(\int g^{-p/(1-p)} d\mu\right)^{1-p}$$

$$= \left(\int fg \, d\mu\right)^p \left(\int g^{p'} d\mu\right)^{1-p}.$$

Take the $1/p$ power of each side to obtain the result.   **QED**

Problem 36. Let $f \geq 0$ and $g \geq 0$ be in $L^p(X, \mathcal{M}, \mu)$, where $0 < p < 1$. Prove that

$$\|f + g\|_p \geq \|f\|_p + \|g\|_p.$$

(**HINT:** Imitate the proof of Minkowski's inequality given in Section A.)

Problem 37. Assume $f \in L^{p_0}(X, \mathcal{M}, \mu)$ for some $0 < p_0 \leq \infty$. Prove that

$$\lim_{p \to 0} \int_X |f|^p d\mu = \mu\left(\{x \in X \mid f(x) \neq 0\}\right).$$

(**HINT:** Integrate over the set on which $0 < |f(x)| \leq 1$ and use LICT. Then integrate over the set on which $|f(x)| > 1$ and use LDCT. In case $p_0 = \infty$ you will need to make a slight modification.)

Problem 38. In addition to the assumptions of Problem 37 also assume $\mu(X) = 1$. Prove that $f \in L^p(X, \mathcal{M}, \mu)$ for $0 < p \leq p_0$, and that

$$\lim_{p \to 0} \|f\|_p = e^{\int_X \log |f| d\mu}.$$

This requires some interpretation in case $\log |f| \notin L^1$. Under our assumptions it is always true that the positive part of $\log |f|$ is integrable, and thus we interpret

$$\int_X \log|f|d\mu = -\infty.$$

The problem thus asserts that in this case

$$\lim_{p\to 0} \|f\|_p = 0.$$

(**HINT**: First assume $|f| > 0$ a.e. With the help of Problem 37 and the mean value theorem prove that

$$\log\|f\|_p = \|f\|_q^{-q} \int_X |f|^q \log|f|d\mu$$

for some $0 < q < p$. Use LICT to prove

$$\int_{|f|\leq 1} |f|^q \log|f|d\mu \to \int_{|f|\leq 1} \log|f|d\mu$$

and use LDCT to prove

$$\int_{|f|>1} |f|^q \log|f|d\mu \to \int_{|f|>1} \log|f|d\mu.$$

In case $f = 0$ on a set A of positive measure, apply what you have proved to $X \sim A$ and the measure $\mu(A^c)^{-1}\mu$.)

Products of Abstract Measures

In Chapter 8 we gave a thorough discussion of Fubini's theorem in the context of Lebesgue integration on $\mathbb{R}^n$. That was rather straightforward mathematics, because in the representation of $\mathbb{R}^n$ as a product space $\mathbb{R}^l \times \mathbb{R}^m$ we already had in our possession three measures, and in essence we verified that one of these was the product of the others. In the present chapter the point of view is somewhat different — we are given two measure spaces and are faced with the task of constructing their product before even being able to state Fubini's theorem. Actually, what we shall do is construct the product measure and prove Fubini's theorem simultaneously.

A. Products of σ-Algebras

Definition: Let $\mathcal{M}$ be a σ-algebra of subsets of a set X and let $\mathcal{N}$ be a σ-algebra of subsets of a set Y. We let $X \times Y$ be the usual Cartesian product of ordered pairs (x, y) with $x \in X$ and $y \in Y$. If $A \in \mathcal{M}$ and $B \in \mathcal{N}$, then $A \times B$ is a subset of $X \times Y$. This particular type of set in the product space $X \times Y$ is called a *measurable rectangle*.

We keep in mind a schematic figure of this sort:

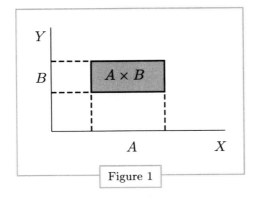

Figure 1

Definition: Using the same situation as above, the *product* of $\mathcal{M}$ and $\mathcal{N}$, denoted $\mathcal{M} \times \mathcal{N}$, is defined to be the smallest σ-algebra of subsets of $X \times Y$ which contains all measurable rectangles.

Note carefully that $\mathcal{M} \times \mathcal{N}$ is *not* a Cartesian product, in spite of the choice of notation.

Recall that the notion of the σ-algebra generated by a collection of sets was thoroughly discussed in Section 5.A.

Notation: (Similar to that in Chapter 8.) If $E \subset X \times Y$ and $y \in Y$, then $E_y \subset X$ is the set

$$E_y = \{x \in X \mid (x,y) \in E\}.$$

If f is a function defined on $X \times Y$, then f_y is the function defined on X by

$$f_y(x) = f(x,y).$$

In particular, if $E \subset X \times Y$,

$$(\chi_E)_y = \chi_{E_y}.$$

On the other hand, if $x \in X$ we use the notation E^x and f^x for the corresponding objects with the roles of x and y switched.

Problem 1. Prove that if $E \in \mathcal{M} \times \mathcal{N}$ and $y \in Y$, then $E_y \in \mathcal{M}$. Prove that if f is $\mathcal{M} \times \mathcal{N}$-measurable and $y \in Y$, then f_y is $\mathcal{M}$-measurable.

(**HINT:** In order to prove the first assertion, define $\mathcal{S}$ by

$$\mathcal{S} = \{E \subset X \times Y \mid E_y \in \mathcal{M}\},$$

and derive relevant properties of $\mathcal{S}$.)

Problem 2. In this problem $X = \mathbb{R}^l$ and $Y = \mathbb{R}^m$, so that $X \times Y = \mathbb{R}^n$, where $n = l + m$. Let

$$\mathcal{B}_n = \text{ the Borel sets in } \mathbb{R}^n,$$
$$\mathcal{L}_n = \text{ the Lebesgue measurable sets in } \mathbb{R}^n.$$

Prove that

$$\mathcal{B}_l \times \mathcal{B}_m = \mathcal{B}_n;$$
$$\mathcal{L}_l \times \mathcal{L}_m \overset{\subsetneq}{\neq} \mathcal{L}_n.$$

In your proof follow this outline:

(a) Let $\mathcal{S} = \{A \subset \mathbb{R}^l \mid A \times \mathbb{R}^m \in \mathcal{B}_n\}$ and prove that $\mathcal{B}_l \subset \mathcal{S}$.

(b) From (a) and the corresponding result with l and m switched, conclude that $\mathcal{B}_n$ contains all measurable rectangles.

(c) Conclude that $\mathcal{B}_l \times \mathcal{B}_m \subset \mathcal{B}_n$.

(d) To prove the reverse inclusion, prove first that $\mathcal{B}_l \times \mathcal{B}_m$ contains all open subsets of $\mathbb{R}^n$.

(e) Use the proposition on p.195.

(f) Consider $E \times \{0\}$, where E is a nonmeasurable subset of $\mathbb{R}^l$.

Lemma: *Let $\mathcal{S}$ be the collection of those subsets of $X \times Y$ which are finite disjoint unions of measurable rectangles. Then $\mathcal{S}$ is an algebra.*

Proof: The intersection of two measurable rectangles is clearly a measurable rectangle. Therefore, it is evident that the intersection of two sets in $\mathcal{S}$ is again a set in $\mathcal{S}$. Now we check the complements. First, if $A \times B$ is a measurable rectangle, then $(A \times B)^c$ is a union of two disjoint measurable rectangles:

$$(A \times B)^c = (A^c \times Y) \cup (A \times B^c).$$

Thus, $(A \times B)^c \in \mathcal{S}$. If $E \in \mathcal{S}$, then E has the form

$$E = \bigcup_{i=1}^{k} E_i,$$

where each E_i is a measurable rectangle. Thus,

$$E^c = \bigcap_{i=1}^{k} E_i^c \ ;$$

since $E_i^c \in \mathcal{S}$ and $\mathcal{S}$ is closed under finite intersections, $E^c \in \mathcal{S}$. Finally, we prove that $\mathcal{S}$ is closed under finite unions. If two sets in $\mathcal{S}$ are disjoint, their union is clearly in $\mathcal{S}$. In general, if $E,\ F \in \mathcal{S}$, then $E \cup F = (E \cap F^c) \cup F$ is a disjoint union of sets in $\mathcal{S}$.   **QED**

B. Monotone Classes

We are going to be working with two measure spaces:

$$X, \mathcal{M}, \mu \quad \text{and} \quad Y, \mathcal{N}, \nu.$$

(In the next section we shall have to make an assumption limiting their "size," but that is unnecessary in the current discussion.) Our goal is to find a measure π on $\mathcal{M} \times \mathcal{N}$ such that

$$X \times Y, \mathcal{M} \times \mathcal{N}, \pi$$

is a measure space and for every measurable rectangle $A \times B$,

$$\pi(A \times B) = \mu(A)\nu(B).$$

This is a rather difficult task. One might think at first that we merely need to define π by the given formula, and then we are finished. However, the formula does not really define a measure π; it only states what values π must have on measurable rectangles.

Not only do we want to prove that such a measure π exists, but also we want to prove a Fubini theorem, which will assert

$$\int\limits_{X \times Y} f \, d\pi = \int\limits_{Y} \left[\int\limits_{X} f_y \, d\mu \right] d\nu(y)$$

$$= \int\limits_{X} \left[\int\limits_{Y} f^x \, d\nu \right] d\mu(x).$$

Actually, the best procedure seems to be to prove the existence of π and Fubini's theorem simultaneously! If $f = \chi_E$, where $E \in \mathcal{M} \times \mathcal{N}$, this amounts to trying to define $\pi(E)$ to be equal to

$$\int\limits_{Y} \mu(E_y) \, d\nu(y) = \int\limits_{X} \nu(E^x) \, d\mu(x).$$

Of course, we shall have to prove that these expressions make sense and that they are equal.

Before proceeding, we have to dispense with a lemma on σ-algebras of a very technical nature.

Definition: Let X be any set and $\mathcal{S} \subset 2^X$. Then $\mathcal{S}$ is a *monotone class* if $\mathcal{S}$ is closed under countable increasing unions and countable decreasing intersections. That is, if A_1, A_2, ... are in $\mathcal{S}$ and

$$\text{(i)} \quad \text{if } A_1 \subset A_2 \subset A_3 \subset \ldots, \text{ then } \bigcup_{k=1}^{\infty} A_k \in \mathcal{S};$$

or

$$\text{(ii)} \quad \text{if } A_1 \supset A_2 \supset A_3 \supset \ldots, \text{ then } \bigcap_{k=1}^{\infty} A_k \in \mathcal{S}.$$

Trivially, any σ-algebra is a monotone class. The converse is false. It is clear that any intersection of monotone classes is also a monotone class. Therefore, exactly as in the case of σ-algebras and algebras (Section 5.A), any collection of subsets of X *generates* a monotone class, the *smallest* monotone class containing the given collection. This smallest monotone class is of course the intersection of all monotone classes which contain the original collection. In general, the monotone class generated this way will be *smaller* than the σ-algebra generated by the same collection of sets.

Problem 3. Prove that if a monotone class is an algebra, then it is a σ-algebra.

Problem 4. Let $\mathcal{S}$ be the collection of all intervals in $\mathbb{R}$. Prove that $\mathcal{S}$ is a monotone class. (Assume $\mathcal{S}$ contains $\emptyset$ and $\mathbb{R}$.)

Lemma: *Let X be any set and let $\mathcal{S} \subset 2^X$ be an* algebra. *Let*

$$\mathcal{S}_\sigma = \text{ the } \sigma\text{-algebra generated by } \mathcal{S},$$
$$\mathcal{S}_m = \text{ the monotone class generated by } \mathcal{S}.$$

Then $\mathcal{S}_\sigma = \mathcal{S}_m$.

Proof: Since $\mathcal{S}_\sigma$ is in particular a monotone class which contains $\mathcal{S}$, $\mathcal{S}_m \subset \mathcal{S}_\sigma$. If we prove that $\mathcal{S}_m$ is an algebra, then Problem 3 implies $\mathcal{S}_m$ is an σ-algebra, and we conclude $\mathcal{S}_\sigma \subset \mathcal{S}_m$. Therefore, it remains to prove that $\mathcal{S}_m$ is an algebra. To prove this, it suffices to prove that A, $B \in \mathcal{S}_m \Rightarrow A^c \in \mathcal{S}_m$ and $A \cup B \in \mathcal{S}_m$.

First define

$$\mathcal{T} = \{A \subset X \mid A^c \in \mathcal{S}_m\}.$$

Then $A \in \mathcal{S} \Rightarrow A^c \in \mathcal{S} \Rightarrow A^c \in \mathcal{S}_m \Rightarrow A \in \mathcal{T}$. That is,

$$\mathcal{S} \subset \mathcal{T}.$$

It is simple to verify that $\mathcal{T}$ is a monotone class (since $\mathcal{S}_m$ is). Thus, $\mathcal{S}_m \subset \mathcal{T}$. That is,

$$A \in \mathcal{S}_m \Rightarrow A^c \in \mathcal{S}_m.$$

Next suppose $A \in \mathcal{S}$ is fixed, and define

$$\mathcal{U} = \{B \subset X \mid A \cup B \in \mathcal{S}_m\}.$$

Since $\mathcal{S}$ is an algebra, $\mathcal{S} \subset \mathcal{U}$. It is easy to check that $\mathcal{U}$ is a monotone class (since $\mathcal{S}_m$ is). Therefore, $\mathcal{S}_m \subset \mathcal{U}$. That is,

$$A \in \mathcal{S}, B \in \mathcal{S}_m \Rightarrow A \cup B \in \mathcal{S}_m.$$

Finally, let $B \in \mathcal{S}_m$ be fixed, and define

$$\mathcal{V} = \{A \subset X \mid A \cup B \in \mathcal{S}_m\}.$$

What we have just proved shows that $\mathcal{S} \subset \mathcal{V}$. Again, we see that $\mathcal{V}$ is a monotone class, proving that $\mathcal{S}_m \subset \mathcal{V}$. That is,

$$A \in \mathcal{S}_m, B \in \mathcal{S}_m \Rightarrow A \cup B \in \mathcal{S}_m.$$

QED

Before proceeding to Fubini's theorem, we give an elementary example of the utility of the lemma. Assume π is a *finite* measure on $\mathcal{M} \times \mathcal{N}$: $\pi(X \times Y) < \infty$. Then π is uniquely determined by its values on the measurable rectangles.

To prove this, suppose that π_1 and π_2 are finite measures on $\mathcal{M} \times \mathcal{N}$ such that

$$\pi_1(A \times B) = \pi_2(A \times B)$$

for all measurable rectangles $A \times B$. Define the classes $\mathcal{S}$ and $\mathcal{T}$ as follows:

    $\mathcal{S}$ is the collection of finite disjoint unions of measurable
    rectangles;

$$\mathcal{T} = \{E \in \mathcal{M} \times \mathcal{N} \mid \pi_1(E) = \pi_2(E)\}.$$

By the lemma of Section A, $\mathcal{S}$ is an algebra. By hypothesis, $\mathcal{S} \subset \mathcal{T}$. Moreover, $\mathcal{T}$ is a *monotone class*: For instance, if $E_1 \supset E_2 \supset E_3 \supset \ldots$ are sets in $\mathcal{T}$, then since $\pi_i(X \times Y) < \infty$,

$$\begin{aligned}
\pi_1(\cap E_k) &= \lim \pi_1(E_k) \\
&= \lim \pi_2(E_k) \\
&= \pi_2(\cap E_k),
\end{aligned}$$

and thus $\cap E_k \in \mathcal{T}$. Likewise, $\mathcal{T}$ is closed under the formation of countable increasing unions.

By the lemma of this section, $\mathcal{S}_\sigma = \mathcal{S}_m \subset \mathcal{T}$. By definition, $\mathcal{S}_\sigma = \mathcal{M} \times \mathcal{N}$. Thus, $\mathcal{M} \times \mathcal{N} \subset \mathcal{T}$, and this proves that $\pi_1 = \pi_2$.

C. Construction of the Product Measure

Throughout this section we assume that X, $\mathcal{M}$, μ and Y, $\mathcal{N}$, ν are *σ-finite measure spaces*. Here is the definition.

Definition: A measure space X, $\mathcal{M}$, μ is *σ-finite* if there exist sets A_1, A_2, A_3, ... in $\mathcal{M}$ such that $\mu(A_k) < \infty$ for every k and $X = \bigcup\limits_{k=1}^{\infty} A_k$. The measure space is simply said to be *finite* if $\mu(X) < \infty$.

Problem 5. Prove that the measure space X, $\mathcal{M}$, μ is σ-finite $\iff$ there exists a measurable function $f : X \to (0, \infty)$ such that

$$\int_X f \, d\mu < \infty.$$

Theorem: *Let* $E \in \mathcal{M} \times \mathcal{N}$, *so that Problem 1 implies that*

$$E_y \in \mathcal{M} \qquad \text{for all } y \in Y,$$
$$E^x \in \mathcal{N} \qquad \text{for all } x \in X.$$

Then

$$\mu(E_y) \text{ is an } \mathcal{N}\text{-measurable function of } y \in Y;$$
$$\nu(E^x) \text{ is an } \mathcal{M}\text{-measurable function of } x \in X;$$

and

$$\int_Y \mu(E_y) \, d\nu(y) = \int_X \nu(E^x) \, d\mu(x).$$

Proof: Let $\mathcal{W}$ be the collection of all sets $E \in \mathcal{M} \times \mathcal{N}$ such that all the assertions of the theorem are valid for E. We are going to establish a number of properties of $\mathcal{W}$, culminating in the fact that $\mathcal{M} \times \mathcal{N} \subset \mathcal{W}$. The theorem will then have been proved.

1. $\mathcal{W}$ is closed with respect to countable disjoint unions. To prove this, suppose the sets E_1, E_2, ... are disjoint and belong to $\mathcal{W}$. Let $E = \bigcup_{k=1}^{\infty} E_k$. Then for each $y \in Y$

$$E_y = \bigcup_{k=1}^{\infty} E_{ky}, \quad \text{a disjoint union,}$$

$$\mu(E_y) = \sum_{k=1}^{\infty} \mu(E_{ky}).$$

Since the functions $\mu(E_{ky})$ are nonnegative and $\mathcal{N}$-measurable,

$$\int_Y \mu(E_y) d\nu(y) = \sum_{k=1}^{\infty} \int_Y \mu(E_{ky}) d\nu(y)$$

$$= \sum_{k=1}^{\infty} \int_X \nu(E_k^x) d\mu(x) \quad (E_k \in \mathcal{W})$$

$$= \int_X \nu(E^x) d\mu(x).$$

Thus $E \in \mathcal{W}$.

2. By the assumption of σ-finiteness, we can express

$$X = \bigcup_{j=1}^{\infty} A_j, \quad \text{a disjoint union of } A_j \in \mathcal{M}, \mu(A_j) < \infty;$$

$$Y = \bigcup_{k=1}^{\infty} B_k, \quad \text{a disjoint union of } B_k \in \mathcal{N}, \nu(B_k) < \infty.$$

(See Problem 10.14(a).) Now suppose the theorem is known to be valid for *finite* measure spaces. Then for any $E \in \mathcal{M} \times \mathcal{N}$, it follows that $E \cap (A_j \times B_k) \in \mathcal{W}$. Since

$$E = \bigcup_{j,k} E \cap (A_j \times B_k),$$

a countable disjoint union, Step 1 implies $E \in \mathcal{W}$.

3. By the preceding step, we are now free to assume both the measure spaces we begin with are *finite*. That is, we assume for the rest of the proof that $\mu(X) < \infty$ and $\nu(Y) < \infty$. We now prove that any measurable rectangle $A \times B$ belongs to $\mathcal{W}$. This is trivial:

$$(A \times B)_y = \begin{cases} A & \text{if } y \in B, \\ \emptyset & \text{if } y \in B^c, \end{cases}$$

$$\mu((A \times B)_y) = \mu(A)\chi_B(y).$$

Likewise,

$$\nu((A \times B)^x) = \nu(B)\chi_A(x).$$

Thus, the integrals in the statement of the theorem exist and are each equal to $\mu(A)\nu(B)$.

4. Let $\mathcal{S}$ be the collection of all finite disjoint unions of measurable rectangles. By Steps 1 and 3, $\mathcal{S} \subset \mathcal{W}$.

5. $\mathcal{W}$ is a monotone class. For instance, suppose $E_1 \supset E_2 \supset \dots$ is a sequence of sets $\mathcal{W}$ and let $E = \bigcap\limits_{k=1}^{\infty} E_k$. Then for all $y \in Y$

$$E_y = \bigcap_{k=1}^{\infty} E_{ky}.$$

Since $\mu(X) < \infty$, we conclude that

$$\mu(E_y) = \lim_{k \to \infty} \mu(E_{ky}).$$

Moreover, $\mu(E_{ky}) \leq \mu(X) < \infty$, and constants are integrable over Y since $\nu(Y) < \infty$. We can therefore apply LDCT to conclude that

$$\int_Y \mu(E_y)d\nu(y) = \lim_{k \to \infty} \int_Y \mu(E_{ky})d\nu(y).$$

Likewise,

$$\int_X \nu(E^x)d\mu(x) = \lim_{k \to \infty} \int_X \nu(E_k^x)d\mu(x).$$

Since the two right sides are equal ($E_k \in \mathcal{W}$), we conclude that

$$\int_Y \mu(E_y)d\nu(y) = \int_X \nu(E^x)d\mu(x),$$

and thus $E \in \mathcal{W}$.

A much simpler argument establishes also that $\mathcal{W}$ is closed under countable increasing unions. The argument is simpler in that we need only invoke LICT — the finiteness assumption is irrelevant.

6. Finally, we exploit the lemmas. The one in Section A shows that $\mathcal{S}$ is an algebra. Thus, the lemma in Section B implies $\mathcal{S}_\sigma = \mathcal{S}_m$. Since $\mathcal{W}$ is a monotone class, $\mathcal{S}_m \subset \mathcal{W}$. By definition, $\mathcal{S}_\sigma = \mathcal{M} \times \mathcal{N}$. Therefore, $\mathcal{M} \times \mathcal{N} \subset \mathcal{W}$.

QED

Corollary: *Under the same assumptions, there exists a unique measure π on $\mathcal{M} \times \mathcal{N}$ such that for every measurable rectangle*

$$\pi(A \times B) = \mu(A)\nu(B).$$

This measure is determined in general by the formula

$$\pi(E) = \int_Y \mu(E_y)d\nu(y) = \int_X \nu(E^x)d\mu(x)$$

for all $E \in \mathcal{M} \times \mathcal{N}$.

Proof: The uniqueness proof in the case of finite measure spaces was presented at the conclusion of Section B. Now we prove uniqueness in the general case of σ-finite measure spaces. Suppose that π_1 and π_2 are measures on $\mathcal{M} \times \mathcal{N}$ such that $\pi_1(A \times B) = \pi_2(A \times B) = \mu(A)\nu(B)$ for all measurable rectangles. We then must prove that $\pi_1(E) = \pi_2(E)$ for all $E \in \mathcal{M} \times \mathcal{N}$. We introduce the decompositions of X and Y precisely as in Step 2 of the preceding proof. For fixed j and k we define for $i = 1$, 2,

$$\tilde{\pi}_i(E) = \pi_i(E \cap (A_j \times B_k)) \qquad \text{for } E \in \mathcal{M} \times \mathcal{N}.$$

In case $E = A \times B$ is a measurable rectangle, then

$$\begin{aligned}
\tilde{\pi}_i(A \times B) &= \pi_i(A \times B \cap A_j \times B_k) \\
&= \pi_i((A \cap A_j) \times (B \cap B_k)) \\
&= \mu(A \cap A_j)\nu(B \cap B_k).
\end{aligned}$$

Thus, $\tilde{\pi}_1(A \times B) = \tilde{\pi}_2(A \times B)$ and also $\tilde{\pi}_i(X \times Y) = \mu(A_j)\nu(B_k) < \infty$. By the uniqueness proved in Section B, $\tilde{\pi}_1 = \tilde{\pi}_2$ on $\mathcal{M} \times \mathcal{N}$. That is, for all $E \in \mathcal{M} \times \mathcal{N}$,

$$\pi_1(E \cap (A_j \times B_k)) = \pi_2(E \cap (A_j \times B_k)).$$

Summing these equations over all j and k yields $\pi_1(E) = \pi_2(E)$. Thus, uniqueness is proved.

The formula we have proposed for π does give the correct value in case E is a measurable rectangle. All that really requires verification is the countable additivity of π. Therefore, assume $E = \bigcup\limits_{k=1}^{\infty} E_k$ is a disjoint union of sets in $\mathcal{M} \times \mathcal{N}$. Then a routine calculation shows that

$$\pi(E) = \int_Y \mu(E_y) d\nu(y)$$

$$= \int_Y \mu\left(\bigcup_{k=1}^{\infty} E_{ky}\right) d\nu(y)$$

$$= \int_Y \sum_{k=1}^{\infty} \mu(E_{ky}) d\nu(y)$$

$$= \sum_{k=1}^{\infty} \int_Y \mu(E_{ky}) d\nu(y)$$

$$= \sum_{k=1}^{\infty} \pi(E_k).$$

QED

Example: This is a counterexample to show that the assumption of σ-finiteness cannot be dropped. Let $X = [0,1] \subset \mathbb{R}$, $\mathcal{M} =$ Lebesgue measurable subsets of $[0,1]$, $\mu =$ Lebesgue measure. Let $Y = [0,1]$, $\mathcal{N} = 2^Y$, and $\nu =$ counting measure (which is *not* σ-finite). Let E be the diagonal $E = \{(x,x) \mid 0 \le x \le 1\}$. Then $E \in \mathcal{M} \times \mathcal{N}$. In fact, $\mathcal{M}$ and $\mathcal{N}$ both contain the Borel subsets of $[0,1]$. Moreover, $\mathcal{B}_1 \times \mathcal{B}_1 = \mathcal{B}_2$, thanks to Problem 2. Since E is closed, it is a Borel set and thus belongs to $\mathcal{B}_1 \times \mathcal{B}_1 \subset \mathcal{M} \times \mathcal{N}$. (Or a direct proof can also easily be given.) But for any $y \in Y$ and any $x \in X$

$$\mu(E_y) = \mu(\{y\}) = 0,$$
$$\nu(E^x) = \nu(\{x\}) = 1.$$

Thus,

$$\int_Y \mu(E_y) d\nu(y) = 0,$$

$$\int_X \nu(E^x) d\mu(x) = \int_X 1 d\mu(x) = \mu(X) = 1,$$

and the two iterated integrals are different.

The next example is tremendously important, as it verifies the fact that integrals can be viewed as "areas" as in the standard elementary discussions of Riemann integration.

Example: Let X, $\mathcal{M}$, μ be an arbitrary σ-finite measure space. The other measure space will be the Lebesgue space $\mathbb{R}$, $\mathcal{L}$, λ. Let π be the corresponding product measure on $X \times \mathbb{R}$, $\mathcal{M} \times \mathcal{L}$. Now suppose

$$f : X \to [0, \infty].$$

Then corresponding to this function we define the "region between the graph of f and the X-axis" to be

$$\Omega = \{(x, y) \mid 0 \le y < f(x)\}.$$

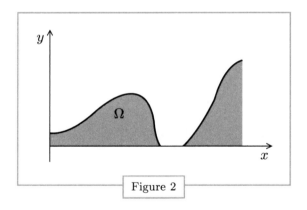

Figure 2

Suppose that f is $\mathcal{M}$-measurable. Then for all $t \in [0, \infty]$

$$\{(x, y) \mid f(x) \le t\} = \{x \mid f(x) \le t\} \times \mathbb{R}$$

is a measurable rectangle. Therefore, the function $(x, y) \longrightarrow f(x)$ is $\mathcal{M} \times \mathcal{L}$-measurable on $X \times \mathbb{R}$. Likewise, the function $(x, y) \longrightarrow y$ is $\mathcal{M} \times \mathcal{L}$-measurable. Therefore, the difference $f(x) - y$ is an $\mathcal{M} \times \mathcal{L}$-measurable function on $X \times \mathbb{R}$. Thus, $\Omega \in \mathcal{M} \times \mathcal{L}$. In fact, the converse is also true:

Problem 6. Let $\mathcal{B}$ denote the Borel sets on $\mathbb{R}$. Keep the above notation, and prove that

$$f \text{ is } \mathcal{M}\text{-measurable} \iff \Omega \in \mathcal{M} \times \mathcal{L} \iff \Omega \in \mathcal{M} \times \mathcal{B}.$$

By the above corollary, the product measure of Ω is given by

$$\pi(\Omega) = \int_X \lambda(\Omega^x)d\mu(x).$$

But

$$\Omega^x = \{y \in \mathbb{R} \mid (x, y) \in \Omega\}$$
$$= \{y \in \mathbb{R} \mid 0 \le y < f(x)\},$$

and thus

$$\lambda(\Omega^x) = \lambda([0, f(x))) = f(x).$$

We conclude that

$$\pi(\Omega) = \int_X f d\mu.$$

This formula asserts that the "area under the graph of f" is equal to the integral of f.

Problem 7. In the same notation as above, let

$$\Omega' = \{(x, y) \mid 0 \le y \le f(x)\}.$$

Prove that the same result is valid:

$$\pi(\Omega') = \int_X f d\mu.$$

We obtain another interesting formula by using the other integral which appears in the conclusion of the corollary. Notice first that

$$\Omega_y = \{x \mid 0 \le y < f(x)\}.$$

If $y < 0$, $\Omega_y = \emptyset$. Thus, the corollary shows that

$$\int_X f d\mu = \int_0^\infty \mu(\{x \mid f(x) > y\})dy.$$

This formula has many interesting features. One of them is that it shows that in a certain sense integration over X can be reduced to *Riemann* (improper) integration on $\mathbb{R}$. (Since $\mu(\{x \mid f(x) > y\})$ is a decreasing function of y, it is Riemann integrable, at least in an improper sense.) We summarize this with a slight generalization:

Theorem: *Let X, $\mathcal{M}$, μ be a measure space and let f be an $\mathcal{M}$-measurable function on X. Let $0 < p < \infty$. Then*

$$\int_X |f|^p d\mu = \int_0^\infty \mu(\{x \mid |f(x)| > s\})ps^{p-1}ds.$$

Proof: Use the previous formula with f replaced by $|f|^p$ and $y = s^p$. This change of variable with $dy = ps^{p-1}ds$ is a standard result from Riemann integration theory, or you may refer to Chapter 15 for complete proofs.   **QED**

Problem 8. This theorem does not require the hypothesis that the measure space is σ-finite. Therefore our proof is incomplete. Finish the proof in the non-σ-finite case. (See Problem 5.)

Problem 9. Show that the theorem remains valid if the inequality sign in the integrand on the right side is replaced by "$\geq$."

Problem 10. Let $0 \leq a_k < \infty$ for $k \in \mathbb{N}$. For $0 < s < \infty$ define

$$N(s) = \text{ the number of indices } k \text{ such that } a_k \geq s.$$

Prove that

$$\sum_{k=1}^\infty a_k = \int_0^\infty N(s)ds.$$

D. The Fubini Theorem

Throughout this section we assume that X, $\mathcal{M}$, μ and Y, $\mathcal{N}$, ν are σ-finite measure spaces, and that $X \times Y$, $\mathcal{M} \times \mathcal{N}$, π is the unique product

measure space whose existence has been established in the preceding
section.

Fubini's Theorem for Nonnegative Functions: *Assume f is a
nonnegative $\mathcal{M} \times \mathcal{N}$-measurable function on $X \times Y$. Then*

$$\int\limits_{X \times Y} f d\pi = \int\limits_{Y} d\nu(y) \int\limits_{X} f(x,y) d\mu(x)$$

$$= \int\limits_{X} d\mu(x) \int\limits_{Y} f(x,y) d\nu(y).$$

INTERPRETATION. We have deliberately omitted the precise statement of the theorem. The theorem's conclusion is actually that for every
$y \in Y$, the section f_y is $\mathcal{M}$-measurable (by Problem 1); the resulting
function F on Y given by

$$F(y) = \int\limits_{X} f_y(x) d\mu(x)$$

is $\mathcal{N}$-measurable;

$$\int\limits_{Y} F(y) d\nu(y) = \int\limits_{X \times Y} f d\pi;$$

and likewise with the roles of x and y interchanged.

Proof: There is no need to provide a detailed proof, as it proceeds
along very standard lines. Indeed, the first theorem of Section C and its
corollary show that the result is valid if f is a characteristic function.
By addition, it is valid for simple functions. Since the general f is the
limit of an increasing sequence of $\mathcal{M} \times \mathcal{N}$-measurable simple functions,
the result follows by a routine limiting argument.   **QED**

Just as in Chapter 8, there is a corresponding result for integrable
functions f. The statement is exactly what you would expect, so we
omit it.

You will have noticed that the present Fubini theorem differs from
that in Chapter 8 in one essential feature: In Chapter 8 it could be
stated only that *almost every* section of f is measurable. The difference

lies in the fact that the product measure space $X \times Y$, $\mathcal{M} \times \mathcal{N}$, π is not always *complete*. In Chapter 8 we did not use the measurable sets $\mathcal{L}_l \times \mathcal{L}_m$ on $\mathbb{R}^n$; rather, we used the complete measure space based on $\mathcal{L}_n$. Remember that Problem 2 implies

$$\mathcal{B}_n \overset{\subset}{\neq} \mathcal{L}_l \times \mathcal{L}_m \overset{\subset}{\neq} \mathcal{L}_n.$$

Recall the concept of the *completion* of a measure space, as discussed at the end of Section 6.E. We now let $\overline{\mathcal{M} \times \mathcal{N}}$, $\overline{\pi}$ represent the completion of the product measure space. We shall state a corresponding Fubini theorem.

In addition to the standing assumptions of this section, we now assume X, $\mathcal{M}$, μ and Y, $\mathcal{N}$, ν are *complete* measure spaces.

Theorem: *Assume f is a nonnegative $\overline{\mathcal{M} \times \mathcal{N}}$-measurable function on $X \times Y$. Then for ν-a.e. $y \in Y$ the section f_y is $\mathcal{M}$-measurable. Furthermore,*

$$\int_X f_y \, d\mu$$

is an $\mathcal{N}$-measurable function of y, and

$$\int_{X \times Y} f \, d\overline{\pi} = \int_Y d\nu(y) \int_X f(x, y) \, d\mu(x).$$

The corresponding statement holds with the roles of x and y interchanged.

Proof: From Example 9 in Section 6.F we see that there exists an $\mathcal{M} \times \mathcal{N}$-measurable function g such that $f = g$ $\overline{\pi}$-a.e. Since we know the result to be valid for g, the theorem will follow if we prove that for any $\overline{\pi}$-null set $E \in \overline{\mathcal{M} \times \mathcal{N}}$, the section $E_y \in \mathcal{M}$ and $\mu(E_y) = 0$ for ν-a.e. y. To prove this, we observe that the definition of the completion of a measure space shows that there exists a π-null set $N \in \mathcal{M} \times \mathcal{N}$ such that $E \subset N$. By the corollary in Section C,

$$0 = \pi(N) = \int_Y \mu(N_y) \, d\nu(y).$$

Therefore, $\mu(N_y) = 0$ for ν-a.e. y. Since μ is complete and $E_y \subset N_y$, it follows that for ν-a.e. y the section $E_y \in \mathcal{M}$ (and $\mu(E_y) = 0$).   **QED**

E. The Generalized Minkowski Inequality

In our discussion of L^p in Chapter 10, it was very important to prove the Minkowski inequality, which states that $\|f + g\|_p \leq \|f\|_p + \|g\|_p$. Of course, a similar inequality is valid for finite sums of functions in L^p and even for infinite sums (see the lemma in Section 10.C). The next theorem generalizes these inequalities quite extensively.

Theorem: Assume X, $\mathcal{M}$, μ and Y, $\mathcal{N}$, ν are σ-finite measure spaces. Assume f is an $\mathcal{M} \times \mathcal{N}$-measurable function on $X \times Y$. Then $\|f_y\|_p$ is an $\mathcal{N}$-measurable function of y, for each $1 \leq p \leq \infty$. Assume that

$$\int_Y \|f_y\|_p d\nu(y) < \infty.$$

Then for μ-a.e. $x \in X$ the section $f^x \in L^1(Y)$. Let

$$F(x) = \int_Y f^x d\nu.$$

Then this is an $\mathcal{M}$-measurable function which satisfies

$$\|F\|_p \leq \int_Y \|f_y\|_p d\nu(y).$$

Remark: Suppose $1 \leq p < \infty$. Then, stripped of all the explanatory comments, the final inequality asserts that

$$\left[\int_X \left| \int_Y f(x,y) d\nu(y) \right|^p d\mu(x) \right]^{1/p}$$
$$\leq \int_Y \left[\int_X \left| f(x,y) \right|^p d\mu(x) \right]^{1/p} d\nu(y).$$

This inequality may look unwieldy and impossible to memorize. In reality it is very simple. Merely regard $f(x,y)$ as a function of x depending on a parameter y, and think of

$$\int_Y f(x,y)d\nu(y)$$

as a "sum" of functions of x. Then the conclusion of the theorem should be read as follows:

"The L^p norm of a sum is $\leq$ the sum of the L^p norms."

In fact, if Y consists of just two points and ν is counting measure, the inequality becomes nothing but Minkowski's inequality. If $Y = \mathbb{N}$ and ν is counting measure, it becomes the lemma of Section 10.C.

Proof: Since

$$|F(x)| \leq \int_Y |f^x|d\nu,$$

there is no loss in generality in assuming $f \geq 0$. Thus, we make that assumption from now on. We also notice that the case $p = 1$ is an immediate consequence of Fubini's theorem, so we assume $1 < p \leq \infty$.

Next we handle the measurability considerations. Specifically, we prove that $\|f_y\|_p$ is an $\mathcal{N}$-measurable function of $y \in Y$. There are two cases, depending on the finiteness or nonfiniteness of p. Suppose first that $p < \infty$. Then the Fubini theorem applied to f^p shows that for every $y \in Y$ the function $(f^p)_y$ is $\mathcal{M}$-measurable on X and that

$$\int (f^p)_y dx = \|f_y\|_p^p$$

is an $\mathcal{N}$-measurable function of $y \in Y$.

Next, we consider the case $p = \infty$. Suppose first that $\mu(X) < \infty$. Then we obtain from Problem 10.16

$$\|f_y\|_\infty = \lim_{p\to\infty} \|f_y\|_p.$$

Thus, $\|f_y\|_\infty$ is a measurable function of y. In general, the σ-finiteness of X implies that $X = \bigcup_{k=1}^\infty A_k$, where $\mu(A_k) < \infty$. It is easy to see that for each y

$$\|f_y\|_\infty = \sup_k \|\chi_{A_k} f_y\|_\infty.$$

Since we already know that $\|\chi_{A_k} f_y\|_\infty$ is a measurable function of y, the same must be true of $\|f_y\|_\infty$.

Let

$$c = \int_Y \|f_y\|_p d\nu(y).$$

Now let $1 < p < \infty$ and define a new function g on $X \times Y$ by the formula

$$g(x,y) = \begin{cases} f(x,y)\|f_y\|_p^{-1/p'} & \text{if} \quad 0 < \|f_y\|_p < \infty \\ 0 & \text{if} \quad \|f_y\|_p = 0, \\ \infty & \text{if} \quad \|f_y\|_p = \infty. \end{cases}$$

Of course, p' is the Hölder conjugate of p. Then for each $y \in Y$,

$$f(x,y) \le g(x,y)\|f_y\|_p^{1/p'} \quad \text{for} \quad \mu\text{-a.e.} \quad x \in X,$$

and

$$\begin{aligned} \|g_y\|_p &= \|f_y\|_p \|f_y\|_p^{-1/p'} \\ &= \|f_y\|_p^{1/p}. \end{aligned}$$

(The latter equation even holds in the cases $\|f_y\|_p = 0$ or ∞.) By Hölder's inequality,

$$\begin{aligned} F(x) &= \int_Y f(x,y)d\nu(y) \\ &\le \int_Y g^x(y)\|f_y\|_p^{1/p'} d\nu(y) \\ &\le \|g^x\|_p \left[\int_Y \|f_y\|_p d\nu(y)\right]^{1/p'} \\ &= \|g^x\|_p c^{1/p'}. \end{aligned}$$

Fubini's theorem now implies

$$\|F\|_p^p \leq \int_X \|g^x\|_p^p c^{p/p'} d\mu(x)$$

$$= c^{p-1} \int_X d\mu(x) \int_Y g(x,y)^p d\nu(y)$$

$$= c^{p-1} \int_Y d\nu(y) \int_X g(x,y)^p d\mu(x)$$

$$= c^{p-1} \int_Y \|g_y\|_p^p d\nu(y)$$

$$= c^{p-1} \int_Y \|f_y\|_p d\nu(y)$$

$$= c^p.$$

Finally, let $p = \infty$. By our measurability check, the set
$$N = \{(x,y) \mid f(x,y) > \|f_y\|_\infty\}$$
is in $\mathcal{M} \times \mathcal{N}$. By definition of the L^∞-norm, for each $y \in Y$ the section
$$N_y = \{x \in X \mid f_y(x) > \|f_y\|_\infty\}$$
is a μ-null set. By the corollary on p.264
$$\nu(N^x) = 0 \qquad \text{for } \mu\text{-a.e. } x \in X.$$
Thus, for μ-a.e. x we have

$$F(x) = \int_Y f(x,y) d\nu(y)$$

$$= \int_{(N^x)^c} f(x,y) d\nu(y)$$

$$\leq \int_{(N^x)^c} \|f_y\|_\infty d\nu(y)$$

$$= \int_Y \|f_y\|_\infty d\nu(y)$$

$$= c.$$

Therefore, $\|F\|_\infty \leq c$.   **QED**

Problem 11. Prove that the theorem remains valid in case the two measure spaces are complete and it is assumed only that f is $\mathcal{M} \times \mathcal{N}$-measurable.

Problem 12. By playing with exponents show that, more generally,

$$\left[\int_X \left(\int_Y |f(x,y)|^q d\nu(y) \right)^{p/q} d\mu(x) \right]^{1/p}$$

$$\leq \left[\int_Y \left(\int_X |f(x,y)|^p d\mu(x) \right)^{q/p} d\nu(y) \right]^{1/q}$$

if $0 < q \leq p < \infty$.

Problem 13 (HARDY'S INEQUALITY). Given a function $f \in L^p(0, \infty)$, define

$$F(x) = x^{-1} \int_0^x f(y) dy.$$

(a) Prove that if $1 < p \leq \infty$, then $F \in L^p(0, \infty)$ and

$$\|F\|_p \leq p' \|f\|_p.$$

(**HINT:** Change the variable by setting $y = xt$. Then use the generalized Minkowski inequality.)

(b) Prove that the constant p' in this inequality is the smallest possible.
(**HINT:** Try $f(x) = x^{\epsilon - 1/p} \chi_{(0,1)}(x)$.)

(c) Prove that if $f \in L^1(0, \infty)$ is nonnegative and not zero, then $F \notin L^1(0, \infty)$.

Problem 14. In a similar way to Problem 13 analyze the function

$$F(x) = \int_x^\infty y^{-1} f(y) dy.$$

Convolutions

We discussed convolutions briefly in the treatment of mollifying in Section 7.C, but we shall now go into more detail.

A. Formal Properties

In this section we shall not bother with integrability or measurability considerations, but shall merely state what we want the definition to be (if it makes sense) and shall state the simple properties we want convolutions to enjoy.

So here is the *formal* definition. If f and g are measurable functions on $\mathbb{R}^n$, we want the *convolution* of f and g to be another function on $\mathbb{R}^n$, denoted $f * g$, and defined in some sense by the equation

$$(f * g)(x) = \int_{\mathbb{R}^n} f(y)g(x - y)dy \qquad \text{for } x \in \mathbb{R}^n.$$

This operation is formally commutative and associative. To prove commutativity let $x - y = y'$ for fixed x:

$$(f * g)(x) = \int_{\mathbb{R}^n} f(x - y')g(y')dy'$$
$$= (g * f)(x).$$

Problem 1. Give a similar formal proof of the associativity:

$$(f * g) * h = f * (g * h).$$

In the next section we shall actually prove that these properties hold and also establish the very existence of $f * g$ in various circumstances. In the meantime, here are some problems which should serve to acquaint you with the idea of convolution.

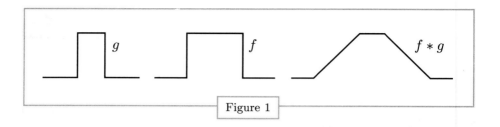

Figure 1

Problem 2. On $\mathbb{R}^1$ let $f = \chi_{(-a,a)}$ and $g = \chi_{(-b,b)}$, where $0 < b \le a$. Verify that

$$(f * g)(x) = \begin{cases} 2b & \text{if } |x| \le a - b, \\ a + b - |x| & \text{if } a - b \le |x| \le a + b, \\ 0 & \text{if } a + b \le |x|. \end{cases}$$

(See Figure 1 above.)

Problem 3. On $\mathbb{R}^1$ verify that for $a > 0$

$$\frac{1}{a^2 + x^2} * \frac{1}{a^2 + x^2} = \frac{2\pi/a}{4a^2 + x^2}.$$

Problem 4. On $\mathbb{R}^1$ let $f(x) = e^{-a|x|}$, $g(x) = e^{-b|x|}$, where $a + b > 0$, and $a \ne b$. Verify that

$$f * g = 2\frac{be^{-a|x|} - ae^{-b|x|}}{b^2 - a^2}.$$

If $a = b > 0$ verify that

$$f * g = \left(|x| + \frac{1}{a}\right) e^{-a|x|}.$$

Problem 5. On $\mathbb{R}^1$ let

$$f(x) = \begin{cases} e^{-ax}, & x \ge 0, \\ 0, & x < 0, \end{cases}$$

$$g(x) = \begin{cases} e^{-bx}, & x \ge 0, \\ 0, & x < 0, \end{cases}$$

where $a \neq b$. Verify that

$$(f * g)(x) = \begin{cases} \dfrac{e^{-ax} - e^{-bx}}{b - a}, & x \geq 0, \\ 0, & x < 0. \end{cases}$$

If $a = b$ show that $f * g = xe^{-ax}$ for $x \geq 0$.

Problem 6. On $\mathbb{R}^1$ show that

$$\frac{1}{x + i} * \frac{1}{x + i} = \frac{-2\pi i}{x + 2i},$$

$$\frac{1}{x + i} * \frac{1}{x - i} = 0.$$

Problem 7. On $\mathbb{R}^1$ show that $\dfrac{1}{(x + i)^2} * \dfrac{1}{(x - i)^2} = 0.$

Problem 8. On $\mathbb{R}^1$ verify that if $a + b > 0$

$$e^{-ax^2} * e^{-bx^2} = \sqrt{\frac{\pi}{a + b}}\, e^{-\frac{ab}{a+b}x^2}.$$

Problem 9. On $\mathbb{R}^n$ verify that

$$e^{-a|x|^2} * e^{-b|x|^2} = \left(\frac{\pi}{a + b}\right)^{n/2} e^{-\frac{ab}{a+b}|x|^2}.$$

Problem 10. Let T be an invertible $n \times n$ matrix and use the notation $(f \circ T)(x) = f(Tx)$. Prove that

$$(f * g) \circ T = |\det T|(f \circ T) * (g \circ T).$$

Problem 11. Prove that if f and g are rotationally symmetric on $\mathbb{R}^n$, then so is $f * g$. Note how this result is reflected in Problems 2, 3, 4, 8, 9.

Problem 12. If supp f is defined as in Problem 7.21, show that

$$\text{supp}(f * g) \subset (\text{supp } f + \text{supp } g)^-.$$

(This is the algebraic sum defined in Section 3.B.)

B. Basic Inequalities

In this section we prove the pertinent facts. First, if f is a Lebesgue measurable function on $\mathbb{R}^n$, then the function $f(x)$ considered as a function of (x, y) in $\mathbb{R}^{2n}$ is also Lebesgue measurable. This follows from Problem 11.2, which implies that $\mathcal{L}_n \times \mathcal{L}_n \subset \mathcal{L}_{2n}$; this fact in turn shows that $f(x)$ is measurable, because the sets we must check have the form

$$\{(x, y) \in \mathbb{R}^{2n} \mid f(x) \le t\} = \{x \in \mathbb{R}^n \mid f(x) \le t\} \times \mathbb{R}^n,$$

and these sets are measurable rectangles.

Now we observe that the transformation of $\mathbb{R}^{2n}$ to $\mathbb{R}^{2n}$ given by $(x, y) \to (x - y, y)$ is linear and invertible, so the theorem in Section 7.B on linear changes of variables implies that $f(x - y)$ is a Lebesgue measurable function of $(x, y) \in \mathbb{R}^{2n}$.

If we are given two measurable functions f and g on $\mathbb{R}^n$, then the above remarks allow us to conclude that

$$f(y)g(x - y) \quad \text{is measurable on} \quad \mathbb{R}^{2n}.$$

Therefore, we can at least hope that Fubini's theorem will be applicable.

The next theorem will assert that if f and g are in $L^1(\mathbb{R}^n)$, then $f * g$ exists a.e. and also belongs to $L^1(\mathbb{R}^n)$. This is not obvious. Even the existence of $f * g$ a.e. is not obvious, as there is no guarantee for a fixed x that the integrable functions of y, $f(y)$ and $g(x - y)$, have an integrable product: The product of two integrable functions is not necessarily integrable.

Theorem: *Assume $f, g \in L^1(\mathbb{R}^n)$. Then for a.e. $x \in \mathbb{R}^n$, $(f * g)(x)$ exists; that is, $f(y)g(x - y)$ is an integrable function of y. Moreover, $f * g \in L^1(\mathbb{R}^n)$, and*

$$\|f * g\|_1 \le \|f\|_1 \|g\|_1.$$

Proof: Assume first that f and g are nonnegative. As we observed just before the theorem, $f(y)g(x-y)$ is a (nonnegative) measurable function on $\mathbb{R}^{2n}$. Therefore, Fubini's theorem for nonnegative functions is applicable and shows that

$$\int dx \int f(y)g(x-y)dy = \int dy \int f(y)g(x-y)dx.$$

The left side is of course $\int (f * g)(x)dx$, while the right side is

$$\int f(y)dy \int g(x-y)dx = \int f(y)dy \cdot \int g(x)dx.$$

Thus, the theorem is valid in this case, and we obtain

$$\|f * g\|_1 = \|f\|_1\|g\|_1.$$

Now for the general case. What we have just proved shows that $|f| * |g|$ exists a.e. Thus, for a.e. x the function of y given by $|f(y)g(x-y)|$ is integrable. But this means that $f(y)g(x-y)$ is integrable. Therefore, we conclude that $f * g$ exists a.e. Since $|f * g| \le |f| * |g|$, we also obtain

$$\|f * g\|_1 \le \| \, |f| * |g| \, \|_1 = \|f\|_1\|g\|_1.$$

QED

The following is an important generalization of this theorem.

Young's Theorem: *Assume* p, q, r, $\in [1, \infty]$ *and*

$$\frac{1}{r} = \frac{1}{p} + \frac{1}{q} - 1.$$

If $f \in L^p(\mathbb{R}^n)$ *and* $g \in L^q(\mathbb{R}^n)$, *then* $f * g$ *exists a.e. and belongs to* $L^r(\mathbb{R}^n)$. *Moreover,*

$$\|f * g\|_r \le \|f\|_p\|g\|_q.$$

Proof: There is no loss in generality in assuming $\|f\|_p = \|g\|_q = 1$. If we prove the theorem for nonnegative functions first, then for general f and g we shall know that $|f| * |g|$ exists a.e. That is, $|f(y)g(x-y)|$ is integrable for a.e. x. But then $f(y)g(x-y)$ is integrable as well, so $(f * g)(x)$ exists, and the result follows.

Thus, we assume $f \geq 0$, $g \geq 0$. We apply Hölder's inequality for three functions (see Problem 10.2) in the following manner:

$$(f * g)(x) = \int \left[f(y)^{p/r} g(x-y)^{q/r} \right] f(y)^{1-p/r} g(x-y)^{1-q/r} dy$$

$$\leq \left[\int f(y)^p g(x-y)^q dy \right]^{1/r} \left[\int f(y)^{(1-p/r)q'} dy \right]^{1/q'}$$

$$\times \left[\int g(x-y)^{(1-q/r)p'} dy \right]^{1/p'} .$$

This is legitimate because

$$\frac{1}{r} + \frac{1}{q'} + \frac{1}{p'} = \frac{1}{r} + \left(1 - \frac{1}{q} \right) + \left(1 - \frac{1}{p} \right) = 1.$$

Note that

$$\left(1 - \frac{p}{r} \right) q' = p \left(\frac{1}{p} - \frac{1}{r} \right) q' = p \left(1 - \frac{1}{q} \right) q' = p;$$

$$\left(1 - \frac{q}{r} \right) p' = q \left(\frac{1}{q} - \frac{1}{r} \right) p' = q \left(1 - \frac{1}{p} \right) p' = q.$$

Thus, the above inequality states simply that

$$(f * g)(x) \leq \left[\int f(y)^p g(x-y)^q dy \right]^{1/r} \cdot 1 \cdot 1,$$

or

$$(f * g)^r (x) \leq \int f(y)^p g(x-y)^q dy.$$

That is,

$$(f * g)^r \leq f^p * g^q.$$

Therefore, the previous theorem implies

$$\int (f * g)^r dx \leq \| f^p * g^q \|_1$$

$$= \| f^p \|_1 \| g^q \|_1$$

$$= \| f \|_p^p \| g \|_q^q$$

$$= 1.$$

QED

Problem 13. Assume $1 \le p_k \le \infty$ for $k = 1, \ldots, N$ and $1 \le r \le \infty$ and

$$\frac{1}{r'} = \frac{1}{p_1'} + \cdots + \frac{1}{p_N'}.$$

Prove that

$$\|f_1 * \cdots * f_N\|_r \le \|f_1\|_{p_1} \cdots \|f_N\|_{p_N}.$$

Problem 14. An important special case of Young's theorem occurs when $q = 1$, so that $r = p$, and the theorem asserts

$$\|f * g\|_p \le \|f\|_p \|g\|_1.$$

Prove this inequality by using the generalized Minkowski inequality of Section 11.E.

You may have noticed that our proof of Young's theorem was deficient, in that we ignored the possibility that one or two of the exponents could be ∞. Nothing was actually lost because the theorem is trivial in such cases: If $p = \infty$, then $r = \infty$ and $q = 1$, and the result follows because $|f * g| \le \|f\|_\infty \|g\|_1$. If $r = \infty$, then $q = p'$, and the result follows by Hölder's inequality: $|f * g| \le \|f\|_p \|g\|_{p'}$. So the missing case in the proof always has $r = \infty$ and we are dealing with a simple application of Hölder's inequality. In this case, not only is the theorem trivial, but even more is true than $f * g \in L^\infty$, as we now show.

> ***Theorem:*** *Assume $1 \le p \le \infty$ and $f \in L^p(\mathbb{R}^n)$, $g \in L^{p'}(\mathbb{R}^n)$. Then the integral defining $(f * g)(x)$ exists for every $x \in \mathbb{R}^n$. The function $f * g$ thus defined is bounded and uniformly continuous on $\mathbb{R}^n$. Moreover, if $1 < p < \infty$, then also $f * g \in C_0$, meaning that $\lim\limits_{|x| \to \infty} (f * g)(x) = 0$.*

Proof: In the general case, one of p, p' must be finite (or both). Assume $p' < \infty$. If $\epsilon > 0$, then the corollary on p.245 shows that there exists $\delta > 0$ such that if $|y| \le \delta$, then $\|\tau_y g - g\|_{p'} \le \epsilon$. Therefore, if $|x - x'| \le \delta$, then

$$\|\tau_x g - \tau_{x'} g\|_{p'} = \|\tau_{x-x'} g - g\|_{p'} \le \epsilon.$$

Thus Hölder's inequality implies

$$|(f * g)(x) - (f * g)(x')| \le \int |f(y)||g(x-y) - g(x'-y)|dy$$

$$= \int |f(-y)||g(x+y) - g(x'+y)|dy$$

$$\le \|f\|_p \|\tau_x g - \tau_{x'} g\|_{p'}$$

$$\le \|f\|_p \epsilon.$$

Therefore, $f * g$ is uniformly continuous. Now assume $1 < p < \infty$. We apply the approximation result on p.245 to produce sequences $f_k \in C_c(\mathbb{R}^n)$ and $g_k \in C_c(\mathbb{R}^n)$ such that $f_k \to f$ in L^p and $g_k \to g$ in $L^{p'}$. Problem 12 shows that $f_k * g_k \in C_c(\mathbb{R}^n)$. Then we estimate as follows:

$$\|f_k * g_k - f * g\|_\infty \le \|f_k * (g_k - g)\|_\infty + \|(f_k - f) * g\|_\infty$$

$$\le \|f_k\|_p \|g_k - g\|_{p'} + \|f_k - f\|_p \|g\|_{p'}$$

$$\to 0 \quad \text{as} \quad k \to \infty.$$

Since $f_k * g_k$ thus converges uniformly to $f * g$, it follows that $f * g$ tends to zero as $|x| \to \infty$.   **QED**

Problem 15. Give an example of $f \in L^1$, $g \in L^\infty$, such that $f * g \notin C_0$.

C. Approximate Identities

The Banach space $L^1(\mathbb{R}^n)$ is an *algebra* with a product (convolution) which is both commutative and associative. We might then wonder whether this algebra has a multiplicative identity; that is, does there exist $\phi \in L^1(\mathbb{R}^n)$ such that $f * \phi = f$ for all $f \in L^1(\mathbb{R}^n)$? We can easily show that no such ϕ exists. For if ϕ does have this property, then in particular $f * \phi = f$ for all $f \in L_c^\infty(\mathbb{R}^n)$. But the last result in Section B implies $f * \phi$ is continuous in this case, and we conclude that every bounded measurable function with compact support is continuous. That is, if f is bounded and measurable and has compact support, then there exists a continuous function equal to it almost everywhere. This is impossible (take $f = \chi_{B(0,1)}$), so we conclude that ϕ does not exist.

Problem 16. Give another proof of the nonexistence of an identity ϕ, based on the following steps. If ϕ exists, use $\chi_{B(0,r)} * \phi = \chi_{B(0,r)}$ to conclude that there exists $x \in B(0,r)$ such that $(\chi_{B(0,r)} * \phi)(x) = 1$. Then show that $\int\limits_{B(0,2r)} |\phi(y)|dy \geq 1$. Now use the theorem on absolute continuity on p.141.

Although the algebra $L^1(\mathbb{R}^n)$ has no identity, it does have an "approximate identity," in the sense that there exists a sequence $\{\phi_k\}$ in $L^1(\mathbb{R}^n)$ such that for all $f \in L^1(\mathbb{R}^n)$, the $L^1(\mathbb{R}^n)$ limit exists:

$$\lim_{k \to \infty} f * \phi_k = f.$$

In fact, this limit even holds for $f \in L^p(\mathbb{R}^n)$ if $1 \leq p < \infty$, as we now prove.

Theorem: *Let $\{\phi_k\}$ be a sequence of functions in $L^1(\mathbb{R}^n)$ such that*

1. $\lim\limits_{k \to \infty} \int \phi_k dx = c$ *exists;*

2. $\int |\phi_k| dx \leq M$ *for some finite constant M;*

3. for all $r > 0$,

$$\lim_{k \to \infty} \int\limits_{|x| \geq r} |\phi_k(x)| dx = 0.$$

Then for every $f \in L^p(\mathbb{R}^n)$, $1 \leq p < \infty$,

$$\lim_{k \to \infty} \|f * \phi_k - cf\|_p = 0.$$

Proof: Let $c_k = \int \phi_k dx$. Then we have by definition

$$(f * \phi_k)(x) - c_k f(x) = \int [f(x - y) - f(x)]\, \phi_k(y) dy.$$

By the generalized Minkowski inequality (p.271) we obtain

$$\|f * \phi_k - c_k f\|_p \leq \int \|\tau_{-y} f - f\|_p |\phi_k(y)| dy.$$

By the continuity of translation in L^p (see the corollary on p.245), for any $\epsilon > 0$ there exists $r > 0$ such that if $|y| < r$,

$$\|\tau_{-y}f - f\|_p \le \frac{\epsilon}{3M}.$$

Also for any $y \in \mathbb{R}^n$ the triangle inequality implies $\|\tau_{-y}f - f\|_p \le 2\|f\|_p$. Therefore,

$$\|f * \phi_k - c_k f\|_p \le \int_{B(0,r)} \frac{\epsilon}{3M}|\phi_k(y)|dy + \int_{B(0,r)^c} 2\|f\|_p|\phi_k(y)|dy$$

$$\le \frac{\epsilon}{3M}\int_{\mathbb{R}^n} |\phi_k(y)|dy + 2\|f\|_p \int_{B(0,r)^c} |\phi_k(y)|dy.$$

By assumptions 1 and 3 there exists k_0 such that for $k \ge k_0$

$$|c_k - c| \le \frac{\epsilon}{3\|f\|_p},$$

$$\int_{B(0,r)^c} |\phi_k(y)|dy \le \frac{\epsilon}{6\|f\|_p}.$$

Using these inequalities and also assumption 2, it follows that for $k \ge k_0$

$$\|f * \phi_k - cf\|_p \le \|f * \phi_k - c_k f\|_p + |c_k - c|\,\|f\|_p$$

$$\le \frac{\epsilon}{3M} \cdot M + 2\|f\|_p \cdot \frac{\epsilon}{6\|f\|_p} + \frac{\epsilon}{3\|f\|_p}\|f\|_p$$

$$= \epsilon.$$

QED

Problem 17. By imitating the steps of the above proof, obtain the substitute results in case $p = \infty$: If $f \in L^\infty(\mathbb{R}^n)$ and f is continuous at x, then

$$\lim_{k \to \infty} (f * \phi_k)(x) = cf(x).$$

If $f \in L^\infty(\mathbb{R}^n)$ and is uniformly continuous, then $f * \phi_k \to cf$ uniformly; that is,

$$\lim_{k \to \infty} \|f * \phi_k - cf\|_\infty = 0.$$

The theorem will usually be applied in a much more concrete situation. The functions ϕ_k will usually be nonnegative so that condition 2 is superfluous, as it is then implied by 1. Moreover, the approximate identity usually will arise from a single function $\phi \in L^1(\mathbb{R}^n)$, by means of the rescaling introduced in Section 7.C: For any $a > 0$ we define

$$\phi_a(x) = a^{-n}\phi\left(\frac{x}{a}\right).$$

If

$$c = \int_{\mathbb{R}^n} \phi\, dx,$$

then we see that

1. $\displaystyle\int \phi_a(x)\,dx = c;$

2. $\displaystyle\int |\phi_a(x)|\,dx = \|\phi\|_1;$

3. $\displaystyle\int_{|x|\geq r} |\phi_a(x)|\,dx = a^{-n}\int_{|x|\geq r} \left|\phi\left(\frac{x}{a}\right)\right|\,dx = \int_{|y|\geq r/a} |\phi(y)|\,dy.$

For any $r > 0$, the last integral has limit 0 as $a \to 0$, by LDCT. Therefore, if we view the parameter a as tending to zero, the family of functions $\{\phi_a\}$ satisfies the hypothesis of the theorem.

Remark: One particularly nice feature of this discussion is its relation to mollifying, which we discussed in Section 7.C. In that analysis we were dealing with a function $\phi \in C_c^\infty(\mathbb{R}^n)$ such that $\int_{\mathbb{R}^n} \phi(x)\,dx = 1$. Thus all the assumptions for approximate identities are satisfied, and we obtain immediately that for all $f \in L^p(\mathbb{R}^n)$, $1 \leq p < \infty$, $f * \phi_a \to f$ in L^p as $a \to 0$. Moreover, $f * \phi_a$ is infinitely differentiable, as we proved in Section 7.C. Thus, the functions $f * \phi_a$ provide an approximation to f in L^p by functions in $C^\infty \cap L^p$.

We cannot use this remark to provide an alternative proof of the approximation theorem for L^p, however. The reason is that the present chapter relies on L^p continuity of translation, and our proof of this property of translation depended on the approximation result.

To finish this chapter we investigate the inequality in Young's theorem in the elementary case $q = 1$, $r = p$ (see Problem 14).

Theorem: *Suppose g is a nonnegative measurable function on $\mathbb{R}^n$. Suppose that for some constant C*

$$\|f * g\|_p \leq C\|f\|_p$$

for all nonnegative $f \in L^p(\mathbb{R}^n)$. Then $C \geq \|g\|_1$.
  On the other hand, suppose $f \in L^p(\mathbb{R}^n)$ and that for some constant D

$$\|f * g\|_p \leq D\|g\|_1$$

for all $g \in L^1(\mathbb{R}^n)$. Then $D \geq \|f\|_p$.

Proof: First assume $g \geq 0$ is fixed. Let $a > 1$ be a constant and define

$$f = \chi_{B(0,ar)}.$$

Then $\|f\|_p = (\lambda(B(0,ar)))^{1/p}$. For $|x| < r$ we have

$$f * g(x) = \int\limits_{|y|<ar} g(x-y)dy$$

$$\geq \int\limits_{|x-y|<ar-r} g(x-y)dy$$

$$= \int\limits_{B(0,(a-1)r)} g d\lambda \quad \text{(a constant)}.$$

Thus

$$\|f * g\|_p \geq \int\limits_{B(0,(a-1)r)} g d\lambda \cdot \|\chi_{B(0,r)}\|_p.$$

Therefore the assumption on C implies

$$\int\limits_{B(0,(a-1)r)} g d\lambda \leq C\frac{\lambda(B(0,ar))^{1/p}}{\lambda(B(0,r))^{1/p}} = Ca^{n/p}.$$

Now let $r \to \infty$, using LICT to conclude

$$\|g\|_1 \leq Ca^{n/p}.$$

Now let $a \to 1$ to obtain $\|g\|_1 \leq C$. (The above argument also handles the case $p = \infty$.)

The second part of the theorem is easily handled in case $p < \infty$ by choosing $g = \phi_k$, where the sequence $\{\phi_k\}$ is an approximate identity. Thus

$$\|f * \phi_k\|_p \leq D\|\phi_k\|_1.$$

Let $k \to \infty$ to obtain $\|f\|_p \leq D$. If $p = \infty$ the hypothesis states

$$\left| \int_{\mathbb{R}^n} f(y)g(x-y)dy \right| \leq D\|g\|_1.$$

This holds for all x, thanks to the last theorem of Section B. Take $x = 0$ and replace $g(y)$ by $g(-y)$ to obtain

$$\left| \int_{\mathbb{R}^n} fg d\lambda \right| \leq D\|g\|_1.$$

By Problem 10.26, the "reverse" of Hölder's inequality, we conclude that $\|f\|_\infty \leq D$.   **QED**

The first part of this theorem can be used in some unlikely situations. For instance, consider Hardy's inequality, as stated in Problem 11.13. There

$$F(x) = x^{-1} \int_0^x f(y)dy \qquad \text{for } 0 < x < \infty.$$

This doesn't appear to be a convolution, but it can be recognized as a disguised one by changing variables. So let

$$x = e^\xi,$$
$$y = e^\eta.$$

Then

$$F(e^\xi) = e^{-\xi} \int_{-\infty}^\xi f(e^\eta)e^\eta d\eta.$$

Notice also that

$$\|f\|_p^p = \int_0^\infty |f(x)|^p dx$$

$$= \int_{-\infty}^\infty |f(e^\xi)|^p e^\xi d\xi,$$

so that

$$\|f\|_{L^p(0,\infty)} = \|e^{\xi/p} f(e^\xi)\|_{L^p(\mathbb{R})}.$$

The same equation is valid for $p = \infty$ when we interpret $e^{\xi/p}$ to be 1. Thus we are led to the equation

$$e^{\xi/p} F(e^\xi) = e^{-\xi/p'} \int_{-\infty}^{\xi} e^{\eta/p} f(e^\eta) e^{\eta/p'} d\eta$$

$$= \int_{\mathbb{R}} e^{\eta/p} f(e^\eta) g(\xi - \eta) d\eta,$$

where

$$g(t) = \begin{cases} e^{-t/p'} & \text{for } 0 < t < \infty, \\ 0 & \text{for } -\infty < t < 0. \end{cases}$$

This formula *is* a convolution on $\mathbb{R}$, so Young's theorem yields immediately

$$\|e^{\xi/p} F(e^\xi)\|_p \le \|g\|_1 \|e^{\xi/p} f(e^\xi)\|_p;$$

and the first part of the theorem shows that $\|g\|_1$ is the best constant. Now

$$\|g\|_1 = \int_0^\infty e^{-t/p'} dt = p'.$$

Thus,

$$\|F\|_{L^p(0,\infty)} \le p' \|f\|_{L^p(0,\infty)},$$

and p' is the best constant.

Problem 18. Analyze Problem 11.14 in a similar way.

Problem 19. Now consider the function

$$F(x) = \int_0^\infty \frac{f(y)}{x + y} dy, \quad 0 < x < \infty.$$

By judicious changes of variables, rewrite this in the form of a convolution over $\mathbb{R}$. Then prove that if $1 < p < \infty$,

$$\|F\|_p \leq \frac{\pi}{\sin \frac{\pi}{p}} \|f\|_p,$$

and show that the constant is the best possible.

(**HINT**: To evaluate the constant you will need Problem 9.39.)

Problem 20. Prove HILBERT'S INEQUALITY:

$$\int_0^\infty \int_0^\infty \frac{|f(x)g(y)|}{x+y} \, dx \, dy \leq \frac{\pi}{\sin \frac{\pi}{p}} \|f\|_p \|g\|_{p'}.$$

Problem 21. Prove the discrete version of Hilbert's inequality: For $a = (a_0, a_1, \ldots) \in l^p$ and $b = (b_0, b_1, \ldots) \in l^{p'}$,

$$\sum_{m,n=0}^\infty \frac{|a_m b_n|}{m+n+1} \leq \frac{\pi}{\sin \frac{\pi}{p}} \|a\|_p \|b\|_{p'}.$$

(**HINT**: Use Problem 20 with appropriate f and g. You should require the estimate

$$\int_m^{m+1} \int_n^{n+1} \frac{dy \, dx}{x+y} \geq \frac{1}{m+n+1}.)$$

Fourier Transform on $\mathbb{R}^n$

In this chapter we shall make constant use of the *inner product* on $\mathbb{R}^n$: If x and $\xi \in \mathbb{R}^n$, then their inner product is denoted

$$x \cdot \xi = \sum_{k=1}^{n} x_k \xi_k.$$

We shall also require the Schwarz inequality (see Problem 1.12)

$$|x \cdot \xi| \leq |x|\,|\xi|.$$

The functions we consider will almost always be thought of as complex-valued. We denote by i a square root of -1, and we also use Euler's formula

$$e^{i\theta} = \cos\theta + i\sin\theta.$$

A. The Fourier Transform of Functions in $L^1(\mathbb{R}^n)$

We shall strive for consistency in denoting the functions to be transformed as depending on $x \in \mathbb{R}^n$ and their Fourier transforms as depending on $\xi \in \mathbb{R}^n$. (We shall not always succeed.)

Definition: If $f \in L^1(\mathbb{R}^n)$, the *Fourier transform* of f is the function on $\mathbb{R}^n$ defined by

$$\widehat{f}(\xi) = \int_{\mathbb{R}^n} f(x)e^{-ix\cdot\xi}dx.$$

The assumption that $f \in L^1$ is indispensable if $\widehat{f}(\xi)$ is to be defined in this manner, because $|f(x)e^{-ix\cdot\xi}| = |f(x)|$. Thus, the integral exists if and only if $f \in L^1$. In Section D, however, we shall see how to define $\widehat{f}$ in case $f \in L^2$. Since $L^2 \not\subset L^1$, a different definition will be required.

The rest of this section contains very basic properties only, all of which are rather easy to prove. Therefore, we shall not state these as theorems, but instead we shall list the properties and prove them as we go.

Properties

FT1 $|\widehat{f}(\xi)| \le \|f\|_1$ for all $\xi \in \mathbb{R}^n$.

Of course this is easy: $|\widehat{f}(\xi)| \le \int |f(x)e^{-ix\cdot\xi}|dx = \int |f(x)|dx = \|f\|_1$.

FT2 $\widehat{f}$ is continuous.

To prove continuity at ξ, suppose $\xi_k \in \mathbb{R}^n$ and $\lim_{k\to\infty} \xi_k = \xi$. Then for all x

$$\lim_{k\to\infty} f(x)e^{-ix\cdot\xi_k} = f(x)e^{-ix\cdot\xi}.$$

Since $|f(x)e^{-ix\cdot\xi_k}| = |f(x)|$, the function $|f|$ serves as a dominating integrable function independent of k. Therefore, LDCT implies $\lim_{k\to\infty} \widehat{f}(\xi_k) = \widehat{f}(\xi)$.

Remark: While this proof is quick and simple, the use of LDCT seems somewhat to obscure a very important principle. So we give a more direct argument. We shall use the simple inequality $|e^{i\theta} - 1| \le |\theta|$ for real θ. We then calculate

$$\widehat{f}(\xi') - \widehat{f}(\xi) = \int f(x) \left[e^{-ix\cdot\xi'} - e^{-ix\cdot\xi} \right] dx$$

$$= \int f(x)e^{-ix\cdot\xi} \left[e^{ix\cdot(\xi-\xi')} - 1 \right] dx;$$

therefore

$$|\widehat{f}(\xi') - \widehat{f}(\xi)| \le \int |f(x)||e^{ix\cdot(\xi-\xi')} - 1|dx.$$

For any $a > 0$

$$|\widehat{f}(\xi') - \widehat{f}(\xi)| \le \int_{|x|\le a} |f(x)||x\cdot(\xi-\xi')|dx + \int_{|x|>a} |f(x)|2dx$$

$$\le |\xi - \xi'| \int_{|x|\le a} |f(x)||x|dx + 2\int_{|x|>a} |f(x)|dx.$$

If $\epsilon > 0$, we can select $a > 0$ such that we have the estimate

$$\int_{|x|>a} |f(x)|dx \le \epsilon/4.$$

For this fixed number a it follows that if $\delta = \epsilon \left[2 \int\limits_{|x| \le a} |f(x)||x|dx \right]^{-1}$,

then

$$|\xi' - \xi| \le \delta \Rightarrow |\widehat{f}(\xi') - \widehat{f}(\xi)| \le \epsilon.$$

Thus we have actually proved more than continuity: $\widehat{f}$ is uniformly continuous. More interesting is the observation that if f is sufficiently small as $|x| \to \infty$, then nice estimates for δ are available. For instance, if $f \in L^1$ and also $|x|f \in L^1$, then

$$|\widehat{f}(\xi') - \widehat{f}(\xi)| \le c|\xi' - \xi|,$$

where $c = \| \, |x| \, f\|_1$. This idea is so important that we paraphrase it as follows:

Scholium 1.   *The decay of $f(x)$ as $|x| \to \infty$ is reflected in the smoothness of $\widehat{f}$.*

FT3   Thus, $\widehat{f}$ is a bounded continuous function on $\mathbb{R}^n$, and $\|\widehat{f}\|_\infty \le \|f\|_1$.

FT4 $\int\limits_{\mathbb{R}^n} f(x)dx = \widehat{f}(0)$.

FT5 $\widehat{f * g} = \widehat{f}\,\widehat{g}$.

This was virtually proved in the proof of the theorem on p.280, where we observed that

$$\int\limits_{\mathbb{R}^n} f * g\, dx = \int\limits_{\mathbb{R}^n} f\, dx \cdot \int\limits_{\mathbb{R}^n} g\, dx.$$

But for fixed ξ we have

$$(f * g)(x)e^{-ix\cdot\xi} = \int f(y)g(x-y)e^{-ix\cdot\xi}dy$$

$$= \int f(y)e^{-iy\cdot\xi}g(x-y)e^{-i(x-y)\cdot\xi}dy$$

$$= ((fe^{-ix\cdot\xi}) * (ge^{-ix\cdot\xi}))(x).$$

Thus,

$$\widehat{f * g}(\xi) = \int (fe^{-ix\cdot\xi}) * (ge^{-ix\cdot\xi})dx$$

$$= \int fe^{-ix\cdot\xi}dx \int ge^{-ix\cdot\xi}dx$$

$$= \widehat{f}(\xi)\widehat{g}(\xi).$$

FT6   For fixed $y \in \mathbb{R}^n$, $\widehat{f(x+y)} = e^{iy\cdot\xi}\widehat{f}$.

For fixed $\eta \in \mathbb{R}^n$, $\widehat{e^{ix\cdot\eta}f(x)} = \widehat{f}(\xi - \eta)$.

FT7 $\widehat{f(-x)} = \widehat{f}(-\xi)$.

FT8   If $a > 0$, $\widehat{a^{-n}f\left(\frac{x}{a}\right)} = \widehat{f}(a\xi)$.

FT9   This is a generalization of FT7 and 8. Let T be an invertible $n \times n$ matrix and let T^{tr} denote the *transpose* of T. Then

$$|\det T|\,\widehat{f(Tx)} = \widehat{f}((T^{\text{tr}})^{-1}\xi).$$

To prove this we simply use Section 7.B:

$$|\det T|\,\widehat{f(Tx)} = |\det T| \int f(Tx)e^{-ix\cdot\xi}dx$$

$$= |\det T| \int f(Tx)e^{-iT^{-1}Tx\cdot\xi}dx$$

$$= \int f(y)e^{-iT^{-1}y\cdot\xi}dy$$

$$= \int f(y)e^{-iy\cdot(T^{-1})^{\text{tr}}\xi}dy$$

$$= \widehat{f}((T^{-1})^{\text{tr}}\xi)$$

$$= \widehat{f}((T^{\text{tr}})^{-1}\xi).$$

FT10   If T is an *orthogonal* matrix (Section 3.A), then $(T^{\text{tr}})^{-1} = T$, so we conclude that

$$\widehat{f \circ T} = \widehat{f} \circ T.$$

FT11   If $f \in L^1(\mathbb{R}^n)$ is a *radial* function, meaning that $f(x)$ depends only on $|x|$, then $\widehat{f}$ is also a radial function.

This follows from FT10, since a function f is radial $\iff f \circ T = f$ for all orthogonal matrices T.

FT12 RIEMANN-LEBESGUE LEMMA: For $f \in L^1$, $\displaystyle\lim_{|\xi| \to \infty} \widehat{f}(\xi) = 0$.

To prove this we first use FT6 to write

$$e^{iy \cdot \xi}\widehat{f}(\xi) = \int f(x+y)e^{-ix \cdot \xi}dx.$$

For fixed ξ choose $y = \pi\xi/|\xi|^2$, so that $e^{iy \cdot \xi} = e^{i\pi} = -1$. Therefore,

$$\widehat{f}(\xi) = -\int f(x+y)e^{-ix \cdot \xi}dx.$$

Add this equation to the defining equation for $\widehat{f}(\xi)$ to obtain

$$2\widehat{f}(\xi) = \int [f(x) - f(x+y)]\, e^{-ix \cdot \xi}dx.$$

Therefore,

$$|\widehat{f}(\xi)| \leq \frac{1}{2}\int |f(x) - f(x+y)|dx.$$

But $|y| = \pi|\xi|^{-1}$, so that $y \to 0$ as $|\xi| \to \infty$. The result therefore follows from the continuity of translation in the L^1 norm, which was proved on p.180.

The *proof* of the Riemann-Lebesgue lemma leads us to state

Scholium 2. *The smoothness of f is reflected in the decay of $\widehat{f}(\xi)$ as $|\xi| \to \infty$.*

In proving the Riemann-Lebesgue lemma we did not actually use any smoothness of f. What we did use was the L^1 continuity of translation, which we could regard as a type of smoothness. But if f is actually smooth, we can say more about the decay of $\widehat{f}$ at ∞. For instance, suppose $f \in C_c^1(\mathbb{R}^n)$. Then f vanishes outside a bounded set and $|f(x) - f(x+y)| \leq C|y|$ for some constant C. The estimate we derived above for $\widehat{f}(\xi)$ then shows

$$|\widehat{f}(\xi)| \leq \text{ const } \cdot |y| \leq \text{ const } \cdot |\xi|^{-1}.$$

In Section C we shall go into this matter in more detail.

FT13 We now show the *formal* relationship between differentiation and multiplication by the independent variable. We omit any hypothesis as we are mainly interested in what we can usually expect to hold. Here are the two properties:

$$\widehat{\frac{\partial f}{\partial x_k}} = i\xi_k \widehat{f},$$

$$\widehat{ix_k f} = -\frac{\partial \widehat{f}}{\partial \xi_k}.$$

Since there is no hypothesis, there is nothing we can actually prove. Nevertheless, we want to indicate how we should like to prove these properties. Then in specific cases we'll only have to check that these methods work.

To "prove" the first property we use Fubini's theorem, perform the integration with respect to x_k first, integrate by parts, and hope the boundary terms (at $\pm\infty$) will contribute nothing:

$$\widehat{\frac{\partial f}{\partial x_k}} = \int \frac{\partial f}{\partial x_k} e^{-ix\cdot\xi} dx$$

$$= -\int f \frac{\partial}{\partial x_k} e^{-ix\cdot\xi} dx$$

$$= -\int f \left(-i\xi_k e^{-ix\cdot\xi}\right) dx$$

$$= i\xi_k \widehat{f}.$$

The second property comes by formally differentiating under the integral sign:

$$-\frac{\partial \widehat{f}}{\partial \xi_k} = -\frac{\partial}{\partial \xi_k} \int f(x) e^{-ix\cdot\xi} dx$$

$$= -\int f(x) \frac{\partial}{\partial \xi_k} e^{-ix\cdot\xi} dx$$

$$= \int f(x) ix_k e^{-ix\cdot\xi} dx$$

$$= \widehat{ix_k f}.$$

Notice how these two properties are harmonious with our two scholia: If f decays quite rapidly as $|x| \to \infty$, then large powers of $|x|$ multiplied by f are integrable, so the second property shows that $\widehat{f}$ can be differentiated often. This fits Scholium 1. On the other hand, if f is very smooth and many integrations by parts are allowable, then the first property shows that large powers of $|\xi|$ multiplied by $\widehat{f}$ result in bounded functions. This illustrates Scholium 2.

Problem 1. Give a rigorous proof of this version of the second part of FT13: If f and $|x|f$ are integrable, then $\widehat{ix_k f} = -\partial\widehat{f}/\partial\xi_k$.

(**HINT**: Show that the corollary in Section 6.G applies.)

FT14 $\widehat{f_1(x_1)\ldots f_n(x_n)} = \widehat{f_1}(\xi_1)\ldots\widehat{f_n}(\xi_n)$. This follows immediately from Fubini's theorem and the property of the exponential,

$$e^{-ix\cdot\xi} = e^{-ix_1\xi_1}\ldots e^{-ix_n\xi_n}.$$

FT15 If $\bar{f}$ denotes the complex conjugate, then $\overline{f(-x)} = \widehat{\bar{f}}(\xi)$. Thus, if $\overline{f(-x)} = f(x)$, then $\widehat{f}$ is real-valued.

FT16 EXAMPLES ON $\mathbb{R}^1$.

a. $f = \chi_{(-a,a)}$. Here

$$\widehat{f}(\xi) = \int_{-a}^{a} e^{-ix\xi}dx$$

$$= \int_{-a}^{a} \cos x\xi\, dx$$

$$= \frac{2\sin a\xi}{\xi}.$$

b. $f(x) = \begin{cases} e^{-x}, & 0 < x < \infty, \\ 0, & -\infty < x < 0. \end{cases}$ Then

$$\widehat{f}(\xi) = \int_{0}^{\infty} e^{-x(1+i\xi)}dx = \frac{1}{1+i\xi}.$$

c. $f(x) = \begin{cases} xe^{-x}, & 0 < x < \infty, \\ 0, & -\infty < x < 0. \end{cases}$ We can calculate directly,

or we can instead use FT13: This function is x times the function of the preceding example, so

$$\widehat{f} = i\frac{d}{d\xi}\frac{1}{1 + i\xi} = \frac{1}{(1 + i\xi)^2}.$$

d. $f(x) = e^{-|x|}$. In this case

$$\widehat{f}(\xi) = \int_{-\infty}^{0} e^{x}e^{-ix\xi}dx + \int_{0}^{\infty} e^{-x}e^{-ix\xi}dx$$

$$= \frac{1}{1 - i\xi} + \frac{1}{1 + i\xi}$$

$$= \frac{2}{1 + \xi^2}.$$

e. $f(x) = \begin{cases} \cos x, & |x| \leq \pi/2, \\ 0, & |x| \geq \pi/2. \end{cases}$ Here for $\xi^2 \neq 1$,

$$\widehat{f}(\xi) = \int_{-\pi/2}^{\pi/2} \cos x\, e^{-ix\xi}dx$$

$$= \int_{-\pi/2}^{\pi/2} \cos x \cos x\xi\, dx$$

$$= 2\int_{0}^{\pi/2} \cos x \cos x\xi\, dx$$

$$= \int_{0}^{\pi/2} [\cos(x + x\xi) + \cos(x - x\xi)]\, dx$$

$$= \frac{\sin(1+\xi)x}{1+\xi}\Big|_0^{\pi/2} + \frac{\sin(1-\xi)x}{1-\xi}\Big|_0^{\pi/2}$$

$$= \frac{\sin(1+\xi)\pi/2}{1+\xi} + \frac{\sin(1-\xi)\pi/2}{1-\xi}$$

$$= \frac{\cos \pi\xi/2}{1+\xi} + \frac{\cos \pi\xi/2}{1-\xi}$$

$$= \frac{2\cos \pi\xi/2}{1-\xi^2}.$$

f. $f(x) = \begin{cases} \sin x, & |x| < \pi/2, \\ 0, & |x| > \pi/2. \end{cases}$ This function is the negative of
the derivative of the preceding, and it is easy to see that FT13
is valid in this case. Thus,

$$\widehat{f}(\xi) = -i\xi\frac{2\cos \pi\xi/2}{1-\xi^2}.$$

g. $f(x) = e^{-x^2}$. This example is extremely important, and the
formula for $\widehat{f}$ can be derived in many ways. Here is a way
which illustrates FT13.

Note that $f' = -2xf$. Thus, FT13 implies

$$\widehat{f'} = 2i\,\widehat{ixf};$$

$$i\xi\widehat{f} = -2i\frac{d\widehat{f}}{d\xi};$$

$$\frac{d\widehat{f}}{d\xi} = -\frac{\xi}{2}\widehat{f}.$$

(This function decays so rapidly and enjoys such smoothness
that the use of the formal properties in FT13 is completely
justified.) The solutions of this ordinary differential equation
are precisely

$$\widehat{f} = ce^{-\xi^2/4},$$

where c is a constant. For $\xi = 0$ we obtain

$$c = \widehat{f}(0) = \int f(x)dx$$

$$= \int e^{-x^2}dx = \sqrt{\pi}.$$

This constant comes from Problem 8.1 or from p.202. Thus, we have found that

$$\widehat{e^{-x^2}} = \sqrt{\pi} e^{-\xi^2/4}.$$

By combining this with FT8, we find for any $a > 0$

$$\widehat{e^{-x^2/a}} = \sqrt{\pi a} \; e^{-a\xi^2/4}.$$

In particular,

$$\widehat{e^{-x^2/2}} = \sqrt{2\pi} e^{-\xi^2/2}.$$

Thus, we have found a function f such that $\widehat{f} = \sqrt{2\pi} f$; namely, $f(x) = e^{-x^2/2}$.

Problem 2. Show that the function $h(x) = xe^{-x^2/2}$ has the property that $\widehat{h} = -\sqrt{2\pi} i h$.

Problem 3. Calculate the Fourier transforms of $x^2 e^{-x^2/2}$ and $x^3 e^{-x^2/2}$. Find constants α and β such that if $\phi(x) = (x^2 + \alpha)e^{-x^2/2}$ and $\psi(x) = (x^3 + \beta x)e^{-x^2/2}$, then

$$\widehat{\phi} = -\sqrt{2\pi} \phi,$$
$$\widehat{\psi} = \sqrt{2\pi} i \psi.$$

Observation.   The example $e^{-x^2/2}$ and Problems 2 and 3 give functions $g \in L^1(\mathbb{R})$ satisfying

$$\widehat{g} = cg,$$

where c is one of the four constants $\sqrt{2\pi}$, $\sqrt{2\pi} i$, $-\sqrt{2\pi}$, $-\sqrt{2\pi} i$. After we have proved the inversion theorem in the next section, we shall see that these constants exhaust the possibilities for the equation $\widehat{g} = cg$.

You have probably noticed that the only Fourier transforms we have computed involve exponentials: e^{-x}, e^{-x^2}, $\cos x \, (= (e^{ix} + e^{-ix})/2)$, etc. This is no accident, for the computation of $\widehat{f}(\xi)$ requires the calculation of the integral of $f(x)e^{-ix\xi}$. We shall succeed in finding more interesting Fourier transforms once we have the inversion theorem.

Remarks: We have two different things to point out about these examples. First, the two scholia are illustrated by them. In Examples (a)–(g) the functions decay rapidly at infinity, at least exponentially fast. Accordingly, all their Fourier transforms are infinitely differentiable. This is consistent with Scholium 1. But even here there is a distinction: Examples (a), (e), and (f) have compact support (and thus have the most rapid "decay" at infinity), and their Fourier transforms are all analytic functions of ξ which can be expanded in Taylor series with radii of convergence equal to infinity. In general, a compactly supported function has a Fourier transform which is so "smooth" that it is an analytic function with infinite radius of convergence. But Examples (b), (c), and (d) have analytic Fourier transforms which have finite radii of convergence. If they are expanded about $\xi = 0$, the common radius of convergence is 1.

Now examine Scholium 2. The functions in (a), (b), and (f) are discontinuous — their Fourier transforms decay at ∞ like $|\xi|^{-1}$. The functions in (c), (d), (e) are continuous but not differentiable — their transforms decay like $|\xi|^{-2}$. The function in Example (g) is infinitely differentiable, and its Fourier transform decays like $e^{-\xi^2/4}$.

The second remark is an observation about $\int_{\mathbb{R}} \widehat{f}(\xi)d\xi$ in the cases in which $\widehat{f} \in L^1$ and we are able to calculate the integral. (The inversion theorem will later take care of this once and for all.) In Examples (a), (b), (f) the function $\widehat{f} \notin L^1$. In (c) we have

$$\int_{-\infty}^{\infty} \widehat{f}(\xi)d\xi = \int_{-\infty}^{\infty} \frac{d\xi}{(1+i\xi)^2} = \frac{i}{1+i\xi} \Big|_{-\infty}^{\infty}$$
$$= 0.$$

In (d)

$$\int_{-\infty}^{\infty} \widehat{f}(\xi)d\xi = \int_{-\infty}^{\infty} \frac{2}{1+\xi^2}d\xi = 2\arctan\xi \Big|_{-\infty}^{\infty}$$
$$= 2\pi.$$

In (e) we are unable at present to do the calculation. In Example (g)

$$\int_{-\infty}^{\infty} \widehat{f}(\xi)d\xi = \int_{-\infty}^{\infty} \sqrt{\pi}e^{-\xi^2/4}d\xi$$
$$= 2\pi.$$

Now notice that in all three of these examples

$$\int_{\mathbb{R}} \widehat{f}(\xi)d\xi = 2\pi f(0).$$

Interesting! The next section will show this not to be accidental.

FT17 Here is an example on $\mathbb{R}^n$:

$$\widehat{e^{-|x|^2}} = \pi^{n/2}e^{-|\xi|^2/4}$$

as follows from FT16 (g) and FT14. Notice that for this example we have

$$\int_{\mathbb{R}^n} \widehat{f}(\xi)d\xi = (2\pi)^n f(0).$$

FT18 If f and g are in $L^1(\mathbb{R}^n)$, then

$$\int \widehat{f}(\xi)g(\xi)d\xi = \int f(x)\widehat{g}(x)dx.$$

Note that to write this equation we have been forced to forsake our notational custom. To prove the equation, we note that the function $f(x)g(\xi)e^{-ix\cdot\xi}$ belongs to $L^1(\mathbb{R}^n \times \mathbb{R}^n)$, so that Fubini's theorem implies

$$\int \widehat{f}(\xi)g(\xi)d\xi = \int g(\xi)d\xi \int f(x)e^{-ix\cdot\xi}dx$$

$$= \int f(x)dx \int g(\xi)e^{-i\xi\cdot x}d\xi$$

$$= \int f(x)\widehat{g}(x)dx.$$

Problem 4. This refers back to Problems 8.3 and 8.5. Those problems show that

$$\int\limits_0^\infty \frac{\sin ax}{x}\,dx = \lim_{b\to\infty} \int\limits_0^b \frac{\sin ax}{x}\,dx = \frac{\pi}{2}\,\mathrm{sgn}\,a.$$

Show that this limit exists *boundedly*, meaning that there exists a constant c such that

$$\left|\int\limits_0^b \frac{\sin ax}{x}\,dx\right| \le c.$$

In fact, show that the smallest such number is $c = \int\limits_0^\pi \frac{\sin x}{x}\,dx$.

Problem 5. This problem is concerned with the line $\mathbb{R}$. FT7 shows that if f is odd, then $\widehat{f}$ is odd. In the following section we shall learn that the converse is true also. Thus, f is odd $\iff$ $\widehat{f}$ is odd. Show that in this case

$$\widehat{f}(\xi) = -2i \int\limits_0^\infty f(x)\sin x\xi\,dx.$$

Problem 6. This is a continuation of Problem 5. Suppose that $f \in L^1(\mathbb{R})$ and that f is odd. Prove that

$$\lim_{\substack{b\to\infty \\ a\to 0+}} \int\limits_a^b \frac{\widehat{f}(\xi)}{\xi}\,d\xi = -\pi i \int\limits_0^\infty f(x)\,dx.$$

(**HINT**: Apply Problem 4.)

Problem 7. We have shown that $f \in L^1 \Rightarrow \widehat{f}$ is continuous and tends to zero at infinity ($\widehat{f} \in C_0$, where C_0 is as defined on p.229). Give an example of a function $g \in C_0$ such that there is no $f \in L^1$ for which $\widehat{f} = g$.

(**HINT**: Apply Problem 6.)

Problem 8. By using Example (f), show that

$$\int\limits_0^\infty \frac{\cos(\pi t/2)}{1 - t^2}\, dt = \frac{\pi}{2}.$$

Problem 9. This problem and the next deal with a *symmetric positive definite* $n \times n$ matrix Q. This means that Q is a real matrix satisfying the conditions that $Q^{\mathrm{tr}} = Q$ ("symmetric") and that for all $x \in \mathbb{R}^n$ with $x \neq 0$, $Qx \cdot x > 0$ ("positive definite"). You will need to use the *spectral representation* for such matrices. That is a theorem which states that there exists an *orthogonal* matrix T and a diagonal matrix

$$\Lambda = \begin{pmatrix} \lambda_1 & 0 & \cdots & 0 \\ 0 & \lambda_2 & \cdots & 0 \\ \vdots & \vdots & & \vdots \\ 0 & 0 & \cdots & \lambda_n \end{pmatrix}$$

such that

$$Q = T^{-1}\Lambda T.$$

This spectral theorem is valid for all symmetric matrices. Since Q is also positive definite, the eigenvalues λ_k satisfy $\lambda_k > 0$. Let $\Lambda^{1/2}$ denote the diagonal matrix with diagonal entries $\sqrt{\lambda_k}$. Show that the quadratic form $Qx \cdot x$ satisfies $Qx \cdot x = |\Lambda^{1/2}Tx|^2$. Then use FT9 to prove that

$$\widehat{e^{-Qx \cdot x}} = \frac{\pi^{n/2}}{\sqrt{\det Q}} e^{-Q^{-1}\xi \cdot \xi/4}.$$

Remark: Proofs of the spectral theorem referred to in Problem 9 can be found in most texts on linear algebra. A very short and somewhat unusual proof can be found in an article by H. Wilf in *American Mathematical Monthly* **88** (1981), 49–50.

Problem 10. Problem 9 gives a "standard" proof of the formula derived there. This problem and the next present a less standard proof. The latter proof is somewhat more fundamental, as it requires no use of the spectral theorem. Let $f(x) = e^{-Qx \cdot x}$, where Q is symmetric and positive definite.

(a) Prove that

$$\frac{\partial f}{\partial x_j} = -2\sum_k q_{jk} x_k f.$$

(b) Prove that

$$\xi_j \widehat{f} = -2\sum_k q_{jk} \frac{\partial \widehat{f}}{\partial \xi_k}.$$

(c) Prove that if $Q^{-1} = (\tilde{q}_{jk})$, then

$$\frac{\partial \widehat{f}}{\partial \xi_j} = -\frac{1}{2}\sum_k \tilde{q}_{jk} \xi_k \widehat{f}.$$

(d) Prove that $\frac{\partial}{\partial \xi_j}\left(e^{Q^{-1}\xi\cdot\xi/4}\widehat{f}\right) = 0$.

(e) Conclude that there exists a constant $\phi = \phi(Q)$ depending only on Q such that
$$\widehat{e^{-Qx\cdot x}} = \phi(Q)e^{-Q^{-1}\xi\cdot\xi/4}.$$

Problem 11. The purpose of this problem is to evaluate the constant $\phi(Q)$ in Problem 10.

(a) Show that

$$\phi(Q) = \int_{\mathbb{R}^n} e^{-Qx\cdot x}\,dx.$$

(b) Prove that for any $a > 0$

$$\phi(aQ) = a^{-n/2}\phi(Q).$$

(c) Make the change of variable $x = Q^{-1}y$ to prove that

$$\phi(Q) = \det Q^{-1}\phi(Q^{-1}).$$

(d) For this step you will have to use the inversion theorem of the next section. That theorem will be applicable to the function $e^{-Qx\cdot x}$ and will show that the Fourier transform of *its* Fourier transform is

$$(2\pi)^n e^{-Qx \cdot x}.$$

That is,

$$\widehat{\phi(Q)e^{-Q^{-1}x \cdot x/4}} = (2\pi)^n e^{-Q\xi \cdot \xi}.$$

Use this formula to prove that

$$\phi(Q)\phi(Q^{-1}) = \pi^n.$$

(e) Now prove that

$$\phi(Q) = \frac{\pi^{n/2}}{\sqrt{\det Q}}.$$

Problem 12. Using the notation of Problem 9 show that for all $y \in \mathbb{R}^n$

$$\int_{\mathbb{R}^n} e^{-Qx \cdot x + y \cdot x} dx = \frac{\pi^{n/2}}{\sqrt{\det Q}} e^{Q^{-1}y \cdot y/4}.$$

(If you are acquainted with elementary properties of analytic functions, you will notice that this result follows immediately from Problem 9 by the complex substitution $\xi = iy$. However, prove the equation of this problem by making a judicious change of variable of the form $x = t + a$, where $a \in \mathbb{R}^n$ is a vector for you to choose depending on y.)

B. The Inversion Theorem

The problem we consider in this section is the following: If we are given the function $\widehat{f}$, can we then determine f? There are two ways to think of this problem. One is simply the question of uniqueness: If $\widehat{f} = \widehat{g}$, then does it follow that $f = g$? By linearity of the Fourier transform, the question can be rephrased as follows: If $\widehat{f} = 0$, does it follow that $f = 0$?

We shall answer this question in the affirmative, but we shall do more than merely prove that Fourier transformation is one-to-one. And this is the second way of viewing the problem. Namely, we shall give a *formula* which expresses f in terms of $\widehat{f}$. That is, we shall not only prove that Fourier transformation is one-to-one, but we shall also compute the inverse transformation.

This inversion theorem will be given in several versions, but they will all state that in some sense

$$f(x) = (2\pi)^{-n} \int\limits_{\mathbb{R}^n} \widehat{f}(\xi) e^{ix \cdot \xi} d\xi.$$

This result is rather deep. It is instructive to see what happens if we try to prove it by substituting the formula for $\widehat{f}(\xi)$ into the above integral and applying Fubini's theorem. If we do just that, we obtain formally

$$\int\limits_{\mathbb{R}^n} \widehat{f}(\xi) e^{ix \cdot \xi} d\xi = \int\limits_{\mathbb{R}^n} e^{ix \cdot \xi} d\xi \int\limits_{\mathbb{R}^n} f(y) e^{-iy \cdot \xi} dy$$

$$\stackrel{?}{=} \int\limits_{\mathbb{R}^n} f(y) dy \int\limits_{\mathbb{R}^n} e^{i(x-y) \cdot \xi} d\xi.$$

But this simply does not make sense, as the integral $\int e^{i(x-y)\cdot\xi} d\xi$ does not exist. However, we do see a way to modify this approach so that Fubini's theorem is applicable. Namely, integrate only over a large ball $B(0,r)$ in the ξ variable and then let $r \to \infty$: The first step works as follows:

$$\int\limits_{B(0,r)} \widehat{f}(\xi) e^{ix \cdot \xi} d\xi = \int\limits_{\mathbb{R}^n} f(y) dy \int\limits_{B(0,r)} e^{i(x-y) \cdot \xi} d\xi$$

$$= \int\limits_{\mathbb{R}^n} f(y) \widehat{\chi_{B(0,r)}}(y - x) dy.$$

This leads to problems, however, because we don't have specific information about $\widehat{\chi_{B(0,r)}}$ at the present time.

But we can make a further modification by replacing $\chi_{B(0,r)}$ by a more nicely behaved function which is "close" to 1 in some sense. First, we apply FT18 of the preceding section to the fixed function $f \in L^1$ we wish to investigate and to another function $g \in L^1$:

$$\int \widehat{f}(\xi) g(\xi) d\xi = \int f(y) \widehat{g}(y) dy.$$

For a fixed $x \in \mathbb{R}^n$ replace g in this formula by $e^{ix \cdot \xi} g(\xi)$. Then FT6 shows that $\widehat{g}(y)$ is to be replaced by $\widehat{g}(y - x)$:

$$\int \widehat{f}(\xi) e^{ix \cdot \xi} g(\xi) d\xi = \int f(y) \widehat{g}(y - x) dy.$$

Now replace $g(\xi)$ by $g(-\xi)$ and use FT7:

$$\int \widehat{f}(\xi)e^{ix\cdot\xi}g(-\xi)d\xi = \int f(y)\widehat{g}(x-y)dy.$$

Finally, let $\phi \in L^1$ and for $0 < a < \infty$ replace $g(\xi) = \phi(a\xi)$. By FT8 we have $\widehat{g}(y) = a^{-n}\widehat{\phi}\left(\frac{y}{a}\right)$. Therefore, we obtain our working formula:

$$(*) \qquad \int \widehat{f}(\xi)e^{ix\cdot\xi}\phi(-a\xi)d\xi = \int f(y)a^{-n}\widehat{\phi}\left(\frac{x-y}{a}\right)dy.$$

We choose the function ϕ to be one with the following properties:

$$\phi \in L^1(\mathbb{R}^n),$$
$$\phi \text{ is bounded and continuous,}$$
$$\phi(0) = 1,$$
$$\widehat{\phi} \in L^1(\mathbb{R}^n).$$

Such functions exist: One which we have already met is $\phi(x) = e^{-|x|^2}$ (see FT17).

Now we state a first version of the inversion theorem.

L^1-**Summability Theorem:** *Assume ϕ satisfies the above hypotheses. Assume $f \in L^1(\mathbb{R}^n)$. Then as $a \to 0$ the following limit exists in the sense of convergence in $L^1(\mathbb{R}^n)$:*

$$f(x) = \lim_{a\to 0}(2\pi)^{-n}\int \widehat{f}(\xi)e^{ix\cdot\xi}\phi(-a\xi)d\xi.$$

The convergence statement means of course that

$$\lim_{a\to 0}\int \left| f(x) - (2\pi)^{-n}\int \widehat{f}(\xi)e^{ix\cdot\xi}\phi(-a\xi)d\xi \right| dx = 0.$$

The word "summability" refers to the fact that we do not actually deal with the *integral* $\int \widehat{f}(\xi)e^{ix\cdot\xi}d\xi$ but instead have a way of "integrating" or "summing" a not necessarily integrable function $\widehat{f}(\xi)e^{ix\cdot\xi}$.

Proof: We refer to the discussion of approximate identities in Section 12.C; in accordance with that section we use the notation

$$(\widehat{\phi})_a(y) = a^{-n}\widehat{\phi}\left(\frac{y}{a}\right).$$

Therefore, the formula (∗) states that

$$\int \widehat{f}(\xi)e^{ix\cdot\xi}\phi(-a\xi)d\xi = (f * (\widehat{\phi})_a)(x).$$

The properties of $\widehat{\phi}$ include the fact that $\widehat{\phi} \in L^1$. Therefore, the special version of the approximate identity result on p.287 shows that

$$f * (\widehat{\phi})_a \rightarrow cf \quad \text{in} \quad L^1(\mathbb{R}^n),$$

where

$$c = \int_{\mathbb{R}^n} \widehat{\phi}(x)dx.$$

Thus, the theorem will be proved as soon as we show that $c = (2\pi)^n$. This *is* true for the special case $\phi(x) = e^{-|x|^2}$, as we showed in Property FT17. But we do not yet know that c is independent of ϕ. This independence will be demonstrated in the following proof, so we postpone the conclusion of the present proof until then.

Fourier Inversion Theorem: *Let $f \in L^1(\mathbb{R}^n)$ and assume that $\widehat{f} \in L^1(\mathbb{R}^n)$. Then f is equivalent to a continuous function. Therefore, we assume with no loss of generality that f is continuous. Then for all $x \in \mathbb{R}^n$*

$$f(x) = (2\pi)^{-n}\int \widehat{f}(\xi)e^{ix\cdot\xi}d\xi.$$

Notice the beautiful symmetry which is present here: Compare this formula with the defining equation

$$\widehat{f}(\xi) = \int f(x)e^{-ix\cdot\xi}dx.$$

Proof: We continue with the notation and the type of function ϕ introduced above. Since $\widehat{f} \in L^1$ and ϕ is bounded and continuous, LDCT implies that for all $x \in \mathbb{R}^n$

$$\lim_{a\to 0} \int \widehat{f}(\xi)e^{ix\cdot\xi}\phi(-a\xi)d\xi = \int \widehat{f}(\xi)e^{ix\cdot\xi}d\xi$$

(recall that $\phi(0) = 1$). But we proved above that this limit exists in $L^1(\mathbb{R}^n)$–convergence as well and that the limit is cf, where $c = \int \widehat{\phi} dx$. By the corollary to the Riesz-Fischer theorem on p.234, there exists a sequence $a_k \to 0$ such that the limit as $k \to \infty$ is $cf(x)$ for a.e. x. We conclude that for a.e. $x \in \mathbb{R}^n$

$$cf(x) = \int \widehat{f}(\xi) e^{ix\cdot\xi} d\xi.$$

We draw several conclusions quickly. First, the only way that ϕ plays a role in this formula is that the constant c is expressed in terms of ϕ. We therefore conclude that c is actually independent of ϕ. As we remarked in the previous proof, the choice $\phi(x) = e^{-|x|^2}$ yields the value $c = (2\pi)^n$. (We have now completed the proof of the L^1-summability theorem.)

Second, we can now finish the present proof. Since $\widehat{f} \in L^1$, the expression

$$F(x) = (2\pi)^{-n} \int \widehat{f}(\xi) e^{ix\cdot\xi} d\xi$$

defines a continuous function of x, as F is virtually the Fourier transform of the function $\widehat{f}$ and the continuity follows from Property FT2. (Actually, $F(x) = (2\pi)^{-n} \widehat{\widehat{f}}(-x)$.) As $F = f$ a.e., the claims of the theorem are verified.   **QED**

Corollary: *If $f \in L^1(\mathbb{R}^n)$ and $\widehat{f} = 0$, then $f = 0$ a.e.*

Proof: Apply either the summability theorem or the inversion theorem.
                                                                      QED

This corollary obviously takes care of the uniqueness question which was phrased at the beginning of this section.

It is of great interest to study summability methods for their own sake. Problems 34–38 will give you a chance to think about some of the issues involved. In Chapter 14 similar summability results are crucial for the study of Fourier series; see 14.E.1 and 2.

Problem 13. In Problem 5 it is stated that if $\widehat{f}$ is an odd function, then so is f. Prove this. Likewise, prove that f is even $\Longleftrightarrow$ $\widehat{f}$ is even.

To apply the inversion theorem one must know that $\widehat{f} \in L^1$. Since $\widehat{f}$ is a continuous function on $\mathbb{R}^n$, the nature of this requirement is that $\widehat{f}$

be "sufficiently small for large $|\xi|$." There are several ways available to discover that $\widehat{f} \in L^1$. One way is to calculate $\widehat{f}$, examine it, and empirically discover that it is integrable. Another way is based on Scholium 2 — to know that f is smooth enough to force $\widehat{f}$ to decay rapidly enough to be in L^1. More will be said on this point in Section C. Another way is given by the following problem.

Problem 14. Assume $f \in L^1 \cap L^\infty$ and $\widehat{f} \geq 0$. Prove that $\widehat{f} \in L^1$.

(**HINT:** Try equation $(*)$ above with $x = 0$ and $\phi(\xi) = e^{-|\xi|^2}$.)

The Fourier inversion theorem can often be used to calculate certain Fourier transforms. Suppose $f \in L^1$ and also $\widehat{f} \in L^1$. We assume f is continuous, in accordance with the inversion theorem. If $F(x) = \widehat{f}(x)$, then the inversion theorem implies

$$\widehat{F}(\xi) = (2\pi)^n f(-\xi),$$

so we have the Fourier transform of F. For instance, Example (d) in the preceding section was

$$\widehat{e^{-|x|}} = \frac{2}{1+\xi^2} \text{ on } \mathbb{R}.$$

(This was an easy calculation.) The resulting function is integrable, so we find that

$$\widehat{\frac{1}{1+x^2}} = \pi e^{-|x|}.$$

This is definitely a nontrivial formula, as you will see if you try directly to calculate the Fourier transform of $1/(1+x^2)$.

Problem 15. Calculate the Fourier transforms (on $\mathbb{R}$) of $\dfrac{1}{(1+x^2)^2}$ and $\dfrac{x}{(1+x^2)^2}$.

Problem 16. Calculate the Fourier transforms (on $\mathbb{R}$) of $\dfrac{1}{(1+ix)^2}$ and $\dfrac{\cos(\pi x/2)}{1-x^2}$.

Problem 17. Assume $0 < \alpha < \infty$. The *Bessel kernel* of order α is the function G_α on $\mathbb{R}^n$ defined by the integral expression

$$G_\alpha(x) = \frac{1}{(4\pi)^{n/2}\Gamma(\frac{\alpha}{2})} \int_0^\infty t^{(\alpha - n)/2 - 1} e^{-|x|^2/4t - t} dt.$$

(a) Prove that $G_\alpha \in L^1(\mathbb{R}^n)$.

(b) Prove that $\widehat{G_\alpha}(\xi) = (1 + |\xi|^2)^{-\alpha/2}$.

(c) Prove that $G_\alpha * G_\beta = G_{\alpha+\beta}$.

Problem 18. One of the most curious formulas for dummy variable transformations is the following: If $f \in L^1(\mathbb{R})$, then $f\left(x - \dfrac{1}{x}\right)$ is also in $L^1(\mathbb{R})$, and

$$\int_{-\infty}^\infty f\left(x - \frac{1}{x}\right) dx = \int_{-\infty}^\infty f(x)dx.$$

Prove this, using both the following methods.

(a) Prove it formally by using these variable changes: First, replace x by $-x^{-1}$ to obtain

$$\int_{-\infty}^\infty f\left(x - \frac{1}{x}\right) dx = \int_{-\infty}^\infty f\left(x - \frac{1}{x}\right) \frac{1}{x^2} dx.$$

Thus, the integral in question equals

$$\frac{1}{2}\int_{-\infty}^\infty f\left(x - \frac{1}{x}\right) \left(1 + \frac{1}{x^2}\right) dx.$$

Now make the substitution $y = x - \dfrac{1}{x}$ to achieve the result. (All these steps are completely justified in Chapter 15.)

(b) Another proof can be based on the constructive method of first proving the formula for simple functions and gradually building up to general nonnegative measurable functions. Do not do this, but do verify directly the truth of the formula for the case of $f = \chi_{(a,b)}$.

Problem 19. By an appropriate substitution or two show that if $a \neq 0$ and $ab \geq 0$, then

$$\int_{-\infty}^{\infty} f\left(ax - \frac{b}{x}\right) dx = \frac{1}{|a|} \int_{-\infty}^{\infty} f(x)dx.$$

Problem 20. Apply Problem 19 to the function $f(x) = e^{-x^2}$. Conclude that for $a > 0$, $b \geq 0$,

$$e^{-2ab} = \frac{a}{\sqrt{\pi}} \int_{0}^{\infty} e^{-a^2 t - b^2/t} \frac{dt}{\sqrt{t}}.$$

Problem 21. Under the same assumptions, show that

$$e^{-2ab} = \frac{a}{\sqrt{\pi}} \int_{0}^{\infty} e^{-b^2 t - a^2/t} \frac{dt}{t^{3/2}}.$$

Problem 22. Here is another way to obtain the formula of Problem 20.

(a) Show that $\widehat{\dfrac{1}{a^2 + x^2}} = \dfrac{\pi}{a} e^{-|a\xi|}$.

(b) Show that $e^{-2ab} = \dfrac{a}{\pi} \displaystyle\int_{-\infty}^{\infty} \dfrac{1}{a^2 + x^2} e^{-2ibx} dx$.

(c) Show that $\dfrac{1}{a^2 + x^2} = \displaystyle\int_{0}^{\infty} e^{-(a^2 + x^2)t} dt$.

(d) Prove that if the equation (c) is inserted into (b), then the desired formula results after an application of Fubini's theorem. The use of Fubini's theorem must be justified. Show that a consideration of the case $b = 0$ provides ample justification.

Problem 23. For certain values of α the Bessel kernel G_α defined in Problem 17 on $\mathbb{R}^n$ can be explicitly evaluated. So let n be fixed and show that

$$G_{n+1}(x) = \frac{\sqrt{\pi}}{(4\pi)^{n/2}\Gamma\left(\frac{n+1}{2}\right)}e^{-|x|};$$

and if $n \geq 2$

$$G_{n-1}(x) = \frac{2\sqrt{\pi}}{(4\pi)^{n/2}\Gamma\left(\frac{n-1}{2}\right)}|x|^{-1}e^{-|x|}.$$

Problem 24. On $\mathbb{R}^n$ show that

$$\widehat{e^{-|x|}} = 2^n \pi^{\frac{n-1}{2}}\Gamma\left(\frac{n+1}{2}\right)\left(1 + |\xi|^2\right)^{-\frac{n+1}{2}}.$$

Problem 25. On $\mathbb{R}^n$ show that

$$\widehat{\left(1 + |x|^2\right)^{-\frac{n+1}{2}}} = \frac{\pi^{\frac{n+1}{2}}}{\Gamma\left(\frac{n+1}{2}\right)}e^{-|\xi|}.$$

One of our first properties of Fourier transforms was the fifth in Section A, that $\widehat{f * g} = \widehat{f}\,\widehat{g}$. A result of the inversion theorem is a corresponding formula for the Fourier transform of a product:

Theorem: *Assume f, $g \in L^1(\mathbb{R}^n)$ and $\widehat{f} \in L^1(\mathbb{R}^n)$. The Fourier inversion theorem then implies that f is bounded, and thus $fg \in L^1(\mathbb{R}^n)$. Then*

$$\widehat{fg} = (2\pi)^{-n}\widehat{f} * \widehat{g}.$$

Proof: By the inversion theorem,

$$\widehat{fg}(\xi) = \int f(x)g(x)e^{-ix\cdot\xi}dx$$

$$= \int g(x)e^{-ix\cdot\xi}dx(2\pi)^{-n}\int \widehat{f}(\eta)e^{ix\cdot\eta}d\eta.$$

Since $\widehat{f}(\eta)g(x)$ belongs to $L^1(\mathbb{R}^n \times \mathbb{R}^n)$, Fubini's theorem can be applied, so that

$$\widehat{fg}(\xi) = (2\pi)^{-n} \int \widehat{f}(\eta)d\eta \int g(x)e^{-ix\cdot(\xi-\eta)}dx$$

$$= (2\pi)^{-n} \int \widehat{f}(\eta)\widehat{g}(\xi - \eta)d\eta$$

$$= (2\pi)^{-n}(\widehat{f} * \widehat{g})(\xi).$$

QED

Problem 26 (THE SINE TRANSFORM).   Let $f \in L^1(0, \infty)$ and define

$$\widetilde{f}(\xi) = \int_0^\infty f(x)\sin x\xi dx \quad \text{for } 0 \le \xi < \infty.$$

Prove the following inversion theorem: If $\widetilde{f} \in L^1(0, \infty)$, then f is e-quivalent to a continuous function on $[0, \infty)$; if f is itself continuous, then

$$f(x) = \frac{2}{\pi} \int_0^\infty \widetilde{f}(\xi)\sin x\xi d\xi \quad \text{for } 0 \le x < \infty.$$

(**HINT:** Do not attempt to give a complete proof patterned after our proof of the inversion theorem, but instead reduce this problem to an easy application of the Fourier inversion theorem.)

Problem 27 (THE COSINE TRANSFORM).   Define a cosine transform corresponding to the sine transform and state and prove an analogous inversion theorem.

Problem 28. In Problem 12.7 an example is given of two complex-valued functions $f, g \in L^1(\mathbb{R})$ such that $f * g = 0$. Give another proof by showing that $\widehat{f}\,\widehat{g} = 0$ for these functions.

Problem 29. Give an example of two real-valued functions $f, g \in L^1(\mathbb{R})$ such that $f * g = 0$ but $f \ne 0$, $g \ne 0$.

Problem 30. Prove that if $f \in L^1(\mathbb{R}^n)$ and $f * f = 0$, then $f = 0$.

Problem 31. Prove that if $f \in L^1(\mathbb{R}^n)$ and $f * f = f$, then $f = 0$.

Problem 32. If $\xi \in \mathbb{R}^n$ and $\xi \neq 0$, and if $c \in \mathbb{R}$, then the set

$$H = \{x \in \mathbb{R}^n \mid x \cdot \xi \leq c\}$$

is called a *closed half space* of $\mathbb{R}^n$. Suppose that $f \in L^1(\mathbb{R}^n)$ and for every closed half space H

$$\int_H f(x)dx = 0.$$

Prove that $f = 0$ a.e.

(**HINT**: You should try to prove $\widehat{f} = 0$. Denote $x' = (x_1, \dots, x_{n-1})$. Why does

$$\int_{-\infty}^{c} dx_n \int_{\mathbb{R}^{n-1}} f(x)dx' = 0$$

for every c? Why does this imply

$$\int_{\mathbb{R}^{n-1}} f(x', x_n)dx' = 0 \text{ for a.e. } x_n \in \mathbb{R}?$$

(See Problem 6.44.) Why does this imply

$$\int_{\mathbb{R}^n} f(x)e^{-itx_n}dx = 0 \text{ for every } t \in \mathbb{R}?)$$

Problem 33. Interpret accurately and prove the following theorem: Let $f \in L^1(\mathbb{R}^2)$ and suppose the integral (from $-\infty$ to ∞) of f along almost every line in each direction vanishes. Then $f = 0$ a.e.

Problem 34. The most basic example of a "summability" result is the following procedure to produce a "value" for the *divergent* series $\sum_{k=0}^{\infty}(-1)^k$. Namely, attempt to calculate

$$\lim_{a \to 0+} \sum_{k=0}^{\infty}(-1)^k e^{-ak}.$$

Prove that this limit exists and equals $\frac{1}{2}$.

Problem 35. For integration here is an analogous procedure to assign a "value" to the divergent integral

$$\int_0^\infty \sin x \, dx.$$

Namely, prove that

$$\lim_{a \to 0+} \int_0^\infty \sin x e^{-ax} \, dx = 1.$$

Problem 36. More generally, show that if ϕ is a C^1 function on $[0, \infty)$ such that $\phi(0) = 1$, $\phi \in L^1$, and $\phi' \in L^1$, then

$$\lim_{a \to 0+} \int_0^\infty \sin x \phi(ax) \, dx = 1.$$

(**HINT:** Integrate by parts and obtain

$$\int_0^\infty \sin x \phi(ax) \, dx = 1 + \int_0^\infty \phi'(y) \cos \frac{y}{a} \, dy,$$

and apply the Riemann-Lebesgue lemma.)

Problem 37. Likewise show that

$$\lim_{a \to 0+} \int_0^\infty \cos x \phi(ax) \, dx = 0.$$

Problem 38. This problem shows that a familiar kind of summability is consistent with the above method. Namely, suppose that f is a bounded measurable function on $[0, \infty)$ and that

$$\lim_{x \to \infty} \int_0^x f(y)dy = L$$

exists. Prove that under the above assumptions on ϕ,

$$\lim_{a \to 0+} \int_0^\infty f(x)\phi(ax)dx = L.$$

(**HINT**: define $F(x) = \int_0^x f(y)dy - L$. You may use integration by parts in this situation (it will be verified in Section 16.F.1) to obtain

$$\int_0^\infty f(x)\phi(ax)dx = F(x)\phi(ax) \Big|_0^\infty - \int_0^\infty F(x)a\phi'(ax)dx$$

$$= L - \int_0^\infty F\left(\frac{y}{a}\right)\phi'(y)dy.)$$

C. The Schwartz Class

The functions to be discussed in this section are important in that they manifest to a considerable degree both the scholia of Section A. Their Fourier transforms, therefore, will enjoy the same properties.

At times it will be convenient to use a notation such as $\mathcal{F}$ for the Fourier transform operator:

$$\mathcal{F}f = \widehat{f}.$$

Definition: The *Schwartz class* of functions on $\mathbb{R}^n$ is the collection $\mathcal{S}$ of all functions $f \in C^\infty(\mathbb{R}^n)$ which, together with their partial derivatives of any order, decay as $|x| \to \infty$ faster than any power $|x|^{-N}$. In other words, if $g = f$ or any partial derivative of f, and if P is any polynomial on $\mathbb{R}^n$, then $P(x)g(x)$ is a bounded function on $\mathbb{R}^n$.

(This is Laurent Schwartz, who developed the theory of distributions in the 1950's, not to be confused with Hermann Amandus Schwarz of the inequality.)

For example, the following functions are in $\mathcal{S}$:

$$e^{-|x|^2}; \quad e^{-|x|^4}; \quad e^{-(1+|x|^2)^\alpha} \text{ for any } \alpha > 0; \quad e^{-(1+x_1^2)|x|^2};$$

$$\frac{1}{\cosh|x|} = \frac{2}{e^{|x|} + e^{-|x|}}; \quad e^{-(\log(1+|x|^2))^2}; \quad \text{any function in } C_c^\infty(\mathbb{R}^n).$$

The following functions are not in $\mathcal{S}$:

$$e^{-|x|}; \quad e^{-|x|^3}; \quad e^{-x_1^2} (\text{if } n \geq 2); \quad \sin x_1; \quad \frac{1}{1+|x|^2};$$

any rational function.

Proposition: If $f \in \mathcal{S}$, then the functions $\frac{\partial f}{\partial x_j}$ and $x_j f$ are in $\mathcal{S}$.

The proof is immediate.

Proposition: $C_c^\infty \subset \mathcal{S} \subset L^1 \cap L^\infty$.

Proof: The first inclusion is trivial. To prove the second, suppose $f \in \mathcal{S}$. Then $x_j^{n+1} f$ is bounded on $\mathbb{R}^n$ for $j = 1, \ldots, n$. Thus, since f is also bounded, there exists a constant c such that

$$\left(1 + |x_1|^{n+1} + \cdots + |x_n|^{n+1}\right)|f(x)| \leq c.$$

By Problem 8.10 there exists another constant c' such that

$$|f(x)| \leq \frac{c'}{1+|x|^{n+1}}.$$

Then Problem 8.11 implies that $f \in L^1$.   **QED**

Theorem: If $f \in \mathcal{S}$, then $\widehat{f} \in \mathcal{S}$. Moreover, $\mathcal{F} : \mathcal{S} \to \mathcal{S}$ provides a bijection of $\mathcal{S}$ onto $\mathcal{S}$.

Proof: By the preceding proposition, $\mathcal{S} \subset L^1$. Thus, $\widehat{f}$ is defined for all $f \in \mathcal{S}$. We designate by $\widehat{\mathcal{S}}$ the collection of all $\widehat{f}$ for $f \in \mathcal{S}$. All the functions in $\widehat{\mathcal{S}}$ are at least bounded and continuous. The first proposition implies that if $\widehat{f} \in \widehat{\mathcal{S}}$, then also $\xi_j \widehat{f}$ and $\partial \widehat{f}/\partial \xi_j$ are in $\widehat{\mathcal{S}}$. This follows from Property FT13:

$$\xi_j \widehat{f} = -i \widehat{\frac{\partial f}{\partial x_j}} \in \widehat{\mathcal{S}};$$

$$\frac{\partial \widehat{f}}{\partial \xi_j} = \widehat{-i x_j f} \in \widehat{\mathcal{S}}.$$

Therefore, a simple induction argument shows that $\widehat{f} \in C^\infty$ and if D is any partial derivative of any order and P any polynomial on $\mathbb{R}^n$, then $P(\xi) D \widehat{f}(\xi) \in \widehat{\mathcal{S}}$ if $f \in \mathcal{S}$. Therefore, $P(\xi) D \widehat{f}(\xi) \in L^\infty$. By definition, $\widehat{f} \in \mathcal{S}$.

We have now shown that $f \in \mathcal{S} \Rightarrow \widehat{f} \in \mathcal{S}$. Thus, $\mathcal{F} : \mathcal{S} \to \mathcal{S}$ is at least an injection, since we know that $\widehat{f} = \widehat{g}$ implies $f = g$. We now prove it is also a surjection. Suppose $g \in \mathcal{S}$. Then define

$$f(x) = (2\pi)^{-n} \int g(\xi) e^{ix \cdot \xi} d\xi.$$

Since $f(x) = (2\pi)^{-n} \widehat{g}(-x)$, the part of the proof already done shows that $f \in \mathcal{S}$. The Fourier inversion theorem then asserts that $f(x) = (2\pi)^{-n} \widehat{\widehat{f}}(-x)$. Therefore, g and $\widehat{f}$ have the same Fourier transform, and we conclude that $\widehat{f} = g$.   **QED**

Remark: The class $\mathcal{S}$ is defined in such a manner that the interplay of the two scholia of Section A produces the result of the theorem. If $f \in \mathcal{S}$, then f decays so rapidly that Scholium 1 implies $\widehat{f} \in C^\infty$; on the other hand, f is so smooth that Scholium 2 implies that $\widehat{f}$ decays rapidly. These two results together had to be used to show that $\widehat{f} \in \mathcal{S}$.

Problem 39. Prove that if $f, g \in \mathcal{S}$, then $fg \in \mathcal{S}$.

Problem 40. Prove that if $f, g \in \mathcal{S}$, then $f * g \in \mathcal{S}$.

(**HINT:** You can do this directly with much hard calculation, or you can be clever.)

Problem 41. In this problem use the notation of Chapter 8:

$$\mathbb{R}^n = \mathbb{R}^l \times \mathbb{R}^m, \text{ so } n = l + m.$$

We shall use the notations (x, y) and (ξ, η) to denote points in $\mathbb{R}^n$, with the understanding that x, $\xi \in \mathbb{R}^l$ and y, $\eta \in \mathbb{R}^m$. Suppose that $f \in \mathcal{S}$ on $\mathbb{R}^n$. Prove that

$$\int_{\mathbb{R}^l} f(x,y)e^{-ix\cdot\xi}dx = (2\pi)^{-m}\int_{\mathbb{R}^m} \widehat{f}(\xi,\eta)e^{iy\cdot\eta}d\eta$$

for all $\xi \in \mathbb{R}^l$, $y \in \mathbb{R}^m$.

(**HINT**: Fix $\xi \in \mathbb{R}^l$ and let $F(y)$ denote the left side of the desired equation. Show that $\widehat{F}(\eta) = \widehat{f}(\xi,\eta)$ and apply the inversion theorem to the function F.)

D. The Fourier-Plancherel Transform

The main problem in this section is to assign a meaning to $\widehat{f}$ if we know only that $f \in L^2(\mathbb{R}^n)$. It is not obvious how to do this, since we have noticed that if $f \notin L^1(\mathbb{R}^n)$, then it is literally impossible to write

$$\widehat{f}(\xi) = \int_{\mathbb{R}^n} f(x)e^{-ix\cdot\xi}dx.$$

This integral exists if and only if $f \in L^1$. Nevertheless, we shall successfully define $\widehat{f}$ for any $f \in L^2$. This new Fourier transform will be called the Fourier-Plancherel transform. We shall see that it has very nice properties, and agrees with the old definition whenever f also belongs to L^1.

We shall give the definition in three stages and summarize at the end.

1. Assume f, $g \in \mathcal{S}$. From Section B we have the formula for $\widehat{fg}$:

$$\widehat{fg}(\xi) = (2\pi)^{-n}\int \widehat{f}(\eta)\widehat{g}(\xi - \eta)d\eta.$$

Evaluating this at $\xi = 0$ yields

$$\int f(x)g(x)dx = (2\pi)^{-n}\int \widehat{f}(\eta)\widehat{g}(-\eta)d\eta.$$

Now let $g(x) = \overline{f(x)}$, the complex conjugate of $f(x)$. By Property 15 in Section A, $\widehat{g}(-\eta) = \overline{\widehat{f}(\eta)}$. Therefore, after replacing η by ξ, we obtain

PARSEVAL'S
IDENTITY
$$\int |f(x)|^2 dx = (2\pi)^{-n} \int |\widehat{f}(\xi)|^2 d\xi.$$

We have thus proved Parseval's identity for all $f \in \mathcal{S}$. This identity will be kept in mind throughout this discussion, and we shall prove that it holds in greater generality as we proceed. Note that it can also be written in the form

$$\|f\|_2 = (2\pi)^{-n/2}\|\widehat{f}\|_2.$$

2. Now assume $f \in L^1 \cap L^2$. We shall then prove that $\widehat{f} \in L^2$ and that Parseval's identity is valid in this situation.

We shall apply the approximation theorem of Section 10.F. Actually, we need the *proof* of the theorem rather than the theorem itself. The proof shows that there exists a sequence $\{\phi_k\}$ of functions in $C_c^\infty(\mathbb{R}^n)$ such that $\lim_{k\to\infty} \phi_k = f$ *both in L^1 and in L^2*. Therefore, we first see that

$$\|\widehat{\phi}_k - \widehat{f}\|_\infty \leq \|\phi_k - f\|_1 \to 0,$$

so that

$$\lim_{k\to\infty} \widehat{\phi}_k(\xi) = \widehat{f}(\xi) \text{ (uniformly) for all } \xi \in \mathbb{R}^n.$$

Second, Parseval's identity holds for the functions $\phi_k - \phi_j \in C_c^\infty \subset \mathcal{S}$, and we conclude

$$\|\phi_k - \phi_j\|_2 = (2\pi)^{-n/2}\|\widehat{\phi}_k - \widehat{\phi}_j\|_2.$$

This tends to zero as $j, k \to \infty$. Thus, for any $\epsilon > 0$ there exists N such that if $j, k \geq N$, then

$$\int |\widehat{\phi}_k(\xi) - \widehat{\phi}_j(\xi)|^2 d\xi \leq \epsilon.$$

Now let $j \to \infty$ and apply Fatou's lemma in Section 6.A: It follows that if $k \geq N$, then

$$\int |\widehat{\phi}_k(\xi) - \widehat{f}(\xi)|^2 d\xi \leq \epsilon.$$

We conclude that $\widehat{f} \in L^2$ and $\lim_{k\to\infty} \widehat{\phi}_k = \widehat{f}$ in L^2. Therefore, we obtain Parseval's identity for any $f \in L^1 \cap L^2$: $\|f\|_2 = (2\pi)^{-n/2}\|\widehat{f}\|_2$.

3. Now we assume *only* that $f \in L^2$. The main problem now is to devise a reasonable definition of a function in L^2 which we are willing to name $\widehat{f}$. In doing this we shall also prove Parseval's identity to hold for f. The crucial fact we need is the *Riesz-Fischer theorem*, Section 10.C.

Given $f \in L^2(\mathbb{R}^n)$, choose *any* sequence $\phi_k \in L^1 \cap L^2$ such that $\lim_{k \to \infty} \phi_k = f$ in L^2. (For instance, we might have $\phi_k \in C_c^\infty$, or $\mathcal{S}$, or we could even use $\phi_k = \chi_{B(0,k)} f$. It doesn't matter.) By Parseval's identity

$$\|\phi_k - \phi_j\|_2 = (2\pi)^{-n/2}\|\widehat{\phi}_k - \widehat{\phi}_j\|_2.$$

We conclude that the functions $\widehat{\phi}_k$ form a *Cauchy sequence* in L^2. Therefore, the Riesz-Fischer theorem guarantees the existence of $F \in L^2$ such that

$$\lim_{k \to \infty} \widehat{\phi}_k = F \text{ in } L^2.$$

Notice that Parseval's identity $\|\phi_k\|_2 = (2\pi)^{-n/2}\|\widehat{\phi}_k\|_2$ implies that

$$\|f\|_2 = (2\pi)^{-n/2}\|F\|_2.$$

This function F is what we shall call the Fourier-Plancherel transform of f, but first we have to demonstrate that F is independent of the choice of the approximating sequence ϕ_k. To prove this, suppose that ϕ_k' is another sequence in $L^1 \cap L^2$ which converges to f in L^2. This sequence also gives rise to a function F' such that $\widehat{\phi}_k' \to F'$ in L^2. But then the sequence $\phi_k - \phi_k' \to 0$ in L^2 and $\widehat{\phi}_k - \widehat{\phi}_k' \to F - F'$ in L^2. The Parseval's identity we have just proved implies that

$$0 = \|0\|_2 = (2\pi)^{-n/2}\|F - F'\|_2.$$

Thus, $F - F' = 0$ a.e., so F and F' represent the same element of L^2.

DEFINITION AND SUMMARY. For any $f \in L^2(\mathbb{R}^n)$, there exists a unique function $\widehat{f} \in L^2(\mathbb{R}^n)$ such that if ϕ_k is any sequence satisfying

$$\phi_k \in L^1 \cap L^2 \quad \text{and} \quad \phi_k \to f \text{ in } L^2,$$

then

$$\widehat{\phi}_k \to \widehat{f} \text{ in } L^2.$$

This function $\widehat{f}$ is called the *Fourier-Plancherel transform* of f. Parseval's identity is valid:

$$\|f\|_2 = (2\pi)^{-n/2}\|\widehat{f}\|_2.$$

It is important to observe that this definition and notation are consistent with the original Fourier transform, since if $f \in L^1 \cap L^2$ then we can choose for the sequence ϕ_k simply $\phi_k = f$ for all k.

We now wish to discuss the inversion theorem for the Fourier-Plancherel transform. Recall that the inversion theorem of Section B can be written in the form

$$f(x) = (2\pi)^{-n}\widehat{\widehat{f}}(-x).$$

Let us introduce the notation

$$g^\vee(x) = g(-x)$$

for any function g. Then the inversion theorem could be written as

$$f^\vee = (2\pi)^{-n}\widehat{\widehat{f}}.$$

As for the case of the Fourier transform, we shall use the notation $\mathcal{F}f$ for the Fourier-Plancherel transform of f; this will be convenient in certain contexts.

Theorem: *The Fourier-Plancherel transform $\mathcal{F} : L^2(\mathbb{R}^n) \to L^2(\mathbb{R}^n)$ is a bijection of $L^2(\mathbb{R}^n)$ onto itself. The inversion theorem is valid:*

$$f^\vee = (2\pi)^{-n}\widehat{\widehat{f}} \text{ for all } f \in L^2.$$

Also, Parseval's identity is satisfied:

$$\|f\|_2 = (2\pi)^{-n/2}\|\widehat{f}\|_2.$$

If $g \in L^2$, the unique $f \in L^2$ satisfying $\widehat{f} = g$ is given by the formula

$$f = (2\pi)^{-n}(\widehat{g})^\vee.$$

Proof: We already know Parseval's identity. It is clear that all the assertions of the theorem are simple consequences of the inversion formula, so that is what we shall prove. Suppose $f \in L^2$, and choose a sequence $\phi_k \in \mathcal{S}$ such that $\phi_k \to f$ in L^2. By definition, $\widehat{\phi_k} \to \widehat{f}$ in L^2. Since $\widehat{\phi_k} \in \mathcal{S}$, the definition of $\widehat{\widehat{f}}$ shows that

$$\widehat{\widehat{\phi_k}} \to \widehat{\widehat{f}} \quad \text{in} \quad L^2.$$

Since the inversion theorem is valid for functions in $\mathcal{S}$, we see that

$$\widehat{\widehat{\phi}}_k = (2\pi)^n \phi_k^\vee \to (2\pi)^n f^\vee \quad \text{in} \quad L^2.$$

Therefore, $\widehat{\widehat{f}} = (2\pi)^n f^\vee$.   **QED**

Example: We consider again Example (b) in Section A. There $f(x) = e^{-x}\chi_{(0,\infty)}$, and we calculated $\widehat{f}(\xi) = (1 + i\xi)^{-1}$. Thus, $\widehat{f} \in L^2$, $\widehat{f} \notin L^1$. The inversion theorem for the Fourier-Plancherel transform applies and asserts that the Fourier-Plancherel transform of $(1 + ix)^{-1}$ is $2\pi f(-\xi)$. That is,

$$\widehat{\frac{1}{1 + ix}} = \begin{cases} 0, & \xi > 0, \\ 2\pi e^\xi, & \xi < 0. \end{cases}$$

In this case we can actually obtain a bit more information. For any $a > 0$ the function $(1 + ix)^{-1}\chi_{(-a,a)}$ is in L^1 and thus has a *Fourier* transform given by

$$\int_{-a}^{a} \frac{e^{-ix\xi}}{1 + ix} dx.$$

As we know, this function of ξ converges in L^2 as $a \to \infty$ to the function $2\pi f(-\xi)$. But a direct calculation shows that it converges for every ξ to some limit. In fact, if $\xi \neq 0$, then an integration by parts yields

$$\int_{-a}^{a} \frac{e^{-ix\xi}}{1 + ix} dx = \frac{-1}{i\xi}\left[\frac{e^{-ia\xi}}{1 + ia} - \frac{e^{ia\xi}}{1 - ia} + i\int_{-a}^{a}\frac{e^{-ix\xi}}{(1 + ix)^2}dx\right].$$

Therefore, there exists

$$\lim_{a\to\infty}\int_{-a}^{a}\frac{e^{-ix\xi}}{1 + ix}dx = -\frac{1}{\xi}\int_{-\infty}^{\infty}\frac{e^{-ix\xi}}{(1 + ix)^2}dx.$$

If $\xi = 0$, then

$$\lim_{a\to\infty}\int_{-a}^{a}\frac{1}{1 + ix}dx = \lim_{a\to\infty}\int_{-a}^{a}\frac{1 - ix}{1 + x^2}dx$$

$$= \int_{-\infty}^{\infty}\frac{1}{1 + x^2}dx$$

$$= \pi.$$

Now since an L^2 limit and an almost everywhere limit of a sequence must be compatible, we conclude that for a.e. ξ

$$\lim_{a \to \infty} \int_{-a}^{a} \frac{e^{-ix\xi}}{1+ix}dx = 2\pi e^{\xi}\chi_{(-\infty,0)}(\xi).$$

In fact, the limiting functions below are continuous functions of ξ except for $\xi = 0$ (where they are equal), so we actually find that for *all* ξ

$$\lim_{a \to \infty} \int_{-a}^{a} \frac{e^{-ix\xi}}{1+ix}dx = \begin{cases} 0, & \xi > 0, \\ \pi, & \xi = 0, \\ 2\pi e^{\xi}, & \xi < 0. \end{cases}$$

Problem 42. Carry out a similar analysis starting with the function $\operatorname{sgn} x \, e^{-|x|}$. Conclude that

$$\lim_{a \to \infty} \int_{-a}^{a} \frac{x \sin x\xi}{1+x^2}dx = \pi \, \operatorname{sgn}\xi \, e^{-|\xi|}.$$

Problem 43. For the sine transform introduced in Problem 26 prove the corresponding Parseval identity: Assuming $f \in L^2(0,\infty)$,

$$\int_{0}^{\infty} |f(x)|^2 dx = \frac{2}{\pi} \int_{0}^{\infty} |\tilde{f}(\xi)|^2 d\xi.$$

Problem 44. Do the same for the cosine transform.

It is an easy matter to extend many properties of the Fourier transform to the Plancherel transform. Some of the properties do not hold, however: We cannot assert that $\widehat{f}$ is continuous or bounded or that the Riemann-Lebesgue lemma holds (since $\widehat{f}$ can be an arbitrary function in L^2). However, the following properties in Section A do remain valid for the Fourier-Plancherel transform, sometimes with certain modifications: Properties FT 5–11, 13–15, 18. For example, let us give a proof of a version of Property FT5:

> ***Theorem:*** *Assume $f \in L^1(\mathbb{R}^n)$ and $g \in L^2(\mathbb{R}^n)$. Then $\widehat{f * g} = \widehat{f}\,\widehat{g}$.*

Proof: The statement does at least make sense, as $f * g \in L^2$ by virtue of Young's theorem on p.281. Now choose $\phi_k \in L^1 \cap L^2$ such that $\phi_k \to g$ in L^2. Then Property FT5 implies

$$\widehat{f * \phi_k} = \widehat{f}\widehat{\phi_k}.$$

But Young's theorem implies

$$\|f * \phi_k - f * g\|_2 \leq \|f\|_1 \|\phi_k - g\|_2 \to 0,$$

and thus Parseval's identity implies

$$\widehat{f * \phi_k} \to \widehat{f * g} \quad \text{in } L^2.$$

On the other hand,

$$\|\widehat{f}\widehat{\phi_k} - \widehat{f}\widehat{g}\|_2 \leq \|\widehat{f}\|_\infty \|\widehat{\phi_k} - \widehat{g}\|_2$$
$$\leq \|f\|_1 \|\widehat{\phi_k} - \widehat{g}\|_2 \to 0.$$

Thus, $\widehat{f}\widehat{\phi_k} \to \widehat{f}\widehat{g}$ in L^2. We conclude that $\widehat{f * g} = \widehat{f}\widehat{g}$.   **QED**

Problem 45. Prove the analog of Property FT18: If $f, g \in L^2(\mathbb{R}^n)$, then

$$\int \widehat{f}(\xi) g(\xi) d\xi = \int f(x) \widehat{g}(x) dx.$$

Problem 46. Prove the analog of the result in Section B on the Fourier transform of a product: if $f, g \in L^2(\mathbb{R}^n)$, then

$$\widehat{fg} = (2\pi)^{-n} \widehat{f} * \widehat{g}.$$

Problem 47. Suppose $f \in L^1(\mathbb{R}^n)$ and $g \in L^2(\mathbb{R}^n)$, and that the Fourier transform of f equals the Fourier-Plancherel transform of $g : \widehat{f} = \widehat{g}$. Prove that $f = g$.

(**HINT:** Show that if $\phi \in \mathcal{S}$, then $\widehat{f}\phi = \widehat{g}\phi$.)

There is one more matter to be taken up in this section. Namely, Parseval's identity has an easy and important generalization:

$$\boxed{\text{For } f, g \in L^2, \int f(x)\overline{g(x)}dx = (2\pi)^{-n} \int \widehat{f}(\xi)\overline{\widehat{g}(\xi)}d\xi.}$$

The process of deducing this generalization from the original identity is called *polarization*. Apply the original identity to $f + g$, and subtract the corresponding identities for f and g, using the fact that for complex numbers

$$|a + b|^2 - |a|^2 - |b|^2 = a\bar{b} + \bar{a}b.$$

The result is:

$$\int (f\bar{g} + \bar{f}g)dx = (2\pi)^{-n} \int (\widehat{f}\,\overline{\widehat{g}} + \overline{\widehat{f}}\,\widehat{g})d\xi.$$

In this relation replace g by ig and then cancel the factor of i:

$$\int (-f\bar{g} + \bar{f}g)dx = (2\pi)^{-n} \int (-\widehat{f}\,\overline{\widehat{g}} + \overline{\widehat{f}}\,\widehat{g})d\xi.$$

By subtracting these two identities we obtain the desired equation.

Parseval's identity can be viewed as a statement about the inversion theorem. To see this, suppose $g \in L^1 \cap L^2$, and apply the identity to $f \in L^2$ and $\bar{g}$. Then

$$\overline{\widehat{\bar{g}}}(\xi) = \int g(x)e^{ix\cdot\xi}dx,$$

so that

$$\int f(x)g(x)dx = (2\pi)^{-n} \int \widehat{f}(\xi) \left[\int g(x)e^{ix\cdot\xi}dx \right] d\xi.$$

Here is the interpretation: the inversion theorem for the Fourier-Plancherel transform says that in some sense (which we have made precise)

$$f(x) = (2\pi)^{-n} \int \widehat{f}(\xi)e^{ix\cdot\xi}d\xi.$$

Though this equation does not hold in a literal sense, we can formally multiply both sides by $g(x) \in L^1 \cap L^2$, integrate over $\mathbb{R}^n$, play like we use Fubini's theorem, and obtain a correct equation! In particular, if $E \subset \mathbb{R}^n$ is a set which is measurable and has finite measure, the choice $g = \chi_E$ yields

$$\int_E f(x)dx = (2\pi)^{-n} \int_{\mathbb{R}^n} \widehat{f}(\xi) \left[\int_E e^{ix\cdot\xi}dx \right] d\xi.$$

For example, let $n = 1$, let $a > 0$, and take $E = (0, a)$. Then for any $f \in L^2(\mathbb{R})$,

$$\int_0^a f(x)dx = \frac{1}{2\pi} \int_{-\infty}^{\infty} \widehat{f}(\xi) \frac{e^{ia\xi} - 1}{i\xi} d\xi.$$

A similar equation holds for $a < 0$ if we take $E = (a, 0)$; in fact, if we define $\int_0^a f(x)dx = -\int_a^0 f(x)dx$, the same equation holds. Now change notation: Replace x by t and a by x to obtain

$$\int_0^x f(t)dt = \frac{1}{2\pi} \int_{-\infty}^{\infty} \widehat{f}(\xi) \frac{e^{ix\xi} - 1}{i\xi} d\xi \quad \text{for} \quad x \in \mathbb{R}.$$

In Chapter 15 we shall establish the theorem of Lebesgue on differentiation of integrals, to the effect that if $F(x) = \int_0^x f(t)dt$, then F is differentiable a.e. and $F'(x) = f(x)$ for a.e. x. Thus, we obtain

$$f(x) = \frac{d}{dx} \frac{1}{2\pi} \int_{-\infty}^{\infty} \widehat{f}(\xi) \frac{e^{ix\xi} - 1}{i\xi} d\xi \quad \text{for} \quad \text{a.e. } x \in \mathbb{R}.$$

We can also apply this formula to $\widehat{f}$ instead of f, and use the inversion formula for the Fourier-Plancherel transform. After changing notation, the result is

$$\widehat{f}(\xi) = \frac{d}{d\xi} \int_{-\infty}^{\infty} f(x) \frac{e^{-ix\xi} - 1}{-ix} dx \quad \text{for} \quad \text{a.e. } \xi \in \mathbb{R}.$$

These two formulas are significant in that they give *explicit* expressions for the Fourier-Plancherel transform and its inverse, not making use of an approximating sequence. The formulas are also quite elegant: They are obtained formally by integrating "under the integral sign" and then differentiating the result. For example,

$$\widehat{f}(\xi) = \int\limits_{-\infty}^{\infty} f(x)e^{-ix\xi}dx \quad \text{(formally)}$$

$$= \frac{d}{d\xi} \int\limits_{-\infty}^{\infty} f(x)\left[\int\limits_{0}^{\xi} e^{-ix\eta}d\eta\right] dx$$

$$= \frac{d}{d\xi} \int\limits_{-\infty}^{\infty} f(x)\frac{e^{-ix\xi} - 1}{-ix}dx.$$

Problem 48 (HILBERT TRANSFORM).

(a) Prove that for any $f \in L^2(\mathbb{R})$ there exists a unique function $Hf \in L^2(\mathbb{R})$ whose Fourier-Plancherel transform satisfies

$$\widehat{Hf} = -i \operatorname{sgn}(\xi)\widehat{f}.$$

(b) Prove that $\|Hf\|_2 = \|f\|_2$.

(c) Prove that $H(Hf) = -f$.

(d) Prove that $H\left(\dfrac{1}{1+x^2}\right) = \dfrac{x}{1+x^2}$.

Problem 49. For $f \in \mathcal{S}$ a more explicit formula can be presented for the Hilbert transform of f.

(a) By writing the inversion formula, show that

$$(Hf)(0) = \lim_{a\to\infty} \frac{1}{\pi} \int\limits_{-\infty}^{\infty} f(y)\frac{\cos ay - 1}{y}dy.$$

(b) Show that

$$(Hf)(0) = \lim_{a\to\infty} \frac{1}{\pi} \int\limits_{-\infty}^{\infty} \frac{f(y) - f(-y)}{2y}(\cos ay - 1)dy.$$

(c) Conclude that

$$(Hf)(0) = \frac{1}{\pi} \int\limits_{-\infty}^{\infty} \frac{f(-y) - f(y)}{2y} \, dy.$$

(d) Show that

$$(Hf)(0) = \lim_{\epsilon \to 0+} \frac{1}{\pi} \int\limits_{|y| > \epsilon} \frac{f(y)}{-y} \, dy.$$

(e) By a simple change of variables, show that for $f \in \mathcal{S}$

$$(Hf)(x) = \lim_{\epsilon \to 0+} \frac{1}{\pi} \int\limits_{|y| > \epsilon} \frac{f(x - y)}{y} \, dy.$$

Problem 50. Let $1 < p < 2$.

(a) Prove that any $f \in L^p(\mathbb{R}^n)$ can be written in the form

$$f = g + h, \quad \text{where } g \in L^1 \text{ and } h \in L^2.$$

(b) Thus you may define $\widehat{f} = \widehat{g} + \widehat{h}$. Prove that $\widehat{f}$ is well defined: It is independent of the choice of g and h.

Remark: The *Hausdorff-Young* inequality asserts that in this situation the transform $\widehat{f} \in L^{p'}(\mathbb{R}^n)$, and, moreover,

$$\|\widehat{f}\|_{p'} \leq (2\pi)^{n/p'} \|f\|_p.$$

We are not going to prove this. Incidentally, it was proved by K.I. Babenko in 1961 that the constant in this inequality is not sharp. Then William Beckner in 1975 discovered the best constant: His inequality is

$$\|\widehat{f}\|_{p'} \leq (2\pi)^{n/p'} A_p^n \|f\|_p.$$

In his result equality is attained for any function $f(x) = e^{-a|x|^2}$, where $a > 0$.

Problem 51. Assuming the above facts, prove that

$$A_p = \frac{p^{1/2p}}{p'^{1/2p'}}.$$

The reference to Beckner's paper is "Inequalities in Fourier analysis," *Annals of Math.*, *102* (1975), 159–182.

E. Hilbert Space

In this section we want to discuss briefly the properties of the Fourier-Plancherel transform viewed as an operator on the Hilbert space $L^2(\mathbb{R}^n)$.

Definition: An *inner product space* is a vector space V together with a function from $V \times V$ to the scalars, denoted $\langle , \rangle$, satisfying:

    (a) $\langle f + g, h \rangle = \langle f, h \rangle + \langle g, h \rangle$ for all f, g, $h \in V$.

    (b) $\langle cf, g \rangle = c \langle f, g \rangle$ for all f, $g \in V$ and c any scalar.

    (c) $\overline{\langle f, g \rangle} = \langle g, f \rangle$ for all f, $g \in V$.

    (d) $0 \le \langle f, f \rangle < \infty$ for all $f \in V$.

    (e) $\langle f, f \rangle = 0 \Longleftrightarrow f = 0$.

This function is called an *inner product.* If V is a complex vector space, then (c) is a statement about the conjugate of the complex number $\langle f, g \rangle$. If V is a real vector space, then (c) merely states that $\langle f, g \rangle = \langle g, f \rangle$.

By combining (a), (b), and (c) it is seen that also

$$\langle f, g + h \rangle = \langle f, g \rangle + \langle f, h \rangle,$$
$$\langle f, cg \rangle = \bar{c} \langle f, g \rangle.$$

Any *inner product* space gives rise to a *normed* space by defining

$$\|f\| = \sqrt{\langle f, f \rangle}.$$

In order to prove that this is a norm, we must prove that the conditions of Section 10.B are satisfied. Of those conditions, only the triangle inequality offers any challenge. It asserts that $\|f + g\| \leq \|f\| + \|g\|$. In this case, the triangle inequality becomes

$$\langle f + g, f + g \rangle = \|f + g\|^2$$
$$\leq (\|f\| + \|g\|)^2$$
$$= \|f\|^2 + 2\|f\|\,\|g\| + \|g\|^2.$$

Since $\langle f + g, f + g \rangle = \langle f, f \rangle + \langle f, g \rangle + \langle g, f \rangle + \langle g, g \rangle$, the inequality becomes

$$\langle f, g \rangle + \overline{\langle f, g \rangle} \leq 2\|f\|\,\|g\|,$$

or

$$\text{Re } \langle f, g \rangle \leq \|f\|\,\|g\|.$$

This is a consequence of the following famous result.

Schwarz Inequality: *For all f, $g \in V$,*

$$|\langle f, g \rangle| \leq \|f\|\,\|g\|.$$

Proof: If $f = 0$ or $g = 0$, the result is trivial. By normalization we thus may assume $\|f\| = \|g\| = 1$. Then

$$0 \leq \|f - g\|^2 = 2 - 2 \text{ Re } \langle f, g \rangle,$$

so we conclude

$$\text{Re } \langle f, g \rangle \leq 1.$$

Choose $\theta \in \mathbb{R}$ such that $\langle f, g \rangle = |\langle f, g \rangle|\, e^{i\theta}$, and apply the inequality just obtained to $e^{-i\theta} f$ and g:

$$1 \geq \text{ Re } \langle e^{-i\theta} f, g \rangle$$
$$= \text{ Re } e^{-i\theta} \langle f, g \rangle$$
$$= |\langle f, g \rangle|.$$

$$\textbf{QED}$$

Since the inner product space V is also a normed space, it makes sense to ask about its completeness (as a metric space). If V is complete, we have called it a Banach space in Section 10.B, but another terminology is used in this case:

Definition: A complete inner product space is called a *Hilbert space.*

We have encountered two examples of Hilbert spaces already. One is $\mathbb{R}^n$, for which we use the notation $x \cdot \xi$ for the inner product and the notation $|x|$ for the associated norm. At the beginning of this chapter we mentioned Schwarz' inequality in this situation.

The other example is L^2. We can even use integration on an arbitrary measure space X, $\mathcal{M}$, μ. The inner product on $L^2(X, \mathcal{M}, \mu)$ is given by

$$\langle f, g \rangle = \int_X f\bar{g}d\mu.$$

Schwarz' inequality states that $|\langle f, g \rangle| \leq \|f\|_2 \|g\|_2$. You will note that this inequality is in this situation a special case of Hölder's inequality (take $p = 2$), but it is not called Hölder's inequality.

The completeness of L^2 follows from the Riesz-Fischer theorem of Section 10.C. The completeness of the Euclidean space $\mathbb{R}^n$ is a consequence of the completeness of the real number system.

Problem 52. Find the logical blunder in the following "proof" of the completeness of $\mathbb{R}^n$: Let μ be counting measure on $X = \{1, 2, \ldots, n\}$. The Riesz-Fischer theorem implies $L^2(X, \mu)$ is complete. But $L^2(X, \mu) = \mathbb{R}^n$.

A continuous linear function $T : V \to V$ on a Hilbert space into itself is almost always called a continuous (or bounded) *operator.* And the effect of operating on $f \in V$ by the operator T is usually denoted by juxtaposition: Tf rather than $T(f)$.

Now suppose V is a complex Hilbert space. Then we have a very important definition:

Definition: A continuous operator $T : V \to V$ is *unitary* if T is a bijection and
$$\langle Tf, Tg \rangle = \langle f, g \rangle \quad \text{for all} \ \ f, g \in V.$$

Problem 53. Use the polarization technique of the preceding section to show that the continuous operator $T : V \to V$ is unitary if we merely assume that it is onto and

$$\|Tf\| = \|f\| \quad \text{for all} \ \ f \in V.$$

One of the most interesting questions about a continuous operator is
that of the nature of its *eigenvalues* and *eigenvectors*. By definition, an
eigenvector for $T : V \to V$ is an element $f \in V$, $f \neq 0$, such that

$$Tf = af,$$

where $a \in \mathbb{C}$. The number a is called an *eigenvalue* of T. An operator
might have or might not have an eigenvalue. If a is an eigenvalue for a
unitary operator T, then necessarily $|a| = 1$. For, if $Tf = af$ and $f \neq 0$
then

$$\|f\| = \|Tf\| = \|af\| = |a|\,\|f\|,$$

so that $|a| = 1$.

What we have been leading up to is a discussion of Parseval's identity,
which says that for $f, g \in L^2(\mathbb{R}^n)$ and $\mathcal{F}$ = Fourier-Plancherel transform,

$$\langle f, g \rangle = (2\pi)^{-n} \langle \mathcal{F}f, \mathcal{F}g \rangle .$$

Except for the numerical factor, this looks like the definition of a unitary
operator. Therefore, let us slightly adjust the operator $\mathcal{F}$ by defining

$$T = (2\pi)^{-n/2}\mathcal{F}.$$

Then T is actually a unitary operator on $L^2(\mathbb{R}^n)$. Further, the inversion
theorem states that

$$T^2 f = f^{\vee}.$$

Therefore, we conclude that

$$T^4 = \text{ id, the identity operator on } L^2(\mathbb{R}^n).$$

If f is an eigenvector for T and $Tf = af$, then $f = T^4 f = a^4 f$. Therefore, $a^4 = 1$. That is,

$$a \in \{1, i, -1, -i\}.$$

Thus, T has at most four eigenvalues. If you will examine the observation
following Problem 3, you will see that at least on $\mathbb{R}$ all four of these
numbers are indeed eigenvalues. Moreover, simple explicit examples of
eigenfunctions were produced there.

Problem 54. Prove that if $f \in L^1(\mathbb{R}^n)$ and $\widehat{f} = cf$, then $f \in L^2$.

Definition: If $a \in \{1, i, -1, -i\}$, let M_a be the corresponding *eigenspace*
of T; that is,

$$M_a = \{f \in L^2(\mathbb{R}^n) \mid Tf = af\}.$$

Problem 55. Prove that each M_a is a closed vector subspace of $L^2(\mathbb{R}^n)$. Also prove that M_1, M_i, M_{-1}, and M_{-i} are mutually *orthogonal* in the sense that if f belongs to one of these eigenspaces and g belongs to a different one, then $\langle f, g \rangle = 0$.

Now it is easy to show with a little algebra that these four eigenspaces *span* all of $L^2(\mathbb{R}^n)$; this means that every $f \in L^2(\mathbb{R}^n)$ can be expressed uniquely in the form

$$f = f_1 + f_2 + f_3 + f_4,$$

where $f_1 \in M_1$, $f_2 \in M_i$, $f_3 \in M_{-1}$, $f_4 \in M_{-i}$. To see this, first operate on this equation with T three times:

$$Tf = f_1 + if_2 - f_3 - if_4,$$
$$T^2 f = f_1 - f_2 + f_3 - f_4,$$
$$T^3 f = f_1 - if_2 - f_3 + if_4.$$

We thus have four equations in four unknowns f_1, f_2, f_3, f_4. These equations have a unique solution.

Problem 56. Prove that these equations have a unique solution and that the solution can be expressed in the form $f_k = P_k f$, $k = 1, 2, 3, 4$, where the operators P_k are expressed as linear combinations of id, T, T^2, T^3. For example

$$P_2 = \frac{\mathrm{id} - iT - T^2 + iT^3}{4}.$$

Problem 57. Prove the following facts about the P_k's:

$$P_j P_k = 0 \text{ if } j \neq k.$$
$$P_k^2 = P_k \quad (P_k \text{ is a } \textit{projection}).$$
$$P_1 + P_2 + P_3 + P_4 = \mathrm{id}.$$
$$\langle P_k f, g \rangle = \langle f, P_k g \rangle \quad (P_k \text{ is } \textit{symmetric}).$$
$$P_1 T = TP_1 = P_1.$$
$$P_2 T = TP_2 = iP_2.$$
$$P_3 T = TP_3 = -P_3.$$
$$P_4 T = TP_4 = -iP_4.$$
$$T = P_1 + iP_2 - P_3 - iP_4.$$

This decomposition of L^2 can be used to give new examples of eigenfunctions for $\mathcal{F}$. For example, consider the function $f(x) = e^{-|x|}$ on $\mathbb{R}$. By Example (d) in Section A, $Tf = \sqrt{\frac{2}{\pi}}(1+\xi^2)^{-1}$. Also $T^2 f = f$ since f is even. Therefore

$$
\begin{aligned}
P_1 f &= \frac{f + Tf + T^2 f + T^3 f}{4} \\
&= \frac{f + Tf}{2}.
\end{aligned}
$$

Thus, if

$$
g(x) = e^{-|x|} + \sqrt{\frac{2}{\pi}}(1+x^2)^{-1},
$$

then

$$
\widehat{g} = \sqrt{2\pi}\, g.
$$

F. Formal Application to Differential Equations

In this section we shall give only a hint of how the Fourier transform can be applied to help in the study of differential equations. One of the most important differential equations is *Laplace's equation*,

$$
\frac{\partial^2 u}{\partial x_1^2} + \cdots + \frac{\partial^2 u}{\partial x_n^2} = 0.
$$

And of all the problems associated with this equation, one of the most important is called the *Dirichlet problem*. Roughly speaking, the problem is this: If $G \subset \mathbb{R}^n$ is an open set and f is a given function defined on the boundary ∂G, then we are supposed to "find" a solution u of Laplace's equation in G such that $u = f$ on ∂G.

Of all the open sets G for which the Dirichlet problem is posed, one of the simplest is a half space.

We shall now treat the Dirichlet problem in a half space and shall use the following notation. We shall work on a space of dimension $n+1$ rather than n and shall denote $y = x_{n+1}$. That is, points in $\mathbb{R}^{n+1}$ will be written (x, y), where $x \in \mathbb{R}^n$ and $y \in \mathbb{R}$. The half space we shall use will be $G = \mathbb{R}^n \times (0, \infty)$. Thus, the given function on $\partial G = \mathbb{R}^n \times \{0\}$ can be described as a function f defined on $\mathbb{R}^n$. The problem is therefore to find a function $u(x,y)$ satisfying

(*)
$$\begin{cases} \dfrac{\partial^2 u}{\partial x_1^2} + \cdots + \dfrac{\partial^2 u}{\partial x_n^2} + \dfrac{\partial^2 u}{\partial y^2} &= 0 \text{ for } y > 0, \\ u(x,0) &= f(x). \end{cases}$$

We emphasize that the things we are about to do are *formal*. We introduce the Fourier transform in the variables $x_1, \ldots, x_n$ which are parallel to ∂G:

$$\widehat{u}(\xi,y) = \int_{\mathbb{R}^n} u(x,y) e^{-ix\cdot\xi} dx.$$

In this equation the variable y appears as a parameter. By Property FT13,

$$\widehat{\dfrac{\partial^2 u}{\partial x_k^2}} = -\xi_k^2 \widehat{u}, \quad k = 1, \ldots, n.$$

And by formally differentiating under the integral sign,

$$\widehat{\dfrac{\partial^2 u}{\partial y^2}} = \dfrac{\partial^2 \widehat{u}}{\partial y^2}.$$

Now take the Fourier transform of the two equations in the problem (*) to obtain the transformed version

(*̂)
$$\begin{cases} -\xi_1^2 \widehat{u} - \cdots - \xi_n^2 \widehat{u} + \dfrac{\partial^2 \widehat{u}}{\partial y^2} &= 0 \text{ for } y > 0, \\ \widehat{u}(\xi,0) &= \widehat{f}(\xi). \end{cases}$$

We rewrite the new differential equation:

$$\dfrac{\partial^2 \widehat{u}}{\partial y^2} - |\xi|^2 \widehat{u} = 0.$$

Notice that this is really "only" an *ordinary* differential equation in the variable y, and that for any fixed $\xi \in \mathbb{R}^n$ it has constant coefficients. For $\xi \neq 0$ a basis of solutions is the pair of functions $e^{|\xi|y}$, $e^{-|\xi|y}$. Thus, $\widehat{u}$ must be a linear combination of these two functions with "constant" coefficients depending only on ξ. But there is only one boundary condition: $\widehat{u}(\xi,0) = \widehat{f}(\xi)$. The other side condition has to be supplied from a desire that u be well behaved "at ∞." This desire may come from either mathematical necessity or physical intuition. Since the function $e^{|\xi|y}$ exhibits poor behavior as $y \to \infty$, it will not be used in constructing the solution. Therefore, $\widehat{u}(\xi, y)$ will be $e^{-|\xi|y}$ times a function of ξ. The boundary condition at $y = 0$ shows that

$$\widehat{u}(\xi, y) = e^{-|\xi|y}\widehat{f}(\xi).$$

In a sense, the problem is now completed. To find $u(x, y)$ we only have to write down the Fourier inversion theorem:

$$u(x, y) = (2\pi)^{-n} \int_{\mathbb{R}^n} e^{-|\xi|y}\widehat{f}(\xi)e^{ix \cdot \xi}d\xi.$$

This is a very significant formula. To see more clearly its significance, it helps to write it immediately below the corresponding formula for $f(x)$:

$$f(x) = (2\pi)^{-n} \int_{\mathbb{R}^n} e^{ix \cdot \xi}\widehat{f}(\xi)d\xi,$$

$$u(x, y) = (2\pi)^{-n} \int_{\mathbb{R}^n} e^{-|\xi|y + ix \cdot \xi}\widehat{f}(\xi)d\xi.$$

Do you see what has happened? We have essentially discovered that it is very easy to solve (*) in case the given function on ∂G is $e^{ix \cdot \xi}$ for some fixed $\xi \in \mathbb{R}^n$; the solution is exactly $e^{-|\xi|y + ix \cdot \xi}$. The expression for $f(x)$ above shows that $f(x)$ is a sort of "linear combination" of the exponentials $e^{ix \cdot \xi}$. We then see that $u(x, y)$ is the corresponding linear combination of the basic solutions coming from the boundary conditions $e^{ix \cdot \xi}$.

Problem 58. By direct calculation show that for any fixed $\xi \in \mathbb{R}^n$, the function $e^{-|\xi|y + ix \cdot \xi}$ is a solution of Laplace's equation in x, y. More generally, show that the exponential $\exp(\alpha_1 x_1 + \cdots + \alpha_n x_n + \alpha_{n+1}y)$ is a solution $\iff \alpha_1^2 + \cdots + \alpha_n^2 + \alpha_{n+1}^2 = 0$.

Often, the above discussion is about as far as this method leads without some very hard additional work. For this particular problem, however, we have already done the additional work which allows us to proceed. Namely, we know explicitly a function on $\mathbb{R}^n$ whose Fourier transform is $e^{-|\xi|y}$. In fact, Problem 25 shows that

$$\frac{\Gamma\left(\frac{n+1}{2}\right)}{\pi^{\frac{n+1}{2}}}\widehat{(1 + |x|^2)^{-\frac{n+1}{2}}} = e^{-|\xi|}.$$

Recall the notation from p.206: $\omega_{n+1} = \dfrac{2\pi^{\frac{n+1}{2}}}{\Gamma\left(\frac{n+1}{2}\right)}$. We thus obtain from Property FT8:

$$\widehat{P}(\xi, y) = e^{-|\xi|y},$$

where

$$P(x, y) = \frac{2}{\omega_{n+1}} \frac{y}{(|x|^2 + y^2)^{\frac{n+1}{2}}}.$$

Therefore, the solution u satisfies

$$\widehat{u}(\xi, y) = \widehat{P}(\xi, y)\widehat{f}(\xi),$$

so that $u = P * f$. This of course refers to convolution on $\mathbb{R}^n$:

$$u(x, y) = \int_{\mathbb{R}^n} P(x - z, y)f(z)dz.$$

We regard this as the final solution of the problem $(*)$. It expresses u explicitly in terms of an integral involving f and an explicit function P. The function P is called the *Poisson kernel* for this Dirichlet problem. The solution we have obtained does not even have a Fourier transform anywhere in it. In summary, we began with a problem $(*)$ we did not know how to solve, transformed it to an easier problem $(\hat{*})$, solved the transformed problem, and finally inverse-transformed the solution to find u itself.

We can now forget about how we arrived at the formula for u in terms of f, and analyze the formula itself.

Problem 59. Prove that the Poisson kernel has the following properties.

(a) $P(x, y) \geq 0$ and $\int_{\mathbb{R}^n} P(x, y)dx = 1$ for $0 < y < \infty$.

(b) $P(x, y) = y^{-n}P\left(\dfrac{x}{y}, 1\right)$.

(c) P is a solution of Laplace's equation.

(**HINT:** You may verify (c) by brute force computation of derivatives, but it is easier to exploit the formula $\widehat{P}(\xi, y) = e^{-|\xi|y}$.)

Problem 60. Refer to Problem 12.17 and prove that if f is a bounded uniformly continuous function on $\mathbb{R}^n$, then the function

$$u(x,y) = \int_{\mathbb{R}^n} P(x - z, y) f(z) dz$$

is a solution of Laplace's equation on $\mathbb{R}^n \times (0, \infty)$, and $\lim_{y \to 0} u(x,y) = f(x)$ uniformly for $x \in \mathbb{R}^n$.

Problem 61. Assume $f \in L^\infty(\mathbb{R}^n)$ and assume f is continuous at $x_0 \in \mathbb{R}^n$. Let u be defined as in Problem 60. Prove that

$$\lim_{(x,y) \to (x_0, 0)} u(x,y) = f(x_0).$$

(Note that you have to prove more than merely $\lim_{y \to 0} u(x_0, y) = f(x_0)$.)

Problem 62. Assume f is a bounded continuous function on $\mathbb{R}^n$ and let u be defined as in Problems 60 and 61. Prove that u is a solution of the Dirichlet problem in the precise sense that if U is defined on $\mathbb{R}^n \times [0, \infty)$ by the formula

$$U(x,y) = \begin{cases} u(x,y) & \text{if } 0 < y < \infty, \\ f(x) & \text{if } y = 0, \end{cases}$$

then U is continuous on $\mathbb{R}^n \times [0, \infty)$ and U is a solution of Laplace's equation on the open half space $\mathbb{R}^n \times (0, \infty)$. Also prove that if a and b are constants such that $a \le f \le b$, then $a \le U \le b$.

There is one obvious defect in Problem 62: The question of uniqueness of the solution to the Dirichlet problem has been omitted. What is needed is a theorem which asserts that if U is continuous on $\mathbb{R}^n \times [0, \infty)$ and satisfies Laplace's equation on $\mathbb{R}^n \times (0, \infty)$, *and* $U(x, 0) = 0$, then $U = 0$. But there is no such theorem: Any function $U = cy$ is a solution. Also $U = e^{x_1} \sin y$, etc. What is true is that *bounded* solutions are unique. Thus, if also $U \in L^\infty(\mathbb{R}^n \times [0, \infty))$, then $U = 0$. The proof of this is not difficult but really belongs to the study of differential equations, not Fourier analysis, so we omit it.

Problem 63. Prove that $P(x, y_1) * P(x, y_2) = P(x, y_1 + y_2)$.

Problem 64. (A long one.) Carry out the entire discussion of this section, through the preceding problem, in the case of the *initial value problem* for the *heat equation*:

$$\begin{cases} \dfrac{\partial^2 u}{\partial x_1^2} + \cdots + \dfrac{\partial^2 u}{\partial x_n^2} - \dfrac{\partial u}{\partial t} & = 0 \text{ for } t > 0, \\ \\ u(x, 0) & = f(x). \end{cases}$$

G. Bessel Functions

You may have wondered why we have neglected balls in our discussion of the Fourier transform. The reason is basically that the Fourier transform of χ_B, where $B \subset \mathbb{R}^n$ is a ball, is a rather complicated function. It is, in fact, a Bessel function.

Definition: The *Bessel function* of *first kind* of *order m* is

$$J_m(z) = \sum_{k=0}^{\infty} (-1)^k \frac{(z/2)^{m+2k}}{k!\,\Gamma(k + m + 1)}.$$

In this expression $-1 < m < \infty$ (though we could allow m to be an arbitrary complex number) and $z \in \mathbb{C}$. It is a simple matter to check that the radius of convergence of the above power series is ∞; the ratio test applies easily.

Problem 65. Prove that

$$\left(z^{-m} J_m\right)' = -z^{-m} J_{m+1}$$

and that

$$\left(z^m J_m\right)' = z^m J_{m-1}.$$

Problem 66. Prove that

$$J_{-1/2}(z) = \sqrt{\frac{2}{\pi z}}\cos z;$$

$$J_{1/2}(z) = \sqrt{\frac{2}{\pi z}}\sin z;$$

$$J_{3/2}(z) = \sqrt{\frac{2}{\pi}}\left(-\frac{\cos z}{\sqrt{z}} + \frac{\sin z}{z^{3/2}}\right).$$

You can see that if m is half an odd integer, then J_m will be an elementary function. (The other J_m's cannot be expressed as elementary functions.)

We are now going to calculate the Fourier transform of the function equal to $(1 - |x|^2)^\delta$ for $|x| < 1$ and equal to 0 for $|x| > 1$. We denote this function by $(1 - |x|^2)^\delta_+$. We assume $\delta > -1$. As we shall see, this assumption is equivalent to the integrability of the function.

Lemma: *For* $\alpha > -1$,

$$\int_{-1}^1 (1 - t^2)^\alpha e^{-ist}\,dt = \Gamma(\alpha + 1)\sqrt{\pi}\,\frac{J_{\alpha+1/2}(s)}{(s/2)^{\alpha+1/2}}.$$

Proof: We use the power series for e^{-ist} and integrate term by term (this will be justified at the end of the proof):

$$\int_{-1}^1 (1 - t^2)^\alpha e^{-ist}\,dt = \sum_{k=0}^\infty \int_{-1}^1 (1 - t^2)^\alpha \frac{(-ist)^k}{k!}\,dt$$

$$= \sum_{k=0}^\infty \frac{(-is)^{2k}}{(2k)!} \int_{-1}^1 (1 - t^2)^\alpha t^{2k}\,dt \quad (\text{odd terms} = 0)$$

$$= \sum_{k=0}^\infty (-1)^k \frac{s^{2k}}{(2k)!} 2 \int_0^1 (1 - \tau)^\alpha \tau^k \tfrac{1}{2}\tau^{-1/2}\,d\tau \quad (\tau = t^2)$$

$$= \sum_{k=0}^\infty (-1)^k \frac{s^{2k}}{(2k)!} B(\alpha + 1, k + \tfrac{1}{2}).$$

By the theorem on the beta function on p.200,

$$\frac{B(\alpha + 1, k + \frac{1}{2})}{(2k)!} = \frac{\Gamma(\alpha + 1)}{\Gamma(\alpha + k + \frac{3}{2})} \cdot \frac{\Gamma(k + \frac{1}{2})}{(2k)!}$$

$$= \frac{\Gamma(\alpha + 1)}{\Gamma(\alpha + k + \frac{3}{2})} \cdot \frac{(k - \frac{1}{2}) \ldots \frac{3}{2} \cdot \frac{1}{2}\sqrt{\pi}}{(2k)!}$$

$$= \frac{\Gamma(\alpha + 1)}{\Gamma(\alpha + k + \frac{3}{2})} \cdot \frac{(2k - 1) \ldots 3 \cdot 1\sqrt{\pi}}{2^k (2k)!} \cdot \frac{2k \cdot (2k - 2) \ldots 4 \cdot 2}{2^k k!}$$

$$= \frac{\Gamma(\alpha + 1)\sqrt{\pi}}{\Gamma(\alpha + k + \frac{3}{2})} \cdot \frac{1}{2^{2k} k!}.$$

Therefore,

$$\int_{-1}^{1} (1 - t^2)^\alpha e^{-ist} dt = \sum_{k=0}^{\infty} (-1)^k \frac{(s/2)^{2k} \Gamma(\alpha + 1)\sqrt{\pi}}{\Gamma(\alpha + k + \frac{3}{2}) k!}$$

$$= \Gamma(\alpha + 1)\sqrt{\pi} \frac{J_{\alpha + 1/2}(s)}{(s/2)^{\alpha + 1/2}}.$$

Now we worry about the interchange of summation and integration which we employed in the calculation. This may be justified very easily by LDCT since the partial sums of the series in question can be dominated as follows:

$$| (1 - t^2)^\alpha \sum_{k=0}^{N} \frac{(-ist)^k}{k!} | \le (1 - t^2)^\alpha \sum_{k=0}^{\infty} \frac{|s|^k}{k!}$$

$$= e^{|s|}(1 - t^2)^\alpha,$$

and this is an integrable function of t since $\alpha > -1$.   **QED**

Theorem: *For $\delta > -1$, the Fourier transform in $\mathbb{R}^n$ satisfies:*

$$\widehat{(1 - |x|^2)_+^\delta} = \Gamma(\delta + 1)\pi^{n/2} \frac{J_{n/2 + \delta}(|\xi|)}{(|\xi|/2)^{n/2 + \delta}}.$$

Proof: If $n = 1$, this is exactly what we have just proved in the lemma. Thus, we assume $n \ge 2$. We write $\mathbb{R}^n = \mathbb{R}^{n-1} \times \mathbb{R}$ and use the notation

$x = (y, t)$, where $y \in \mathbb{R}^{n-1}$, $t \in \mathbb{R}$. Since the function $(1-|x|^2)_+^\delta$ is radial, we know from Property FT11 in Section A that its Fourier transform is also radial. Therefore, we may assume $\xi = (0, \ldots, 0, \rho)$, where $\rho = |\xi|$. Therefore,

$$\widehat{(1 - |x|^2)_+^\delta}(\xi) = \int\limits_{|x|<1} (1 - |x|^2)^\delta e^{-i\rho x_n} dx$$

$$= \int_{-1}^{1} e^{-i\rho t} dt \int\limits_{|y|<\sqrt{1-t^2}} (1 - |y|^2 - t^2)^\delta dy$$

(by Fubini's theorem). We now apply the formula on p.205 for integrating radial functions:

$$\int\limits_{|y|<\sqrt{1-t^2}} (1 - |y|^2 - t^2)^\delta dy = \frac{2\pi^{\frac{n-1}{2}}}{\Gamma(\frac{n-1}{2})} \int_0^{\sqrt{1-t^2}} (1 - r^2 - t^2)^\delta r^{n-2} dr$$

$$= \frac{\pi^{\frac{n-1}{2}}}{\Gamma(\frac{n-1}{2})} \int_0^1 (1 - t^2)^{\delta + \frac{n-1}{2}} (1 - u)^\delta u^{\frac{n-3}{2}} du,$$

where we have substituted $r = \sqrt{1 - t^2} u^{1/2}$. We have thus obtained a beta function, and our last expression equals

$$\frac{\pi^{\frac{n-1}{2}}}{\Gamma(\frac{n-1}{2})} (1 - t^2)^{\delta + \frac{n-1}{2}} \frac{\Gamma(\delta + 1)\Gamma(\frac{n-1}{2})}{\Gamma(\delta + \frac{n+1}{2})}.$$

Therefore,

$$\widehat{(1 - |x|^2)_+^\delta}(\xi) = \frac{\pi^{\frac{n-1}{2}}\Gamma(\delta + 1)}{\Gamma(\delta + \frac{n+1}{2})} \int_{-1}^{1} e^{-i\rho t} (1 - t^2)^{\delta + \frac{n-1}{2}} dt$$

$$= \frac{\pi^{\frac{n-1}{2}}\Gamma(\delta + 1)}{\Gamma(\delta + \frac{n+1}{2})} \Gamma(\delta + \frac{n+1}{2})\sqrt{\pi} \frac{J_{\delta + n/2}(\rho)}{(\rho/2)^{\delta + n/2}}$$

$$= \Gamma(\delta + 1)\pi^{n/2} \frac{J_{\delta + n/2}(\rho)}{(\rho/2)^{\delta + n/2}}. \qquad \textbf{QED}$$

Corollary: *We have the formula for the Fourier transform of the characteristic function of the unit ball $B(0, 1) \subset \mathbb{R}^n$:*

$$\widehat{\chi_{B(0,1)}}(\xi) = \left(\frac{2\pi}{|\xi|}\right)^{n/2} J_{n/2}(|\xi|).$$

Proof: Set $\delta = 0$.   **QED**

We see, for example, that for

$$n = 1, \quad \widehat{\chi_{B(0,1)}}(\xi) = \frac{2\sin\xi}{\xi} \text{ (agreeing with Property FT16a)};$$

$$n = 2, \quad \widehat{\chi_{B(0,1)}}(\xi) = \frac{2\pi}{|\xi|} J_1(|\xi|) \text{ (a nonelementary function)};$$

$$n = 3, \quad \widehat{\chi_{B(0,1)}}(\xi) = 4\pi\left(-\frac{\cos|\xi|}{|\xi|^2} + \frac{\sin|\xi|}{|\xi|^3}\right).$$

It is clear that $\widehat{\chi}_{B(0,1)} \notin L^1(\mathbb{R}^n)$; otherwise, the inversion theorem would imply that $\chi_{B(0,1)}$ is equivalent to a continuous function. Which it is not. It is possible, however, that for some $\delta > 0$ the function $(1 - |x|^2)_+^\delta$ has a Fourier transform belonging to $L^1(\mathbb{R}^n)$. To examine this situation we need to study the behavior of $J_{n/2+\delta}(|\xi|)$ as $|\xi| \to \infty$, since the Fourier transform is automatically bounded and continuous on $\mathbb{R}^n$. Fortunately this study has been worked out in detail — the asymptotic behavior of J_m is known. We shall simply quote part of the result, using the famous book of G.N. Watson, *A Treatise on the Theory of Bessel Functions*, 2nd ed., 1944, University Press, Cambridge, p. 199. There a full asymptotic expansion for J_m is obtained. The first term is all we require:

$$J_m(t) = \sqrt{\frac{2}{\pi t}}\cos\left(t - \frac{m\pi}{2} - \frac{\pi}{4}\right) + O\left(t^{-3/2}\right),$$

where $O\left(t^{-3/2}\right)$ stands for a function of t whose absolute value is bounded by $Ct^{-3/2}$ as $t \to \infty$, where C is a constant. Thus, for $|\xi| \to \infty$ we obtain

$$\widehat{(1 - |x|^2)_+^\delta} = \frac{\Gamma(\delta+1)\pi^{\frac{n-1}{2}} 2^{\frac{n+1}{2}+\delta}}{|\xi|^{\frac{n+1}{2}+\delta}}\cos\left(|\xi| - \frac{n+1}{4}\pi - \frac{\delta\pi}{2}\right)$$

$$+ O\left(|\xi|^{-\frac{n+3}{2}-\delta}\right).$$

It is easy to see that the cosine term does not affect the integrability of the right side of this formula, nor does the remainder term. By Problem 9.5 we conclude that the right side is integrable $\iff (n+1)/2 + \delta > n$. That is,

$$\widehat{(1 - |x|^2)_+^\delta} \in L^1(\mathbb{R}^n) \iff \delta > \frac{n-1}{2}.$$

As an immediate consequence of the L^1-summability theorem of Section B we therefore have the following result:

Theorem: *Assume $\delta > (n-1)/2$ and let $f \in L^1(\mathbb{R}^n)$. Then as $R \to \infty$ the following limit exists in the sense of convergence in $L^1(\mathbb{R}^n)$:*

$$f(x) = \lim_{R \to \infty} (2\pi)^{-n} \int_{|\xi| < R} \widehat{f}(\xi) e^{ix \cdot \xi} \left(1 - \frac{|\xi|^2}{R^2}\right)^{\delta} d\xi.$$

Proof: The L^1-summability theorem is applied with $a = R^{-1}$ and $\phi(\xi) = (1 - |\xi|^2)^{\delta}_+$. Since $\delta > (n-1)/2$, $\widehat{\phi} \in L^1(\mathbb{R}^n)$.   **QED**

Note.   The result of this theorem and others similar to it are called the *Bochner-Riesz* method of summability. What occurs when $\delta = (n-1)/2$ and when δ is even smaller is quite interesting and is still being investigated. The number $(n-1)/2$ is called the *critical index*.

We finish this section by discussing the following question. If $f \in L^1(\mathbb{R}^n)$ is a radial function, then $\widehat{f}$ is also radial. Now a radial function can be viewed as a function on $(0, \infty) \subset \mathbb{R}$: $f(x) = \phi(|x|)$. Therefore, the Fourier transform sets up an operator which transforms functions on $(0, \infty)$ into functions on $(0, \infty)$. This operator is called the *Hankel transform*. We want to give an expression for this transform which is essentially one-dimensional in character. We shall abuse the notation by using the same letter to designate a radial function on $\mathbb{R}^n$ and the corresponding function on $(0, \infty)$: $f(x) = f(|x|)$ if f is radial.

Theorem: *The Hankel transform on $\mathbb{R}^n$ is given by*

$$\widehat{f}(\rho) = (2\pi)^{n/2} \int_0^{\infty} f(r) r^{n/2} \rho^{1-n/2} J_{n/2-1}(r\rho) dr.$$

Proof: If $n = 1$, this follows from Problem 66. Assuming $n \geq 2$ we write $x = (y, t) \in \mathbb{R}^{n-1} \times \mathbb{R}$ and $|\xi| = \rho$. Then as in the proof of the first theorem of this section, we have

$$\widehat{f}(\rho) = \int_{\mathbb{R}^n} f\left(\sqrt{|y|^2 + t^2}\right) e^{-it\rho} dy dt$$

$$= \int_{-\infty}^{\infty} e^{-it\rho} dt \int_{\mathbb{R}^{n-1}} f\left(\sqrt{|y|^2 + t^2}\right) dy.$$

We now apply the integration formula found on p.205 and then the substitution $s^2 + t^2 = r^2$:

$$\int_{\mathbb{R}^{n-1}} f\left(\sqrt{|y|^2 + t^2}\right) dy = \frac{2\pi^{\frac{n-1}{2}}}{\Gamma\left(\frac{n-1}{2}\right)} \int_0^{\infty} f\left(\sqrt{s^2 + t^2}\right) s^{n-2} ds$$

$$= \frac{2\pi^{\frac{n-1}{2}}}{\Gamma\left(\frac{n-1}{2}\right)} \int_{|t|}^{\infty} f(r)(r^2 - t^2)^{\frac{n-3}{2}} r \, dr.$$

Therefore,

$$\widehat{f}(\rho) = \frac{2\pi^{\frac{n-1}{2}}}{\Gamma\left(\frac{n-1}{2}\right)} \int_{-\infty}^{\infty} e^{-it\rho} dt \int_{|t|}^{\infty} f(r)(r^2 - t^2)^{\frac{n-3}{2}} r \, dr$$

$$= \frac{2\pi^{\frac{n-1}{2}}}{\Gamma\left(\frac{n-1}{2}\right)} \int_0^{\infty} f(r) r \, dr \int_{-r}^{r} e^{-it\rho}(r^2 - t^2)^{\frac{n-3}{2}} dt$$

$$= \frac{2\pi^{\frac{n-1}{2}}}{\Gamma\left(\frac{n-1}{2}\right)} \int_0^{\infty} f(r) r^{n-1} dr \int_{-1}^{1} e^{-iur\rho}(1 - u^2)^{\frac{n-3}{2}} du$$

$$= \frac{2\pi^{\frac{n-1}{2}}}{\Gamma\left(\frac{n-1}{2}\right)} \int_0^{\infty} f(r) r^{n-1} \Gamma\left(\frac{n-1}{2}\right) \sqrt{\pi} \frac{J_{\frac{n-2}{2}}(r\rho)}{(r\rho/2)^{\frac{n-2}{2}}} dr$$

(by the above lemma). Therefore,

$$\widehat{f}(\rho) = (2\pi)^{n/2} \int\limits_0^\infty f(r)r^{n/2}\rho^{1-n/2}J_{n/2-1}(r\rho)dr.$$

QED

The inversion theorem of course has the form

$$f(r) = (2\pi)^{-n/2} \int\limits_0^\infty \widehat{f}(\rho)\rho^{-n/2}r^{1-n/2}J_{n/2-1}(r\rho)d\rho.$$

Remark: These formulas can be generalized. To see how, let $\phi(r) = f(r)r^{(n-1)/2}$ and $\psi(\rho) = \widehat{f}(\rho)\rho^{(n-1)/2}$. Then the above formulas take the form

$$\psi(\rho) = (2\pi)^{n/2} \int\limits_0^\infty \phi(r)\sqrt{r\rho}J_{n/2-1}(r\rho)dr;$$

$$\phi(r) = (2\pi)^{-n/2} \int\limits_0^\infty \psi(r)\sqrt{r\rho}J_{n/2-1}(r\rho)d\rho.$$

Here, then, is the generalization. Let m be any number satisfying $m \geq -\frac{1}{2}$. Then define $\psi(\rho)$ by the formula

$$\psi(\rho) = (2\pi)^{n/2} \int\limits_0^\infty \phi(r)\sqrt{r\rho}J_m(r\rho)dr.$$

The inverse formula is then

$$\phi(r) = (2\pi)^{-n/2} \int\limits_0^\infty \psi(\rho)\sqrt{r\rho}J_m(r\rho)d\rho.$$

We do not prove this result.

There is one more thing we want to mention about Bessel functions. The Bessel function of "imaginary argument" is defined simply as

$$I_m(z) = e^{-m\pi i/2}J_m(iz), \quad 0 < z < \infty.$$

Then the "modified Bessel function of third kind" is

$$K_m(z) = \frac{\pi}{2} \frac{I_{-m}(z) - I_m(z)}{\sin m\pi}.$$

Now recall the Bessel kernel of order α defined in Problem 17. It can be shown that it is related to K_m by the formula

$$G_\alpha(x) = \frac{|x|^{\frac{n-\alpha}{2}} K_{\frac{n-\alpha}{2}}(|x|)}{2^{\frac{n+\alpha}{2}-1} \pi^{n/2} \Gamma\left(\frac{\alpha}{2}\right)}.$$

H. Special Results for $n = 1$

In the case of Fourier transforms of functions of *one* real variable, the critical index is 0, according to the work of the preceding section. This is the index which we are now going to investigate. Thus, we wish to study and interpret an equation of the form

$$f(x) = \lim_{R\to\infty} \frac{1}{2\pi} \int_{-R}^{R} \widehat{f}(\xi) e^{ix\xi} d\xi.$$

If $f \in L^1(\mathbb{R}^n)$, we can calculate the integral on the right side by using Fubini's theorem or can equivalently apply equation $(*)$ of Section B, with $\phi = \chi_{(-1,1)}$. The result is the same:

$$\int_{-R}^{R} \widehat{f}(\xi) e^{ix\xi} d\xi = \int_{-\infty}^{\infty} f(y) \frac{2\sin(x-y)R}{x-y} dy.$$

This equation is also valid if $f \in L^2(\mathbb{R})$ and $\widehat{f}$ is the Fourier-Plancherel transform. This follows for instance from Problem 45. If we rewrite the above convolution, we have

$$\frac{1}{2\pi} \int_{-R}^{R} \widehat{f}(\xi) e^{ix\xi} d\xi = \frac{1}{\pi} \int_{-\infty}^{\infty} f(x-y) \frac{\sin Ry}{y} dy.$$

Our results in this section are all based on the following observations: If $f(x) = 0$ for a certain $x \in \mathbb{R}$, then it *might* happen that $f(x-y)/y$ is an integrable function of y. On any interval $y > \epsilon$ or $y < -\epsilon$ (where $\epsilon > 0$), this function is integrable: If $f \in L^1$ because $|\, f(x-y)/y\,| \leq \epsilon^{-1}|f(x-y)|$, and if $f \in L^2$ because of Schwarz' inequality and the fact that $y^{-1} \in L^2$ on these intervals. Thus, the question of the integrability of $f(x-y)/y$ boils down to the behavior of this function near $y = 0$. In any case, if $f(x-y)/y$ is integrable, then the Riemann-Lebesgue lemma implies that

$$\lim_{R \to \infty} \frac{1}{\pi} \int_{-\infty}^{\infty} f(x-y)\frac{\sin Ry}{y}dy = 0.$$

Now let us be very specific:

Theorem: *Assume $f \in L^1(\mathbb{R})$ or $f \in L^2(\mathbb{R})$. Let $x \in \mathbb{R}$, and assume the existence of the limits*

$$f(x+) = \lim_{\substack{y \to x \\ y > x}} f(y),$$

$$f(x-) = \lim_{\substack{y \to x \\ y < x}} f(y).$$

Further, assume that there exists a constant C such that

$$| f(y) - f(x+)\,| \leq C(y - x) \quad \text{for } y > x,$$
$$| f(y) - f(x-)\,| \leq C(x - y) \quad \text{for } y < x.$$

Then

$$\frac{f(x+) + f(x-)}{2} = \lim_{R \to \infty} \frac{1}{2\pi} \int_{-R}^{R} \widehat{f}(\xi)e^{ix\xi}d\xi.$$

Proof: Since $\dfrac{\sin Ry}{y}$ is even, we have

$$\frac{1}{2\pi} \int_{-R}^{R} \widehat{f}(\xi)e^{ix\xi}d\xi = \frac{1}{\pi} \int_{-\infty}^{\infty} f(x+y)\frac{\sin Ry}{y}dy.$$

Let $L = (f(x+) + f(x-))/2$. Then we have

$$\frac{1}{2\pi} \int_{-R}^{R} \widehat{f}(\xi) e^{ix\xi} d\xi = \frac{1}{\pi} \int_{-\infty}^{\infty} \frac{f(x-y) + f(x+y)}{2} \frac{\sin Ry}{y} dy$$

$$= \frac{2}{\pi} \int_{0}^{\infty} \frac{f(x-y) + f(x+y)}{2} \frac{\sin Ry}{y} dy$$

$$= \frac{2}{\pi} \int_{0}^{1} \left[\frac{f(x-y) + f(x+y)}{2} - L \right] \frac{\sin Ry}{y} dy$$

$$+ \frac{2}{\pi} \int_{1}^{\infty} \frac{f(x-y) + f(x+y)}{2y} \sin Ry \, dy + L \frac{2}{\pi} \int_{0}^{1} \frac{\sin Ry}{y} dy.$$

The second integral on the right side tends to zero as $R \to \infty$ by the Riemann-Lebesgue lemma. The third integral has been treated in Problem 8.3:

$$\lim_{R \to \infty} \int_{0}^{1} \frac{\sin Ry}{y} dy = \lim_{R \to \infty} \int_{0}^{R} \frac{\sin y}{y} dy$$

$$= \frac{\pi}{2}.$$

The square-bracketed term in the first integral satisfies the estimate

$$\left| \frac{f(x-y) + f(x+y)}{2} - L \right|$$

$$\leq \tfrac{1}{2} | f(x-y) - f(x-) | + \tfrac{1}{2} | f(x+y) - f(x+) |$$

$$\leq \tfrac{1}{2} Cy + \tfrac{1}{2} Cy$$

$$= Cy.$$

Therefore,

$$\left[\frac{f(x-y) + f(x+y)}{2} - L \right] \frac{1}{y}$$

is a bounded function of y, hence integrable on $[0, 1]$. So the Riemann-Lebesgue lemma implies the first integral on the right side above tends to zero as $R \to \infty$.   **QED**

Example: We treat the same example that was previously considered in Section D: $f(x) = e^{-x}$ for $x > 0$, 0 for $x < 0$. Then $\widehat{f}(\xi) = (1 + i\xi)^{-1}$. This function satisfies the conditions of the theorem, so we immediately conclude

$$\lim_{R \to \infty} \frac{1}{2\pi} \int_{-R}^{R} \frac{e^{ix\xi}}{1 + i\xi} d\xi = \begin{cases} e^{-x}, & x > 0, \\ \frac{1}{2}, & x = 0, \\ 0, & x < 0. \end{cases}$$

The considerations of this section lead to an important principle, called the *principle of localization*. This states the following: Suppose $f \in L^1 \cup L^2$ and $g \in L^1 \cup L^2$. Let $x \in \mathbb{R}$, and suppose f and g are equal in some neighborhood of x. Then the limits

$$\lim_{R \to \infty} \frac{1}{2\pi} \int_{-R}^{R} \widehat{f}(\xi) e^{ix\xi} d\xi,$$

$$\lim_{R \to \infty} \frac{1}{2\pi} \int_{-R}^{R} \widehat{g}(\xi) e^{ix\xi} d\xi$$

simultaneously exist, and have the same value. That is, if one of the limits exists, then so does the other, and then they are equal.

The proof is evident, for the function $f - g$ vanishes near x, and so satisfies the conditions of the theorem. Therefore,

$$\lim_{R \to \infty} \left[\frac{1}{2\pi} \int_{-R}^{R} \widehat{f}(\xi) e^{ix\xi} d\xi - \frac{1}{2\pi} \int_{-R}^{R} \widehat{g}(\xi) e^{ix\xi} d\xi \right] = 0.$$

Problem 67. The above theorem is very much a "summability" result in case $\widehat{f}$ is not integrable. The conclusion cannot be strengthened to read

$$\frac{f(x+) + f(x-)}{2} = \lim_{R,S \to \infty} \frac{1}{2\pi} \int_{-R}^{S} \widehat{f}(\xi) e^{ix\xi} d\xi.$$

Prove this by using the above example with $x = 0$ and calculating

$$\lim_{R \to \infty} \frac{1}{2\pi} \int\limits_{-R}^{2R} \frac{1}{1 + i\xi} d\xi.$$

(It is not equal to $\frac{1}{2}$.)

I. Hermite Polynomials

The purpose of this section is to discuss some functions in $L^2(\mathbb{R})$ which not only form an orthonormal basis but which are also eigenvectors for the Fourier-Plancherel transform, in the sense of Problems 2 and 3.

Definition: For $k = 0, 1, 2, \ldots$, the *Hermite polynomial of order k* is

$$H_k(x) = (-1)^k e^{x^2} \left(\frac{d}{dx} \right)^k (e^{-x^2}).$$

Problem 68. Prove that $H_k' = -H_{k+1} + 2xH_k$.

Problem 69. Prove that $H_{k+1} = 2xH_k - 2kH_{k-1}$. Calculate H_0, H_1, H_2, H_3, H_4.

Problem 70. Prove that $H_k' = 2kH_{k-1}$.

Problem 71. Prove that H_k is even if k is even and odd if k is odd. Prove that the highest degree term in the polynomial H_k is $2^k x^k$.

We now turn to the orthogonality relations satisfied by the Hermite polynomials. We shall use the standard inner product for $L^2(\mathbb{R})$,

$$\langle f, g \rangle = \int\limits_{\mathbb{R}} f(x)\overline{g(x)}dx.$$

Orthogonality Relations:

$$\left\langle H_j e^{-x^2/2}, H_k e^{-x^2/2} \right\rangle = \begin{cases} 0 & \text{if } j \neq k, \\ \sqrt{\pi} 2^k k! & \text{if } j = k. \end{cases}$$

Proof: Let $D = d/dx$ for this proof. Since we are dealing with improper Riemann integrals of C^∞ functions which decay rapidly, we can integrate by parts as follows:

$$\langle Df, g \rangle = - \langle f, Dg \rangle.$$

If $j > k$,

$$\begin{aligned}
\left\langle H_j e^{-x^2/2}, H_k e^{-x^2/2} \right\rangle &= \left\langle e^{-x^2} H_j, H_k \right\rangle \\
&= (-1)^j \left\langle D^j e^{-x^2}, H_k \right\rangle \\
&= (-1)^{j-1} \left\langle D^{j-1} e^{-x^2}, D H_k \right\rangle \\
&= \text{etc.} \\
&= \left\langle e^{-x^2}, D^j H_k \right\rangle \\
&= 0
\end{aligned}$$

since $D^j H_k = 0$ (the jth derivative of a polynomial of degree k). Likewise, the inner product is zero if $j < k$. If $j = k$, then

$$\begin{aligned}
\left\langle H_k e^{-x^2/2}, H_k e^{-x^2/2} \right\rangle &= (-1)^k \left\langle D^k e^{-x^2}, H_k \right\rangle \\
&= \left\langle e^{-x^2}, D^k H_k \right\rangle.
\end{aligned}$$

Since $D^k H_k$ is the constant $2^k k!$ by Problem 71, the last inner product is

$$2^k k! \left\langle e^{-x^2}, 1 \right\rangle = 2^k k! \sqrt{\pi}.$$

QED

A standard device for investigating sequences of polynomials defined in similar ways is the use of *generating functions*. Now we present a result which shows that $e^{2xt - t^2}$ is the generating function for the Hermite polynomials.

Generating Function: *For any* x, $t \in \mathbb{C}$,

$$\sum_{k=0}^{\infty} H_k(x) \frac{t^k}{k!} = e^{2xt - t^2}.$$

Proof: We are going to use a basic result of analytic function theory: The function e^{-z^2} is represented by its Taylor series. That is,

$$\sum_{k=0}^{\infty} \left(\frac{d}{dz}\right)^k (e^{-z^2}) \frac{w^k}{k!} = e^{-(z+w)^2}.$$

Therefore,

$$\sum_{k=0}^{\infty} H_k(x) \frac{t^k}{k!} = e^{x^2} \sum_{k=0}^{\infty} D^k(e^{-x^2}) \frac{(-t)^k}{k!}$$

$$= e^{x^2} e^{-(x-t)^2}$$

$$= e^{2xt - t^2}.$$

                                                                            QED

As seen from the proof, the above series converges for each x as a power series in t. We shall need a statement about its convergence when both sides are interpreted as functions of x. The next result will suffice.

Lemma: *For each* $t \in \mathbb{C}$,

$$\sum_{k=0}^{\infty} H_k(x) e^{-x^2/2} \frac{t^k}{k!} = e^{-x^2/2 + 2xt - t^2},$$

where the convergence takes place in $L^2(\mathbb{R})$.

Proof: Since the equation holds for each $x \in \mathbb{R}$, the corollary to the Riesz-Fischer theorem in Section 10.C shows that it suffices to prove merely that the left side converges in $L^2(\mathbb{R})$. That is, thanks to the orthogonality relations, we want to prove

$$\sum_{k=0}^{\infty} \|H_k e^{-x^2/2}\|_{L^2}^2 \frac{|t|^{2k}}{(k!)^2} < \infty.$$

This means

$$\sum_{k=0}^{\infty} \frac{2^k |t|^{2k}}{k!} < \infty,$$

which is certainly true. **QED**

Now we can easily establish a Fourier transform formula.

> **Theorem:** *For any* $k = 0, 1, 2, \ldots,$
>
> $$\mathcal{F}(H_k(x)e^{-x^2/2}) = \sqrt{2\pi}(-i)^k H_k(\xi)e^{-\xi^2/2}.$$

Proof: We are of course using the notation $\mathcal{F}$ for the Fourier transform with respect to x. Since the lemma establishes convergence in $L^2(\mathbb{R})$ and the Fourier-Plancherel transform is continuous on $L^2(\mathbb{R})$, we obtain for any $t \in \mathbb{C}$,

$$\sum_{k=0}^{\infty} \mathcal{F}(H_k e^{-x^2/2}) \frac{t^k}{k!} = \mathcal{F}(e^{-x^2/2 + 2xt - t^2})$$

$$= \mathcal{F}(e^{-(x-2t)^2/2 + t^2})$$

$$= e^{t^2} e^{-2it\xi} \mathcal{F}(e^{-x^2/2}) \text{ (Property 6, Section A)}$$

$$= e^{t^2 - 2it\xi} \sqrt{2\pi} e^{-\xi^2/2},$$

$$= \sqrt{2\pi} e^{-\xi^2/2} e^{-\tau^2 + 2\tau\xi},$$

where we have set $t = i\tau$. Using the generating function once again,

$$\sum_{k=0}^{\infty} \mathcal{F}(H_k e^{-x^2/2}) \frac{t^k}{k!} = \sqrt{2\pi} e^{-\xi^2/2} \sum_{k=0}^{\infty} H_k(\xi) \frac{\tau^k}{k!}$$

$$= \sqrt{2\pi} \sum_{k=0}^{\infty} H_k(\xi) e^{-\xi^2/2} (-i)^k \frac{t^k}{k!}.$$

Equating the coefficients of t^k in this equation yields the result.   **QED**

Theorem: *The* Hermite functions *are defined as follows:*

$$\phi_k(x) = \pi^{-1/4} 2^{-k/2} (k!)^{-1/2} H_k(x) e^{-x^2/2} \text{ for } k = 0, 1, 2, \dots .$$

The Hermite functions form an orthonormal basis of $L^2(\mathbb{R})$. That is,

$$\langle \phi_j, \phi_k \rangle = \begin{cases} 0 & \text{if } j \neq k, \\ 1 & \text{if } j = k; \end{cases}$$

and if $f \in L^2(\mathbb{R})$ satisfies $\langle f, \phi_k \rangle = 0$ for all k, then $f = 0$.

Proof: The statement about $\langle \phi_j, \phi_k \rangle$ is a restatement of the orthogonality relations. We now prove the second result. The hypothesis on f means that

$$\left\langle f, H_k e^{-x^2/2} \right\rangle = 0 \quad \text{for } k = 0, 1, 2, \dots .$$

That is,

$$\int_{\mathbb{R}} f(x) H_k(x) e^{-x^2/2} dx = 0.$$

Let $t \in \mathbb{C}$, multiply this equation by $t^k / k!$, and sum over all k. Since $f \in L^2(\mathbb{R})$, the lemma shows that the result is

$$\int_{\mathbb{R}} f(x) e^{-x^2/2 + 2xt} dx = 0.$$

Now let $\xi \in \mathbb{R}$ and set $t = -i\xi/2$ to obtain

$$\int_{\mathbb{R}} f(x) e^{-x^2/2} e^{-ix\xi} dx = 0.$$

This equation just states $\mathcal{F}(f e^{-x^2/2})(\xi) = 0$. Since ξ is arbitrary, $\mathcal{F}(f e^{-x^2/2}) = 0$. Therefore, $f e^{-x^2/2} = 0$.   **QED**

This orthonormal basis for $L^2(\mathbb{R})$ has the additional property connected with the Fourier transform that

$$\mathcal{F}\phi_k = \sqrt{2\pi}(-i)^k \phi_k, k = 0, 1, 2, \dots .$$

(Remember Problems 2 and 3, which essentially contain this result for $k = 0, 1, 2, 3$.) This result is a more precise version of the facts established in Problems 55–57. In that notation, the eigenspaces M_a are spanned by the ϕ_k's. For instance, consider

$$M_i = \{f \in L^2(\mathbb{R}) \mid \mathcal{F}f = \sqrt{2\pi}if\}.$$

Then M_i is spanned by $\phi_3, \phi_7, \phi_{11}, \phi_{15}, \ldots$. That is, every $f \in M_i$ can be expressed as

$$f = \sum_{k=0}^{\infty} a_k \phi_{3+4k},$$

where the series converges in $L^2(\mathbb{R})$; and conversely.

Another interesting formula for H_k follows.

Proposition: *For all* $k = 0, 1, 2, \ldots,$

$$H_k(x) = \frac{2^k}{\sqrt{\pi}} \int_{\mathbb{R}} (x + iy)^k e^{-y^2}\, dy.$$

Proof: Let H_k^* be the function defined by the right side of the proposed formula. Then

$$H_0^*(x) = \frac{1}{\sqrt{\pi}} \int_{\mathbb{R}} e^{-y^2}\, dy = 1 = H_0(x),$$

$$H_1^*(x) = \frac{2}{\sqrt{\pi}} \int_{\mathbb{R}} (x + iy)e^{-y^2}\, dy = 2x = H_1(x).$$

The result will follow by induction if we prove that H_k^* satisfies the recursion relation of Problem 69. Let us calculate

$$H_{k+1}^* - 2x H_k^* = \frac{2^{k+1}}{\sqrt{\pi}} \int_{\mathbb{R}} [(x+iy)^{k+1} - x(x+iy)^k] e^{-y^2} dy$$

$$= \frac{2^{k+1}}{\sqrt{\pi}} \int_{\mathbb{R}} (x+iy)^k iy e^{-y^2} dy$$

$$= -\frac{2^k}{\sqrt{\pi}} \int_{\mathbb{R}} (x+iy)^k \frac{d}{dy}(ie^{-y^2}) dy$$

$$= \frac{2^k}{\sqrt{\pi}} \int_{\mathbb{R}} k(x+iy)^{k-1} i(ie^{-y^2}) dy \quad \text{(partial integration)}$$

$$= -2k H_{k-1}^*.$$

QED

Problem 72. In this problem you will generalize the Fourier transform formula obtained above by proving that for $0 < \alpha < \infty$ and $\alpha \neq 1$,

$$\mathcal{F}(H_k(x) e^{-\alpha x^2}) = \sqrt{\frac{\pi}{\alpha}} (-i)^k \left(\frac{1}{\alpha} - 1\right)^{k/2} H_k\left(\frac{\xi}{2\sqrt{\alpha(1-\alpha)}}\right) e^{-\xi^2/4\alpha}.$$

Note that the choice $\alpha = \frac{1}{2}$ gives our earlier results. The method you are to follow will give a bit of practice in working with the recursion relation in Problem 68.

(a) Show that $\mathcal{F}(H_k e^{-\alpha x^2})$ must be of the form

$$\mathcal{F}(H_k e^{-\alpha x^2}) = \sqrt{\frac{\pi}{\alpha}} F_k(\xi) e^{\xi^2/4\alpha},$$

where F_k is a *polynomial* in the variable ξ.

(b) Show that $F_0 = 1$.

(c) Use the relation of Problem 68 to conclude that

$$2i(\alpha - 1)F_k'(\xi) = -F_{k+1}(\xi) - \frac{i\xi}{\alpha}F_k(\xi).$$

(d) This recursion formula looks almost like that of Problem 68. Prove that it is possible to choose $A, B \in \mathbb{C}$ such that if $F_k(\xi) = A^k h_k(B\xi)$, then h_k *does* satisfy exactly the relation of Problem 68.

(e) Conclude that the function h_k of (d) is precisely the Hermite polynomial of order k.

(f) By choosing $B = 1/2\sqrt{\alpha(1-\alpha)}$, derive the desired formula.

Problem 73. If $0 < \alpha < 1$, all terms in the above formula are *real* except perhaps $(-i)^k$. Now show that even if $1 < \alpha < \infty$, then the product

$$\left(\frac{1}{\alpha} - 1\right)^{k/2} H_k\left(\frac{\xi}{2\sqrt{\alpha(1-\alpha)}}\right)$$

is still real. In fact, show that this product can be interpreted as

$$\alpha^{-k/2}\left(\sqrt{(1-\alpha)}\right)^k H_k\left(\frac{\xi}{2\sqrt{\alpha}\sqrt{1-\alpha}}\right),$$

where $\sqrt{1-\alpha}$ denotes either of $\pm i\sqrt{\alpha - 1}$ (but the same in both appearances), and the product is independent of the choice of $\pm$.

Problem 74. The formula in Problem 72 breaks down if $\alpha = 1$. Show that
$$\mathcal{F}(H_k(x)e^{-x^2}) = \sqrt{\pi}(-i)^k \xi^k e^{-\xi^2/4}.$$

Problem 75. Prove the *addition formula* for the Hermite polynomials:

$$2^{k/2}H_k(x+y) = \sum_{m=0}^{k}\binom{k}{m}H_{k-m}(x\sqrt{2})H_m(y\sqrt{2}).$$

(**HINT:** Work from the right side, using the formula of the proposition in this section. Then apply the binomial theorem to obtain the following expression for the right side:

$$\frac{2^k}{\pi} \int_{\mathbb{R}^2} \left(\sqrt{2}x + \sqrt{2}y + is + it \right)^k e^{-s^2 - t^2}\, ds\, dt.$$

Now introduce the linear change of variable $\dfrac{s-t}{\sqrt{2}} = u,\ \dfrac{s+t}{\sqrt{2}} = v.$)

Problem 76. Derive the following "explicit" formula for H_k:

$$H_k(x) = \sum_{0 \le j \le k/2} 2^{k-2j} \frac{k(k-1)\cdots(k-2j+1)}{j!} (-1)^j x^{k-2j}.$$

Problem 77. In this and the following problem let V be the Hilbert space $L^2(\mathbb{R}, \mathcal{L}, e^{-x^2}\, dx)$. For $f,\ g \in V$ denote their inner product as

$$[f, g] = \int_{\mathbb{R}} f(x)\overline{g(x)}e^{-x^2}\, dx.$$

(a) Prove that the Hermite polynomials H_0, H_1, ... form an orthogonal basis of V, and that for any $f \in V$

$$[f, f] = \sum_{k=0}^{\infty} \frac{|[f, H_k]|^2}{[H_k, H_k]}.$$

(b) Prove that if $f \in C^1(\mathbb{R})$ and has compact support, then

$$[f', H_k] = [f, H_{k+1}].$$

(c) Prove that

$$[f', f'] = \sum_{k=0}^{\infty} 2k \frac{|[f, H_k]|^2}{[H_k, H_k]}.$$

(d) Prove that

$$\frac{1}{2}[f', f'] + \frac{1}{\sqrt{\pi}}|[f, 1]|^2 \ge [f, f].$$

Problem 78. Prove that if $f \in C^1(\mathbb{R})$ and both

$$\int_{\mathbb{R}} |f'|^2 e^{-x^2} \, dx < \infty$$

and

$$\int_{\mathbb{R}} |f| e^{-x^2} \, dx < \infty,$$

then

$$\int_{\mathbb{R}} |f|^2 e^{-x^2} \, dx \le \frac{1}{\sqrt{\pi}} \left| \int_{\mathbb{R}} f e^{-x^2} \, dx \right|^2 + \frac{1}{2} \int_{\mathbb{R}} |f'|^2 e^{-x^2} \, dx.$$

Use the following outline.

(a) Prove that for $y \ge 0$

$$|f(y)| \le |f(0)| + \left[\int_{\mathbb{R}} |f'|^2 e^{-x^2} \, dx \right]^{1/2} \left[\int_0^y e^{x^2} \, dx \right]^{1/2}.$$

(b) Prove that

$$\int_0^y e^{x^2} \, dx \le e^{y^2} \quad \text{for} \quad y \ge 0.$$

(c) Conclude that for some constant c depending only on f,

$$|f(x)| \le c e^{x^2/2} \quad \text{for all} \quad x \in \mathbb{R}.$$

(d) Apply the result of Problem 77(d) to ϕf, where $\phi \in C_c^\infty(\mathbb{R})$ and $\phi(0) = 1$ and insert the estimate

$$\left[\int_{\mathbb{R}} |(\phi f)'|^2 e^{-x^2} \, dx \right]^{1/2} \le \left[\int_{\mathbb{R}} |\phi|^2 |f'|^2 e^{-x^2} \, dx \right]^{1/2} + c \left[\int_{\mathbb{R}} |\phi'|^2 \, dx \right]^{1/2}.$$

(e) In (d) replace $\phi(x)$ by $\phi(\epsilon x)$, where $\epsilon > 0$. Let $\epsilon \to 0$ to obtain the result. Give complete justification for each limit that occurs.

Problem 79. Prove that equality holds in the inequality of Problem 78 in case f is an affine function.

Problem 80. An orthogonal basis for $L^2(\mathbb{R}^n, \mathcal{L}, e^{-|x|^2} dx)$ is the set of functions $H_{k_1}(x_1) \ldots H_{k_n}(x_n)$, where each $k_i = 0, 1, 2, \ldots$. Carry out the *formal* manipulations which produce the inequality which extends Problem 78:

$$\int_{\mathbb{R}^n} |f|^2 e^{-|x|^2} dx \leq \frac{1}{2} \int_{\mathbb{R}^n} \sum_{i=1}^{n} \left| \frac{\partial f}{\partial x_i} \right|^2 e^{-|x|^2} dx + \pi^{-n/2} \left| \int_{\mathbb{R}^n} f e^{-|x|^2} dx \right|^2 .$$

Fourier Series in One Variable

In this chapter we restrict attention to functions of one variable only. Some of the more elementary results have easy extensions to functions of several variables, but many do not.

A. Periodic Functions

The functions we are going to discuss will be *periodic* functions defined on $\mathbb{R}$. We consistently assume that the period is 2π, so that our functions satisfy the equation

$$f(x + 2\pi) = f(x) \qquad \text{for all } x \in \mathbb{R}.$$

There is another fruitful way to regard such functions. This arises because of the natural mapping of $\mathbb{R}$ onto the unit circle $\{z \in \mathbb{C} \mid |z| = 1\}$ given by $x \to e^{ix}$. It is clear that a function f defined on $\mathbb{R}$ is periodic with period 2π if and only if there exists a function f_0 defined on the unit circle such that

$$f(x) = f_0(e^{ix}) \qquad \text{for all } x \in \mathbb{R}.$$

There is some group theory lurking in this discussion. Suppose that G is a topological group with group operation written additively. We assume G is commutative. The adjective "topological" simply means that G is a topological space for which the algebraic operations are continuous. Don't worry about this at all if these concepts are unfamiliar to you, as all the examples we have in mind are quite concrete. A *character* of G is a continuous "homomorphism" of G into the unit circle. That is, ϕ is a character of G if

$$\phi : G \to \mathbb{C} \text{ is continuous,}$$
$$|\phi(x)| = 1 \text{ for all } x \in G, \text{ and}$$
$$\phi(x + y) = \phi(x)\phi(y) \text{ for all } x, y \in G.$$

Note that $\phi(0) = \phi(0)\phi(0)$, so that $\phi(0) = 1$.

Example: The real line $\mathbb{R}$ is a topological group. For any $\xi \in \mathbb{R}$, it is evident that $\phi(x) = e^{ix\xi}$ defines a character of $\mathbb{R}$. Conversely, suppose that ϕ is an arbitrary character of $\mathbb{R}$. Then we can prove that there exists $\xi \in \mathbb{R}$ such that $\phi(x) = e^{ix\xi}$. One way to see this is as follows: Let

$$f(x) = \int_0^x \phi(t)dt.$$

Then $f \in C^1(\mathbb{R})$ and

$$f(x + a) = \int_0^{x+a} \phi(t)dt$$

$$= \int_0^x \phi(t)dt + \int_x^{x+a} \phi(t)dt$$

$$= f(x) + \int_0^a \phi(x + t)dt$$

$$= f(x) + \int_0^a \phi(x)\phi(t)dt$$

$$= f(x) + \phi(x)f(a).$$

Since $\phi(0) = 1$ and ϕ is continuous at 0, there exists $a \in \mathbb{R}$ such that $f(a) \neq 0$. Therefore, $\phi(x) = f(a)^{-1}[f(x + a) - f(x)]$ is differentiable. Therefore, for all $x, y \in \mathbb{R}$

$$\phi'(x + y) = \phi(x)\phi'(y).$$

Now set $y = 0$ and let $k = \phi'(0)$:

$$\phi'(x) = k\phi(x).$$

Thus, $(\phi(x)e^{-kx})' = (\phi'(x) - k\phi(x))e^{-kx} = 0$, so that $\phi(x)e^{-kx}$ is constant. Set $x = 0$ to see that the constant is 1, and thus $\phi(x) = e^{kx}$. Since $|\phi(x)| = 1$, $k = i\xi$ must be pure imaginary.

Problem 1. Prove that the characters of $\mathbb{R}^n$ are precisely the functions

$$\phi(x) = e^{ix \cdot \xi},$$

for arbitrary $\xi \in \mathbb{R}^n$.

Problem 2. The unit circle is a group of the sort we are considering. The group operation is written multiplicatively; zw is the usual complex multiplication; and the identity is 1. Prove that its characters are precisely the functions

$$\phi(z) = z^n,$$

where n is an arbitrary integer.

(**HINT**: Consider the function on $\mathbb{R}$ given by $x \to \phi(e^{ix})$.)

Problem 3. Let $\mathbb{Z}$ be the set of all integers. Then $\mathbb{Z}$ is a group (the topology is trivial and irrelevant). Prove that the characters of $\mathbb{Z}$ are precisely the functions

$$\phi(n) = z^n,$$

where z is an arbitrary member of the unit circle.

(**HINT**: This is genuinely trivial. Let $z = \phi(1)$.)

In general, the set of characters of G can be made into a group in a very natural way, and can also be given an appropriate topology. The resulting topological group is called the *character group* of G. Problems 1, 2, 3 then assert that

> the character group of $\mathbb{R}^n \cong \mathbb{R}^n$;
>
> the character group of the unit circle $\cong \mathbb{Z}$;
>
> the character group of $\mathbb{Z} \cong$ the unit circle.

There is a deep theorem which asserts that if G is also locally compact, then the character group of the character group of G is G itself. Note how these examples bear out this theorem, which is known as the *Pontryagin duality theorem*.

Now we return to $\mathbb{R}$. When we say that a function on $\mathbb{R}$ is *periodic* we always mean that the period equals 2π. Typical examples are e^{inx}, $\cos nx$, $\sin nx$, where $n \in \mathbb{Z}$. We shall use the notation

$$\mathbb{T} = [0, 2\pi),$$

but we mean more: We think of $\mathbb{T}$ as the *group* obtained by identifying $[0, 2\pi)$ with the unit circle. Thus, if we say $f \in L^1(\mathbb{T})$, we actually mean that f is defined on $\mathbb{R}$, is periodic, and is integrable on $[0, 2\pi)$. Likewise, if we say $f \in C^m(\mathbb{T})$, we actually mean that f is defined on $\mathbb{R}$, is periodic, and belongs to $C^m(\mathbb{R})$. This is an extremely important convention. Thus, the periodic function f defined by $f(x) = x$ on $[0, 2\pi)$ is *not* continuous. Here is its graph:

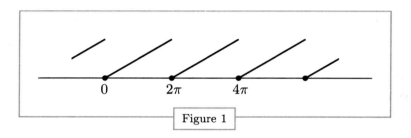

Figure 1

Likewise, the function $f \in C(\mathbb{T})$ defined by $f(x) = x^2$ on $[-\pi, \pi)$ is *not* in $C^1(\mathbb{T})$:

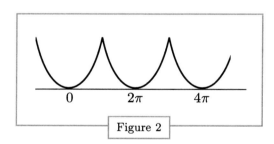

Figure 2

Problem 4. Suppose f is a periodic function on $\mathbb{R}$. Prove that $f \in L^1_{\mathrm{loc}}(\mathbb{R}) \Longleftrightarrow f \in L^1(\mathbb{T})$. Also prove that for all $a \in \mathbb{R}$

$$\int_0^{2\pi} f(x)dx = \int_a^{a+2\pi} f(x)dx.$$

It would be much more convenient if the Lebesgue measure of $[0, 2\pi)$ were equal to 1 instead of 2π. We shall not redefine Lebesgue measure, but instead shall reserve the notation $\int_{\mathbb{T}} \ldots dx$ to include this normaliza-tion:

$$\int_{\mathbb{T}} f(x)dx = \frac{1}{2\pi} \int_0^{2\pi} f(x)dx.$$

Moreover, we also use the notation

$$\|f\|_{L^1(\mathbb{T})} = \frac{1}{2\pi} \int_0^{2\pi} |f(x)|dx;$$

more generally,

$$\|f\|_{L^p(\mathbb{T})} = \left[\frac{1}{2\pi} \int_0^{2\pi} |f(x)|^p dx \right]^{1/p}.$$

Problem 5. If f and $g \in L^1(\mathbb{T})$, then we *define* the convolution by

$$(f * g)(x) = \int_{\mathbb{T}} f(y)g(x-y)dy.$$

Establish the following properties (reflecting the properties in Chapter 12):

(a) $f * g$ is periodic;

(b) $f * g \in L^1(\mathbb{T})$;

(c) $\int_{\mathbb{T}} f * g dx = \int_{\mathbb{T}} f dx \cdot \int_{\mathbb{T}} g dx$;

(d) $f * g = g * f$;

(e) $f * (g * h) = (f * g) * h$;

(f) $f * e^{inx} = c e^{inx}$.

Problem 6. Verify Figure 3:
  Here $f(x) = \chi_{(-\pi/2,\pi/2)}(x)$ for $-\pi \le x < \pi$ and $(f * f)(x) = (\pi - |x|)/2\pi$ for $-\pi \le x \le \pi$.

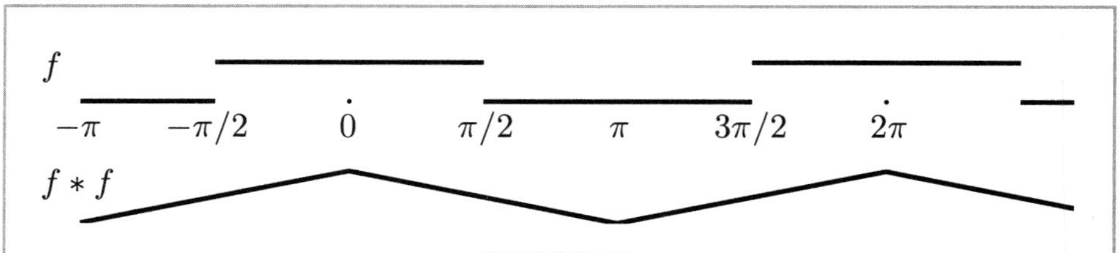

f

$-\pi$ $-\pi/2$ 0 $\pi/2$ π $3\pi/2$ 2π

$f * f$

Figure 3

Problem 7. Refer to Young's theorem in Chapter 12 and prove that in this case as well

$$\|f * g\|_{L^r(\mathbb{T})} \le \|f\|_{L^p(\mathbb{T})}\|g\|_{L^q(\mathbb{T})},$$

where $1/r = 1/p + 1/q - 1$. Prove by a simple example that the inequality is sharp in this periodic case.

Problem 8. Prove that the characters of $\mathbb{T}$ are orthogonal:

$$\int_{\mathbb{T}} e^{inx}\overline{e^{imx}}dx = 0 \quad \text{if} \ \ n \ne m.$$

Prove also that

$$\int_{\mathbb{T}} \cos nx \cos mx dx = 0 \quad \text{if} \ \ 0 \le n < m;$$

$$\int_{\mathbb{T}} \sin nx \sin mx dx = 0 \quad \text{if} \ \ 1 \le n < m;$$

$$\int_{\mathbb{T}} \cos nx \sin mx dx = 0 \quad \text{for all} \ \ n, m \in \mathbb{Z}.$$

Also show that for $n > 0$,

$$\int_{\mathbb{T}} \cos^2 nx dx = \int_{\mathbb{T}} \sin^2 nx dx = \frac{1}{2}.$$

B. Trigonometric Series

Remember that we are still considering periodic functions on $\mathbb{R}$. A *trigonometric series* is a formal expression

$$\sum_{n=-\infty}^{\infty} c_n e^{inx},$$

where $c_n \in \mathbb{C}$. We make no assumption about convergence at the present time. If the series terminates, then we do obtain a function on $\mathbb{R}$, called a *trigonometric polynomial.*

1.   Some Important Examples

One of the most important trigonometric polynomials is the *Dirichlet kernel*:

$$D_N(x) = \sum_{n=-N}^{N} e^{inx}.$$

This series can be summed quite easily by a trick:

$$\left(e^{ix/2} - e^{-ix/2}\right) D_N(x) = \sum_{-N}^{N} e^{i(n+1/2)x} - \sum_{-N}^{N} e^{i(n-1/2)x}$$

$$= \sum_{-N}^{N} e^{i(n+1/2)x} - \sum_{-N-1}^{N-1} e^{i(n+1/2)x}$$

$$= e^{i(N+1/2)x} - e^{i(-N-1/2)x}.$$

That is, $2i \sin \dfrac{x}{2} D_N(x) = 2i \sin(N + \dfrac{1}{2})x$. Thus,

$$D_N(x) = \frac{\sin(N + \frac{1}{2})x}{\sin \frac{x}{2}}.$$

Problem 9. Eschew this trick and obtain this formula by simply summing the geometric series used in defining $D_N(x)$.

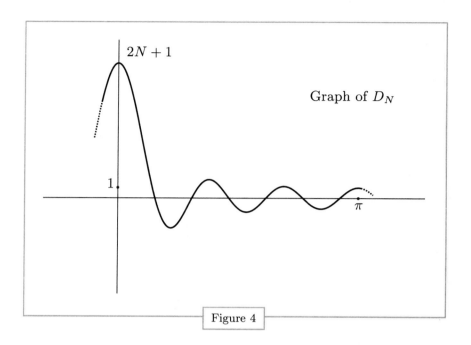

2N + 1

Graph of D_N

1.

π

Figure 4

This figure is inserted to indicate that D_N does not tend to zero as $N \to \infty$, but does oscillate more and more rapidly. It is an even, periodic function with $D_N(0) = 2N + 1$, $D_N(\pi) = (-1)^N$. Note that

$$\int_{\mathbb{T}} D_N(x)dx = 1.$$

The last equation is obvious from the equation defining D_N, since $\int_{\mathbb{T}} e^{inx}dx = 0$ if $n \neq 0$. It is highly nonobvious if one uses the formula for D_N which was just derived, and actually leads to a quick proof of the equation

$$\int_0^\infty \frac{\sin x}{x}dx = \frac{\pi}{2}$$

which was explained in Problem 8.3 (where a different proof was given).

Problem 10. Prove that the function $\csc(x/2) - 2/x$ is integrable on

$(0, \pi)$. In fact, prove that it is bounded. In fact, prove that it tends to zero as $x \to 0$. Use this to show that

$$\lim_{N \to \infty} \int_0^\pi \left(\frac{1}{\sin \frac{x}{2}} - \frac{2}{x} \right) \sin \left(N + \tfrac{1}{2} \right) x dx = 0.$$

Then prove that

$$\lim_{N \to \infty} \int_0^\pi \frac{\sin(N + \frac{1}{2})x}{x} dx = \frac{\pi}{2}.$$

Finally, prove that

$$\int_0^\infty \frac{\sin x}{x} dx = \frac{\pi}{2}.$$

The next trigonometric series we consider is another polynomial, called the *Fejér kernel*. It is defined to be the average of the Dirichlet kernels $D_0, D_1, \ldots, D_N$:

$$F_N = \frac{\sum_{k=0}^N D_k}{N + 1}.$$

Problem 11. Show that

$$F_N(x) = \sum_{n=-N}^N \left(1 - \frac{|n|}{N + 1} \right) e^{inx}.$$

We can also calculate F_N explicitly. We start from the equation obtained above:

$$2i \sin \frac{x}{2} D_k(x) = e^{i(k+1/2)x} - e^{-i(k+1/2)x}.$$

We employ the same trick:

$$2i \sin \frac{x}{2} \left(e^{ix/2} - e^{-ix/2} \right) D_k(x) = \left[e^{i(k+1)x} - e^{ikx} \right] - \left[e^{-ikx} - e^{-i(k+1)x} \right].$$

Summing on k from 0 to N produces

$$\left(2i\sin\frac{x}{2}\right)^2(N+1)F_N(x) = \left[e^{i(N+1)x}-1\right] - \left[1-e^{-i(N+1)x}\right]$$
$$= e^{i(N+1)x} - 2 + e^{-i(N+1)x}$$
$$= \left(e^{i(N+1)x/2} - e^{-i(N+1)x/2}\right)^2$$
$$= \left(2i\sin\frac{N+1}{2}x\right)^2.$$

Thus, we obtain

$$F_N(x) = \frac{1}{N+1}\left(\frac{\sin\frac{N+1}{2}x}{\sin\frac{x}{2}}\right)^2.$$

An extraordinary thing has occurred. The new kernel F_N is *nonnegative*. We also indicate its behavior with a sketch:

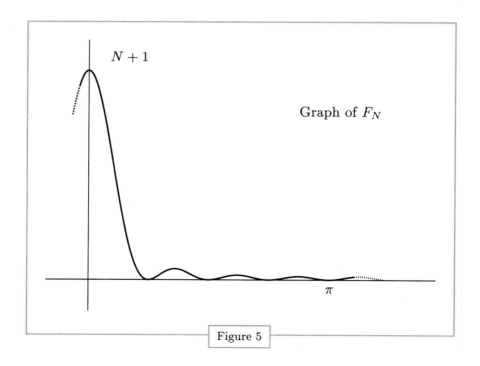

$N+1$

Graph of F_N

π

Figure 5

This kernel is also an even, periodic function. It satisfies $F_N(0) = N + 1$, but is nonnegative and for $0 < x \le \pi$ tends to zero as $N \to \infty$. Note that

$$\int_{\mathbb{T}} F_N(x)dx = 1.$$

This equation is obvious from the similar fact for D_k and the definition of F_N as an average of the D_k's. It also follows immediately from the formula of Problem 11.

Problem 12. Prove that $\csc^2(x/2) - 4/x^2$ is bounded on $(0, \pi)$. As in Problem 10, show then that

$$\int_0^\infty \frac{\sin^2 x}{x^2}dx = \frac{\pi}{2}.$$

A third trigonometric series of great importance is the *Poisson kernel*: For $0 < r < 1$ it is the series

$$P_r(x) = \sum_{n=-\infty}^{\infty} r^{|n|}e^{inx}.$$

This is of course not a trigonometric polynomial. Since the formula can be viewed as a sum of two geometric series (which converge since $0 < r < 1$), the kernel P_r can be evaluated explicitly:

Problem 13. Show that

$$P_r(x) = \frac{1 - r^2}{1 - 2r\cos x + r^2}.$$

Also show that

$$\int_{\mathbb{T}} P_r(x)dx = 1.$$

It is quite easy to sketch the graph of the Poisson kernel. Thinking of r as being rather close to 1, the graph appears as shown. The kernel P_r is even, periodic, positive, and monotone on the interval $[0, \pi]$.

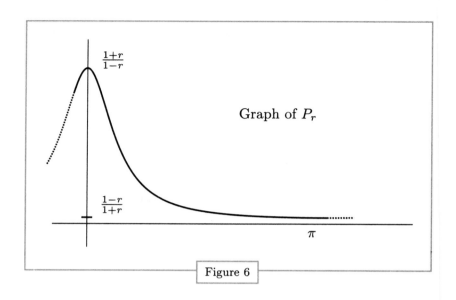

$$\frac{1+r}{1-r}$$

Graph of P_r

$$\frac{1-r}{1+r}$$

π

Figure 6

2.   Absolutely Convergent Series

The only series we have considered thus far which is not actually a polynomial is the Poisson kernel. It is a series which is absolutely convergent. In general, if $\sum\limits_{n=-\infty}^{\infty} |c_n| < \infty$, then the series

$$f(x) = \sum_{n=-\infty}^{\infty} c_n e^{inx}$$

converges for all $x \in \mathbb{R}$ and thus defines a periodic function f on $\mathbb{R}$. This function is actually continuous, as the series converges uniformly also.

The main thing we want to observe is the following result.

Proposition: *In the above situation we have the equations*

$$c_n = \int_{\mathbb{T}} f(x) e^{-inx} dx \quad \textit{for all } n \in \mathbb{Z}.$$

Proof: Let $m \in \mathbb{Z}$ be fixed. Then

$$f(x) e^{-imx} = \sum_{n=-\infty}^{\infty} c_n e^{i(n-m)x}.$$

The uniform convergence of this series implies immediately that we can integrate term by term (we could also employ LDCT):

$$\int_{\mathbb{T}} f(x)e^{-imx}dx = \sum_{n=-\infty}^{\infty} c_n \int_{\mathbb{T}} e^{i(n-m)x}dx$$

$$= c_m \int_{\mathbb{T}} dx = c_m$$

by Problem 8.   **QED**

3. "Real" and "Complex" Forms

The trigonometric series we have mentioned to this point have been presented in the so-called "complex" form — we have used the exponentials e^{inx}. If we choose to employ $\cos nx$, $\sin nx$ instead, then the series will be called a "real" trigonometric series, though the coefficients themselves need not be real. The two are equivalent because of Euler's formula

$$e^{inx} = \cos nx + i \sin nx$$

and the converse

$$\cos nx = \frac{e^{inx} + e^{-inx}}{2}, \quad \sin nx = \frac{e^{inx} - e^{-inx}}{2i}.$$

Problem 14. Verify the *formal* equivalency:

$$\sum_{n=-\infty}^{\infty} c_n e^{inx} = \frac{1}{2}a_0 + \sum_{n=1}^{\infty}(a_n \cos nx + b_n \sin nx),$$

where

$$\begin{cases} a_0 &= 2c_0, \\ a_n &= c_n + c_{-n}, \\ b_n &= i(c_n - c_{-n}), \end{cases}$$

and conversely

$$\begin{cases} c_0 &= \frac{1}{2}a_0, \\ c_n &= \frac{1}{2}(a_n - ib_n) \text{ for } n > 0, \\ c_n &= \frac{1}{2}(a_{-n} + ib_{-n}) \text{ for } n < 0. \end{cases}$$

For example, we have

$$D_N(x) = 1 + 2\cos x + \cdots + 2\cos Nx;$$

$$F_N(x) = 1 + 2\sum_{n=1}^{N}\left(1 - \frac{n}{N+1}\right)\cos nx;$$

$$P_r(x) = 1 + 2\sum_{n=1}^{\infty} r^n \cos nx.$$

The choice of which form of the trigonometric series we use is dictated by the types of functions investigated or the types of questions which we ask.

Problem 15. Let

$$f(x) = \sum_{n=-\infty}^{\infty} c_n e^{inx}$$

be an absolutely convergent trigonometric series. Prove that the sum $f(x)$ is real-valued for all $x \in \mathbb{R} \Longleftrightarrow c_{-n} = \overline{c_n}$ for all n. Prove that another equivalent condition is that in the associated "real" trigonometric series all the coefficients a_n and b_n are real numbers.

Problem 16. Prove that $\sum\limits_{n=-\infty}^{\infty} |c_n| < \infty$ if and only if $\sum\limits_{n=1}^{\infty} (|a_n| + |b_n|)$ $< \infty$. If $f(x) = \sum\limits_{-\infty}^{\infty} c_n e^{inx}$ in this event, show that

$$a_n = 2\int_{\mathbb{T}} f(x)\cos nx\,dx \quad \text{for } n \geq 0,$$

$$b_n = 2\int_{\mathbb{T}} f(x)\sin nx\,dx \quad \text{for } n \geq 1.$$

Problem 17. Let K_N be the trigonometric polynomial

$$K_N(x) = \sin x + \sin 2x + \cdots + \sin Nx.$$

Show that

$$K_N(x) = \frac{\cos\frac{x}{2} - \cos(N + \frac{1}{2})x}{2\sin\frac{x}{2}}.$$

Problem 18. Since the Fejér kernel is nonnegative, you might expect it to be the square of some real trigonometric polynomial. Show that if N is even, then indeed

$$F_N(x) = \left(\frac{1}{\sqrt{N+1}} D_{N/2}(x)\right)^2.$$

However, if N is odd this is no longer true: e.g., $F_1(x) = \frac{1}{2}\left(\sin x / \sin \frac{x}{2}\right)^2$ $= 2\cos^2 \frac{x}{2}$. But $\sqrt{2}\cos \frac{x}{2}$ is not periodic (of period 2π). Prove that for odd N in general F_N cannot be expressed as the square of a real trigonometric polynomial (of period 2π).

Problem 19. Prove that for odd N it is the case that

$$F_N(x) = \left(\frac{1}{\sqrt{N+1}} E_N \left(\frac{x}{2}\right)\right)^2,$$

where

$$E_N(x) = \sum_{\substack{n=-N \\ n \text{ odd}}}^{N} e^{inx}.$$

Problem 20. Prove that for even N

$$F_N(x) = \left| \frac{1}{\sqrt{N+1}} \sum_{k=-N/2}^{N/2} e^{ikx} \right|^2$$

and that for odd N

$$F_N(x) = \left| \frac{1}{\sqrt{N+1}} \sum_{k=-(N+1)/2}^{(N+1)/2} e^{ikx} \right|^2.$$

Thus, for every N the nonnegative polynomial F_N is the square of the *modulus* of a trigonometric polynomial.

An interesting theorem of Fejér and Riesz shows that in general every nonnegative trigonometric polynomial is the square of the modulus of a trigonometric polynomial (of the same period). In the next four problems a simple proof of this result is given.

Problem 21. Let $f(x) = \sum c_n e^{inx}$ be a trigonometric polynomial. It then makes sense to define f on $\mathbb{C}$ by allowing x in this formula to be any complex number. Suppose $f(z_0) = 0$ for some $z_0 \in \mathbb{C}$. Prove that

$$f(x) = (e^{ix} - e^{iz_0})f_1(x),$$

where $f_1(x)$ is also a trigonometric polynomial.

Problem 22. Assume $f(x) = \sum c_n e^{inx}$ is a trigonometric polynomial which is *real* for all real x. (See Problem 15.) Assume $f(z_0) = 0$ and $z_0 \notin \mathbb{R}$. Prove that $f(\overline{z_0}) = 0$. Prove also that for all real x

$$f(x) = \mid e^{ix} - e^{iz_0} \mid^2 g(x),$$

where $g(x)$ is a trigonometric polynomial.

Problem 23. Assume $f(x) = \sum c_n e^{inx}$ is a trigonometric polynomial which is real and *nonnegative* for all real x. Assume $f(x_0) = 0$ and $x_0 \in \mathbb{R}$. Prove that the derivative $f'(x_0) = 0$. Then prove that for all real x

$$f(x) = \mid e^{ix} - e^{ix_0} \mid^2 g(x),$$

where $g(x)$ is also a trigonometric polynomial.

Problem 24 (FEJÉR-RIESZ THEOREM). Assume $f(x) = \sum_{n=-N}^{N} c_n e^{inx}$ is a trigonometric polynomial which is nonnegative for all real x. Prove that, when restricted to real x, $f(x)$ is the square of the modulus of a trigonometric polynomial.

(**HINT:** Proceed by induction on N, using Problems 22 and 23.)

There is an interesting question which arises in connection with the absolute convergence of trigonometric series in the real form. The situation differs from the case of the complex form because it is possible that for a given x the series

$$\frac{1}{2}|a_0| + \sum_{n=1}^{\infty} \mid a_n \cos nx + b_n \sin nx \mid$$

converges and yet the series

$$\frac{1}{2}|a_0| + \sum_{n=1}^{\infty} (|a_n| + |b_n|)$$

diverges. For example, this frequently happens for $x = 0$. But the following result shows this cannot happen for all x.

Lusin-Denjoy Theorem: *Let $E \subset \mathbb{T}$ be a measurable set with positive measure. Assume that for all $x \in E$ the series*

$$\frac{1}{2}a_0 + \sum_{n=1}^{\infty}(a_n \cos nx + b_n \sin nx)$$

converges absolutely. Then the series

$$\frac{1}{2}|a_0| + \sum_{n=1}^{\infty}(|a_n| + |b_n|)$$

converges.

Proof: We are not assuming that a_n and b_n are real. Nevertheless, by splitting the trigonometric series into its real and imaginary parts, we see that we can assume $a_n, b_n \in \mathbb{R}$ with no loss of generality. Then we use "polar coordinates,"

$$a_n = r_n \cos\theta_n, \quad b_n = r_n \sin\theta_n,$$

where $r_n \geq 0$ and $0 \leq \theta_n < 2\pi$. The hypothesis is therefore that for all $x \in E$

$$\phi(x) = \sum_{n=1}^{\infty} r_n|\cos(nx - \theta_n)| < \infty.$$

Let

$$E_k = \{x \in E \mid \phi(x) \leq k\}, \quad k \in \mathbb{N}.$$

Since E is the union of the E_k's, there exists k such that E_k has positive measure. Now we observe that

$$2\pi k \geq \int_{E_k} \phi(x)\,dx$$

$$= \sum_{n=1}^{\infty} r_n \int_{E_k} |\cos(nx - \theta_n)|\,dx$$

$$\geq \sum_{n=1}^{\infty} r_n \int_{E_k} \cos^2(nx - \theta_n)\,dx$$

$$= \sum_{n=1}^{\infty} r_n \int_{E_k} \left[\frac{1}{2} + \frac{1}{2}\cos(2nx - 2\theta_n)\right]\,dx.$$

The Riemann-Lebesgue lemma implies that

$$\lim_{n \to \infty} \int_{E_k} \cos(2nx - 2\theta_n)\,dx = 0.$$

(If you are surprised at this result, it might help you to rewrite the integral as follows:

$$\int_{\mathbb{R}} \chi_{E_k}(x)\frac{1}{2}(e^{2inx - 2i\theta_n} + e^{-2inx + 2i\theta_n})\,dx$$

$$= \frac{1}{2}e^{-2i\theta_n}\widehat{\chi}_{E_k}(-2n) + \frac{1}{2}e^{2i\theta_n}\widehat{\chi}_{E_k}(2n).)$$

Therefore, there exists a positive integer N such that for all $n \geq N$,

$$\int_{E_k} \cos^2(nx - \theta_n)\,dx \geq \frac{1}{4}\lambda(E_k).$$

We then conclude that

$$2\pi k \geq \sum_{n=N}^{\infty} r_n \frac{1}{4}\lambda(E_k).$$

Since $\lambda(E_k) > 0$, we conclude

$$\sum_{n=1}^{\infty} r_n = \sum_{n=1}^{\infty} \sqrt{a_n^2 + b_n^2} < \infty.$$

QED

Problem 25. Consider the trigonometric series $\sum\limits_{n=-\infty}^{\infty} c_n e^{inx}$. Suppose that $E \subset \mathbb{T}$ has positive measure and that for all $x \in E$

$$\sum_{n=1}^{\infty} |c_n e^{inx} + c_{-n} e^{-inx}| < \infty.$$

Prove that

$$\sum_{n=-\infty}^{\infty} |c_n| < \infty.$$

4.   A Necessary Condition for Convergence

Definition: A trigonometric series $\sum\limits_{n=-\infty}^{\infty} c_n e^{inx}$ *converges* at $x \in \mathbb{T}$ if

$$\lim_{N \to \infty} \sum_{n=-N}^{N} c_n e^{inx} \text{ exists.}$$

You may wonder why this is a definition. The reason is that the usual (and correct) meaning of convergence of a doubly infinite series is that the limit

$$\lim_{M, N \to \infty} \sum_{n=-M}^{N} c_n e^{inx}$$

exists. We are therefore looking at a particular method of summation, which is somewhat justified by the next problem. See the remark on p.408.

Problem 26. If $\frac{1}{2}a_0 + \sum\limits_{n=1}^{\infty} (a_n \cos nx + b_n \sin nx)$ is the real form of the above series, show that the convergence of the complex series at x is equivalent to the existence of

$$\lim_{N \to \infty} \frac{1}{2}a_0 + \sum_{n=1}^{N} (a_n \cos nx + b_n \sin nx).$$

Cantor-Lebesgue Theorem: *Assume $E \subset \mathbb{T}$ is a measurable set having positive measure. Assume that the series*

$$\frac{1}{2}a_0 + \sum_{n=1}^{\infty}(a_n \cos nx + b_n \sin nx)$$

converges for all $x \in E$. Then

$$\lim_{n \to \infty} a_n = \lim_{n \to \infty} b_n = 0.$$

Proof: The hypothesis implies that $a_n \cos nx + b_n \sin nx \to 0$ for every $x \in E$. *In fact, this weaker condition is all we shall require for the proof.* As in the preceding proof, we can assume a_n and b_n are real. By using the same polar coordinates, our assumption is that $r_n \cos(nx + \theta_n) \to 0$ for every $x \in E$. We then must prove that $r_n \to 0$. We proceed by contradiction: If $r_n \to 0$ is false, then we obtain for a subsequence n_k

$$\cos(n_k x + \theta_{n_k}) \to 0 \quad \text{for all} \quad x \in E.$$

Therefore,

$$\cos^2(n_k x + \theta_{n_k}) \to 0 \quad \text{for all} \quad x \in E.$$

Therefore, LDCT and the Riemann-Lebesgue lemma imply

$$0 = \lim_{k \to \infty} \int_E \cos^2(n_k x + \theta_{n_k})dx$$

$$= \lim_{k \to \infty} \int_E \left[\frac{1}{2} + \frac{1}{2}\cos(2n_k x + 2\theta_{n_k})\right] dx$$

$$= \int_E \frac{1}{2}dx$$

$$= \frac{1}{2}\lambda(E).$$

This contradicts the hypothesis $\lambda(E) > 0$.   **QED**

Problem 27. Let $x \in \mathbb{R}$. Prove that

$$\lim_{n \to \infty} \sin nx \text{ exists} \iff x \in \pi\mathbb{Z}$$

and

$$\lim_{n \to \infty} \cos nx \text{ exists} \iff x \in 2\pi\mathbb{Z}.$$

(**HINT**: The cases in which x is an integral multiple of π are transparent. In the other cases show that $\lim_{n \to \infty} \sin nx$ exists $\Leftrightarrow \lim_{n \to \infty} \cos nx$ exists by using the addition formulas for $\sin(n+1)x$ and $\cos(n+1)x$. Knowing then that $\lim_{n \to \infty} e^{inx}$ exists, show that $e^{ix} = 1$.)

5.   Some Special Trigonometric Series

The Cantor-Lebesgue theorem implies that the convergence of the series

$$\frac{1}{2}a_0 + \sum_{n=1}^{\infty}(a_n \cos nx + b_n \sin nx)$$

on a set of positive measure necessitates the condition $\lim_{n \to \infty} a_n = \lim_{n \to \infty} b_n = 0$. The converse statement is false. In fact, there exist trigonometric series of this form with $\lim_{n \to \infty} a_n = \lim_{n \to \infty} b_n = 0$ which *diverge for all values of* x. An example provided by Steinhaus in 1929 is the trigonometric series

$$\sum_{n=2}^{\infty} \frac{\cos n(x - \log \log n)}{\log n}.$$

This series does have the correct form, as shown by the addition formula for cosine; the coefficients are

$$a_n = \frac{\cos(n \log \log n)}{\log n}, \quad b_n = \frac{\sin(n \log \log n)}{\log n}.$$

The proof of this strange behavior is quite simple. For a large positive integer N let $I_N = [\log \log N, \log \log(N + 1)]$. Assume that $x \in I_N$. Then part of the above series is the sum

$$A_N = \sum_{N < n < N + \log N} \frac{\cos n(x - \log \log n)}{\log n}.$$

For these values of n and for $x \in I_N$ we obtain from the mean value theorem

$$|x - \log \log n| = \log \log n - x$$
$$\leq \log \log n - \log \log N$$
$$= (n - N)\frac{1}{\xi \log \xi}$$

for some $N < \xi < n$. Thus,

$$n|x - \log \log n| \leq n \log N \frac{1}{N \log N}$$
$$= \frac{n}{N}$$
$$< 1 + \frac{\log N}{N}$$
$$< \frac{\pi}{3}$$

(if N is sufficiently large). Therefore, $\cos n(x - \log \log n) > \cos \frac{\pi}{3} = \frac{1}{2}$ and we conclude

$$A_N > \sum_{N < n < N + \log N} \frac{1/2}{\log n}$$
$$> \frac{1}{2\log(N + \log N)} \sum_{N < n < N + \log N} 1$$
$$> \frac{\log N - 1}{2\log(N + \log N)}.$$

As the last expression has limit $\frac{1}{2}$ as $N \to \infty$, we conclude that $A_N > \frac{1}{4}$ for all sufficiently large N. If $x \in \mathbb{R}$ is arbitrary, then there will be infinitely many values of N such that $x \in I_N$ modulo 2π; i.e., such that for some integer m_N, $x - m_N 2\pi \in I_N$. Then $A_N > \frac{1}{4}$ for infinitely many N, proving that the series does not converge at x.

This strange behavior does not occur if $a_n \to 0$ and $b_n \to 0$ monotonically. The reason is that the rapid oscillation of e^{inx} for large n has a chance to cause lots of cancellation in the partial sum of the series. In Steinhaus' counterexample the main point was that $\cos n(x - \log \log n) > \frac{1}{2}$ for a large interval of values of n. This took care of the possible cancellation.

The cancellation can be seen in the Dirichlet kernel of Section B.1:

$$\sum_{n=-N}^{N} e^{inx} = \frac{\sin(N + \frac{1}{2})x}{\sin \frac{x}{2}}.$$

Therefore,

$$\left| \sum_{n=-N}^{N} e^{inx} \right| \leq \left| \csc \frac{x}{2} \right|.$$

Problem 28. Prove that if $M \leq N$, then

$$\left| \sum_{n=M}^{N} e^{inx} \right| \leq \left| \csc \frac{x}{2} \right|.$$

(**HINT:** Start by summing the geometric series.)

Lemma: *Let $M \leq N$ be integers, and assume $c_M \geq c_{M+1} \geq \cdots \geq c_N \geq 0$. Then*

$$\left| \sum_{n=M}^{N} c_n e^{inx} \right| \leq c_M \left| \csc \frac{x}{2} \right|.$$

Proof: The following method of proof is very important. It is called "summation by parts." Define

$$E_k = \sum_{n=M}^{k} e^{inx}, \quad M \leq k \leq N.$$

Then

$$\sum_{n=M}^{N} c_n e^{inx} = \sum_{n=M+1}^{N} c_n (E_n - E_{n-1}) + c_M E_M$$

$$= \sum_{n=M+1}^{N} c_n E_n - \sum_{n=M}^{N-1} c_{n+1} E_n + c_M E_M$$

$$= \sum_{n=M}^{N} c_n E_n - \sum_{n=M}^{N-1} c_{n+1} E_n$$

$$= c_N E_N + \sum_{n=M}^{N-1} (c_n - c_{n+1}) E_n,$$

Now we estimate the modulus, using Problem 28 and the monotonicity of the c_n's:

$$\left| \sum_{n=M}^{N} c_n e^{inx} \right| \leq c_N |E_N| + \sum_{n=M}^{N-1} (c_n - c_{n+1}) |E_n|,$$

$$\leq \left\{ c_N + \sum_{n=M}^{N-1} (c_n - c_{n+1}) \right\} \left| \csc \frac{x}{2} \right|$$

$$= c_M \left| \csc \frac{x}{2} \right|.$$

QED

Theorem: *Assume that $c_0 \geq c_1 \geq c_2 \geq \ldots$ and that $\lim\limits_{n \to \infty} c_n = 0$. Then the series*

$$\sum_{n=0}^{\infty} c_n e^{inx}$$

converges for $0 < |x| \leq \pi$. The convergence is uniform on the set $\delta \leq |x| \leq \pi$ for any $\delta > 0$.

Proof: This is an immediate consequence of the lemma and the Cauchy criterion for convergence. If $\delta \leq |x| \leq \pi$, then $| \sin x/2 | \geq \sin \delta/2$, so that

$$\left| \sum_{n=M}^{N} c_n e^{inx} \right| \leq c_M \csc \frac{\delta}{2} \to 0 \text{ as } M, N \to \infty.$$

QED

We shall later require the next lemma, which follows easily from the preceding one.

Lemma: *Assume the hypothesis of the theorem, and also that $c_n \leq C/n$ for some constant C. Then for any $N > 0$*

$$\left| \sum_{n=1}^{N} c_n \sin nx \right| \leq 5C.$$

Proof: Since the terms are odd functions, we may assume $0 < x \leq \pi$. We require the elementary inequality $\sin x/2 \geq x/\pi$ (see Figure 7). Then for any m such that $1 \leq m \leq N$

$$\left| \sum_{n=1}^{N} c_n \sin nx \right| \leq \sum_{n=1}^{m} |c_n| \, |\sin nx| + \left| \sum_{n=m+1}^{N} c_n e^{inx} \right|.$$

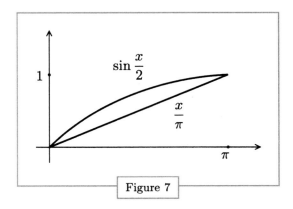

Figure 7

(If $m = N$ we interpret the second term to be zero.) Since $|\sin nx| \leq nx$, the preceding lemma implies

$$\left| \sum_{n=1}^{N} c_n \sin nx \right| \leq \sum_{n=1}^{m} Cx + c_{m+1} \csc \frac{x}{2}$$

$$\leq Cmx + \frac{C}{m+1} \frac{\pi}{x}.$$

Now there are two cases. First, if $N \leq 1/x$, then we choose $m = N$ (so that there is no second term) and obtain the estimate $CNx \leq C$. But if $N > 1/x$, then we choose m to be the unique integer satisfying $1/x - 1 < m \leq 1/x$. (If $m = 0$ there is no first term in the splitting into two sums.) Then the estimate is

$$Cmx + \frac{C}{m+1} \frac{\pi}{x} \leq C + \frac{C\pi}{1}$$

$$= C(1 + \pi)$$

$$\leq 5C.$$

QED

The lemma we have just proved has a converse:

Proposition: *Assume the hypothesis of the preceding theorem, and assume that for some constant B*

$$\left| \sum_{n=1}^{N} c_n \sin nx \right| \leq B \quad \textit{for all } x \in \mathbb{R} \quad \textit{and all } N > 0.$$

Then $c_n \leq 9B/n$ for all $n \geq 1$.

Proof: Take $x = \pi/4N$ and use two of the given inequalities to obtain

$$2B \geq \left| \sum_{n=N+1}^{2N} c_n \sin \frac{n\pi}{4N} \right|$$

$$\geq \sum_{n=N+1}^{2N} c_n \sin \frac{\pi}{4}$$

$$\geq c_{2N} N \sin \frac{\pi}{4}.$$

Thus $c_{2N} \leq 2B\sqrt{2}/N$ and the inequality for c_{2N+1} follows by the monotonicity. **QED**

C. Fourier Coefficients

We are still considering only functions which are periodic (with period 2π) on $\mathbb{R}$.

Definition: Let $f \in L^1(\mathbb{T})$. The *Fourier coefficients* of f are the numbers

$$\widehat{f}(n) = \int_{\mathbb{T}} f(x)e^{-inx}dx, \quad n \in \mathbb{Z}.$$

Several remarks need to be made about this definition. First, you notice that we use the same notation $\widehat{f}$ as was used in the preceding chapter to denote Fourier transforms. At first glance, it would seem that problems could arise from this double use of a notation. Actually, no ambiguity is possible, since we can define the Fourier transform of f only if $f \in L^1(\mathbb{R})$ (or perhaps $f \in L^2(\mathbb{R})$), and the only function which is both periodic and in $L^1(\mathbb{R})$ (or $L^2(\mathbb{R})$) is zero. Thus, for a given function f which is not zero a.e., it may have a Fourier transform $\widehat{f}(\xi)$ or it may have Fourier coefficients $\widehat{f}(n)$, but it cannot have both.

Second, we have used only those exponentials $e^{-i\xi x}$ with $\xi = n \in \mathbb{Z}$. The reason is basically that only such exponentials are periodic. Another way of expressing the same thing is given in Problem 2, which shows that the characters of $\mathbb{T}$ are precisely the functions $\phi(x) = e^{inx}$.

Third, we have divided by 2π at the outset of this discussion. There are two good reasons for doing this. The first is that $dx/2\pi$ represents Lebesgue measure on $\mathbb{T}$ if $\mathbb{T}$ is to have total measure 1. (No such possibility was open to us when we treated the Fourier transform, since $\mathbb{R}$ has infinite measure.) The other reason is that in the case of Fourier series it is really the inversion formula that will capture our attention, rather than the properties of the Fourier coefficients *per se*.

The Fourier coefficients are very similar to the Fourier transforms; we regard $\widehat{f}$ as a function defined on $\mathbb{Z}$.

Properties

FC1 $|\widehat{f}(n)| \leq \|f\|_{L^1(\mathbb{T})}$ for all $n \in \mathbb{Z}$.

FC2 $\widehat{f * g} = \widehat{f}\,\widehat{g}$.

Problem 29. Prove the preceding properties.

FC3 For fixed $y \in \mathbb{R}$, $\widehat{f(x+y)}(n) = e^{iny}\widehat{f}(n)$.

For fixed $m \in \mathbb{Z}$, $\widehat{e^{imx}f}(n) = \widehat{f}(n-m)$.

FC4 $\widehat{f(-x)}(n) = \widehat{f}(-n)$.

FC5 $\displaystyle\lim_{|n|\to\infty} \widehat{f}(n) = 0$.

FC6 If $\bar{f}$ denotes the complex conjugate, then $\widehat{\overline{f(-x)}} = \overline{\widehat{f}}$. Thus, if $\overline{f(-x)} = f(x)$, then $\widehat{f}(n) \in \mathbb{R}$ for all n.

FC7 If $f \in C^1(\mathbb{T})$, then $\widehat{\dfrac{df}{dx}}(n) = in\widehat{f}(n)$.

Detailed proofs of these properties do not need to be given, as they are all similar to properties of the Fourier transform. For instance, the fifth property is an immediate consequence of the Riemann-Lebesgue lemma on p.297. In fact, if $g(x) = f(x)\chi_{(0,2\pi)}(x)$, then $g \in L^1(\mathbb{R})$ and

$2\pi \widehat{f}(n) = \widehat{g}(n)$ for $n \in \mathbb{Z}$. Since $\lim\limits_{|\xi| \to \infty} \widehat{g}(\xi) = 0$ by the Riemann-Lebesgue lemma, the result follows.

We also give the proof of FC7. An integration by parts gives

$$\widehat{f'}(n) = \int_{\mathbb{T}} f'(x)e^{-inx}dx$$

$$= \frac{f(x)e^{-inx}}{2\pi} \Big|_0^{2\pi} - \int_{\mathbb{T}} f(x)(-ine^{-inx})dx$$

$$= \frac{f(2\pi) - f(0)}{2\pi} + in \int_{\mathbb{T}} f(x)e^{-inx}dx$$

$$= in\widehat{f}(n).$$

(Note that $f(2\pi) = f(0)$ by periodicity.) Note that if $f \in C(\mathbb{T})$ and f' has only a finite number of jump discontinuities, the same relation is valid.

Examples:

1. $f(x) = \text{sgn}(x)$ on $(-\pi, \pi)$. (We re-emphasize: f is periodic, so this function represents a "square wave":)

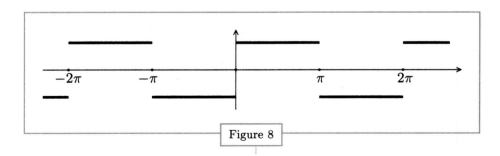

Figure 8

Here we calculate

$$\widehat{f}(n) = \int_{\mathbb{T}} f(x) e^{-inx} dx$$

$$= \frac{1}{2\pi} \int_{-\pi}^{\pi} \mathrm{sgn}(x)\, e^{-inx} dx$$

$$= \frac{1}{\pi} \int_{0}^{\pi} -i \sin nx\, dx$$

$$= \frac{i}{n\pi} \cos nx \Big|_{0}^{\pi}$$

$$= \frac{i}{n\pi} (\cos n\pi - 1) \quad (\text{if } n \neq 0).$$

Thus,

$$\widehat{f}(n) = \begin{cases} -\dfrac{2i}{n\pi} & \text{if } n \text{ is odd,} \\ 0 & \text{if } n \text{ is even.} \end{cases}$$

2. $f(x) = \dfrac{\pi - x}{2}$ on $(0, 2\pi)$. This graph is a "sawtooth":

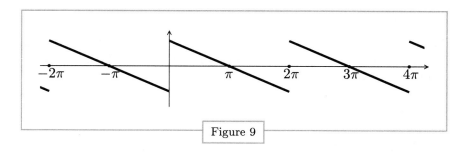

Figure 9

In this case also $\widehat{f}(0) = 0$. If $n \neq 0$, then an integration by parts yields

$$\widehat{f}(n) = \int_{\mathbb{T}} f(x)e^{-inx}dx$$

$$= \frac{1}{2\pi}\int_0^{2\pi}\frac{\pi-x}{2}e^{-inx}dx$$

$$= \frac{1}{-2\pi in}e^{-inx}\frac{\pi-x}{2}\Big|_0^{2\pi} - \int_0^{2\pi}\left(-\frac{1}{2}\right)\frac{e^{-inx}}{-2\pi in}dx$$

$$= \frac{-1}{4\pi in}\left[-\pi e^{-2\pi in} - \pi e^0\right]$$

$$= \frac{1}{2in}.$$

3. $g(x) = \dfrac{(x-\pi)^2}{4}$ on $(0, 2\pi)$.

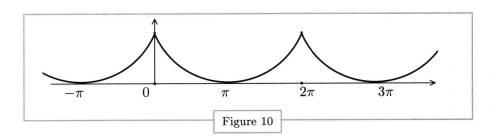

Figure 10

In this case most of the work in calculating $\widehat{g}$ has already been accomplished. For if f refers to the function in Example 2, then $g' = -f$. Therefore, Property FC7 yields

$$-\widehat{f}(n) = in\widehat{g}(n).$$

Therefore, for $n \neq 0$ we obtain

$$\widehat{g}(n) = \frac{1}{2n^2}.$$

For $n = 0$ we must calculate:

$$\widehat{g}(0) = \int_{\mathbb{T}} g(x)dx$$

$$= \frac{1}{2\pi} \int_{0}^{2\pi} \frac{(x - \pi)^2}{4} dx$$

$$= \frac{1}{24\pi} (x - \pi)^3 \Big|_{0}^{2\pi}$$

$$= \frac{\pi^2}{12}.$$

Problem 30. Let $h(x) = |x|$ for $|x| < \pi$, and $h \in C(\mathbb{T})$. Sketch the graph of h and show that

$$\widehat{h}(n) = \begin{cases} -2/\pi n^2 & \text{if } n \text{ is odd,} \\ \pi/2 & \text{if } n = 0, \\ 0 & \text{if } n \text{ is even and } \neq 0. \end{cases}$$

Problem 31. Let $f(x) = |\sin x|$. Show that

$$\widehat{f}(n) = \begin{cases} \dfrac{2}{\pi(1 - n^2)} & \text{if } n \text{ is even,} \\ 0 & \text{if } n \text{ is odd.} \end{cases}$$

We are now going to discuss the concept of a *Fourier series*. Before we do, however, we state a simple result that we already have proved.

Proposition: *Assume* $\displaystyle\sum_{n=-\infty}^{\infty} |c_n| < \infty$ *and assume* $f \in C(\mathbb{T})$ *is defined by*

$$f(x) = \sum_{n=-\infty}^{\infty} c_n e^{inx}.$$

Then

$$\widehat{f}(n) = c_n.$$

Proof: This is precisely the proposition on p.378, restated.   **QED**

Definition: Let $f \in L^1(\mathbb{T})$. The *Fourier series* of f is the formal expression

$$\sum_{n=-\infty}^{\infty} \widehat{f}(n)e^{inx}.$$

We say nothing about the actual convergence of this series, although we are thinking and hoping that in some sense it represents the original function $f(x)$. The preceding proposition of course guarantees this in a simple case. What is needed is precisely some sort of *inversion theorem* which will contain hypotheses to ensure that indeed

$$f(x) = \sum_{n=-\infty}^{\infty} \widehat{f}(n)e^{inx}.$$

But even if we do not know this is valid, we nevertheless would like to indicate the relation between f and its Fourier series by some sort of equation like the preceding one. To do this, we use the following device:

Notation: For $f \in L^1(\mathbb{T})$,

$$f(x) \sim \sum_{n=-\infty}^{\infty} \widehat{f}(n)e^{inx}.$$

This notation is therefore just shorthand for the actual equations

$$\widehat{f}(n) = \int_{\mathbb{T}} f(x)e^{-inx}dx, \quad n \in \mathbb{Z}.$$

Thus, Example 1 could be rewritten

$$f(x) \sim \sum_{\substack{n=-\infty \\ n \text{ odd}}}^{\infty} \frac{-2i}{n\pi}e^{inx}.$$

Example 2:

$$f(x) \sim \sum_{n \neq 0} \frac{e^{inx}}{2in}.$$

Example 3:

$$g(x) \sim \frac{\pi^2}{12} + \sum_{n \neq 0} \frac{e^{inx}}{2n^2}.$$

Problem 31:

$$|\sin x| \sim \sum_{n=-\infty}^{\infty} \frac{2e^{2inx}}{\pi(1 - 4n^2)}.$$

Usually, when dealing with real functions as these are, we prefer to use the "real" forms of the Fourier series, as discussed in Section B.3. This means that we shall also write

$$f(x) \sim \frac{a_0}{2} + \sum_{n=1}^{\infty} (a_n \cos nx + b_n \sin nx).$$

This notation means nothing more nor less than the equations

$$a_n = 2 \int_{\mathbb{T}} f(x) \cos nx \, dx \quad \text{for } n \geq 0,$$

$$b_n = 2 \int_{\mathbb{T}} f(x) \sin nx \, dx \quad \text{for } n \geq 1$$

(cf. Problem 16). The preceding four examples can now be written as follows:

$$\text{sgn}(x)(\text{on } (-\pi, \pi)) \sim \frac{4}{\pi} \sum_{\substack{n=1 \\ n \text{ odd}}}^{\infty} \frac{\sin nx}{n};$$

$$\frac{\pi - x}{2} (\text{on } (0, 2\pi)) \sim \sum_{n=1}^{\infty} \frac{\sin nx}{n};$$

$$\frac{(x - \pi)^2}{4} (\text{on } (0, 2\pi)) \sim \frac{\pi^2}{12} + \sum_{n=1}^{\infty} \frac{\cos nx}{n^2};$$

$$|\sin x| \sim \frac{2}{\pi} + \frac{4}{\pi} \sum_{n=1}^{\infty} \frac{\cos 2nx}{1 - 4n^2}.$$

This formal way of writing the Fourier coefficients makes some of the basic properties we gave for $\widehat{f}$ much more readily remembered. For instance, Property FC3 contains the statement $\widehat{f(x + y)}(n) = e^{iny}\widehat{f}(n)$. This takes the following form: Suppose

$$f(x) \sim \sum_{n=-\infty}^{\infty} c_n e^{inx};$$

then

$$f(x+y) \sim \sum_{n=-\infty}^{\infty} c_n e^{iny} e^{inx}.$$

The other statement in Property FC3 becomes

$$e^{imx} f(x) \sim \sum_{n=-\infty}^{\infty} c_n e^{i(m+n)x} = \sum_{n=-\infty}^{\infty} c_{n-m} e^{inx}.$$

Property FC4 states

$$f(-x) \sim \sum_{n=-\infty}^{\infty} c_n e^{-inx} = \sum_{n=-\infty}^{\infty} c_{-n} e^{inx}.$$

And Property FC7,

$$\frac{df}{dx} \sim \sum_{n=-\infty}^{\infty} inc_n e^{inx}.$$

Problem 32. In the above notation, prove that if m is a non-zero integer, then

$$f(mx) \sim \sum_{n=-\infty}^{\infty} c_n e^{inmx}.$$

(You cannot work this problem by making the substitution $x \to mx$. Rather you must demonstrate that

$$\int_{\mathbb{T}} f(mx) e^{-ikx} dx = \begin{cases} 0 & \text{if } m \text{ does not divide } k, \\ \widehat{f}\left(\frac{k}{m}\right) & \text{if } m \text{ divides } k.\end{cases}$$

D. Convergence of Fourier Series

   This section and the following one are exactly analogous to Sections 13.H and B, respectively, which treated the inversion theorem for the Fourier transform. The problem is the same: If $f \in L^1(\mathbb{T})$ and the Fourier coefficients $\widehat{f}(n)$ are given, then determine the function f itself. Because of the historical terminology, the results in the present case are not called "inversion theorems," but rather are called "convergence of the Fourier series to the function." They really are inversion theorems, however.

These results all state that in some sense

$$f(x) = \sum_{n=-\infty}^{\infty} \widehat{f}(n)e^{inx}.$$

We shall first give the analog of the theorem of Section 13.H, and then give some summability results in Section E.

Notation: Given $f \in L^1(\mathbb{T})$ and $N \geq 0$, the Nth order partial sum of the Fourier series of f is the trigonometric polynomial

$$s_N(x) = \sum_{n=-N}^{N} \widehat{f}(n)e^{inx}.$$

We now give a sufficient condition for the convergence of $s_N(x)$ to $f(x)$, or, more generally, to $\frac{1}{2}[f(x+) + f(x-)]$. Recall that by definition

$$f(x+) = \lim_{\substack{y \to x \\ y > x}} f(y),$$
$$f(x-) = \lim_{\substack{y \to x \\ y < x}} f(y).$$

Theorem: *Assume $f \in L^1(\mathbb{T})$. Let $x \in \mathbb{R}$ and assume $f(x+)$ and $f(x-)$ both exist. Further, assume that there exists a constant C such that*
$$|f(y) - f(x+)| \leq C(y - x) \quad \text{for } y > x,$$
$$|f(y) - f(x-)| \leq C(x - y) \quad \text{for } y < x,$$
in both cases for y in a neighborhood of x. Then

$$\frac{f(x+) + f(x-)}{2} = \lim_{N \to \infty} s_N(x).$$

Proof: By definition,

$$s_N(x) = \sum_{n=-N}^{N} \int_{\mathbb{T}} f(y)e^{-iny}dy\; e^{inx}$$

$$= \int_{\mathbb{T}} f(y) \sum_{n=-N}^{N} e^{in(x-y)}dy$$

$$= \int_{\mathbb{T}} f(y)D_N(x-y)dy,$$

where D_N is the Dirichlet kernel defined in Section B.1. Thus, $s_N = f*D_N$ according to the definition given in Problem 5. Since $s_N = D_N*f$, we can use the formula for D_N given on p.373 to write

$$s_N(x) = \int_{\mathbb{T}} f(x-y)\frac{\sin(N+\frac{1}{2})y}{\sin\frac{y}{2}}dy.$$

Let $L = \frac{1}{2}[f(x+) + f(x-)]$. Since $\int_{\mathbb{T}} D_N(y)dy = 1$, we find that

$$s_N(x) - L = \int_{\mathbb{T}} [f(x-y) - L]\frac{\sin(N+\frac{1}{2})y}{\sin\frac{y}{2}}dy.$$

We now write this integration as $\int_0^{\pi} + \int_{-\pi}^{0}$, and on the interval $(-\pi, 0)$ replace y by $-y$. The result is

$$s_N(x) - L = \frac{1}{2\pi}\int_0^{\pi}[f(x-y) - L]\frac{\sin(N+\frac{1}{2})y}{\sin\frac{y}{2}}dy$$

$$+ \frac{1}{2\pi}\int_0^{\pi}[f(x+y) - L]\frac{\sin(N+\frac{1}{2})y}{\sin\frac{y}{2}}dy$$

$$= \int_0^{\pi}\phi(y)\sin\left(N+\frac{1}{2}\right)y\; dy,$$

where
$$\phi(y) = \frac{f(x+y) + f(x-y) - 2L}{2\pi \sin \dfrac{y}{2}}.$$

The hypothesis on f shows that ϕ is integrable on $[\epsilon, \pi]$ for any $\epsilon > 0$, and ϕ is *bounded* on $(0, \epsilon]$. Thus, $\phi \in L^1(0, \pi)$. By the Riemann-Lebesgue lemma,

$$\lim_{|\xi| \to \infty} \int_0^\pi \phi(y) e^{-iy\xi} dy = 0.$$

In particular, for $\xi = \pm \left(N + \frac{1}{2}\right)$ we obtain the same limit, showing that $\lim_{N \to \infty} [s_N(x) - L] = 0$.   **QED**

This theorem applies beautifully to all the explicit examples we have given up to this point. The results look like the following:

$$\sum_{n=0}^\infty \frac{\sin(2n+1)x}{2n+1} = \frac{\pi}{4} \qquad \text{for } 0 < x < \pi;$$

$$\sum_{n=1}^\infty \frac{\sin nx}{n} = \frac{\pi - x}{2} \qquad \text{for } 0 < x < 2\pi;$$

$$\sum_{n=1}^\infty \frac{\cos nx}{n^2} = \frac{x^2}{4} - \frac{\pi x}{2} + \frac{\pi^2}{6} \qquad \text{for } 0 \leq x \leq 2\pi;$$

$$\frac{2}{\pi} - \frac{4}{\pi} \sum_{n=1}^\infty \frac{\cos 2nx}{4n^2 - 1} = |\sin x| \qquad \text{for } x \in \mathbb{R}.$$

These equations yield certain interesting series for various specific values of the variable x. For instance, if the first is evaluated at $x = \pi/2$, the result is

$$\sum_{n=0}^\infty \frac{(-1)^n}{2n+1} = \frac{\pi}{4}.$$

The choice $x = 0$ in the third series gives

$$\sum_{n=1}^\infty \frac{1}{n^2} = \frac{\pi^2}{6}.$$

Problem 33. Use the fourth series to show that $\displaystyle\sum_{n=1}^\infty \frac{1}{4n^2 - 1} = \frac{1}{2}$. Then show that this is actually trivial, since it is a telescoping series.

Problem 34. Prove that

$$|\sin x| = \frac{8}{\pi} \sum_{n=1}^{\infty} \frac{\sin^2 nx}{4n^2 - 1}.$$

Problem 35. Let $t \in \mathbb{R} \sim \mathbb{Z}$ be fixed. Calculate the Fourier coefficients of the function equal to $\cos tx$ for $-\pi \leq x \leq \pi$, and show that

$$\frac{\pi \cos tx}{\sin t\pi} = \frac{1}{t} + \sum_{n=1}^{\infty} \frac{2t}{t^2 - n^2}(-1)^n \cos nx, \quad -\pi \leq x \leq \pi.$$

Problem 36. Show that for $t \in \mathbb{R} \sim \mathbb{Z}$

$$\frac{\pi}{\sin t\pi} = \frac{1}{t} + \sum_{n=1}^{\infty} (-1)^n \frac{2t}{t^2 - n^2}.$$

Problem 37. Problem 35 implies that

$$\frac{\pi \cos t\pi}{\sin t\pi} = \frac{1}{t} + \sum_{n=1}^{\infty} \frac{2t}{t^2 - n^2}, \quad t \notin \mathbb{Z}.$$

Show that for $0 < t < 1$

$$\log \sin t\pi = \log t\pi + \sum_{n=1}^{\infty} \log\left(1 - \frac{t^2}{n^2}\right).$$

Then show that

$$\frac{\sin t\pi}{\pi} = t \prod_{n=1}^{\infty} \left(1 - \frac{t^2}{n^2}\right) \quad \text{for } 0 < t < 1.$$

Problem 38. Prove that

$$\frac{\sin t\pi}{\pi} = t \prod_{n=1}^{\infty} \left(1 - \frac{t^2}{n^2}\right) \quad \text{for all } t \in \mathbb{R}.$$

(This result was previously derived in Problem 9.34 by another method.)

(**HINT:** You may clearly assume $t \notin \mathbb{Z}$. Define $F_N(t) = t \prod\limits_{n=1}^{N} \left(1 - \dfrac{t^2}{n^2}\right)$
and prove that

$$F_N(t) = (-1)^N (N!)^{-2} \prod_{n=-N}^{N} (t - n).$$

Then prove that $\lim\limits_{N \to \infty} F_N(t+1)/F_N(t) = -1$, and use Problem 37.)

Problem 39. Set $t = \frac{1}{2}$ and obtain another proof of Wallis' formula (Problem 9.14).

As a sort of corollary of the proof of the above theorem, we include the following result.

> **Theorem:** *If f satisfies a Lipschitz condition on $\mathbb{T}$, then its Fourier series converges uniformly (to f).*

Proof: We are assuming f is periodic on $\mathbb{R}$ and

$$|f(x) - f(x')| \leq C|x - x'| \quad \text{for all } x, x' \in \mathbb{R}.$$

As in the previous proof, we have

$$s_N(x) - f(x) = \int_0^\pi \phi(y) \sin\left(N + \frac{1}{2}\right) y \, dy,$$

where
$$\phi(y) = \frac{[f(x+y) - f(x)] + [f(x-y) - f(x)]}{2\pi \sin \dfrac{y}{2}}.$$

We make two observations about ϕ. First,

$$|\phi(y)| \leq C.$$

To prove this, we simply recall from Figure 7 that $\pi \sin \dfrac{y}{2} \geq y$. Therefore,

$$|\phi(y)| \leq \frac{Cy + Cy}{2y} = C.$$

Second, suppose $0 < y < \pi$ and $0 < h < \pi/2$. Then

$$\phi(y + h) - \phi(y) =$$

$$\frac{1}{2\pi}[f(x+y+h) - f(x) + f(x-y-h) - f(x)]\left[\csc\frac{y+h}{2} - \csc\frac{y}{2}\right]$$

$$+ \frac{1}{2\pi\sin y/2}[f(x+y+h) - f(x+y) + f(x-y-h) - f(x-y)].$$

The difference of cosecants can be estimated from the mean value theorem:

$$\left|\csc\frac{y+h}{2} - \csc\frac{y}{2}\right| = \frac{|\sin\frac{y}{2} - \sin\frac{y+h}{2}|}{\sin\frac{y+h}{2}\sin\frac{y}{2}}$$

$$\leq \frac{h}{2\sin\frac{y+h}{2}\sin\frac{y}{2}}.$$

If $y + h \leq \pi$, then we have the estimate

$$\frac{\pi^2 h}{2(y+h)y}.$$

If $y + h > \pi$, then $y > \pi/2$ and $y + h < 3\pi/2$, so we have the estimate

$$\frac{h}{2(1/\sqrt{2})^2} = h < \frac{3\pi^2 h}{2(y+h)y}.$$

Therefore, the first term in the formula for $\phi(y + h) - \phi(y)$ can be estimated by

$$\frac{2C(y+h)}{2\pi}\frac{3\pi^2 h}{2(y+h)h} = \frac{3\pi C h}{2y}.$$

The second term is dominated by

$$\frac{1}{2y}(Ch + Ch) = \frac{Ch}{y}.$$

Therefore,

$$|\phi(y+h) - \phi(y)| < \frac{3\pi C h}{2y} + \frac{Ch}{y} < \frac{6Ch}{y}.$$

Putting our two observations together, we obtain

$$|\phi(y+h) - \phi(y)| \leq \begin{cases} \dfrac{6Ch}{y} & \text{if } 0 < 2h < y < \pi, \\ 2C & \text{if } 0 < y < 2h < \pi. \end{cases}$$

Now replace y by $y + h$ in the formula for $s_N - f$:

$$s_N(x) - f(x) = \int_{-h}^{\pi-h} \phi(y+h) \sin\left(N + \frac{1}{2}\right)(y+h)\, dy$$

$$= \int_0^{\pi} \phi(y+h) \sin\left(N + \frac{1}{2}\right)(y+h)\, dy + E,$$

where the "error term" E satisfies the estimate

$$|E| \le 2Ch$$

(there are two intervals each of length h and the integrand is bounded by C). Now for large N choose

$$h = \frac{\pi}{N + \frac{1}{2}}$$

(see p.297, the proof of the Riemann-Lebesgue lemma). Thus,

$$s_N(x) - f(x) = -\int_0^{\pi} \phi(y+h) \sin\left(N + \frac{1}{2}\right)y\, dy + E.$$

Adding our two expressions for $s_N(x) - f(x)$ yields

$$2[s_N(x) - f(x)] = \int_0^{\pi} [\phi(y) - \phi(y+h)] \sin\left(N + \frac{1}{2}\right)y\, dy + E.$$

Now we estimate:

$$2|s_N(x) - f(x)| \le \int_0^{2h} 2C\, dy + \int_{2h}^{\pi} \frac{6Ch}{y}\, dy + 2Ch$$

$$= 6Ch + 6Ch \log \frac{\pi}{2h}.$$

That is,

$$|s_N(x) - f(x)| \le \frac{3C\pi}{N + \frac{1}{2}} \left[1 + \log \frac{N + \frac{1}{2}}{2}\right].$$

Therefore, $s_N(x) - f(x)$ has limit zero as $N \to \infty$, uniformly for all x.

QED

Problem 40. Prove that the conclusion of the theorem remains valid if it is assumed only that f satisfies a Hölder condition; i.e., that there exist constants C and $0 < \alpha < 1$ such that f (is periodic and) satisfies

$$|f(x) - f(x')| \leq C|x - x'|^{\alpha}.$$

Just as in Section 13.H there is a *principle of localization* for Fourier series:

Corollary: Assume f, $g \in L^1(\mathbb{T})$. Let $x \in \mathbb{R}$ and assume $f = g$ in a neighborhood of x. Then

$$\sum_{n=-\infty}^{\infty} \widehat{f}(n)e^{inx} = \sum_{n=-\infty}^{\infty} \widehat{g}(n)e^{inx},$$

in the sense that if one of these series converges, then the other also converges and the two sums are equal.

Proof: This is obvious as the theorem applies to the function $f - g$ and this function vanishes in a neighborhood of x. Therefore,

$$0 = \sum_{n=-\infty}^{\infty} [\widehat{f}(n) - \widehat{g}(n)]e^{inx}.$$

QED

This result is called a *localization* principle because it asserts that the convergence of the series

$$\sum_{n=-\infty}^{\infty} \widehat{f}(n)e^{inx}$$

depends only on the nature of the integrable function in a neighborhood of x.

Remark: This is a good place to stress again what we intend the symbol $\sum_{n=-\infty}^{\infty}$ to mean in this context. The definition is precisely

$$\sum_{n=-\infty}^{\infty} \widehat{f}(n)e^{inx} = \lim_{N \to \infty} \sum_{n=-N}^{N} \widehat{f}(n)e^{inx}.$$

This is not the same as another possible definition, namely

$$\lim_{M,N\to\infty} \sum_{n=-M}^{N} \widehat{f}(n)e^{inx}.$$

For example, if $c_n = 1/n$ for $n \neq 0$, $c_n = 0$ for $n = 0$, then

$$\sum_{n=-\infty}^{\infty} c_n = 0$$

but

$$\lim_{M,N\to\infty} \sum_{n=-M}^{N} c_n$$

does not exist.

The next problem is analogous to Problem 13.6.

Problem 41. Assume $f \in L^1(\mathbb{T})$ is an odd function, so that

$$f \sim \sum_{n=1}^{\infty} b_n \sin nx.$$

Prove that

$$\sum_{n=1}^{\infty} \frac{b_n}{n} = \int_0^{\pi} \left(1 - \frac{x}{\pi}\right) f(x)dx.$$

(**HINT:** Write

$$\sum_{n=1}^{N} \frac{b_n}{n} = \int_0^{\pi} \left(\frac{2}{\pi} \sum_{n=1}^{N} \frac{\sin nx}{n}\right) f(x)dx$$

and let $N \to \infty$. You should use a lemma of Section B.5 to show that the integrand is dominated by a constant times $|f(x)|$, and then use LDCT.)

Problem 42. Let $f \in L^1(\mathbb{T})$ and suppose

$$f \sim \frac{a_0}{2} + \sum_{n=1}^{\infty}(a_n \cos nx + b_n \sin nx).$$

Prove that $\displaystyle\sum_{n=1}^{\infty} \frac{b_n}{n}$ converges and that

$$\sum_{n=1}^{\infty} \frac{b_n}{n} = \int_0^{\pi} \left(1 - \frac{x}{\pi}\right) \frac{f(x) - f(-x)}{2} dx$$

$$= \frac{1}{2\pi} \int_0^{2\pi} (\pi - x)f(x)dx.$$

Problem 43. Give an example of a sequence c_n, $-\infty < n < \infty$, such that $\displaystyle\lim_{|n|\to\infty} c_n = 0$, for which no $f \in L^1(\mathbb{T})$ exists with $\widehat{f}(n) = c_n$ for all n.

(**HINT:** Use Problem 42.)

Problem 44. Using Problem 41, show that $\displaystyle\sum_{n=1}^{\infty} \frac{1}{n^2} = \frac{\pi^2}{6}$.

Problem 45. Use directly the result of Problem 44 to show that $\displaystyle\sum_{n=1}^{\infty} \frac{1}{(2n-1)^2} = \frac{\pi^2}{8}$.

E. Summability of Fourier Series

Even if $f \in C(\mathbb{T})$, it may happen for a particular point x that the series

$$\sum_{n=-\infty}^{\infty} \widehat{f}(n)e^{inx}$$

fails to converge. And if we know only that $f \in L^1(\mathbb{T})$, the situation is even worse. Kolmogorov has given an example of a function $f \in L^1(\mathbb{T})$

whose Fourier series diverges for *every* $x \in \mathbb{R}$! We shall not present Kolmogorov's example but shall present later a function $f \in C(\mathbb{T})$ for which the Fourier series fails to converge at $x = 0$ (see Section F below). (The trigonometric series in Section B.5 which was everywhere divergent was not a Fourier series.) Nevertheless, we can recover $f(x)$ from the Fourier coefficients $\widehat{f}(n)$. To do this we can use various methods of "summing" series which may diverge. These methods are analogous to the L^1-summability of Section 13.B.

1.   Cesàro Summability

Given $f \in L^1(\mathbb{T})$, we have defined the partial sums $s_0(x)$, $s_1(x)$, $s_2(x)$, ... of the Fourier series of f. We now define the *Cesàro means*:

$$\sigma_N(x) = \frac{s_0(x) + s_1(x) + \cdots + s_N(x)}{N+1}.$$

We shall investigate the limiting behavior of $\sigma_N(x)$ as $N \to \infty$. First, you should be aware that if $\lim_{N\to\infty} s_N(x)$ exists, then $\lim_{N\to\infty} \sigma_N(x)$ exists and is the same:

Problem 46. Suppose s_0, s_1, s_2, ... is a convergent sequence. Prove that
$$\lim_{N\to\infty} \frac{s_0 + s_1 + \cdots + s_N}{N+1} = \lim_{N\to\infty} s_N.$$

Now refer to Section B for the discussion of the Dirichlet and Fejér kernels. Since $s_N = f * D_N$ as shown in Section D, we find

$$\sigma_N = \frac{1}{N+1} \sum_{k=0}^{N} s_k$$

$$= \frac{1}{N+1} \sum_{k=0}^{N} f * D_k$$

$$= f * \frac{1}{N+1} \sum_{k=0}^{N} D_k$$

$$= f * F_N.$$

Theorem: *The Cesàro means of the Fourier series of f converge to f in the following ways.*

> *(a) If $f \in C(\mathbb{T})$, $\sigma_N \to f$ uniformly.*
>
> *(b) If $f \in L^1(\mathbb{T})$ and f is continuous at x_0, $\sigma_N(x_0) \to f(x_0)$.*
>
> *(c) If $f \in L^p(\mathbb{T})$, $\sigma_N \to f$ in $L^p(\mathbb{T})$ if $1 \leq p < \infty$.*

Proof: The details about the Fejér kernel F_N are given in Section B. In particular, the hypotheses of the theorem on approximate identities in Section 12.C are satisfied (with $c = 1$ in that notation). Therefore, (c) follows immediately from the formula $\sigma_N = f * F_N$. And (a) is a direct consequence of Problem 12.17. The proof of (b) is slightly different, so we give the details. Given $\epsilon > 0$, there exists $0 < \delta < \pi$ such that $|f(x) - f(x_0)| \leq \epsilon/2$ for all x satisfying $|x - x_0| \leq \delta$. Then

$$\sigma_N(x_0) - f(x_0) = \int_{\mathbb{T}} f(x_0 - y) F_N(y) dy - f(x_0)$$

$$= \int_{\mathbb{T}} [f(x_0 - y) - f(x_0)] F_N(y) dy$$

$$= \frac{1}{2\pi} \int_{-\pi}^{\pi} [f(x_0 - y) - f(x_0)] F_N(y) dy.$$

We estimate in the following way:

$$|\sigma_N(x_0) - f(x_0)| \leq \frac{\epsilon/2}{2\pi} \int_{|y| \leq \delta} F_N(y) dy$$

$$+ \frac{1}{2\pi} \int_{\delta \leq |y| \leq \pi} |f(x_0 - y) - f(x_0)| F_N(y) dy$$

$$\leq \frac{\epsilon}{2} + \sup_{\delta \leq |y| \leq \pi} F_N(y) \, \|f - f(x_0)\|_{L^1(\mathbb{T})}.$$

By the explicit formula for $F_N(y)$ on p.376 it follows that

$$F_N(y) \leq \frac{1}{N \sin^2(y/2)}.$$

Therefore,

$$|\sigma_N(x_0) - f(x_0)| \leq \frac{\epsilon}{2} + \frac{\|f - f(x_0)\|_{L^1(\mathbb{T})}}{N \sin^2(\delta/2)}.$$

The right side is therefore less than ϵ for all sufficiently large N.   **QED**

Corollary: If $f \in L^1(\mathbb{T})$ and $\widehat{f}(n) = 0$ for all $n \in \mathbb{Z}$, then $f = 0$.

Proof: Since $\sigma_N \to f$ in $L^1(\mathbb{T})$ and $\sigma_N = 0$, it follows that $f = 0$.

                                                                              QED

As another corollary we have a result corresponding to the inversion theorem of Section 13.B:

Fourier Inversion Theorem: Let $f \in L^1(\mathbb{T})$ and assume that the Fourier series of f converges absolutely:

$$\sum_{n=-\infty}^{\infty} |\widehat{f}(n)| < \infty.$$

Then f is equivalent to a continuous function. Assuming that f is continuous, then for all $x \in \mathbb{R}$,

$$f(x) = \sum_{n=-\infty}^{\infty} \widehat{f}(n)e^{inx}.$$

Proof: Define

$$g(x) = \sum_{n=-\infty}^{\infty} \widehat{f}(n)e^{inx}.$$

Since this series converges uniformly, g is continuous and its Fourier coefficients satisfy $\widehat{g} = \widehat{f}$. By the preceding corollary, $g = f$ as elements of $L^1(\mathbb{T})$. The theorem follows.   **QED**

Problem 47. Suppose $f \in L^1(\mathbb{T})$ and has Fourier series represented either as

$$f \sim \sum_{n=-\infty}^{\infty} c_n e^{inx}$$

or as

$$f \sim \frac{a_0}{2} + \sum_{n=1}^{\infty} (a_n \cos nx + b_n \sin nx).$$

Prove that f is odd $\iff \widehat{f}(-n) = -\widehat{f}(n)$ for all $n \iff c_{-n} = -c_n$ for all $n \iff a_n = 0$ for all n.

Problem 48. Under the same assumptions of Problem 47, prove that f is real-valued $\iff \overline{c_n} = c_{-n}$ for all $n \iff a_n$, b_n are real for all n.

Problem 49. Suppose $f \in L^1(\mathbb{T})$ and f is continuous at x. Also suppose that

$$\sum_{n=-\infty}^{\infty} \widehat{f}(n) e^{inx}$$

converges. Prove that

$$f(x) = \sum_{n=-\infty}^{\infty} \widehat{f}(n) e^{inx}.$$

(**HINT:** Use Problem 46.)

Problem 50. Suppose $f \in L^1(\mathbb{T})$ and $f(x+)$, $f(x-)$ exist. Prove that

$$\lim_{N \to \infty} \sigma_N(x) = \frac{f(x+) + f(x-)}{2}.$$

Another corollary is a famous theorem on approximation:

> **Weierstrass Approximation Theorem:** *The trigonometric polynomials are dense in* $C(\mathbb{T})$.

Proof: If $f \in C(\mathbb{T})$, then $\sigma_N \to f$ uniformly and σ_N is a trigonometric polynomial. **QED**

Problem 51. Suppose $f \in L^1(\mathbb{T})$. Prove that $f \in C^\infty(\mathbb{T})$ if and only if the Fourier coefficients $\widehat{f}(n)$ "decrease rapidly" as $|n| \to \infty$. That is, for any $\alpha > 0$ there exists a constant C_α such that

$$|\widehat{f}(n)| \le C_\alpha |n|^{-\alpha} \quad \text{for all } n \in \mathbb{Z}.$$

(**HINT**: If $f \in C^\infty$, use the relation $\widehat{f^{(m)}} = (in)^m \widehat{f}$ to estimate $\widehat{f}$. If $\widehat{f}$ decreases rapidly, use the inversion theorem to show $f \in C^\infty$.)

2.   Abel Summability

Again, we consider the Fourier series of a function $f \in L^1(\mathbb{T})$. The *Abel means* are defined as follows for $0 < r < 1$:

$$A_r(x) = \sum_{n=-\infty}^{\infty} r^{|n|} \widehat{f}(n) e^{inx}.$$

This function is not a trigonometric polynomial, but the rapid decay of $r^{|n|}$ as $|n| \to \infty$ guarantees splendid convergence of the series. In fact, since

$$\int_{\mathbb{T}} \sum_{n=-\infty}^{\infty} r^{|n|} |f(y)| dy = \int_{\mathbb{T}} \left(\frac{2}{1-r} - 1 \right) |f(y)| dy$$

$$= \frac{1+r}{1-r} \|f\|_{L^1(\mathbb{T})} < \infty,$$

we can insert the definition of $\widehat{f}(n)$ into the definition of $A_r(x)$ and interchange summation and integration to obtain

$$A_r(x) = \sum_{n=-\infty}^{\infty} r^{|n|} \left(\int_{\mathbb{T}} f(y) e^{-iny} dy \right) e^{inx}$$

$$= \int_{\mathbb{T}} \left(\sum_{n=-\infty}^{\infty} r^{|n|} e^{in(x-y)} \right) f(y) dy$$

$$= \int_{\mathbb{T}} P_r(x-y) f(y) dy.$$

Here P_r is the Poisson kernel defined in Section B.1.

Since the behavior of P_r as $r \to 1$ is similar to that of the Fejér kernel F_N as $N \to \infty$, the same proof as in the preceding section shows at once that a similar result is valid:

Theorem: *The Abel means of the Fourier series of f enjoy the following properties as $r \to 1-$.*

    (a) If $f \in C(\mathbb{T})$, $A_r \to f$ uniformly.

    (b) If $f \in L^1(\mathbb{T})$ and f is continuous at x_0, $A_r(x_0) \to f(x_0)$.

    (c) If $f \in L^p(\mathbb{T})$, $A_r \to f$ in $L^p(\mathbb{T})$ if $1 \le p < \infty$.

---

3. Application of Abel Summability to the Dirichlet Problem

In Section 13.F we showed how the Fourier transform could be employed as an effective tool for solving the Dirichlet problem for Laplace's equation in a half space. As the heuristic development of that section is directly analogous to the present section, we dispense with the motivation and go directly to the result.

Let G be the unit disk in $\mathbb{R}^2$: $G = \{(x, y) | x^2 + y^2 < 1\}$. We use polar coordinates $x = r \cos \theta$, $y = r \sin \theta$, so that G is described by the inequality $r < 1$. The Laplace operator in polar coordinates has the form

$$\frac{\partial^2}{\partial x^2} + \frac{\partial^2}{\partial y^2} = \frac{\partial^2}{\partial r^2} + \frac{1}{r}\frac{\partial}{\partial r} + \frac{1}{r^2}\frac{\partial^2}{\partial \theta^2}.$$

It is therefore an easy calculation to show that the functions $r^{|n|}e^{in\theta}$ are solutions of Laplace's equation for any $n \in \mathbb{Z}$:

$$\left(\frac{\partial^2}{\partial x^2} + \frac{\partial^2}{\partial y^2} \right) \left(r^{|n|}e^{in\theta} \right) = 0.$$

In rectangular coordinates these functions are equal to $(x + iy)^n$ if $n \ge 0$ and $(x - iy)^{-n}$ if $n \le 0$, so they are infinitely differentiable on $\mathbb{R}^2$.

> **Theorem:** *Assume $f \in C(\mathbb{T})$. Then there exists a function u defined on G^- which satisfies*
>
> **(a)** $\left(\dfrac{\partial^2}{\partial x^2} + \dfrac{\partial^2}{\partial y^2} \right) u = 0$ *in G;*
>
> **(b)** $u \in C(G^-)$;
>
> **(c)** *on ∂G, $u(1, \theta) = f(\theta)$.*

Proof: We use the Fourier series of f, using θ as the variable in $\mathbb{T}$:

$$f(\theta) \sim \sum_{n=-\infty}^{\infty} \widehat{f}(n) e^{in\theta}.$$

Then we define

$$u(r, \theta) = \sum_{n=-\infty}^{\infty} r^{|n|} \widehat{f}(n) e^{in\theta}, \quad r < 1.$$

By the fact that $r^{|n|} e^{in\theta}$ is a solution of Laplace's equation we conclude that (a) is satisfied; the rapid convergence of the series permits termwise differentiation of u. Since $u(r, \theta) = A_r(\theta)$, part (a) of the preceding theorem implies that $u(r, \theta) \to f(\theta)$ uniformly as $r \to 1-$. Therefore, we simply define $u(1, \theta) = f(\theta)$ and conclude that (b) and (c) are valid.

QED

Problem 52. Show that if the real form of the Fourier series of f is

$$f \sim \frac{a_0}{2} + \sum_{n=1}^{\infty} (a_n \cos n\theta + b_n \sin n\theta),$$

then for $r < 1$

$$u(r, \theta) = \frac{a_0}{2} + \sum_{n=1}^{\infty} r^n (a_n \cos n\theta + b_n \sin n\theta).$$

Problem 53. Why did we not write above

$$u(r,\theta) = \sum_{n=-\infty}^{\infty} r^{|n|}\widehat{f}(n)e^{in\theta} \quad \text{for } r \leq 1?$$

Problem 54. Given $f \in C(\mathbb{T})$, show that there exists a solution of Laplace's equation for $r > 1$ which is continuous for $r \geq 1$ and is equal to f for $r = 1$.

Problem 55. Refer to Problem 13 and show that a solution $u(r,\theta)$ for Problem 54 can be written in the form $u(r,\theta) = P_{1/r} * f$.

F. A Counterexample

We now give an elegant example of Fejér of a function $f \in C(\mathbb{T})$ whose Fourier series does not converge everywhere. Since all points of the group $\mathbb{T}$ look alike, we shall construct $f \in C(\mathbb{T})$ such that its Fourier series does not converge for $x = 0$:

$$\frac{a_0}{2} + \sum_{n=1}^{\infty} a_n \quad \text{diverges.}$$

First, for any $m \in \mathbb{N}$ define the trigonometric polynomial Q_m by the formula

$$Q_m(x) = \frac{\cos mx}{m} + \frac{\cos(m+1)x}{m-1} + \cdots + \frac{\cos(2m-2)x}{2} + \frac{\cos(2m-1)x}{1}$$
$$- \frac{\cos(2m+1)x}{1} - \frac{\cos(2m+2)x}{2} - \cdots - \frac{\cos(3m-1)x}{m-1} - \frac{\cos 3mx}{m}.$$

We have written Q_m according to increasing indices, which run from m to $3m$. Using the addition formula for cosine, we have

$$Q_m(x) = \sum_{j=1}^{m} \frac{\cos(2m-j)x - \cos(2m+j)x}{j}$$

$$= 2\sin 2mx \sum_{j=1}^{m} \frac{\sin jx}{j}.$$

Therefore, the lemma on p.390 implies that for all x and m

$$|Q_m(x)| \leq 10.$$

Next we choose an increasing sequence $m_1 < m_2 < m_3 < \ldots$ such that the corresponding index intervals $[m_k, 3m_k]$ are disjoint. That is,

$$3m_k < m_{k+1}.$$

For example, we select

$$m_k = 2^{k^2}.$$

With this choice of m_k we define

$$f(x) = \sum_{k=1}^{\infty} \frac{1}{k^2} Q_{m_k}(x).$$

Because of the estimate $|Q_{m_k}(x)| \leq 10$, this series converges uniformly; therefore, $f \in C(\mathbb{T})$. Moreover, the uniform convergence implies that if the Fourier series of f is

$$f \sim \frac{a_0}{2} + \sum_{n=1}^{\infty} (a_n \cos nx + b_n \sin nx),$$

then

$$a_n = \sum_{k=1}^{\infty} \frac{1}{k^2} 2 \int_{\mathbb{T}} Q_{m_k}(x) \cos nx dx,$$

$$b_n = \sum_{k=1}^{\infty} \frac{1}{k^2} 2 \int_{\mathbb{T}} Q_{m_k}(x) \sin nx dx.$$

All $b_n = 0$ because Q_{m_k} contains no sine terms. Also, since the index intervals $[m_k, 3m_k]$ are disjoint, at most one term in the above series for a_n is nonzero. We conclude that

$$a_{2m_k - j} = \frac{1}{k^2 j} \quad \text{for } 1 \leq j \leq m_k,$$

$$a_{2m_k + j} = \frac{-1}{k^2 j} \quad \text{for } 1 \leq j \leq m_k,$$

and all other $a_n = 0$. Therefore, the Fourier series for f is just

$$f \sim \sum_{k=1}^{\infty} \sum_{j=1}^{m_k} \left(\frac{\cos(2m_k - j)x}{k^2 j} - \frac{\cos(2m_k + j)x}{k^2 j} \right),$$

where we think of the terms being written in order of increasing frequency. The beautiful point of this example is this: Whereas this Fourier series does *not* converge for all x, when the terms are regrouped and the series is summed as in the definition of f, the rearranged series converges uniformly.

To see that the Fourier series diverges for $x = 0$ consider the partial sums $s_{2m_k}(x)$ and $s_{m_k-1}(x)$. Their difference is the polynomial

$$s_{2m_k}(x) - s_{m_k-1}(x) = \sum_{j=1}^{m_k} \frac{\cos(2m_k - j)x}{k^2 j}.$$

If the Fourier series of f converges at x, this difference must tend to zero as $k \to \infty$. However, for $x = 0$ we have

$$s_{2m_k}(0) - s_{m_k-1}(0) = \frac{1}{k^2} \sum_{j=1}^{m_k} \frac{1}{j}$$

$$> \frac{1}{k^2} \log m_k = \log 2.$$

Therefore, the Fourier series of f fails to converge for $x = 0$.

Remarks: This example can be modified to produce even more pathological behavior. It can be shown that for any countable set $A \subset \mathbb{T}$, there exists $f \in C(\mathbb{T})$ whose Fourier series diverges for all $x \in A$ and converges for all $x \in \mathbb{T} \sim A$. There also exists $f \in C(\mathbb{T})$ whose Fourier series diverges on an uncountable set.

For many years one of the most intriguing unsolved problems in real analysis was this: If $f \in C(\mathbb{T})$, is it true that the Fourier series of f converges almost everywhere? The answer was finally given in a paper of Carleson in 1966. He was able to show that if $f \in L^2(\mathbb{T})$, then the Fourier series of f converges a.e. Subsequently, Hunt extended this positive result to all $f \in L^p(\mathbb{T})$, $1 < p < \infty$. This is quite impressive, in view of the example of Kolmogorov of a function in $L^1(\mathbb{T})$ whose Fourier series diverges everywhere.[1]

---

[1] Carleson, L., On convergence and growth of partial sums of Fourier series, *Acta Math. 116* (1966), 135–157.

Hunt, R.A., On the convergence of Fourier series, *Orthogonal Expansions and Their Continuous Analogues*, pp. 235–255, Southern Illinois Univ. Press, Carbondale, Illinois (1968).

G. Parseval's Identity

This section is analogous to Section 13.D, but with a significant simplification which is due to the fact that $L^2(\mathbb{T}) \subset L^1(\mathbb{T})$. In Chapter 13 we had to face the fact that $L^2(\mathbb{R}^n)$ is not a subset of $L^1(\mathbb{R}^n)$, and therefore it was not clear at the outset how to define the Fourier transform of an element of $L^2(\mathbb{R}^n)$. For this reason we defined the Fourier-Plancherel transform. No such problem faces us on $\mathbb{T}$, and we can immediately state the result.

Parseval's Identity: *Assume* $f,\, g \in L^2(\mathbb{T})$. *Then*

$$\int_{\mathbb{T}} f(x)\overline{g(x)}dx = \sum_{n=-\infty}^{\infty} \widehat{f}(n)\overline{\widehat{g}(n)}.$$

Proof: Assume first that $f = g = $ a trigonometric polynomial. Thus,

$$f(x) = \sum_{|n| \leq N} \widehat{f}(n)e^{inx}.$$

Therefore,

$$|f(x)|^2 = \sum_{\substack{|m| \leq N \\ |n| \leq N}} \widehat{f}(n)\overline{\widehat{f}(m)}e^{i(n-m)x}.$$

Integrating,

$$\int_{\mathbb{T}} |f(x)|^2 dx = \sum_{|n| \leq N} |\widehat{f}(n)|^2,$$

and the result is proved in this case.

Next, assume $f = g \in L^2(\mathbb{T})$. According to Section E.1, the Cesàro means σ_n converge to f in $L^2(\mathbb{T})$. Since the function σ_N is a trigonometric polynomial, we have already proved

$$\int_{\mathbb{T}} |\sigma_N(x)|^2 dx = \sum_{|n| \leq N} |\widehat{\sigma_N}(n)|^2.$$

By definition of σ_N,

$$\widehat{\sigma_N}(n) = \left(1 - \frac{|n|}{N+1}\right)\widehat{f}(n) \quad \text{for } |n| \le N.$$

Therefore, $|\widehat{\sigma_N}(n)|$ *increases* to $|\widehat{f}(n)|$ for each n as $N \to \infty$. It follows from LICT that

$$\int_{\mathbb{T}} |f(x)|^2 dx = \lim_{N\to\infty} \int_{\mathbb{T}} |\sigma_N(x)|^2 dx$$

$$= \lim_{N\to\infty} \sum_{|n|\le N} |\widehat{\sigma_N}(n)|^2$$

$$= \sum_{n=-\infty}^{\infty} |\widehat{f}(n)|^2.$$

This completes the proof of Parseval's identity in case $f = g$. The general case follows by the polarization technique as in Section 13.D.

QED

This result can be applied in many ways. One of these yields various summation formulas for infinite series. By Example 2 of Section C, the function $(\pi - x)/2$ on $(0, 2\pi)$ has Fourier coefficients $1/2in$ for $n \ne 0$. Therefore, Parseval's identity yields

$$\frac{1}{2\pi} \int_0^{2\pi} \left(\frac{\pi - x}{2}\right)^2 = \sum_{n\ne 0} \frac{1}{4n^2}.$$

Evaluating the integral yields the familiar equation

$$\sum_{n=1}^{\infty} \frac{1}{n^2} = \frac{\pi^2}{6}.$$

Problem 56. Use the function $(x - \pi)^2/4$ in the same way (Example 3 of Section C) to prove that

$$\sum_{n=1}^{\infty} \frac{1}{n^4} = \frac{\pi^4}{90}.$$

Problem 57. Suppose $f \in L^2(\mathbb{T})$ and

$$f \sim \frac{a_0}{2} + \sum_{n=1}^{\infty} (a_n \cos nx + b_n \sin nx).$$

Prove that

$$\frac{1}{\pi} \int_0^{2\pi} |f(x)|^2 dx = \frac{|a_0|^2}{2} + \sum_{n=1}^{\infty} (|a_n|^2 + |b_n|^2).$$

Here is another application. Let $g = \chi_{(0,a)}$, where $0 < a < 2\pi$; that is, g is supposed to be periodic, equal to 1 on $(0, a)$ and to 0 on $(a, 2\pi)$. Thus,

$$\widehat{g}(n) = \frac{1}{2\pi} \int_0^a e^{-inx} dx \quad \text{for all } n \in \mathbb{N}.$$

Parseval's identity implies that for any $f \in L^2(\mathbb{T})$,

$$\frac{1}{2\pi} \int_0^a f(x) dx = \sum_{n=-\infty}^{\infty} \widehat{f}(n) \overline{\widehat{g}(n)}.$$

That is,

$$\int_0^a f(x) dx = \sum_{n=-\infty}^{\infty} \widehat{f}(n) \int_0^a e^{inx} dx.$$

Thus, the Fourier series of f can be integrated termwise and equality is obtained. The result holds for any a, as the following problem shows.

Problem 58. Prove that if $f \in L^1(\mathbb{T})$, $\int_0^a f(x) dx - \widehat{f}(0)a$ is a periodic function of $a \in \mathbb{R}$, and

$$\int_0^a f(x) dx - \widehat{f}(0)a \sim \sum_{n \neq 0} \frac{\widehat{f}(n)}{in} e^{ina} + c_0,$$

where

$$c_0 = \frac{1}{2\pi} \int\limits_0^{2\pi} (\pi - x) f(x) dx.$$

Prove that if $f \in L^2(\mathbb{T})$, then

$$\int\limits_0^a f(x) dx = \sum_{n=-\infty}^{\infty} \widehat{f}(n) \int\limits_0^a e^{inx} dx, \quad a \in \mathbb{R},$$

and that the infinite series both converge uniformly.

Problem 59. Apply the preceding problem to Example 3 of Section C to obtain

$$\frac{x(x - \pi)(x - 2\pi)}{12} = \frac{x^3 - 3\pi x^2 + 2\pi^2 x}{12} = \sum_{n=1}^{\infty} \frac{\sin nx}{n^3}, \quad 0 \le x \le 2\pi.$$

Problem 60. Obtain from Problem 59 the relations

$$\frac{1}{1^3} - \frac{1}{3^3} + \frac{1}{5^3} - \frac{1}{7^3} + \cdots = \frac{\pi^3}{32};$$

$$\frac{1}{1^6} + \frac{1}{2^6} + \frac{1}{3^6} + \frac{1}{4^6} + \cdots = \frac{\pi^6}{945}.$$

Problem 61. Let $t \in \mathbb{R} \sim \mathbb{Z}$ be fixed, and investigate Parseval's identity for the periodic function equal to e^{itx} for $-\pi < x < \pi$. Conclude that

$$\frac{\pi^2}{\sin^2 t\pi} = \sum_{n=-\infty}^{\infty} \frac{1}{(t - n)^2}.$$

(I learned this elegant proof from the paper by Robert M. Young, "An elementary proof of a trigonometric identity," *Amer. Math. Monthly* **86** (1979), 296–297.)

The most important application of Parseval's identity lies in its implications about the Hilbert spaces (see Section 13.E) $L^2(\mathbb{T})$ and l^2. Recall the definition of l^p as given in Section 10.E.3. Specifically, we are treating l^2 of the integers $\mathbb{Z}$; that is, l^2 consists of all sequences $c = (c_n)$ with

$n \in \mathbb{Z}$ such that

$$\|c\|_{l^2} = \left(\sum_{n=-\infty}^{\infty} |c_n|^2 \right)^{1/2} < \infty.$$

Then Parseval's identity implies that for all $f \in L^2(\mathbb{T})$

$$\|f\|_{L^2(\mathbb{T})} = \|\widehat{f}\|_{l^2}.$$

It is the Riesz-Fischer theorem which shows that every sequence in l^2 is equal to $\widehat{f}$ for some $f \in L^2(\mathbb{T})$, as we now prove.

Theorem: *The operator $f \to \widehat{f}$ is a bijection of $L^2(\mathbb{T})$ onto l^2.*

Proof: Since $\widehat{f} = 0 \Rightarrow f = 0$, we have only to show that the operator is a surjection. Suppose that $c = (c_n) \in l^2$. Then let f_n be the trigonometric polynomial

$$f_n(x) = \sum_{|k| \leq n} c_k e^{ikx}, n = 0, 1, 2, \dots .$$

Of course,

$$\widehat{f_n}(k) = \begin{cases} c_k & \text{if } |k| \leq n, \\ 0 & \text{if } |k| > n. \end{cases}$$

Therefore in particular

$$\lim_{n \to \infty} \widehat{f_n}(k) = c_k \quad \text{for all } k \in \mathbb{Z}.$$

Parseval's identity shows that for $m < n$

$$\|f_m - f_n\|_{L^2(\mathbb{T})}^2 = \sum_{m < |k| \leq n} |c_k|^2.$$

Since $c \in l^2$, we conclude that

$$\lim_{m,n \to \infty} \|f_m - f_n\|_{L^2(\mathbb{T})} = 0.$$

The space $L^2(\mathbb{T})$ is complete, as shown by the Riesz-Fischer theorem (Section 10.C). Therefore, there exists $f \in L^2(\mathbb{T})$ such that $\lim_{n \to \infty} f_n = f$ in $L^2(\mathbb{T})$. In particular, for all $k \in \mathbb{Z}$ we have

$$\lim_{n \to \infty} \widehat{f_n}(k) = \widehat{f}(k).$$

Therefore, $c_k = \widehat{f}(k)$ for all $k \in \mathbb{Z}$.   **QED**

Problem 62. The above proof is completely abstract, requiring only the completeness of $L^2(\mathbb{T})$. Let the inner product on $L^2(\mathbb{T})$ be defined by

$$\langle f, g \rangle = \int_{\mathbb{T}} f(x)\overline{g(x)}dx.$$

Prove that the functions e^{inx}, $n \in \mathbb{Z}$, form an *orthonormal basis* of $L^2(\mathbb{T})$. That is, prove that

$$\langle e^{inx}, e^{imx} \rangle = 0 \text{ if } m \neq n,$$

$$\langle e^{inx}, e^{inx} \rangle = 1,$$

and if $f \in L^2(\mathbb{T})$ satisfies

$$\langle f, e^{inx} \rangle = 0 \quad \text{for all } n \in \mathbb{Z},$$

then $f = 0$.

Problem 63 (HILBERT TRANSFORM). This problem is the analog of Problem 13.48.

(a) Prove that for any $f \in L^2(\mathbb{T})$ there exists a unique function $Hf \in L^2(\mathbb{T})$ such that

$$\widehat{Hf}(n) = -i\operatorname{sgn}(n)\widehat{f}(n) \quad \text{for all } n \in \mathbb{Z}.$$

(b) Prove that the Fourier series of f and Hf are related as follows:

$$f \sim \frac{a_0}{2} + \sum_{n=1}^{\infty} (a_n \cos nx + b_n \sin nx),$$

$$Hf \sim \sum_{n=1}^{\infty} (a_n \sin nx - b_n \cos nx).$$

(c) Prove that $\|Hf\|_{L^2(\mathbb{T})} = \|f\|_{L^2(\mathbb{T})}$ if and only if $\int_{\mathbb{T}} f\,dx = 0$.

(d) Assume $\int_{\mathbb{T}} f\,dx = 0$. Prove that $H(Hf) = -f$.

(e) Let $0 < a < 1$. Prove that

$$H\left(\frac{e^{ix}}{1 - ae^{ix}}\right) = -i\frac{e^{ix}}{1 - ae^{ix}},$$

$$H\left(\frac{e^{-ix}}{1 - ae^{-ix}}\right) = i\frac{e^{-ix}}{1 - ae^{-ix}},$$

and combine these to prove

$$H\left(\frac{1 - a^2}{1 - 2a\cos x + a^2}\right) = \frac{2a\sin x}{1 - 2a\cos x + a^2}.$$

Problem 64. Assume that $f \in C^\infty(\mathbb{T})$ throughout this problem.

(a) Prove that $Hf \in C^\infty(\mathbb{T})$ (cf. Problem 51).

(b) Show that

$$(Hf)(0) = \sum_{n=1}^\infty -2\int_{\mathbb{T}} f(x)\sin nx\,dx.$$

(c) By using the kernel defined in Problem 17, show that

$$(Hf)(0) = \lim_{N\to\infty}\int_{\mathbb{T}} \frac{\cos(N + \frac{1}{2})x - \cos\frac{x}{2}}{\sin\frac{x}{2}} f(x)\,dx.$$

(d) Show that

$$(Hf)(0) = \lim_{N \to \infty} \int_{\mathbb{T}} \frac{\cos(N + \frac{1}{2})x - \cos \frac{x}{2}}{\sin \frac{x}{2}} \frac{f(x) - f(-x)}{2} dx.$$

(e) Conclude that

$$(Hf)(0) = \int_{\mathbb{T}} \frac{f(x) - f(-x)}{-2 \tan \frac{x}{2}} dx.$$

(f) Show that

$$(Hf)(0) = \lim_{\epsilon \to 0+} \frac{1}{2\pi} \int_{\epsilon < |x| < \pi} \frac{f(x)}{-\tan \frac{x}{2}} dx.$$

(g) Finally show that for all x

$$(Hf)(x) = \lim_{\epsilon \to 0+} \int_{\epsilon < |y| < \pi} \frac{f(x - y)}{2\pi \tan \frac{y}{2}} dy.$$

H. Poisson Summation Formula

The remarkable formula we are about to discuss ties together the two concepts of Fourier transform and Fourier series. Given a function $f \in L^1(\mathbb{R})$, we might ask for a procedure for associating with f in some natural way a function $F \in L^1(\mathbb{T})$. A little thought leads to two reasonable possibilities. One is to sum infinitely many translates of f and define

$$F(x) = \sum_{n=-\infty}^{\infty} f(x + 2\pi n).$$

This function is then formally periodic. Another is to consider the Fourier transform $\widehat{f}(\xi)$. This function is continuous on $\mathbb{R}$, so it makes good sense to evaluate it on $\mathbb{Z}$. Then we can formally consider the Fourier (?) series

$$\sum_{n=-\infty}^{\infty} \widehat{f}(n)e^{inx},$$

and thus obtain a periodic function. The fact is that these two methods are essentially equivalent, as we now prove.

Proposition: *Assume $f \in L^1(\mathbb{R})$. Then the series*

$$F(x) = \sum_{n=-\infty}^{\infty} f(x + 2\pi n)$$

converges a.e. and locally in $L^1(\mathbb{R})$ to a function $F \in L^1(\mathbb{T})$. The Fourier coefficients of F are given by

$$\widehat{F}(n) = \frac{1}{2\pi}\widehat{f}(n), \quad n \in \mathbb{Z}.$$

Proof: We first carry out the formal calculation of $\widehat{F}(m)$ for fixed $m \in \mathbb{Z}$. Thus,

$$2\pi\widehat{F}(m) = 2\pi \int_{\mathbb{T}} F(x)e^{-imx}dx$$

$$= \int_0^{2\pi} \sum_{n=-\infty}^{\infty} f(x + 2\pi n)e^{-imx}dx$$

$$= \sum_{n=-\infty}^{\infty} \int_0^{2\pi} f(x + 2\pi n)e^{-imx}dx$$

$$= \sum_{n=-\infty}^{\infty} \int_{2\pi n}^{2\pi(n+1)} f(y)e^{-im(y-2\pi n)}dy \; ;$$

here we have made the substitution $x + 2\pi n = y$. Notice that $e^{2\pi imn} = 1$. Therefore,

$$2\pi \widehat{F}(m) = \sum_{n=-\infty}^{\infty} \int_{2\pi n}^{2\pi(n+1)} f(y)e^{-imy}dy$$

$$= \int_{-\infty}^{\infty} f(y)e^{-imy}dy$$

$$= \widehat{f}(m).$$

We must now justify the interchange of summation and integration. This depends only on the observation that if we take $m = 0$ and apply the above calculation to $|f|$ rather than f, it is legitimate and shows that

$$\int_0^{2\pi} \sum_{-\infty}^{\infty} |f(x + 2\pi n)|dx = \sum_{-\infty}^{\infty} \int_0^{2\pi} |f(x + 2\pi n)|dx$$

$$= \int_{-\infty}^{\infty} |f(y)|dy$$

$$< \infty.$$

Therefore, $\sum_{-\infty}^{\infty} |f(x + 2\pi n)|$ converges for a.e. x and the series defining F converges in $L^1(0, 2\pi)$.   **QED**

The above proof is of course quite elementary. The significance of the Poisson summation formula lies in the expression of $F(x)$ in terms of its Fourier coefficients $\widehat{F}(n) \left(= \widehat{f}(n)/2\pi \right)$. In order to obtain this we must decide on some reasonable hypothesis for f which will insure that the inversion theorem applies. Many choices are available, but one which will suffice for our purposes is a Lipschitz condition of the form: For certain positive constants C and α,

$$|f(x) - f(x')| \leq \frac{C|x - x'|}{1 + x^2} \quad \text{for } |x - x'| \leq \alpha.$$

It then follows that for $|x - x'| \leq \alpha$,

$$|F(x) - F(x')| \leq \sum_{n=-\infty}^{\infty} |f(x + 2\pi n) - f(x' + 2\pi n)|$$

$$\leq \sum_{n=-\infty}^{\infty} \frac{C|x - x'|}{1 + (x + 2\pi n)^2}$$

$$\leq C'|x - x'|,$$

where C' is another constant. Thus, F satisfies the hypothesis of the theorem in Section D. We therefore obtain immediately from the proposition the following result:

Poisson Summation Formula: *Assume $f \in L^1(\mathbb{R})$ and assume f satisfies the Lipschitz condition*

$$|f(x) - f(x')| \leq \frac{C|x - x'|}{1 + x^2} \quad \text{for } |x - x'| \leq \alpha.$$

Then for all $x \in \mathbb{R}$

$$\sum_{n=-\infty}^{\infty} f(x + 2\pi n) = \frac{1}{2\pi} \sum_{n=-\infty}^{\infty} \widehat{f}(n) e^{inx}.$$

Corollary: *Under the same hypothesis on f,*

$$\sum_{n=-\infty}^{\infty} f(2\pi an) = \frac{1}{2\pi a} \sum_{n=-\infty}^{\infty} \widehat{f}\left(\frac{n}{a}\right), \quad 0 < a < \infty.$$

Proof: Apply the theorem to the function $f(ax)$, whose Fourier transform is $a^{-1}\widehat{f}(\xi/a)$. Then set $x = 0$. (See the next problem.)   **QED**

Problem 65. Prove that $f(ax)$ satisfies a Lipschitz condition of the required form.

   Example: Take $f(x) = e^{-x^2}$. Then $\widehat{f}(\xi) = \sqrt{\pi}e^{-\xi^2/4}$, and the corollary shows that

$$\sum_{-\infty}^{\infty} e^{-4\pi^2 a^2 n^2} = \frac{1}{2\sqrt{\pi}a}\sum_{-\infty}^{\infty} e^{-n^2/4a^2}.$$

One of the *theta functions* of Jacobi is the function

$$\theta(t) = \sum_{-\infty}^{\infty} e^{-\pi t n^2}, 0 < t < \infty.$$

By choosing $4\pi a^2 = t$ in the above formula, we obtain

$$\theta(t) = \frac{1}{\sqrt{t}}\theta(t^{-1}).$$

This identity of Jacobi is very important. For example, the series for $\theta(t)$ converges more rapidly the larger t is. For $t \to 0+$, the convergence is very slow. But Jacobi's identity expresses $\theta(t)$ as $t^{-1/2}\theta(t^{-1})$, and the series for $\theta(t^{-1})$ converges very rapidly for small t. Thus, in particular

$$\lim_{t\to 0+} \sqrt{t}\theta(t) = 1.$$

Problem 66. Show that for any $a > 0$

$$\sum_{n=-\infty}^{\infty} e^{-a(x+2\pi n)^2} = \frac{1}{\sqrt{4\pi a}}\sum_{n=-\infty}^{\infty} e^{-n^2/4a}\cos nx.$$

Problem 67. Apply the Poisson summation formula to $f(x) = e^{-a|x|}$.

Conclude that

$$\frac{\cosh a(\pi - x)}{\sinh a\pi} = \frac{1}{a\pi} + \frac{2}{\pi} \sum_{n=1}^{\infty} \frac{a}{a^2 + n^2} \cos nx, \quad 0 \le x \le 2\pi.$$

The result of this problem gives the Fourier series of the function $\cosh a(\pi - x)$ for $0 \le x \le 2\pi$. This function is of course in $C(\mathbb{T})$. Its derivative $-a \sinh a(\pi - x)$ has discontinuities for $x = 2\pi n$. The Fourier coefficients of this derivative are still given by FC7 on p.393, however. That is, we have the Fourier series

$$\frac{-a \sinh a(\pi - x)}{\sinh a\pi} \sim \frac{2}{\pi} \sum_{n=1}^{\infty} \frac{-an}{a^2 + n^2} \sin nx, \quad 0 < x < 2\pi.$$

The function on the left side satisfies the hypothesis of the inversion theorem of Section D. Thus, equality holds for $0 < x < 2\pi$.

We are now going to derive from this relation an interesting Fourier transform. First, let $x = \pi/2$:

$$\frac{a \sinh(a\pi/2)}{\sinh a\pi} = \frac{2}{\pi} \sum_{k=0}^{\infty} \frac{a(2k+1)}{a^2 + (2k+1)^2} \sin \frac{2k+1}{2}\pi.$$

Therefore, since $\sinh 2x = 2 \sinh x \cosh x$,

$$\frac{1}{2} \operatorname{sech} \frac{a\pi}{2} = \frac{2}{\pi} \sum_{k=0}^{\infty} \frac{2k+1}{a^2 + (2k+1)^2}(-1)^k.$$

Replace a by x:

$$\operatorname{sech} \frac{\pi x}{2} = \frac{4}{\pi} \sum_{k=0}^{\infty} \frac{2k+1}{x^2 + (2k+1)^2}(-1)^k.$$

Now we want to take the Fourier transform of all these functions of x. We want to interchange integration and summation, but none of our convergence theorems applies to this situation as it stands. We resort to a subterfuge. Group the terms on the right side to obtain

$$\operatorname{sech} \frac{\pi x}{2} = \frac{4}{\pi} \sum_{j=0}^{\infty} \left[\frac{4j+1}{x^2 + (4j+1)^2} - \frac{4j+3}{x^2 + (4j+3)^2} \right].$$

The resulting series converges in $L^2(\mathbb{R})$. To see this, use the mean value theorem to write (where $4j + 1 < m < 4j + 3$)

$$\left| \frac{4j+1}{x^2 + (4j+1)^2} - \frac{4j+3}{x^2 + (4j+3)^2} \right| = \left| \frac{2(x^2 - m^2)}{(x^2 + m^2)^2} \right|$$

$$\leq \frac{2}{x^2 + m^2}$$

$$< \frac{2}{x^2 + (4j+1)^2}.$$

The $L^2(\mathbb{R})$ norm of this function of x is

$$2 \left[\int_{\mathbb{R}} \frac{1}{(x^2 + (4j+1)^2)^2} \, dx \right]^{1/2} = \frac{c}{(4j+1)^{3/2}}.$$

Since $\sum_{j=0}^{\infty} (4j+1)^{-3/2}$ converges, the convergence in $L^2(\mathbb{R})$ follows. Since the Fourier-Plancherel transform is a continuous operator on $L^2(\mathbb{R})$, we obtain

$$\widehat{\operatorname{sech} \frac{\pi x}{2}} = \frac{4}{\pi} \sum_{j=0}^{\infty} \left[\frac{4j+1}{x^2 + (4j+1)^2} - \frac{4j+3}{x^2 + (4j+3)^2} \right]^{\wedge}.$$

These are Fourier-Plancherel transforms, and the convergence is in $L^2(\mathbb{R})$. Now recall that $\widehat{\frac{\alpha}{x^2 + \alpha^2}} = \pi e^{-\alpha|\xi|}$ for $\alpha > 0$. Therefore,

$$\widehat{\operatorname{sech} \frac{\pi x}{2}} = \frac{4}{\pi} \sum_{j=0}^{\infty} \left(\pi e^{-(4j+1)|\xi|} - \pi e^{-(4j+3)|\xi|} \right).$$

We finally see that this convergence actually occurs pointwise also, so we calculate for $\xi \neq 0$

$$\widehat{\operatorname{sech}\frac{\pi x}{2}} = 4\sum_{k=0}^{\infty}(-1)^k e^{-(2k+1)|\xi|}$$

$$= 4e^{-|\xi|}\sum_{k=0}^{\infty}(-1)^k e^{-2k|\xi|}$$

$$= \frac{4e^{-|\xi|}}{1+e^{-2|\xi|}}$$

$$= \frac{4}{e^{|\xi|}+e^{-|\xi|}}$$

$$= \frac{4}{e^{\xi}+e^{-\xi}}$$

$$= 2\operatorname{sech}\xi.$$

Problem 68. Let $f(x) = \operatorname{sech}\sqrt{\frac{\pi}{2}}x$. Show that $\widehat{f} = \sqrt{2\pi}f$.

Problem 69. Let $f(x) = \sqrt{\frac{\pi}{2}}x\operatorname{sech}\sqrt{\frac{\pi}{2}}x\tanh\sqrt{\frac{\pi}{2}}x - \frac{1}{2}\operatorname{sech}\sqrt{\frac{\pi}{2}}x$. Show that $\widehat{f} = -\sqrt{2\pi}f$.

Problem 70. Let $f(x) = \begin{cases} 1-|x| & \text{if } |x| < 1, \\ 0 & \text{if } |x| \geq 1 \end{cases}$. Show that $\widehat{f}(\xi) = \left(\frac{\sin(\xi/2)}{\xi/2}\right)^2$. Let $0 < \alpha < \infty$ and let k be the largest integer which is smaller than α/π. Show that the corollary yields

$$\sum_{n=-\infty}^{\infty}\left(\frac{\sin\alpha n}{\alpha n}\right)^2 = \frac{\pi}{\alpha}\left[1+2k - \frac{\pi k}{\alpha}(k+1)\right].$$

Show that for $0 < \alpha \le \pi$,

$$\sum_{n=-\infty}^{\infty} \left(\frac{\sin \alpha n}{\alpha n}\right)^2 = \int_{-\infty}^{\infty} \left(\frac{\sin \alpha t}{\alpha t}\right)^2 dt.$$

Problem 71. Apply the corollary to the function equal to xe^{-x} for $x \ge 0$ and zero for $x \le 0$. Conclude that

$$\sum_{n=-\infty}^{\infty} \frac{1}{(n+ia)^2} = -\pi^2 \, \mathrm{csch}^2 \pi a \qquad \text{for } a \in \mathbb{R}.$$

I. A Special Class of Sine Series

Throughout this section we assume that a_n is a decreasing sequence with limit 0:

$$a_1 \ge a_2 \ge a_3 \ge \ldots, \quad \lim_{n\to\infty} a_n = 0.$$

We are going to discuss in some detail the trigonometric series

$$(*) \qquad\qquad \sum_{n=1}^{\infty} a_n \sin nx.$$

From the theorem on p.390 it is known that the *function*

$$f(x) = \sum_{n=1}^{\infty} a_n \sin nx$$

exists for all $x \in \mathbb{R}$. It is clearly an odd, periodic function and thus is completely determined by its behavior on the interval $[0, \pi]$. We also know that $(*)$ converges uniformly on $[\delta, \pi]$ for all $\delta > 0$; therefore f is continuous on the interval $(0, \pi]$.

We are now going to state the theorem, which is in reality three theorems. Because of their similarities, however, we prefer to state the three theorems in one. These results all connect the convergence properties of $(*)$, the nature of f, and the properties of the coefficients.

Theorem: *We use the above notation, and still assume a_n decreases to 0.*

(a) *The following conditions are equivalent:*

    (i)   *na_n is bounded;*

    (ii) *($*$) converges boundedly (has uniformly bounded partial sums);*

    (iii) *($*$) is the Fourier series of a bounded function;*

    (iv) *f is bounded.*

(b) *The following conditions are equivalent:*

    (i)   *$na_n \to 0$ as $n \to \infty$;*

    (ii) *($*$) converges uniformly;*

    (iii) *($*$) is the Fourier series of a continuous function;*

    (iv) *f is continuous.*

(c) *The following conditions are equivalent:*

    (i) *$\displaystyle\sum_{n=1}^{\infty} \frac{a_n}{n} < \infty$;*

    (ii) *($*$) converges in $L^1(\mathbb{T})$;*

    (iii) *($*$) is the Fourier series of a function in $L^1(\mathbb{T})$;*

    (iv) *$f \in L^1(\mathbb{T})$.*

Proof of (a):

The lemma on p.390 and proposition on p.391 show that (i)$\Longleftrightarrow$(ii). If (ii) holds, then $f \in L^{\infty}(\mathbb{T})$ and LDCT implies that ($*$) is the Fourier series of f. Thus, (ii)$\Rightarrow$(iii) and (iv).

Proof that (iii)$\Rightarrow$(i): Assume that ($*$) is the Fourier series of a bounded function g, and assume $g(x) \leq B$ on $[0, \pi]$. Let σ_N be the Cesáro means of the Fourier series ($*$), as defined on p.411:

$$\sigma_N(x) = \sum_{n=1}^{N} \left(1 - \frac{n}{N+1}\right) a_n \sin nx.$$

Replace N by $2N$ and use this equality at $x = \pi/2N$:

$$\sigma_{2N}\left(\frac{\pi}{2N}\right) = \sum_{n=1}^{2N}\left(1 - \frac{n}{2N+1}\right) a_n \sin\frac{n\pi}{2N}.$$

Since $\sin(t/2) \geq t/\pi$ for $0 \leq t \leq \pi$ (see Figure 7 on p.391),

$$\sigma_{2N}\left(\frac{\pi}{2N}\right) \geq \sum_{n=1}^{N}\left(1 - \frac{n}{2N+1}\right) a_n \sin\frac{n\pi}{2N}$$

$$\geq \sum_{n=1}^{N}\left(1 - \frac{N}{2N+1}\right) a_N \frac{n}{N}$$

$$= \frac{N+1}{2N+1}a_N\frac{1}{N}\sum_{n=1}^{N} n$$

$$= \frac{(N+1)^2}{2(2N+1)}a_N$$

$$\geq \frac{N+1}{4}a_N$$

(notice the use of the monotonicity of a_n). Since $\sigma_{2N} = g * F_{2N}$ and the Fejér kernel $F_{2N} \geq 0$, it follows that $\sigma_{2N}(x) \leq B$ for all x, N. Hence $B \geq (N+1)a_N/4$. This proves that Na_N is bounded.

Proof that (iv)$\Rightarrow$(i): This proof seems to be considerably more difficult. We are going to exploit the monotonicity of a_n by summing $(*)$ by parts. Recall the notation of Problem 17,

$$K_n(x) = \sin x + \sin 2x + \cdots + \sin nx.$$

There follows

$$s_N(x) = \sum_{n=1}^{N} a_n \sin nx$$

$$= a_1 K_1(x) + \sum_{n=2}^{N} a_n(K_n(x) - K_{n-1}(x))$$

$$= \sum_{n=1}^{N} a_n K_n(x) - \sum_{n=1}^{N-1} a_{n+1}K_n(x)$$

$$= \sum_{n=1}^{N}(a_n - a_{n+1})K_n(x) + a_{N+1}K_N(x).$$

By Problem 17,

$$K_n(x) = \frac{\cos \frac{1}{2}x - \cos(n + \frac{1}{2})x}{2 \sin \frac{1}{2}x}.$$

For each x it follows that $K_N(x)$ is bounded; since $a_n \to 0$ we conclude that

$$f(x) = \sum_{n=1}^{\infty} (a_n - a_{n+1}) K_n(x).$$

Now we are going to observe that it is almost the case that $K_n \geq 0$ on $[0, \pi]$. Note that

$$K_n(x) = \frac{\cos \frac{1}{2}x - \cos nx \cos \frac{1}{2}x + \sin nx \sin \frac{1}{2}x}{2 \sin \frac{1}{2}x}$$

$$= \frac{1 - \cos nx}{2 \tan \frac{1}{2}x} + \frac{1}{2} \sin nx.$$

Define

$$K_n^*(x) = \sin x + \sin 2x + \cdots + \sin(n - 1)x + \frac{1}{2} \sin nx$$

$$= K_n(x) - \frac{1}{2} \sin nx$$

$$= \frac{1 - \cos nx}{2 \tan(x/2)}$$

$$= \frac{\sin^2(nx/2)}{\tan(x/2)}.$$

Then $K_n^* \geq 0$ on $[0, \pi]$, and

$$f(x) = \sum_{n=1}^{\infty} (a_n - a_{n+1}) K_n^*(x) + \frac{1}{2} \sum_{n=1}^{\infty} (a_n - a_{n+1}) \sin nx.$$

Note that

$$\left| \sum_{n=1}^{\infty} (a_n - a_{n+1}) \sin nx \right| \leq \sum_{n=1}^{\infty} (a_n - a_{n+1}) = a_1.$$

Assume that $f(x) \leq B$ on $[0, \pi]$. We then obtain for $0 \leq x \leq \pi$

$$\sum_{n=1}^{\infty} (a_n - a_{n+1}) K_n^*(x) \leq B + \frac{1}{2} a_1.$$

Since all $K_n^*(x) \geq 0$ and $a_n - a_{n+1} \geq 0$, we obtain for any N

$$\sum_{n=1}^{N} (a_n - a_{n+1}) \frac{\sin^2(nx/2)}{\tan(x/2)} \leq B + \frac{1}{2} a_1.$$

Now let $x = \pi/N$ in this inequality, and use the inequalities

$$\sin \frac{n\pi}{2N} \geq \frac{n}{N} \quad \text{and} \quad \tan \frac{\pi}{2N} \leq \frac{\text{const}}{N}$$

to obtain for some constant C

$$\sum_{n=1}^{N} (a_n - a_{n+1}) n^2 \leq CN.$$

Now we write

$$a_N = \sum_{n=N}^{\infty} (a_n - a_{n+1})$$

$$= \sum_{k=0}^{\infty} \sum_{2^k N \leq n < 2^{k+1} N} (a_n - a_{n+1})$$

$$\leq \sum_{k=0}^{\infty} 2^{-2k} N^{-2} \sum_{2^k N \leq n < 2^{k+1} N} (a_n - a_{n+1}) n^2$$

$$\leq \sum_{k=0}^{\infty} 2^{-2k} N^{-2} \sum_{n=1}^{2^{k+1} N} (a_n - a_{n+1}) n^2$$

$$\leq \sum_{k=0}^{\infty} 2^{-2k} N^{-2} C 2^{k+1} N$$

$$= CN^{-1} \sum_{k=0}^{\infty} 2^{-k+1}$$

$$= 4CN^{-1}.$$

Therefore, Na_N is bounded, and we have completed the proof of (a).

Remark: Notice that in our use of both (iii) and (iv), we require only that the function be bounded above.

Proof of (b):
   Proof that (iii)⇒(i): Assume that (∗) is the Fourier series of the continuous function g, and let σ_N be the Cesàro means of (∗). As in the proof of (a), we obtain the inequality

$$\sigma_{2N}\left(\frac{\pi}{2N}\right) \geq \frac{N+1}{4}a_N.$$

By the theorem on p.411, $\sigma_N \to g$ uniformly. Therefore, $g(0) = 0$ and $\sigma_{2N}(\pi/2N) \to g(0)$. Therefore, $Na_N \to 0$.
   Proof that (i)⇒(ii): By the lemma on p.390,

$$\left|\sum_{n=M}^{N} a_n \sin nx \right| \leq 5 \sup_{n\geq M} na_n.$$

Therefore, $\sum\limits_{n=M}^{N} a_n \sin nx$ converges uniformly to zero as $N > M \to \infty$.
This proves that (∗) converges uniformly.
   Proof that (ii)⇒(iii): This is easy. We are given that $s_N \to f$ uniformly. Therefore, f is continuous and (∗) is the Fourier series of f. We also notice that we have proved (ii)⇒(iv).
   Proof that (iv)⇒(iii): We assume f is continuous. In particular, it is bounded, so we can use a. Therefore, (∗) is the Fourier series of the bounded function f. Since f is continuous, (iii) follows.
Proof of (c):
   The fact that (iii)⇒(i) is an immediate consequence of Problem 41. The assertion (ii)⇒(iv) is trivial. And (ii)⇒(iii) follows by multiplying by $\sin nx$ and integrating. We shall now prove (i)⇒(ii) and (iv)⇒(i) to finish the proof.
   Proof that (i)⇒(ii): First notice that the hypothesis (i) implies

$$\lim_{n\to\infty} a_n \log n = 0.$$

To see this, choose N such that $N^2 \leq n < (N+1)^2$. Then

$$\sum_{k=N}^{N^2} \frac{a_k}{k} \geq a_n \sum_{k=N}^{N^2} \frac{1}{k}.$$

This sum is greater than the integral

$$\int\limits_{N}^{N^2} \frac{1}{t}dt = \log N$$

$$> \frac{1}{2}\log(N+1)$$

$$> \frac{1}{4}\log n.$$

Therefore,

$$a_n \log n < \text{ const } \cdot \sum_{k=N}^{\infty} \frac{a_k}{k} \to 0.$$

Now we use the formulas for s_N and f obtained during the proof of (a) to write

$$f(x) - s_N(x) = \sum_{n=N+1}^{\infty} (a_n - a_{n+1})K_n(x) - a_{N+1}K_N(x).$$

We are going to have to estimate $\|K_n\|_{L^1(\mathbb{T})}$. This may be done as follows: $|K_n(x) - K_n^*(x)| \le \frac{1}{2}$ for all x, so $\|K_n\|_{L^1(\mathbb{T})}$ and $\|K_n^*\|_{L^1(\mathbb{T})}$ differ by at most $\frac{1}{2}$. Since $K_n^* \ge 0$ on $[0, \pi]$,

$$\int\limits_{-\pi}^{\pi} |K_n^*(x)|dx = 2\int\limits_{0}^{\pi} K_n^*(x)dx$$

$$= 2\sum_{k=1}^{n-1}\int\limits_{0}^{\pi} \sin kx\,dx + \int\limits_{0}^{\pi} \sin nx\,dx$$

$$= 4\sum_{\substack{1 \le k \le n-1 \\ k \text{ odd}}} \frac{1}{k} + \frac{1 - \cos n\pi}{n}.$$

It is easy to show that the last sum is approximately $\frac{1}{2}\log n$ for large n. Therefore both $\|K_n\|_{L^1(\mathbb{T})}$ and $\|K_n^*\|_{L^1(\mathbb{T})}$ are approximately

$\log(n+1)/\pi$. Therefore, there exists a constant C such that

$$\|f - s_N\|_{L^1(\mathbb{T})} \le \sum_{n=N+1}^{\infty} (a_n - a_{n+1})\|K_n\|_{L^1(\mathbb{T})} + a_{N+1}\|K_N\|_{L^1(\mathbb{T})}$$

$$\le C \sum_{n=N+1}^{\infty} (a_n - a_{n+1})\log(n+1) + Ca_{N+1}\log(N+1)$$

$$= C \lim_{M\to\infty} \left[\sum_{n=N+1}^{M} a_n \log(n+1) - \sum_{n=N+2}^{M+1} a_n \log n\right] + Ca_{N+1}\log(N+1)$$

$$= C \lim_{M\to\infty} \left[\sum_{n=N+1}^{M} a_n \log \frac{n+1}{n} - a_{M+1}\log(M+1) + a_{N+1}\log(N+1)\right]$$
$$+ Ca_{N+1}\log(N+1)$$

$$= C \sum_{n=N+1}^{\infty} a_n \log\left(1 + \frac{1}{n}\right) + 2Ca_{N+1}\log(N+1)$$

$$\le C \sum_{n=N+1}^{\infty} \frac{a_n}{n} + 2Ca_{N+1}\log(N+1).$$

As $N \to \infty$ we therefore obtain the convergence of s_N to f in $L^1(\mathbb{T})$.

Proof that (iv)$\Rightarrow$(i): We essentially want to reverse the above steps. To do this we need to have nonnegative terms, so we use the relation

$$f(x) = \sum_{n=1}^{\infty} (a_n - a_{n+1})K_n^*(x) + \frac{1}{2}\sum_{n=1}^{\infty}(a_n - a_{n+1})\sin nx.$$

Therefore,

$$\sum_{n=1}^{\infty}(a_n - a_{n+1})K_n^* \le f + \frac{1}{2}a_1,$$

and we conclude

$$\sum_{n=1}^{\infty}(a_n - a_{n+1})\|K_n^*\|_{L^1(\mathbb{T})} \le \|f + \frac{1}{2}a_1\|_{L^1(\mathbb{T})}.$$

Therefore, there exists a constant C such that

$$\sum_{n=1}^{\infty}(a_n - a_{n+1})\log(n+1) \le C.$$

Next note that for any N

$$\sum_{n=N}^{\infty} (a_n - a_{n+1}) \log(n+1) \geq \log(N+1) \sum_{n=N}^{\infty} (a_n - a_{n+1}) = \log(N+1) \cdot a_N,$$

so that $a_N \log N \to 0$. Therefore,

$$
\begin{aligned}
C &\geq \sum_{n=1}^{N} (a_n - a_{n+1}) \log(n+1) \\
&= \sum_{n=1}^{N} a_n \log(n+1) - \sum_{n=1}^{N+1} a_n \log n \\
&= \sum_{n=1}^{N} a_n \log \frac{n+1}{n} - a_{N+1} \log(N+1) \\
&\geq \text{const} \cdot \sum_{n=1}^{N} \frac{a_n}{n} - a_{N+1} \log(N+1).
\end{aligned}
$$

Let $N \to \infty$ to conclude that

$$\sum_{n=1}^{\infty} \frac{a_n}{n} < \infty.$$

QED

Problem 72. Prove that the conditions in (b) of the theorem are e-quivalent to the *equicontinuity* of s_N at 0: That is, for any $\epsilon > 0$ there exists $\delta > 0$ such that $|s_N(x)| \leq \epsilon$ for $0 \leq x \leq \delta$ and all $N = 1, 2, 3, \ldots$

.

Problem 73. Prove that the conditions in (c) of the theorem are equivalent to the condition that $\sup_N \|s_N\|_{L^1(\mathbb{T})} < \infty$.

Remark: The situation for cosine series is quite different. For example, there exist sequences a_n tending monotonically to zero *as slowly as one wishes* such that

$$\frac{a_0}{2} + \sum_{n=1}^{\infty} a_n \cos nx$$

is the Fourier series of a function in $L^1(\mathbb{T})$. One particular example is this: There exists $f \in L^1(\mathbb{T})$ whose Fourier series is

$$f \sim \sum_{n=2}^{\infty} \frac{\cos nx}{\log n}.$$

Our results show, of course, that the corresponding sine series

$$\sum_{n=2}^{\infty} \frac{\sin nx}{\log n}$$

is not the Fourier series of a function in $L^1(\mathbb{T})$.

A very readable and interesting account of these cosine series is found in A. Zygmund, *Trigonometric Series, Vol. I*, Cambridge Univ. Press 1968, pp. 183–184.

Example: In case $a_n = 1/n$ the corresponding sine series has a sum which is known explicitly from Section D:

$$\sum_{n=1}^{\infty} \frac{\sin nx}{n} = \frac{\pi - x}{2} \quad \text{for } 0 < x < 2\pi.$$

Notice how parts (a) and (b) of the theorem are illustrated by this example. The function f is bounded but not continuous on $\mathbb{T}$. It is interesting to note that not only is it true that

$$\sum_{n=1}^{\infty} \frac{\sin nx}{n} > 0 \quad \text{for } 0 < x < \pi,$$

but that the same inequality holds for each of the partial sums. This fact has what Robert Burckel calls a "stunningly elegant proof." This proof was discovered by E. Landau, "Über eine trigonometrische Ungleichung," *Math. Zeit. 37* (1933), 36–37, and is reproduced in the following exercise.

Problem 74. Let $s_N(x) = \sum_{n=1}^{N} \frac{\sin nx}{n}$. Prove by induction on N that $s_N(x) > 0$ for $0 < x < \pi$.

(**HINT:** Let x be a critical point of s_N on $(0, \pi)$. Then

$$
\begin{aligned}
s_N'(x) &= \frac{D_N(x) - 1}{2} \\
&= \frac{\sin(N + \frac{1}{2})x - \sin\frac{1}{2}x}{2\sin\frac{1}{2}x} \\
&= 0.
\end{aligned}
$$

Show that $\sin Nx = 0$ or $\sin x$. Conclude that $s_N(x) \geq s_{N-1}(x)$.)

Problem 75. Another example is the sine series

$$
\sum_{n=1}^{\infty} r^n \sin nx,
$$

where $0 < r < 1$ is fixed. This of course fits part (b) of the Theorem. Show that the sum of this series is the function

$$
\frac{r\sin x}{1 - 2r\cos x + r^2},
$$

which is positive on $(0, \pi)$. However, show that it is not necessarily true that even the second partial sum $r\sin x + r^2\sin 2x$ is positive on $(0, \pi)$.

Problem 76. Use the theorem to prove that there exists a continuous function on $\mathbb{T}$ whose Fourier series converges uniformly but not absolutely.

Differentiation

One of the most important theorems in mathematics is the fundamental theorem of calculus, which implies that if f is a continuous function on an interval $[a, b]$ and if

$$F(x) = \int_a^x f(t)dt \quad \text{for } a \leq x \leq b,$$

then F is differentiable on $[a, b]$ and its derivative is given by

$$F'(x) = f(x) \quad \text{for } a \leq x \leq b.$$

This fundamental theorem is quite easy to prove. But an amazing theorem of Lebesgue extends this result to the situation in which f is assumed only to be integrable. Then F as defined above is a continuous function; this follows from the theorem on absolute continuity on p.141. Lebesgue's theorem asserts that F is differentiable a.e. and that

$$F'(x) = f(x) \quad \text{for a.e. } x \in [a, b].$$

The proof we are going to present depends on a basic principle called the Vitali covering theorem. Although it will not be obvious at first glance why the Vitali theorem has any relevance at all to differentiation, we choose to prove the covering theorem right away and allow the applications themselves to reveal its importance. We shall also work on $\mathbb{R}^n$ instead of $\mathbb{R}$, since Lebesgue's theorem is valid on $\mathbb{R}^n$ with a suitable interpretation. Section A contains the Vitali covering theorem. Section B introduces an important technical device, the Hardy-Littlewood maximal function. Lebesgue's theorem will then follow easily in Section C.

Remark: The *mise en scène* of the Vitali theorem involves a rather arbitrary set $E \subset \mathbb{R}^n$ and, for each $x \in E$, an open ball centered at x. The radii of these balls are quite arbitrary. The aim of the theorem is to try to achieve the following two conflicting objectives:

(1) select *disjoint* balls from among the given balls, such that

(2) E is *covered* by these disjoint balls.

Since these two objectives could hardly ever both be realized, we must relent slightly with respect to one or the other and settle for less. The *Vitali* covering theorem modifies (2). The *Besicovitch* covering theorem, which will be discussed in Section H, modifies (1).

Notation: If B is an open ball in $\mathbb{R}^n$, we denote by rad B the radius of B. If $0 < a < \infty$, we denote by aB the ball concentric with B such that rad $aB = a$ rad$B$. This conflicts with the notation of Section 3.B, but no confusion should arise.

A. The Vitali Covering Theorem

> *Vitali Covering Theorem:* *Assume $E \subset \mathbb{R}^n$ is a bounded set. Assume that $\mathcal{F}$ is a collection of open balls which are centered at points of E such that every point of E is the center of some ball in $\mathcal{F}$. Then there exists a sequence (possibly terminating) $B_1, B_2, \ldots$ of balls from $\mathcal{F}$ such that*
>
> *(1) the balls $B_1, B_2, \ldots$ are disjoint,*
>
> *(2) $E \subset \bigcup_{\alpha \geq 1} 3B_\alpha$.*

(Notice that E is not covered by the disjoint balls but is covered by the concentric balls of triple the radius.)

Proof: This proof is actually attributed to Banach. It is based upon a very simple idea: Select the balls inductively, at each stage choosing the largest one which is disjoint from the previous selections. This recipe has to be modified, however, since there may be infinitely many radii involved and there may not be a largest radius available. We shall just be sure to select a ball whose radius is almost as large as possible.

Before starting the selection, we observe that if the radii of the balls in $\mathcal{F}$ are not bounded above, then since E is bounded we can choose a single ball $B \in \mathcal{F}$ whose radius is so large (and of course centered at a point of E) that $E \subset B$. Thus, (1) and (2) hold trivially in this case.

Therefore, we assume the radii of the balls in $\mathcal{F}$ to be bounded above. We select the balls $B_1, B_2, \ldots$ inductively in the following manner:

Assume that $B_1, \ldots, B_{\alpha-1}$ have been selected, where $\alpha \geq 1$. Define

$$d_\alpha = \sup \left\{ \mathrm{rad}\ B \mid B \in \mathcal{F} \text{ and } B \cap \bigcup_{\beta < \alpha} B_\beta = \emptyset \right\}.$$

If there are no $B \in \mathcal{F}$ satisfying $B \cap \bigcup_{\beta < \alpha} B_\beta = \emptyset$, the process terminates with $B_{\alpha-1}$; otherwise, choose $B_\alpha \in \mathcal{F}$ such that

$$\tfrac{1}{2} d_\alpha < \text{ rad } B_\alpha \quad \text{and} \quad B_\alpha \cap \bigcup_{\beta < \alpha} B_\beta = \emptyset.$$

This scheme not only serves to select the balls inductively, but also in the case $\alpha = 1$ gives the method for selecting the first ball B_1.

The selection certainly makes sense as long as it can be performed, since our assumptions guarantee that $0 < d_\alpha < \infty$. Of the two properties the balls are required to have, (1) is clear. In order to prove (2), let $x \in E$ be arbitrary. There exists $B \in \mathcal{F}$ having center x; let $\rho = $ rad B. We first notice that B must have a nonempty intersection with at least one of the selected balls $B_1, B_2, \ldots$. Otherwise, $B \cap B_\alpha = \emptyset$ for all α. This implies that the selection never terminates, and, indeed, that

$$\rho \le d_\alpha \quad \text{for } \alpha = 1, 2, \ldots .$$

This in turn implies that we have a countable infinity of balls B_α which are disjoint, whose centers lie in a bounded set E, and whose radii satisfy

$$\text{rad } B_\alpha > \tfrac{1}{2} d_\alpha \ge \tfrac{1}{2} \rho > 0.$$

This is clearly impossible since $\bigcup_{\alpha=1}^{\infty} B_\alpha$ is a bounded set and thus has finite measure, yet

$$\lambda \left(\bigcup_{\alpha=1}^{\infty} B_\alpha \right) = \sum_{\alpha=1}^{\infty} \lambda(B_\alpha) = \infty.$$

Since B meets at least one B_α, there exists a *smallest* $\alpha \ge 1$ such that $B \cap B_\alpha \ne \emptyset$. Therefore,

$$B \cap \bigcup_{\beta < \alpha} B_\beta = \emptyset,$$

and we conclude

$$\rho \le d_\alpha < 2 \text{ rad } B_\alpha.$$

Let $y \in B \cap B_\alpha$. Then if z is the center of B_α,

$$\begin{aligned} |x - z| &\le |x - y| + |y - z| \\ &< \rho + \text{ rad } B_\alpha \\ &< 3 \text{ rad } B_\alpha. \end{aligned}$$

Therefore, $x \in 3B_\alpha$.   **QED**

Remark: The factor 3 which appears in conclusion (2) of the theorem is not the best one can do. In fact, a trivial modification of the above proof shows that this factor can be replaced by $2 + \epsilon$ for any $\epsilon > 0$. All that is necessary is to choose $B_\alpha \in \mathcal{F}$ to satisfy

$$\frac{1}{1+\epsilon} d_\alpha < \text{ rad } B_\alpha.$$

The factor cannot be lowered further, in the sense that it cannot be guaranteed that $E \subset \bigcup_{\alpha \geq 1} 2B_\alpha$. Here is an example for the case $n = 1$:

Problem 1. Let $E = (-1, 1)$. For $x \in E$ let $r(x) = (1 + 2|x|)/3$ and let $B_x = (x - r(x), x + r(x))$. Let $\mathcal{F} = \{B_x | x \in E\}$. Prove that the conclusion of the Vitali theorem does not hold if the factor 3 is replaced by 2.

(**HINT:** Each ball in $\mathcal{F}$ contains 0.)

B. The Hardy-Littlewood Maximal Function

In the following section we are going to establish Lebesgue's theorem on differentiation of "indefinite integrals." The n-dimensional version of this theorem states that if $f \in L^1_{\text{loc}}(\mathbb{R}^n)$ (see Section 10.E.4), then for a.e. $x \in \mathbb{R}^n$

$$\lim_{r \to 0} \frac{1}{\lambda(B(x,r))} \int_{B(x,r)} f(y)dy = f(x).$$

(Recall that $B(x, r)$ is the open ball with center x and radius r.) In proving this theorem we shall need to examine very carefully the quotient in the above equation. That is why the following definition is given.

Definition: Assume $f \in L^1_{\text{loc}}(\mathbb{R}^n)$. Then the *Hardy-Littlewood maximal function* for f is the function Mf defined on $\mathbb{R}^n$ by

$$Mf(x) = \sup_{0 < r < \infty} \frac{1}{\lambda(B(x,r))} \int_{B(x,r)} |f(y)|dy.$$

We now derive some properties of this function. The first thing we need to know is that $Mf : \mathbb{R}^n \to [0, \infty]$ is a measurable function. In fact, it is Borel measurable. In fact, it is lower semicontinuous (Section 7.A). To see this, suppose $t < Mf(x)$. Then there exists $0 < r < \infty$ such that

$$t < \frac{1}{\lambda(B(x,r))} \int\limits_{B(x,r)} |f(y)| dy.$$

Choose $r' > r$ such that the inequality

$$t < \frac{1}{\lambda(B(x,r'))} \int\limits_{B(x,r)} |f(y)| dy$$

holds. If $|x - x'| \le r' - r$, then $B(x,r) \subset B(x',r')$ (Problem 1.17) and therefore

$$t < \frac{1}{\lambda(B(x,r'))} \int\limits_{B(x',r')} |f(y)| dy$$

$$= \frac{1}{\lambda(B(x',r'))} \int\limits_{B(x',r')} |f(y)| dy$$

$$\le Mf(x').$$

This proves that Mf is lower semicontinuous at x.

The second property is introduced primarily as a warning — the function Mf must be thought of as definitely larger than $|f|$, for

$$\text{it is } not \text{ true that } f \in L^1(\mathbb{R}^n) \implies Mf \in L^1(\mathbb{R}^n).$$

In fact, if $Mf \in L^1(\mathbb{R}^n)$, then $f = 0$. This is easily seen: If $a > 0$ is arbitrary and $|x| > a$, then

$$Mf(x) \ge \frac{1}{\lambda(B(x,2|x|))} \int\limits_{B(x,2|x|)} |f(y)| dy$$

$$\ge \frac{1}{\lambda(B(0,2|x|))} \int\limits_{B(0,a)} |f(y)| dy$$

$$= \frac{\text{const}}{|x|^n} \int\limits_{B(0,a)} |f(y)| dy.$$

Since $|x|^{-n}$ is not integrable for $|x| > a$, it follows that

$$\int_{B(0,a)} |f(y)|dy = 0.$$

Since a is arbitrary, we conclude that $f = 0$.

Not only this, we cannot even prove that if $f \in L^1(\mathbb{R}^n)$, then $f \in L^1_{\text{loc}}(\mathbb{R}^n)$. Here we give an example in case $n = 1$. Let

$$f(x) = \begin{cases} \dfrac{1}{x \log^2 x}, & 0 < x < \tfrac{1}{2}, \\ 0, & \text{all other } x. \end{cases}$$

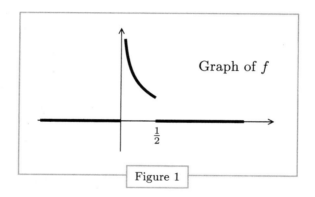

Graph of f

$\frac{1}{2}$

Figure 1

If $0 < x < \tfrac{1}{2}$, use $r = x$ in the definition of $Mf(x)$ to obtain the lower bound

$$Mf(x) \geq \frac{1}{2x} \int_0^{2x} f(y)dy$$

$$> \frac{1}{2x} \int_0^x f(y)dy$$

$$= \frac{1}{2x} \int_0^x \frac{dy}{y \log^2 y}$$

$$= \frac{1}{2x} \frac{-1}{\log y} \Big|_0^x$$

$$= \frac{-1}{2x \log x}.$$

Since $\dfrac{-1}{2x \log x}$ is not integrable near $x = 0$, it follows that $Mf \notin L^1_{\text{loc}}(\mathbb{R})$.

In spite of this negative situation, there is a substitute result, which says roughly that $f \in L^1(\mathbb{R}^n) \implies Mf$ belongs to a weakened version of $L^1(\mathbb{R}^n)$. In order to appreciate the significance of this result, it is necessary to realize that any $g \in L^1(\mathbb{R}^n)$ satisfies the *Chebyshev inequality*

$$\lambda\left(\{x \in \mathbb{R}^n \mid |g(x)| \geq t\}\right) \leq \frac{\|g\|_1}{t} \quad \text{for } 0 < t < \infty.$$

The converse is not valid, however. That is, if g is a measurable function on $\mathbb{R}^n$ which satisfies an inequality of the form

$$\lambda\left(\{x \in \mathbb{R}^n \mid |g(x)| \geq t\}\right) \leq \frac{C}{t} \quad \text{for } 0 < t < \infty,$$

it does not follow that $g \in L^1(\mathbb{R}^n)$.

Problem 2. Prove that the function $g(x) = |x|^{-n}$ on $\mathbb{R}^n$ satisfies an inequality of the above type.

Problem 3. Prove the following more general form of Chebyshev's inequality: If $1 \leq p < \infty$ and $g \in L^p(X, \mathcal{M}, \mu)$, then

$$\mu\left(\{x \in X \mid |g(x)| \geq t\}\right) \leq \left(\frac{\|g\|_p}{t}\right)^p \quad \text{for } 0 < t < \infty.$$

Now we come to the main property of the Hardy-Littlewood maximal function, and we also see the important part played by the Vitali theorem.

Hardy-Littlewood Theorem: *Let $f \in L^1(\mathbb{R}^n)$. Then*

$$\lambda\left(\{x \mid Mf(x) > t\}\right) \leq \frac{3^n \|f\|_1}{t} \quad \text{for } 0 < t < \infty.$$

Proof: Let $E = \{x \mid Mf(x) > t\}$. Consider any point $x \in E$. Then $Mf(x) > t$ and the definition of the maximal function implies there exists $0 < r < \infty$ (depending on x) such that

$$\frac{1}{\lambda(B(x,r))} \int\limits_{B(x,r)} |f(y)| dy > t.$$

We express this as follows: For any $x \in E$ there exists a ball B with center x such that

$$\lambda(B) < \frac{1}{t} \int_B |f(y)| dy.$$

We assume $E \neq \emptyset$, of course, since the result is trivial otherwise. We would like to apply the Vitali covering theorem since we have a huge number of balls to deal with, but one of the hypotheses is missing: We do not know that E is bounded. This is easily handled by considering $E \cap B(0, k)$ instead of E, for a fixed radius k. After we obtain an estimate for the measure of $E \cap B(0, k)$, we can let $k \to \infty$.

Now let $\mathcal{F}$ be the collection of open balls B with centers in $E \cap B(0, k)$ and satisfying the above inequality for $\lambda(B)$. Then the hypothesis of the Vitali covering theorem is satisfied. Thus, if $E \cap B(0, k) \neq \emptyset$, then there exist balls B_1, B_2, ... in $\mathcal{F}$ such that

(1) B_1, B_2, ... are disjoint,

(2) $E \cap B(0, k) \subset \bigcup_{\alpha \geq 1} 3 B_\alpha$.

All we have to do is assemble this information. Here is the method: First we use the inclusion (2), then the fact $\lambda(3 B_\alpha) = 3^n \lambda(B_\alpha)$, then the inequality for $\lambda(B_\alpha)$, and finally (1), the disjointness of the selected balls. We obtain

$$\lambda(E \cap B(0, k)) \leq \sum_{\alpha \geq 1} \lambda(3 B_\alpha)$$

$$= \sum_{\alpha \geq 1} 3^n \lambda(B_\alpha)$$

$$< \sum_{\alpha \geq 1} 3^n t^{-1} \int_{B_\alpha} |f(y)| dy$$

$$= 3^n t^{-1} \int_{\bigcup_{\alpha \geq 1} B_\alpha} |f(y)| dy$$

$$\leq 3^n t^{-1} \int_{\mathbb{R}^n} |f(y)| dy.$$

Finally, let $k \to \infty$ to obtain $\lambda(E) \leq 3^n t^{-1} \|f\|_1$.   **QED**

Remark: Our remark in Section A shows that the number 3 in our theorem can be replaced by $2 + \epsilon$ for any $\epsilon > 0$. Since nothing in the statement of the theorem depends on this ϵ, the Hardy-Littlewood theorem can immediately be sharpened to the conclusion

$$\lambda\left(\{x \mid Mf(x) > t\}\right) \leq \frac{2^n \|f\|_1}{t}.$$

Moreover, by applying this inequality to $t - 1/j$ and then letting $j \to \infty$, we obtain a still sharper inequality

$$\lambda\left(\{x \mid Mf(x) \geq t\}\right) \leq \frac{2^n \|f\|_1}{t}.$$

(I do not know of any applications in which this refinement is needed; the size of the constant in the Hardy-Littlewood theorem seems unimportant.)

The following result, on the other hand, represents an important refinement.

Problem 4. Prove that for any measurable function f defined on $\mathbb{R}^n$,

$$\lambda\left(\{x \mid Mf(x) > t\}\right) \leq \frac{2 \cdot 3^n}{t} \int\limits_{\{|f(x)| > t/2\}} |f(x)| dx.$$

(**HINT:** Let g be the function which equals f wherever $|f| > t/2$, and equals zero otherwise (t being fixed). Show that $Mf(x) > t \Rightarrow Mg(x) > t/2$, and then apply the Hardy-Littlewood theorem to g.)

Problem 5. Let $1 < p < \infty$, and suppose $f \in L^p(\mathbb{R}^n)$. Prove that also $Mf \in L^p(\mathbb{R}^n)$ and

$$\|Mf\|_p \leq 2(3^n p')^{1/p} \|f\|_p.$$

(**HINT:** Use the formula from Section 11.C,

$$\|Mf\|_p^p = p \int\limits_0^\infty \lambda\left(\{x \mid Mf(x) > t\}\right) t^{p-1} dt.$$

Apply Problem 4 and then Fubini's theorem.)

C. Lebesgue's Differentiation Theorem

We are now ready to prove this famous theorem.

> **Lebesgue's Theorem:** *Assume* $f \in L^1_{\text{loc}}(\mathbb{R}^n)$. *Then for a.e.*
> $x \in \mathbb{R}^n$
>
> $$\lim_{r \to 0} \frac{1}{\lambda(B(x,r))} \int\limits_{B(x,r)} |f(y) - f(x)| dy = 0.$$
>
> *In particular, it follows that for a.e.* $x \in \mathbb{R}^n$
>
> $$\lim_{r \to 0} \frac{1}{\lambda(B(x,r))} \int\limits_{B(x,r)} f(y) dy = f(x).$$

Proof: This theorem is really *local* in nature: If we want to establish the result for points x which belong to an open set G, the behavior of f outside G is irrelevant. Therefore, we may as well assume from the outset that $f \in L^1(\mathbb{R}^n)$.

The second conclusion of the theorem follows from the first by the simple observation

$$\left| \frac{1}{\lambda(B(x,r))} \int\limits_{B(x,r)} f(y) dy - f(x) \right| = \left| \frac{1}{\lambda(B(x,r))} \int\limits_{B(x,r)} [f(y) - f(x)] \, dy \right|$$

$$\leq \frac{1}{\lambda(B(x,r))} \int\limits_{B(x,r)} |f(y) - f(x)| dy.$$

Therefore, we concentrate on the first result. Because of the nature of the result, it is reasonable and convenient to introduce a local version of the Hardy-Littlewood maximal function, namely the function f^* defined by

$$f^*(x) = \limsup_{r \to 0} \frac{1}{\lambda(B(x,r))} \int\limits_{B(x,r)} |f(y) - f(x)| dy.$$

The rest of the proof is a matter of deriving six properties of this function and then quickly using them to finish the proof by showing that $f^* = 0$ a.e.

1. $f^* \geq 0$. (Obvious.)

2. $(f + g)^* \leq f^* + g^*$.

To see this, note that

$$\int\limits_{B(x,r)} |f(y) + g(y) - f(x) - g(x)| dy$$

$$\leq \int\limits_{B(x,r)} |f(y) - f(x)| dy + \int\limits_{B(x,r)} |g(y) - g(x)| dy.$$

Now all that is necessary is to divide by $\lambda(B(x,r))$ and then use the simple general property of the limit superior: The limsup of a sum of two functions is no larger than the sum of their limsups.

3. If g is continuous at x, then $g^*(x) = 0$.

This property is "trivial," though it is essentially a statement of the *fundamental theorem of calculus*. If $\epsilon > 0$, then there exists $\delta > 0$ such that $|g(y) - g(x)| \leq \epsilon$ for all $y \in B(x, \delta)$. Therefore, if $0 < r \leq \delta$,

$$\frac{1}{\lambda(B(x,r))} \int\limits_{B(x,r)} |g(y) - g(x)| dy \leq \epsilon.$$

4. If g is continuous on $\mathbb{R}^n$, $(f - g)^* = f^*$.

This follows from Properties 2 and 3, as follows:

$$(f - g)^* \leq f^* + (-g)^* = f^*;$$
$$f^* \leq (f - g)^* + g^* = (f - g)^*.$$

5. $f^* \leq Mf + |f|$.

This is an utterly crude estimate:

$$\frac{1}{\lambda(B(x,r))} \int\limits_{B(x,r)} |f(y) - f(x)| dy$$

$$\leq \frac{1}{\lambda(B(x,r))} \int\limits_{B(x,r)} (|f(y)| + |f(x)|) \, dy$$

$$= \frac{1}{\lambda(B(x,r))} \int\limits_{B(x,r)} |f(y)| dy + |f(x)|$$

$$\leq Mf(x) + |f(x)|.$$

6. We have the following inequality for outer Lebesgue measure:

$$\lambda^* \left(\{x \mid f^*(x) > t\} \right) \leq \frac{2(3^n + 1)}{t} \|f\|_1, 0 < t < \infty.$$

This is a consequence of the Hardy-Littlewood theorem and a Chebyshev inequality. We first apply Property 5 to see that if $f^*(x) > t$, then either $Mf(x) > t/2$ or $|f(x)| > t/2$:

$$\lambda^* \left(\{x \mid f^*(x) > t\} \right) \leq \lambda \left(\{x \mid Mf(x) > t/2\} \right) + \lambda \left(\{x \mid |f(x)| > t/2\} \right)$$
$$\leq \frac{3^n \|f\|_1}{t/2} + \frac{\|f\|_1}{t/2}.$$

Finally, we are ready to prove the theorem. Let $\epsilon > 0$. Then the lemma on p.173 implies that there exists a function $g \in C_c(\mathbb{R}^n)$ such that $\|f - g\|_1 \leq \epsilon$. Therefore, Properties 4 and 6 imply

$$\lambda^* \left(\{x \mid f^*(x) > t\} \right) = \lambda^* \left(\{x \mid (f - g)^*(x) > t\} \right)$$
$$\leq \frac{2(3^n + 1)}{t} \|f - g\|_1$$
$$\leq \frac{2(3^n + 1)}{t} \epsilon.$$

Since ϵ is arbitrary, it follows that

$$\lambda^* \left(\{x \mid f^*(x) > t\} \right) = 0.$$

Thus, $\{x \mid f^*(x) > k^{-1}\}$ is a null set for all $k \in \mathbb{N}$. The union of these sets is therefore the null set $\{x \mid f^*(x) > 0\}$. That is, $f^*(x) \leq 0$ for a.e. x. Finally, Property 1 shows that $f^* = 0$ a.e.   **QED**

D. The Lebesgue Set of a Function

Definition: Suppose $f \in L^1_{\text{loc}}(\mathbb{R}^n)$ and $x \in \mathbb{R}^n$. Then x is a point in the *Lebesgue set* of f if there exists a number A such that

$$\lim_{r \to 0} \frac{1}{\lambda(B(x,r))} \int_{B(x,r)} |f(y) - A| dy = 0.$$

We first observe that there can be no more than one number A which fulfills this condition. In fact, just as in the proof of the second assertion of Lebesgue's theorem in the preceding section, it follows that

$$\lim_{r \to 0} \frac{1}{\lambda(B(x,r))} \int_{B(x,r)} f(y)dy = A.$$

Therefore, A is unique (and the limit on the left side exists).

Next, we observe that whether x belongs to the Lebesgue set of f is completely independent of the value $f(x)$. In fact, f does not even need to be defined at the point x. Moreover, if $f = g$ a.e., then the Lebesgue set of f equals the Lebesgue set of g. Thus, the Lebesgue set is well defined for each of the equivalence classes which constitute $L^1_{\mathrm{loc}}(\mathbb{R}^n)$.

Here is what Lebesgue's theorem has to say about this concept: If $f \in L^1_{\mathrm{loc}}(\mathbb{R}^n)$, then *almost every point of $\mathbb{R}^n$ belongs to the Lebesgue set of f.* Moreover, if f is a particular representative of the equivalence class $f \in L^1_{\mathrm{loc}}$, then for a.e. x the number A is just $f(x)$. Therefore, f can be modified on a set of measure zero so that for *every* x in the Lebesgue set of f

$$\lim_{r \to 0} \frac{1}{\lambda(B(x,r))} \int_{B(x,r)} |f(y) - f(x)|dy = 0.$$

From now on in this chapter we shall employ this convention. That is, if $f \in L^1_{\mathrm{loc}}(\mathbb{R}^n)$ and x is a point belonging to the Lebesgue set of f, then we designate by $f(x)$ that number which satisfies the definition.

Problem 6. Let H be the Heaviside function:

$$H(x) = \begin{cases} 1 & \text{if } x > 0, \\ \frac{1}{2} & \text{if } x = 0, \\ 0 & \text{if } x < 0. \end{cases}$$

Prove that for all $x \in \mathbb{R}$

$$H(x) = \lim_{r \to 0} \frac{1}{2r} \int_{x-r}^{x+r} H(y)dy,$$

yet show that 0 is not in the Lebesgue set of H. Explain.

We now make an important remark. The use of *balls* in this situation is not crucial. All of the theory we have discussed up to this point could as well have been done with *cubes*, for instance. (On the other hand, if we tried to use all possible rectangles the theory would *not* work.) Even cubes are not necessary. Many interesting situations fit the following defintion.

Definition: A sequence of measurable sets E_1, E_2, ... *converges regularly to x* if there exist a positive constant c and a sequence of positive numbers r_1, r_2, ... such that

$$E_k \subset B(x, r_k),$$
$$\lim_{k \to \infty} r_k = 0,$$

and

$$\lambda(B(x, r_k)) \leq c\lambda(E_k).$$

Theorem: *Assume $f \in L^1_{\text{loc}}(\mathbb{R}^n)$ and let $x \in \mathbb{R}^n$. Assume x is in the Lebesgue set of f. If E_1, E_2, ... converges regularly to x, then*

$$f(x) = \lim_{k \to \infty} \frac{1}{\lambda(E_k)} \int_{E_k} f(y) dy.$$

Proof: This is immediate:

$$\left| \frac{1}{\lambda(E_k)} \int_{E_k} f(y) dy - f(x) \right| \leq \frac{1}{\lambda(E_k)} \int_{E_k} |f(y) - f(x)| dy$$

$$\leq \frac{c}{\lambda(B(x, r_k))} \int_{B(x, r_k)} |f(y) - f(x)| dy$$

$$\to 0 \quad \text{as } k \to \infty.$$

QED

Of course, the basic idea here is that the sets E_k are nice and "fat" in the sense that they fill up a good percentage of a sequence of balls which shrink to the point x. The converse of the preceding theorem is valid:

Problem 7. Assume $f \in L^1_{\text{loc}}(\mathbb{R}^n)$ and let $x \in \mathbb{R}^n$. Assume that for every sequence $E_1, E_2, \ldots$ converging regularly to x there exists

$$\lim_{k \to \infty} \frac{1}{\lambda(E_k)} \int\limits_{E_k} f(y)dy.$$

Prove that x belongs to the Lebesgue set of f.

(**HINT**: Show first that you may assume f is real valued. Then show by interlacing two sequences that the above limit is independent of the particular sequence $\{E_k\}$. Then show that you can assume the limit is zero. Now let $r_k \to 0$ be arbitrary and take each E_k as follows:

$$E_k = B(x, r_k) \cap \{y \mid f(y) \geq 0\} \quad \text{or}$$
$$E_k = B(x, r_k) \cap \{y \mid f(y) < 0\},$$

depending on which choice satisfies $\lambda(E_k) \geq \frac{1}{2}\lambda(B(x, r_k))$. Prove that

$$\frac{1}{\lambda(B(x, r_k))} \int\limits_{B(x, r_k)} |f(y)|dy \to 0.)$$

As an example of the use of regular sequences we prove the following theorem of Lebesgue for dimension one.

Theorem: *Assume $f \in L^1_{\text{loc}}(\mathbb{R})$ and let $a \in \mathbb{R}$. Define*

$$F(x) = \int\limits_a^x f(y)dy$$

(with the usual convention if $x < a$). Then F is differentiable a.e. and

$$F' = f \quad a.e.$$

Proof: We know that almost every number $x \in \mathbb{R}$ is in the Lebesgue set of f and thus satisfies the conclusion of the preceding theorem. It is therefore sufficient to prove that $F'(x) = f(x)$ for such a point x. We are now assuming that for any regular sequence E_1, E_2, ... converging to x

$$\lim_{k \to \infty} \frac{1}{\lambda(E_k)} \int\limits_{E_k} f(y)dy = f(x).$$

Let r_k be any sequence of positive numbers converging to zero. Then let $E_k = (x, x + r_k)$. These sets are obviously a sequence converging regularly to x. Therefore,

$$\lim_{k \to \infty} \frac{1}{r_k} \int\limits_{x}^{x+r_k} f(y)dy = f(x);$$

that is,

$$\lim_{k \to \infty} \frac{F(x + r_k) - F(x)}{r_k} = f(x).$$

Since the sequence r_k is arbitrary, we conclude that

$$\lim_{h \to 0+} \frac{F(x + h) - F(x)}{h} = f(x).$$

By choosing instead $E_k = (x - r_k, x)$, we obtain by the same argument

$$\lim_{h \to 0-} \frac{F(x + h) - F(x)}{h} = f(x).$$

Therefore, $F'(x) = f(x)$.   **QED**

Problem 8. Here is an example which shows that it is possible that $F'(x) = f(x)$ without having x belong to the Lebesgue set of f. Namely, define

$$f(x) = \begin{cases} (x^2 \cos x^{-1})' = \sin x^{-1} + 2x \cos x^{-1} & \text{if } x \neq 0, \\ 0 & \text{if } x = 0. \end{cases}$$

Define

$$F(x) = \int\limits_0^x f(y)dy,$$

and show that

$$F(x) = \begin{cases} x^2 \cos x^{-1} & \text{if } x \neq 0, \\ 0 & \text{if } x = 0. \end{cases}$$

Prove that 0 is not in the Lebesgue set of f. Prove that $F'(0) = f(0)$.

Problem 9. Let
$$g(x) = \begin{cases} \sin x^{-1} & \text{if } x \neq 0, \\ 0 & \text{if } x = 0. \end{cases}$$
and define
$$G(x) = \int_0^x g(y)dy.$$

Prove that 0 is not in the Lebesgue set of g. Prove that $G'(0) = g(0)$.

E. Points of Density

We now are going to treat a special case of the differentiation theory we have been discussing. Namely, let $E \subset \mathbb{R}^n$ be a measurable set and apply Lebesgue's theorem of Section C to the characteristic function χ_E. We first note that for a fixed $x \in \mathbb{R}^n$ the function $\chi_E - \chi_E(x)$ never changes sign. Therefore, we might as well use the second conclusion in the statement of Lebesgue's theorem. Thus, for a.e. $x \in \mathbb{R}^n$ it is true that
$$\lim_{r \to 0} \frac{\lambda(E \cap B(x,r))}{\lambda(B(x,r))} = \chi_E(x).$$

In particular, almost every point $x \in E$ satisfies
$$\lim_{r \to 0} \frac{\lambda(E \cap B(x,r))}{\lambda(B(x,r))} = 1.$$

If x satisfies this condition, we say that x is a *point of density* of E. Thus, almost every point of E is a point of density of E.

Likewise, almost every $x \in E^c$ satisfies
$$\lim_{r \to 0} \frac{\lambda(E \cap B(x,r))}{\lambda(B(x,r))} = 0.$$

It is a curious fact that some of these results are valid without any assumptions on the set E. In order to state the next theorem, we use the outer measure λ^* to define for a general set $E \subset \mathbb{R}^n$
$$DE(x) = \lim_{r \to 0} \frac{\lambda^*(E \cap B(x,r))}{\lambda(B(x,r))},$$

provided the limit exists.

Theorem: *Let $E \subset \mathbb{R}^n$. Then*

$$DE(x) = 1 \quad for\ a.e.\ x \in E.$$

Moreover, E is measurable if and only if

$$DE(x) = 0 \quad for\ a.e.\ x \in E^c.$$

Proof: We use Problem 2.39, which asserts that E has a *measurable hull* A. That is, A is measurable, $E \subset A$, and $\lambda_*(A \sim E) = 0$. Then it is true that for every measurable set B

$$\lambda^*(E \cap B) = \lambda(A \cap B).$$

This follows from Property M11 on p.50:

$$\lambda(A \cap B) = \lambda^*(E \cap B) + \lambda_*((A \sim E) \cap B)$$
$$= \lambda^*(E \cap B).$$

Therefore, in particular

$$\frac{\lambda^*(E \cap B(x,r))}{\lambda(B(x,r))} = \frac{\lambda(A \cap B(x,r))}{\lambda(B(x,r))}.$$

Since A is measurable, we conclude that $DE(x) = 1$ for a.e. $x \in A$. Since $E \subset A$, this establishes the first assertion of the theorem. To prove the second assertion, we first remark that if E is measurable, we already have proved that $DE(x) = 0$ for a.e. $x \in E^c$. Therefore, we assume conversely that $DE(x) = 0$ for a.e. $x \in E^c$. We have to prove that E is measurable. All we actually need to assume is that for a.e. $x \in E^c$, $DE(x) \neq 1$. Then, since $DE = 1$ a.e. in A, we conclude that $A \cap E^c$ is a null set. Since $E = A \sim (A \cap E^c)$, E is measurable.   **QED**

Problem 10. Prove that no set $E \subset \mathbb{R}^n$ exists having the property that $\lambda^*(E \cap B(x,r)) = \frac{1}{2}\lambda(B(x,r))$ for all x and r. (Generalization of Problem 6.45.)

Problem 11. Construct a measurable set $E \subset \mathbb{R}$ such that

$$\limsup_{r \to 0} \frac{\lambda(E \cap (-r, r))}{2r} = 1,$$

$$\liminf_{r \to 0} \frac{\lambda(E \cap (-r, r))}{2r} = 0.$$

(**HINT:** Let E be symmetric about 0, with $E \cap (0, \infty) = \bigcup_{k=1}^{\infty} [a_k, b_k]$, a countable union of disjoint intervals tending to 0. Show that if the right sides exist,

$$\limsup_{r \to 0} \frac{\lambda(E \cap (0, r))}{r} \geq \lim_{k \to \infty} \frac{b_k - a_k}{b_k}$$

and

$$\liminf_{r \to 0} \frac{\lambda(E \cap (0, r))}{r} \leq \lim_{k \to \infty} \frac{b_k}{a_{k-1}}.$$

Show that you can choose a_k and b_k such that

$$\lim_{k \to \infty} \frac{a_k}{b_k} = 0 \quad \text{and} \quad \lim_{k \to \infty} \frac{b_k}{a_{k-1}} = 0.)$$

Problem 12. Let $0 < \theta < 1$. Construct a measurable set $E \subset \mathbb{R}$ such that

$$\lim_{r \to 0} \frac{\lambda(E \cap (0, r))}{r} = \theta.$$

(**HINT:** Consider the function of r given by $\lambda(E \cap (0, r))$. Think of this as an infinite polygonal function with slopes 0 and 1, and choose it so that $\theta r \leq \lambda(E \cap (0, r)) \leq \theta r + r^2$.)

Problem 13. Let $A \subset \mathbb{R}^n$ be an arbitrary nonempty set, and let $0 < \rho < \infty$ be fixed. Recall the *distance function* $d(x, A)$ as defined in Section 1.F. Define the set

$$E = \{x \in \mathbb{R}^n \mid d(x, A) = \rho\}.$$

(a) Prove that E is closed.

(b) From Section 1.F it is known that if $x \in E$, there exists $x_0 \in A^-$ such that $|x - x_0| = \rho$. Prove that $B(x_0, \rho) \cap E = \emptyset$.

(c) Prove that

$$\limsup_{r \to 0} \frac{\lambda(E \cap B(x, r))}{\lambda(B(x, r))} \leq \frac{1}{2}.$$

(d) Prove that $\lambda(E) = 0$.

F. Applications

Lebesgue's theorem is a very important tool in many phases of analysis. In this section we are going to see some examples of its use.

1. The Fourier-Plancherel Transform

In Section 13.D we discussed in detail this transformation of functions in $L^2(\mathbb{R}^n)$. In case $n = 1$ we found that the function $f \in L^2(\mathbb{R})$ and its Fourier-Plancherel transform $\widehat{f} \in L^2(\mathbb{R})$ are related by the formula

$$\int_0^x f(t)dt = \frac{1}{2\pi} \int_{-\infty}^{\infty} \widehat{f}(\xi) \frac{e^{ix\xi} - 1}{i\xi} d\xi, \quad \text{all } x \in \mathbb{R}.$$

Therefore we can now state immediately that

$$f(x) = \frac{d}{dx} \frac{1}{2\pi} \int_{-\infty}^{\infty} \widehat{f}(\xi) \frac{e^{ix\xi} - 1}{i\xi} d\xi, \quad \text{for a.e. } x \in \mathbb{R}.$$

Likewise,

$$\widehat{f}(\xi) = \frac{d}{d\xi} \int_{-\infty}^{\infty} f(x) \frac{e^{-ix\xi} - 1}{-ix} dx \quad \text{for a.e. } \xi \in \mathbb{R}.$$

2. Approximate Identities

The results of Section 12.C imply the following result. For $0 < a < \infty$ let ϕ_a be a function in $L^1(\mathbb{R}^n)$, and assume that

1. $\lim\limits_{a\to 0} \int \phi_a dx = c$ exists;

2. $\int |\phi_a| dx \le M$ for some constant M;

3. for every $r > 0$,

$$\lim_{a\to 0} \int\limits_{|x|\ge r} |\phi_a(x)| dx = 0.$$

Then for every $f \in L^p(\mathbb{R}^n)$, $1 \le p < \infty$, $f * \phi_a \to cf$ in $L^p(\mathbb{R}^n)$ as $a \to 0$. Note that we are not necessarily assuming that ϕ_a has the specific form $\phi_a(x) = a^{-n}\phi_1\left(\frac{x}{a}\right)$. The results of Section 12.C had nothing to say about the validity of the equation

$$\lim_{a\to 0} f * \phi_a(x) = cf(x)$$

for individual points $x \in \mathbb{R}^n$. However, with an additional assumption on the approximate identity ϕ_a we can prove that this pointwise limit exists a.e. Since this assumption is rather technical, we prefer to discuss it in advance of stating the theorems.

For the remainder of this discussion of approximate identities we assume that ψ is a positive decreasing function on $(0, \infty)$ such that $\psi(|x|) \in L^1(\mathbb{R}^n)$, and that

$$|\phi_a(x)| \le a^{-n}\psi\left(\frac{|x|}{a}\right) \qquad \text{for all } x \in \mathbb{R}^n, \ 0 < a < \infty.$$

Note that Assumptions 2 and 3 now hold automatically, and thus only Assumption 1 has to be verified in practice.

By a slight abuse of notation we set

$$\|\psi\|_1 = \int\limits_{\mathbb{R}^n} \psi(|x|) dx.$$

From Section 9.C this norm satisfies

$$\|\psi\|_1 = \omega_n \int_0^\infty \psi(r) r^{n-1} dr$$

$$= \sum_{k=-\infty}^\infty \omega_n \int_{2^{k-1}}^{2^k} \psi(r) r^{n-1} dr$$

$$\geq \sum_{k=-\infty}^\infty \omega_n \psi(2^k) \int_{2^{k-1}}^{2^k} r^{n-1} dr$$

$$= \sum_{k=-\infty}^\infty \omega_n \psi(2^k) \frac{1}{n} \left(2^{kn} - 2^{(k-1)n} \right)$$

$$= \frac{\omega_n}{n} \sum_{k=-\infty}^\infty \psi(2^k) 2^{kn} (1 - 2^{-n})$$

$$\geq \frac{\omega_n}{2n} \sum_{k=-\infty}^\infty \psi(2^k) 2^{kn}.$$

Problem 14. Prove that

$$\|\psi\|_1 \leq \frac{\omega_n}{n} \sum_{k=-\infty}^\infty \psi(2^k) 2^{(k+1)n}.$$

From these estimates we see that little is lost in replacing $\|\psi\|_1$ by the convergent series

$$\sum_{k=-\infty}^\infty \psi(2^k) 2^{kn}.$$

In most applications, the functions ϕ_a satisfy inequalities of the form

$$|\phi_a(x)| \leq a^{-n} \psi\left(\frac{|x|}{a} \right),$$

where

$$\psi(|x|) \leq \frac{\text{constant}}{(1 + |x|)^{n+\epsilon}}$$

for some $\epsilon > 0$.

In what follows we use the notation

$$c_a = \int_{\mathbb{R}^n} \phi_a(x)dx,$$

so that

$$\lim_{a \to 0} c_a = c.$$

Theorem: *Suppose the functions ϕ_a satisfy the above assumptions. Let $1 \le p \le \infty$ and assume $f \in L^p(\mathbb{R}^n)$. Then*

$$\lim_{a \to 0} f * \phi_a = cf \ \text{almost everywhere.}$$

Proof: What we actually prove is the more precise statement, that if x is a point of the Lebesgue set of f, and if $f(x) = A$, then

$$\lim_{a \to 0} \int_{\mathbb{R}^n} f(x - y)\phi_a(y)dy = cA.$$

We regard x as fixed, and we define

$$g(r) = \frac{1}{r^n} \int_{B(x,r)} |f(y) - A|dy$$

$$= \frac{1}{r^n} \int_{|y|<r} |f(x - y) - A|dy.$$

Then the assumption about x means that $\lim_{r \to 0} g(r) = 0$. Clearly, g is bounded for r not close to zero: Hölder's inequality yields

$$g(r) \le \frac{1}{r^n} \int_{B(x,r)} |f(y)|dy + \ \text{constant} \ |A|$$

$$\le \frac{1}{r^n} \left(\int_{B(x,r)} |f|^p dy \right)^{1/p} \left(\int_{B(x,r)} dy \right)^{1/p'} + \ \text{constant}$$

$$\le \frac{1}{r^n} \|f\|_p \ \text{constant} \ r^{n/p'} + \ \text{constant}$$

$$\le \ \text{constant} \ r^{-n/p} + \ \text{constant}.$$

Thus, g is a bounded function for $0 < r < \infty$, and $\lim\limits_{r \to 0} g(r) = 0$.

Since $\int\limits_{\mathbb{R}^n} \phi_a(y)dy = c_a$, we now obtain

$$
|f * \phi_a(x) - c_a A| = \left| \int\limits_{\mathbb{R}^n} [f(x - y) - A]\,\phi_a(y)dy \right|
$$

$$
\leq \int\limits_{\mathbb{R}^n} |f(x - y) - A||\phi_a(y)|dy
$$

$$
= \sum_{k=-\infty}^{\infty} \int\limits_{2^k \leq |y|/a < 2^{k+1}} |f(x - y) - A||\phi_a(y)|dy
$$

$$
\leq \sum_{k=-\infty}^{\infty} \int\limits_{2^k \leq |y|/a < 2^{k+1}} |f(x - y) - A|a^{-n}\psi\left(\frac{|y|}{a}\right)dy
$$

$$
\leq \sum_{k=-\infty}^{\infty} a^{-n}\psi(2^k) \int\limits_{2^k \leq |y|/a < 2^{k+1}} |f(x - y) - A|dy
$$

$$
\leq \sum_{k=-\infty}^{\infty} a^{-n}\psi(2^k) \int\limits_{|y| < 2^{k+1}a} |f(x - y) - A|dy
$$

$$
= \sum_{k=-\infty}^{\infty} a^{-n}\psi(2^k)(2^{k+1}a)^n g(2^{k+1}a)
$$

$$
= \sum_{k=-\infty}^{\infty} \psi(2^k)2^{(k+1)n}g(2^{k+1}a).
$$

The rest is easy. We want to let $a \to 0$. Each term in this series is bounded by a constant (the supremum of g) times $\psi(2^k)2^{(k+1)n}$, and we know

$$
\sum_{k=-\infty}^{\infty} \psi(2^k)2^{(k+1)n} < \infty.
$$

Therefore, LDCT implies the limit of the sum is the sum of the limits, and since $\lim\limits_{a \to 0} g(2^{k+1}a) = 0$, it follows that

$$
\lim_{a \to 0} |f * \phi_a(x) - c_a A| = 0.
$$

QED

Problem 15. Under the assumptions of the theorem, prove that

$$|f * \phi_a(x)| \le 2^{n+1} M f(x) \|\psi\|_1.$$

In case the function ψ is bounded, we can prove a little more about the pointwise behavior of these approximate identities. There are many applications for which it is desirable to know not only that $f * \phi_a(x) \to cf(x)$ as $a \to 0$, but also that $f * \phi_a(x') \to cf(x)$ as $a \to 0$ and $x' \to x$. Many of these applications require that $x' \to x$ "at least as rapidly as $a \to 0$." We express this by requiring that for some constant $0 < m < \infty$,

$$|x' - x| < ma.$$

Theorem: *Continue with the same assumptions on ϕ_a. In addition, assume that ψ is bounded. Let $1 \le p \le \infty$ and assume $f \in L^p(\mathbb{R}^n)$. Then for almost every $x \in \mathbb{R}^n$ it follows that for all $0 < m < \infty$*

$$\lim_{\substack{a \to 0 \\ |x'-x|<ma}} f * \phi_a(x') = cf(x).$$

Proof: We need to make only a simple modification of the previous proof. We maintain the same notation, where x is a particular point of the Lebesgue set of f, and $A = f(x)$.

Note that the assumption on ψ means that $\psi(0) < \infty$. Then as before we obtain

$$|f * \phi_a(x') - c_a A| \le \int_{|y|/a<1} |f(x' - y) - A| a^{-n} \psi\left(\frac{|y|}{a}\right) dy$$

$$+ \sum_{k=0}^{\infty} \int_{2^k \le |y|/a < 2^{k+1}} |f(x' - y) - A| a^{-n} \psi\left(\frac{|y|}{a}\right) dy.$$

After estimating ψ, we shall change the variable y by setting $x' - y = x - z$

in each integral. Thus, noting that $|z| \leq |y| + |x' - x| < |y| + ma$,

$$|f * \phi_a(x') - c_a A| \leq a^{-n}\psi(0) \int_{|z|<(1+m)a} |f(x-z) - A|dz$$

$$+ \sum_{k=0}^{\infty} a^{-n}\psi(2^k) \int_{|z|<(2^{k+1}+m)a} |f(x-z) - A|dz$$

$$\leq \psi(0)(1+m)^n g((1+m)a)$$

$$+ \sum_{k=0}^{\infty} \psi(2^k)(2^{k+1}+m)^n g((2^{k+1}+m)a).$$

The rest of the proof is completed in the same way.   **QED**

Problem 16. Under the assumptions of the theorem, prove that for $|x' - x| < ma$,

$$|f * \phi_a(x')| \leq (2+m)^n M f(x) \left[\frac{\omega_n}{n}\psi(0) + 2\|\psi\|_{L^1(\mathbb{R}^n)}\right].$$

Remark: It is easy to see that some restriction must be placed on the rate at which x' approaches x in the above theorem and problem. It cannot be expected that for almost every $x \in \mathbb{R}^n$

$$\lim_{\substack{a \to 0 \\ x' \to x}} f * \phi_a(x') = cf(x).$$

The reason is that for fixed x', we expect $f * \phi_a(x')$ to be close to $cf(x')$ for small enough a. If $c \neq 0$, this would require $f(x') \to f(x)$ as $x' \to x$. This in turn requires some sort of continuity of f. The next problem contains a specific example.

Problem 17. Let $A \subset [0,1]$ be a fat Cantor set (Section 4.B) and let $f = \chi_A$. Let $\phi_a = a^{-1}\chi_{(-a/2,a/2)}$. Prove that for every $x \in A$ it is false that

$$\lim_{\substack{a \to 0 \\ x' \to x}} f * \phi_a(x') = f(x).$$

(**HINT:** f is continuous on A^c.)

It is not difficult to see that in the preceding theorem the assumption that ψ is bounded cannot be dropped. Here is a typical example. Choose

$$\phi_a(x) = \begin{cases} a^{-n/2}|x|^{-n/2} & \text{if } |x| < a, \\ 0 & \text{if } |x| \geq a. \end{cases}$$

Then choose $f_0 = \phi_1$. Both f_0 and ϕ_a are in $L^1(\mathbb{R}^n)$, but

$$\int_{\mathbb{R}^n} f_0 \phi_a dx = \infty \quad \text{for } 0 < a < \infty.$$

Now let $\{x_1, x_2, x_3, \ldots\}$ be a countable dense set in $\mathbb{R}^n$ and define

$$f(x) = \sum_{k=1}^{\infty} 2^{-k} f_0(x - x_k).$$

Then $f \in L^1(\mathbb{R}^n)$ and $\|f\|_1 = \|f_0\|_1$. Let $x \in \mathbb{R}^n$ be any point. Then it is false that

$$\lim_{\substack{a \to 0 \\ |x'-x|<a}} f * \phi_a(x') = cf(x).$$

In fact, the limit on the left side does not even exist. To see this, note that for any $a > 0$ there exists k such that $|x_k - x| < a$. Then

$$f * \phi_a(x_k) = \int f(x_k - y)\phi_a(y)dy$$

$$\geq 2^{-k} \int_{\mathbb{R}^n} f_0(x_k - y - x_k)\phi_a(y)dy$$

$$= 2^{-k} \int_{\mathbb{R}^n} f_0(y)\phi_a(y)dy$$

$$= \infty.$$

3.   Summation of Fourier Series

Cesàro summability. Refer to Section 14.E.1 for the notation. For $f \in L^1(\mathbb{T})$ we have the Fourier series

$$f \sim \sum_{n=-\infty}^{\infty} \widehat{f}(n)e^{inx}.$$

The Cesàro means are defined by

$$\sigma_N(x) = \sum_{|n| \leq N} \left(1 - \frac{|n|}{N+1}\right)\widehat{f}(n)e^{inx}.$$

This function can also be represented as a convolution on $\mathbb{T}$,

$$\sigma_N = f * F_N,$$

where the Fejér kernel is

$$F_N(x) = \frac{1}{N+1} \left(\frac{\sin \frac{N+1}{2} x}{\sin \frac{x}{2}} \right)^2.$$

This situation doesn't quite fit the scheme we have been using, because we now are dealing with the group $\mathbb{T}$ rather than $\mathbb{R}$. However, a simple change of viewpoint takes care of the difference. We simply write

$$\sigma_N(x) = \frac{1}{2\pi} \int_{-\pi}^{\pi} f(x - y) F_N(y) dy$$

and think of F_N as vanishing outside $(-\pi, \pi)$. Then the constant c is equal to

$$\int_{\mathbb{R}} \frac{1}{2\pi} F_N dx = 1.$$

The parameter $a = 2/(N + 1)$. Since $|\sin \frac{x}{2}| \geq \frac{|x|}{\pi}$ for $|x| < \pi$,

$$F_N(x) \leq \frac{a}{2} \left(\frac{\sin(x/a)}{x/\pi} \right)^2$$

$$= \frac{\pi^2}{2a} \left(\frac{\sin(x/a)}{x/a} \right)^2,$$

so the function

$$\psi(x) = \frac{\pi^2}{2} \left(\frac{\sin x}{x} \right)^2,$$

and $\psi \in L^1(\mathbb{R})$. Moreover ψ is dominated by an integrable decreasing function on $(0, \infty)$, so our theorems apply. We conclude that for any $f \in L^1(\mathbb{T})$

$$\lim_{N \to \infty} \sigma_N(x) = f(x) \quad \text{a.e. on } \mathbb{T}.$$

Abel summability. This was discussed in Section 14.E.2. A corresponding analysis shows that for any $f \in L^1(\mathbb{T})$

$$\lim_{r \to 1-} \sum_{n=-\infty}^{\infty} r^{|n|} \widehat{f}(n) e^{inx} = f(x) \quad \text{a.e. on } \mathbb{T}.$$

Problem 18. Prove this result.

(**HINT**: Let $a = 1 - r$ and write for $|x| < \pi$ and $\frac{1}{2} \le r < 1$

$$
\begin{aligned}
P_r(x) &= \frac{1 - r^2}{(1 - r)^2 + 4r \sin^2(x/2)} \\
&\le \frac{2a}{a^2 + 2x^2/\pi^2} \\
&= \frac{1}{a} \psi\left(\frac{x}{a}\right).)
\end{aligned}
$$

4.   Partial Differential Equations

Now we shall apply the more sophisticated results of Section 2, dealing with limits of the form

$$
\lim_{\substack{a \to 0 \\ |x' - x| < ma}} f * \phi_a(x') = c f(x).
$$

Dirichlet problem for a half space. This problem was discussed in Section 13.F, and we continue to use that notation. We assume for simplicity that $f \in L^1(\mathbb{R}^n)$, and we write

$$
u(x, y) = \int_{\mathbb{R}^n} P(x - z, y) f(z) dz,
$$

where P is the Poisson kernel, given explicitly by

$$
P(x, y) = \frac{2}{\omega_{n+1}} \frac{y}{(|x|^2 + y^2)^{(n+1)/2}}.
$$

Then u is a solution of Laplace's equation on the half space $\mathbb{R}^n \times (0, \infty)$. We recognize u to have the form of convolution of f with an approximate identity on $\mathbb{R}^n$, where y is a parameter tending to 0. All our assumptions are clearly satisfied, with

$$
\psi(x) = \frac{2}{\omega_{n+1}} \frac{1}{(|x|^2 + 1)^{(n+1)/2}}.
$$

So we conclude first that

$$
\lim_{y \to 0+} \|u(x, y) - f(x)\|_{L^1(\mathbb{R}^n)} = 0.
$$

Second,
$$\lim_{y \to 0+} u(x, y) = f(x) \quad \text{for a.e. } x \in \mathbb{R}^n.$$

Third, a.e. $x \in \mathbb{R}^n$ satisfies the following: For any $0 < m < \infty$

$$\lim_{\substack{y \to 0+ \\ |x'-x|<my}} u(x', y) = f(x).$$

This last relation has an interesting and important geometrical interpretation. It states that $u(x', y)$ converges to $f(x)$ *nontangentially*:

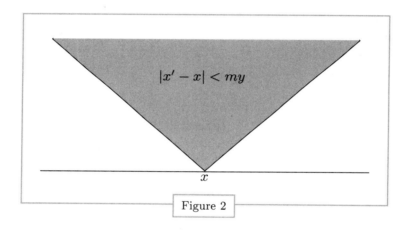

$$|x' - x| < my$$

$$x$$

Figure 2

For a given m, the set $\{(x', y) \mid |x' - x| < my\}$ is a *cone* in the half space where $y > 0$, with vertex x and generators having slope m^{-1}. As $y \to 0$ with fixed m, this forces $x' \to x$ in such a way that (x', y) cannot approach $(x, 0)$ tangent to the boundary $\mathbb{R}^n \times \{0\}$.

Dirichlet problem for the unit disk. This problem is connected with Abel summability. It was discussed in Section 14.E.3. Given $f \in L^1(\mathbb{T})$, define

$$u(r, \theta) = \sum_{n=-\infty}^{\infty} r^{|n|} \widehat{f}(n) e^{in\theta} \quad \text{for } r < 1.$$

Then u is a solution of Laplace's equation in the unit disk in $\mathbb{R}^2$, and we can now prove that for a.e. $\theta \in \mathbb{T}$, $u(r, \theta') \to f(\theta)$ "nontangentially." Geometrically, the situation is like the one in Figure 3:

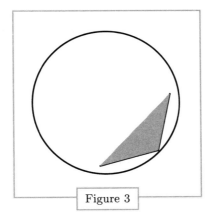

Figure 3

As a point with polar coordinates (r, θ') approaches $(1, \theta)$ inside any nontangential angle as illustrated,

$$u(r, \theta') \to f(\theta).$$

Problem 19. Demonstrate that an inequality of the form $|\theta' - \theta| < m(1 - r)$ leads to the geometric interpretation given in Figure 3.

Initial value problem for the heat equation. This problem was briefly introduced in Problem 13.64. The result of that problem is the following: let

$$Z(x, t) = (4\pi t)^{-n/2} e^{-|x|^2/4t} \quad \text{for } x \in \mathbb{R}^n, \ 0 < t < \infty.$$

Then $\int_{\mathbb{R}^n} Z(x, t) dx = 1$ and Z is a solution of the heat equation. If $f \in L^1(\mathbb{R}^n)$, define

$$u(x, t) = \int_{\mathbb{R}^n} Z(x - y, t) f(y) dy.$$

Then u satisfies the heat equation on $\mathbb{R}^n \times (0, \infty)$:

$$\frac{\partial^2 u}{\partial x_1^2} + \cdots + \frac{\partial^2 u}{\partial x_n^2} - \frac{\partial u}{\partial t} = 0.$$

Our previous results on approximate identities imply that $\|u(x, t) - f(x)\|_{L^1(\mathbb{R}^n)}$ has limit zero as $t \to 0+$. The results we have obtained in this chapter also apply, if we simply choose the parameter $a = \sqrt{t}$. Then in fact

$$Z(x,t) = a^{-n}\psi\left(\frac{|x|}{a}\right),$$

where

$$\psi(|x|) = (4\pi)^{-n/2}e^{-|x|^2/4}.$$

The result on "nontangential" convergence becomes the following: For a.e. $x \in \mathbb{R}^n$ and for all $0 < m < \infty$

$$\lim_{\substack{a \to 0 \\ |x'-x|<ma}} u(x',t) = f(x).$$

Replacing a by $\sqrt{t}$, this says

$$\lim_{\substack{t \to 0 \\ |x'-x|<m\sqrt{t}}} u(x',t) = f(x).$$

In this situation the word "nontangential" is actually a misnomer, because the regions $|x' - x| < m\sqrt{t}$ are parabolic, as we illustrate in Figure 4.

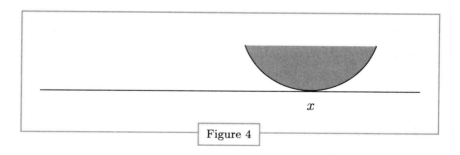

Figure 4

G. The Vitali Covering Theorem (Again)

To prepare for the discussion of monotone functions in the next chapter, we require another version of the Vitali theorem.

> ***Vitali Covering Theorem (Infinitesimal Version):***   *Let*
> $E \subset \mathbb{R}^n$ *be arbitrary. Assume that $\mathcal{F}$ is a collection of closed ball-*
> *s with positive radii which satisfies the following "Vitali condition"*
> *relative to E:*
>
> > *If $x \in E$ and $\epsilon > 0$, there exists $B \in \mathcal{F}$ such that*
> > *$x \in B$ and the radius of B is less than ϵ.*
>
> *Then there exists a sequence (possibly terminating) B_1, B_2, ... of*
> *balls from $\mathcal{F}$ such that*
>
> *(1) the balls B_1, B_2, ... are disjoint,*
>
> *(2) $E \subset \bigcup_{\alpha \geq 1} B_\alpha$ except for a null set.*

Proof: It suffices to prove this theorem in the case that E is bounded. The reason is that except for a null set E is the countable union of the sets

$$E \cap \{x \in \mathbb{R}^n \mid k < |x| < k+1\}, \quad k = 0, 1, 2, \ldots .$$

We then would prove the theorem for each of these sets, in each case using only balls contained in $\{x \mid k < |x| < k+1\}$.

Because of the Vitali condition, we can also assume that all the balls in $\mathcal{F}$ have radii less than a positive constant. Moreover, we can assume each ball in $\mathcal{F}$ contains a point in E.

One of the interesting things about this proof is the fact that the selection procedure is virtually identical to that employed in the proof of the Vitali theorem in Section A.

Assume that $B_1, \ldots, B_{\alpha-1}$ have been selected, where $\alpha \geq 1$. In case $E \subset \bigcup_{\beta < \alpha} B_\beta$, the process terminates with $B_{\alpha-1}$. Otherwise, the Vitali condition guarantees the existence of balls $B \in \mathcal{F}$ which are disjoint from the *closed* set $\bigcup_{\beta < \alpha} B_\beta$.

Define

$$d_\alpha = \sup\{\operatorname{rad} B \mid B \in \mathcal{F} \quad \text{and} \quad B \cap \bigcup_{\beta < \alpha} B_\beta = \emptyset\}.$$

Then choose $B_\alpha \in \mathcal{F}$ such that

$$\tfrac{1}{2}d_\alpha \leq \operatorname{rad} B_\alpha \quad \text{and} \quad B_\alpha \cap \bigcup_{\beta < \alpha} B_\beta = \emptyset.$$

Of course, if the process terminates at some stage, the theorem is established. Thus we assume that the process never terminates. Property (1) is obvious, so it is only (2) which requires verification.

Since the balls B_α are disjoint, have bounded radii, and have nonvoid intersection with the bounded set E, we conclude that

$$\sum_{\alpha=1}^{\infty} \lambda(B_\alpha) < \infty.$$

In particular, $\lim\limits_{\alpha \to \infty} \operatorname{rad} B_\alpha = 0$, and thus $\lim\limits_{\alpha \to \infty} d_\alpha = 0$. Now we are going to prove that for any $k \in \mathbb{N}$

$$E \subset \bigcup_{\alpha=1}^{k-1} B_\alpha \cup \bigcup_{\alpha=k}^{\infty} 5B_\alpha.$$

Assume then that $x \in E \sim \bigcup\limits_{\alpha=1}^{k-1} B_\alpha$. By the Vitali condition there exists $B \in \mathcal{F}$ such that

$$x \in B \quad \text{and} \quad B \cap \bigcup_{\alpha=1}^{k-1} B_\alpha = \emptyset.$$

It cannot be the case that $B \cap \bigcup\limits_{\alpha=1}^{\infty} B_\alpha = \emptyset$. Otherwise, the definition of d_α would show that

$$d_\alpha \geq \operatorname{rad} B \quad \text{for all } \alpha \in \mathbb{N},$$

contradicting the fact that $d_\alpha \to 0$. There is thus a smallest α_0 such that $B \cap B_{\alpha_0} \neq \emptyset$, and we note that $\alpha_0 \geq k$. Since

$$B \cap \bigcup_{\beta < \alpha_0} B_\beta = \emptyset,$$

the definition of d_{α_0} implies $d_{\alpha_0} \geq \operatorname{rad} B$. Therefore, the choice of B_{α_0} implies

$$\operatorname{rad} B \leq 2 \operatorname{rad} B_{\alpha_0}$$

This fact together with $B \cap B_{\alpha_0} \neq \emptyset$ implies $B \subset 5B_{\alpha_0}$. See Figure 5.

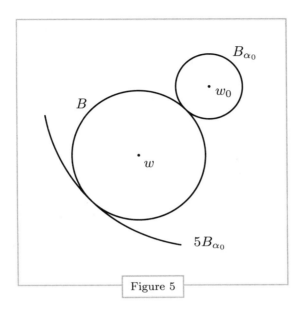

Figure 5

(Here are the details: If B has center w and B_{α_0} has center w_0 and if $y \in B \cap B_{\alpha_0}$, then for any $z \in B$,

$$\begin{aligned} |z - w_0| &\leq |z - w| + |w - y| + |y - w_0| \\ &\leq \text{ rad } B + \text{ rad } B + \text{ rad } B_{\alpha_0} \\ &\leq 5 \text{ rad } B_{\alpha_0}.) \end{aligned}$$

Therefore, $x \in B \subset B_{\alpha_0}$, and our claim is established. It follows that

$$E \sim \bigcup_{\alpha=1}^{\infty} B_\alpha \subset \bigcup_{\alpha=k}^{\infty} 5B_\alpha$$

for any $k \in \mathbb{N}$. Therefore,

$$\lambda^* \left(E \sim \bigcup_{\alpha=1}^{\infty} B_\alpha \right) \leq \sum_{\alpha=k}^{\infty} 5^n \lambda(B_\alpha).$$

As this tends to zero as $k \to \infty$, $\lambda^* \left(E \sim \bigcup_{\alpha=1}^{\infty} B_\alpha \right) = 0$ (cf. Problem 2.41).   **QED**

Problem 20. Show that the theorem remains valid if the word "closed" in its statement is replaced with the word "open."

Problem 21. Prove that, except for a null set, $\mathbb{R}^n$ can be expressed as the union of a countable disjoint collection of closed balls (cf. Problem 2.36).

Problem 22. Let E be a set in $\mathbb{R}^n$ which is a union (*not a countable union*) of closed balls with positive radii. Prove that E is measurable. More generally, prove the same thing if E is a union of sets X such that for each X there corresponds an open ball B such that $B \subset X \subset B^-$.

Problem 23. Let $E \subset \mathbb{R}^n$ be arbitrary. Prove that

$$\lambda^*(E) = \inf\left\{ \sum_{k=1}^{\infty} \lambda(B_k) \mid E \subset \bigcup_{k=1}^{\infty} B_k \right\},$$

and the B_k's are closed balls. This result is similar to but more difficult than Problem 2.27.

(**HINT:** The inequality "$\geq$" is the one which requires proof. You may assume $\lambda^*(E) < \infty$. First choose bounded open sets G_m such that $E \subset \bigcup_{m=1}^{\infty} G_m$ and $\sum_{m=1}^{\infty} \lambda(G_m) < \lambda^*(E) + \epsilon$. Write each $G_m \subset \bigcup_{\alpha=1}^{k-1} B_\alpha \cup \bigcup_{\alpha=k}^{\infty} 5B_\alpha$, with all $B_\alpha \subset G_m$.)

H.   The Besicovitch Covering Theorem

We include this section for the sake of completeness. No particular application of the theorem will be made in this book, although we shall give an illustration of its use at the end of this section. The idea of the present covering technique goes back to the discussion at the beginning of this chapter. We want to be able to cover E with the very same balls in the given family but are willing for the balls to have some overlap. Notice that the hypothesis of the following theorem is identical to the hypothesis of the Vitali covering theorem in Section A, except that we prefer to use cubes instead of balls.

When we speak of cubes in this setting, we intend that they be oriented with edges parallel to the coordinate axes. If I is a cube with center x

and edge length l, and if I is open, we denote it as $I = I(x, l/2)$. If we use the l^∞ norm on $\mathbb{R}^n$,

$$\|x\| = \max_{1 \le i \le n} |x_i|,$$

then

$$I(x, r) = \{y \in \mathbb{R}^n \mid \|y - x\| < r\}.$$

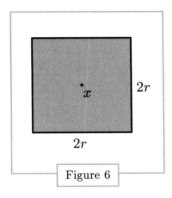

Figure 6

Besicovitch Covering Theorem: *Assume $E \subset \mathbb{R}^n$ is a bounded set. Assume that $\mathcal{F}$ is a collection of open cubes which are centered at points of E such that every point of E is the center of some cube in $\mathcal{F}$. Then there exists a sequence (possibly terminating) I_1, I_2, ... of cubes from $\mathcal{F}$ such that*

(1) no point of $\mathbb{R}^n$ belongs to more than 4^n of the cubes I_α,

(2) $E \subset \bigcup_{\alpha \ge 1} I_\alpha$.

Proof: If the edge lengths of the cubes in $\mathcal{F}$ are not bounded above, there exists a single cube which covers E. Therefore, we assume the edge lengths are bounded above.

Now we select the cubes inductively. Assume that $I_1, \ldots, I_{\alpha-1}$ have been selected, where $\alpha \ge 1$ (so this recipe will also show how to begin the selection). If $E \subset \bigcup_{\beta < \alpha} I_\beta$, the procedure terminates with $I_{\alpha-1}$.

Otherwise, the idea of the proof is to select as large a cube as possible with center outside of $\bigcup_{\beta < \alpha} I_\beta$. Thus we define

$$d_\alpha = \sup\{r \mid I(x,r) \in \mathcal{F} \quad \text{and} \quad x \in E \sim \bigcup_{\beta < \alpha} I_\beta\}.$$

We then choose

$$I_\alpha = I(x_\alpha, r_\alpha)$$

such that

$$x_\alpha \in E \sim \bigcup_{\beta < \alpha} I_\beta,$$

$$r_\alpha > \tfrac{1}{2} d_\alpha.$$

Notice the following: If $\alpha < \alpha'$, then $I(x_{\alpha'}, r_{\alpha'})$ is in the running during the election of $I(x_\alpha, r_\alpha)$. Therefore, $d_\alpha \geq r_{\alpha'}$, and so $r_\alpha > \tfrac{1}{2} r_{\alpha'}$. Changing the notation, it follows that

$$\beta < \alpha \Longrightarrow r_\alpha < 2r_\beta \quad \text{and} \quad x_\alpha \notin I_\beta.$$

Now we have to verify (1) and (2). First we assume that (1) is valid and give a proof of (2). If the selection process terminates, then (2) is granted. Thus, assume the process does not terminate. Then (1) implies

$$\sum_{\alpha=1}^{\infty} \chi_{I_\alpha} \leq 4^n.$$

Since the cubes I_α have bounded edge lengths and have centers lying in the bounded set E, there exists a large cube I which contains all I_α. Thus,

$$\sum_{\alpha=1}^{\infty} \chi_{I_\alpha} \leq 4^n \chi_I.$$

Integrate this inequality to obtain

$$\sum_{\alpha=1}^{\infty} (2r_\alpha)^n \leq 4^n \lambda(I) < \infty.$$

Therefore, $\lim r_\alpha = 0$. Now suppose (2) is false. Then there exists $x \in E$ and yet $x \notin \bigcup_{\alpha=1}^{\infty} I_\alpha$. By hypothesis, there exists $I(x,r) \in \mathcal{F}$. Therefore, all d_α satisfy $d_\alpha \geq r$. Therefore, $r_\alpha > \frac{1}{2}d_\alpha \geq \frac{1}{2}r$, contradicting $r_\alpha \to 0$. Thus, (2) is established.

Now we give the proof of (1). It is essentially a combinatorial argument. We are given a sequence of cubes $I_1, I_2, \ldots$ such that if $\beta < \alpha$, then $r_\alpha \leq 2r_\beta$ and $x_\alpha \notin I_\beta$. Assume that some point in $\mathbb{R}^n$ belongs to more than 4^n of these cubes. By translation we can assume this point to be the origin. And by extracting from the I_α's just those which contain the origin, we can assume

$$ 0 \in \bigcap_{\alpha=1}^{4^n+1} I_\alpha. $$

Now $\mathbb{R}^n$ can be split into 2^n "quadrants," depending on the sign of the coordinates of the points in $\mathbb{R}^n$. One of these quadrants must contain more than 2^n of the x_α's. By a change of notation we can assume it is the "first" quadrant $\mathcal{Q} = [0, \infty) \times \cdots \times [0, \infty)$. We then renumber those I_α's whose centers belong to $\mathcal{Q}$, keeping them in the same order so that the order relations are still valid. Thus, we now assume

$$ 0 \in \bigcap_{\alpha=1}^{2^n+1} I(x_\alpha, r_\alpha) \quad \text{and} \quad x_\alpha \in \mathcal{Q}. $$

We then make the following observations:

(a) $\mathcal{Q} \cap I(0, r_1) \subset I(x_1, r_1)$.

This follows because $0 \in I(x_1, r_1) \Rightarrow \|x_1\| < r_1$. Therefore, if $\|y\| < r_1$ and $y \in \mathcal{Q}$, then since all coordinates of y and x_1 are nonnegative, $\|y - x_1\| < r_1$.

(b) If $\alpha > 1$, $r_\alpha > r_1$.

Since $x_\alpha \notin I(x_1, r_1)$ and $x_\alpha \in \mathcal{Q}$, (a) $\Rightarrow x_\alpha \notin I(0, r_1)$. Since also $0 \in I(x_\alpha, r_\alpha)$, we conclude $r_1 \leq \|x_\alpha\| < r_\alpha$.

(c) If $\alpha > 1$, $x_\alpha \in I(0, 2r_1)$.

This is trivial: $\|x_\alpha\| < r_\alpha < 2r_1$.

(d) If $\alpha > 1$, $x_\alpha \in I(0, 2r_1) \sim I(0, r_1)$.

As we noted under (b), $x_\alpha \notin I(0, r_1)$.

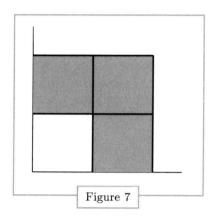

Figure 7

The region $[I(0, 2r_1) \sim I(0, r_1)] \cap \mathcal{Q}$ splits into $2^n - 1$ cubes, as illustrated in Figure 7 for the case $n = 2$. Indeed, a point $x \in \mathcal{Q}$ belongs to this region $\Longleftrightarrow r_1 \leq \|x\| < 2r_1$. This means that all the coordinates of x are in the interval $[0, 2r_1)$ and at least one is in the interval $[r_1, 2r_1)$; there are $2^n - 1$ ways to choose nonvoid subsets of $\{1, \ldots, n\}$. Since we are dealing with centers numbered $x_2, x_3, \ldots, x_{2^n+1}$, we have 2^n of them distributed in $2^n - 1$ cubes. Therefore, two of them at least belong to one of these cubes. By renaming the coordinates, we may assume that $1 < \beta < \alpha$ and that

(e) $x_\beta, x_\alpha \in [r_1, 2r_1)^m \times [0, r_1)^{n-m}$,

where $1 \leq m \leq n$. Finally, we observe

(f) $[r_1, 2r_1)^m \times [0, r_1)^{n-m} \subset I(x_\beta, r_\beta)$.

Suppose $y \in [r_1, 2r_1)^m \times [0, r_1)^{n-m}$. Then the coordinates of y and of x_β lie in the same intervals of length r_1, respectively, so $\|y - x_\beta\| < r_1 < r_\beta$ (by (b)).

By (e) and (f), $x_\alpha \in I(x_\beta, r_\beta) = I_\beta$. This contradicts the fact that $x_\alpha \notin I_\beta$ for $\beta < \alpha$. As this contradiction was derived from the assumption that some point of $\mathbb{R}^n$ belongs to more than 4^n of the cubes, that assumption is untenable. This proves (1).   **QED**

Remark: If balls are used instead of cubes, this theorem is still valid, but with the number 4^n replaced by a larger one (depending only on n). We have chosen this version because there are additional geometric complexities if balls are used.

We now want to provide an indication of why the Besicovitch theorem is of such importance. We shall consider a measure μ defined on the Borel sets $\mathcal{B}$ of $\mathbb{R}^n$. We assume μ is *locally finite* in the sense that

$$\mu(K) < \infty \text{ for every compact set } K \subset \mathbb{R}^n.$$

We also assume μ is *regular* in the sense that for every Borel set A

$$\mu(A) = \inf\{\mu(G) \mid A \subset G, G \text{ open}\}.$$

Problem 24. Prove that for every open set $G \subset \mathbb{R}^n$,

$$\mu(G) = \sup\{\mu(K) \mid K \subset G, K \text{ compact}\}.$$

Lemma: Assume μ satisfies the above conditions. Then for any fixed $0 < r < \infty$,

$$\mu(I(x,r)) \text{ is a lower semicontinuous function of } x.$$

In addition, for any fixed $x \in \mathbb{R}^n$

$$\mu(I(x,r)) \text{ is a left-continuous function of } r.$$

Proof: Since $\mu(I(x,r))$ is a nondecreasing function of r, both results follow from the fact that $\mu(I(x,r))$ is a lower semicontinuous function of $(x,r) \in \mathbb{R}^n \times (0,\infty)$. Suppose then that $t < \mu(I(x,r))$. By Problem 24 there exists a compact set $K \subset I(x,r)$ such that $t < \mu(K)$. If (x',r') is close enough to (x,r) that $K \subset I(x',r')$, then

$$t < \mu(K) \leq \mu(I(x',r')).$$

QED

For the rest of this section we assume μ is a regular measure on the Borel sets of $\mathbb{R}^n$ such that for every cube $I(x,r)$,

$$0 < \mu(I(x,r)) < \infty.$$

The following result is a generalization of the Hardy-Littlewood theorem of Section B.

Theorem: *Assume also that ν is a locally finite regular measure on $\mathcal{B}$. Let $0 < t < \infty$, and let*

$$E = \left\{ x \mid \sup_{0 < r < \infty} \frac{\nu(I(x,r))}{\mu(I(x,r))} > t \right\}.$$

Then E is a Borel set, and

$$\mu(E) \le \frac{4^n \nu(\mathbb{R}^n)}{t}.$$

Proof: By the left-continuity of $\nu(I(x,r))$ and $\mu(I(x,r))$, $x \in E$ if and only if there exists a *rational r* such that

$$\frac{\nu(I(x,r))}{\mu(I(x,r))} > t.$$

For each $r \in \mathbb{Q} \cap (0, \infty)$ the quotient $\nu(I(x,r))/\mu(I(x,r))$ is a Borel measurable function of x, since both the numerator and denominator are lower semicontinuous (and therefore Borel measurable). Then the *countable* supremum

$$\sup_{\substack{0 < r < \infty \\ r \in \mathbb{Q}}} \frac{\nu(I(x,r))}{\mu(I(x,r))}$$

is also Borel measurable. Therefore $E \in \mathcal{B}$.

Now we focus attention on the bounded set $E \cap B(0,k)$. Let $\mathcal{F}$ be the collection of open cubes I with centers in $E \cap B(0,k)$ and satisfying the inequality

$$\frac{\nu(I)}{\mu(I)} > t.$$

The hypotheses of the Besicovitch covering theorem are satisfied. We conclude that if $E \cap B(0,k) \ne \emptyset$, then there exist cubes $I_1, I_2, \ldots$ in $\mathcal{F}$ such that

(1) $\sum_{\alpha \ge 1} \chi_{I_\alpha} \le 4^n$,

(2) $E \cap B(0,k) \subset \bigcup_{\alpha \ge 1} I_\alpha$.

We thus obtain

$$\mu(E \cap B(0,k)) \leq \sum_{\alpha \geq 1} \mu(I_\alpha)$$

$$< \sum_{\alpha \geq 1} t^{-1}\nu(I_\alpha)$$

$$= t^{-1} \sum_{\alpha \geq 1} \int_{\mathbb{R}^n} \chi_{I_\alpha} d\nu$$

$$= t^{-1} \int_{\mathbb{R}^n} \left(\sum_{\alpha \geq 1} \chi_{I_\alpha} \right) d\nu$$

$$\leq t^{-1} \int_{\mathbb{R}^n} 4^n d\nu$$

$$= t^{-1} 4^n \nu(\mathbb{R}^n).$$

Now let $k \to \infty$ in order to obtain the conclusion of the theorem.

QED

Remark: The reason the *Vitali* covering theorem cannot be applied to this situation is very clear. In the Vitali theorem the set E is covered with enlarged balls (or cubes) $3B_\alpha$, and in this situation we do not have at hand an estimate of the form

$$\mu(3B_\alpha) \leq c\mu(B_\alpha).$$

We can now establish a differentiation theorem like that of Lebesgue in Section C. First, we prove a lemma concerning approximation by continuous functions.

Lemma: C_c *is dense in* $L^1(\mu)$.

Proof: Recall that C_c stands for the space of continuous functions on $\mathbb{R}^n$ which have compact support. In Section 7.C.2 we proved this lemma for the case of Lebesgue measure. We do not need to repeat the details of that proof, as they are identical in this case except for one particular. According to Part 5 of the proof on p.174, we need one fact: If A is a bounded Borel set and $\epsilon > 0$, then there exist a compact set K and an open set G such that $K \subset A \subset G$ and

$$\mu(G \sim K) < \epsilon.$$

Here is the proof: Since μ is regular, there exists an open set G such that $A \subset G$ and $\mu(G \sim A) < \epsilon/2$. Then there exists an open set H such that $G \sim A \subset H$ and $\mu(H) < \epsilon/2$. By Problem 24 there exists a compact set $L \subset G$ such that $\mu(G \sim L) < \epsilon/2$. Now define $K = L \sim H = L \cap H^c$, which is compact. Since

$$G \sim K \subset (G \sim L) \cup H,$$

it follows that $\mu(G \sim K) \leq \mu(G \sim L) + \mu(H) < \epsilon$.   **QED**

Theorem: *Assume $f \in L^1(\mu)$. Then for μ-a.e. $x \in \mathbb{R}^n$*

$$\lim_{r \to 0} \frac{1}{\mu(B(x,r))} \int_{B(x,r)} |f(y) - f(x)| d\mu(y) = 0.$$

Proof: We do not need to give many details but instead follow the proof of Lebesgue's theorem in Section C. As in that proof, we introduce

$$f^*(x) = \limsup_{r \to 0} \frac{1}{\mu(B(x,r))} \int_{B(x,r)} |f(y) - f(x)| d\mu(y).$$

Properties 1–4 in the previous proof are valid without change. Likewise for Property 5, if we use the maximal function based on μ,

$$Mf(x) = \sup_{r>0} \frac{1}{\mu(B(x,r))} \int_{B(x,r)} |f| d\mu.$$

Thus, $f^* \leq Mf + |f|$. We also introduce the measure associated with f,

$$\nu(A) = \int_A |f| d\mu.$$

Then $\{x \mid f^*(x) > t\} \subset \{x \mid Mf(x) > t/2\} \cup \{x \mid |f(x)| > t/2\}$. By the maximal theorem of this section,

$$\mu(\{x \mid Mf(x) > t/2\}) \leq \frac{4^n \nu(\mathbb{R}^n)}{t/2}$$

$$= \frac{2 \cdot 4^n}{t} \|f\|_{L^1(\mu)}.$$

By Chebyshev's inequality,

$$\mu(\{x \mid |f(x)| > t/2\}) \le \frac{2}{t} \|f\|_{L^1(\mu)}.$$

Now let $\epsilon > 0$. By the preceding lemma, there exists $g \in C_c$ such that $\|f - g\|_{L^1(\mu)} < \epsilon$. Since $(f - g)^* = f^*$,

$$\{x \mid f^*(x) > t\} \subset \{x \mid M(f-g)(x) > t/2\} \cup \{x \mid |f(x) - g(x)| > t/2\}.$$

The first set on the right has μ-measure not greater than $2 \cdot 4^n t^{-1} \|f - g\|_{L^1(\mu)} < 2 \cdot 4^n t^{-1} \epsilon$, and the second has μ-measure not greater than $2t^{-1}\epsilon$. Therefore, $\{x \mid f^*(x) > t\}$ is contained in a Borel set whose μ-measure is not greater than $2(4^n + 1)t^{-1}\epsilon$. Since ϵ is arbitrary, $\{x \mid f^*(x) > t\}$ is contained in a Borel set whose μ-measure is zero. Using a sequence $t = k^{-1}$, it follows that there exists a Borel set N such that

$$\{x \mid f^*(x) > 0\} \subset N,$$
$$\mu(N) = 0.$$

Thus, if $x \notin N$, $f^*(x) = 0$.   **QED**

I. The Lebesgue Set of Order p

In this section we return to Lebesgue measure on $\mathbb{R}^n$ and generalize the theorem of Lebesgue in Section C. The point is this: If $f \in L^p_{\text{loc}}(\mathbb{R}^n)$, then we are giving up something to consider only the Lebesgue set as defined for functions in L^1_{loc}. The exponent p can be incorporated into the result in the following manner. We assume $1 \le p < \infty$.

Theorem: *Assume $f \in L^p_{\text{loc}}(\mathbb{R}^n)$. Then for a.e. $x \in \mathbb{R}^n$*

$$\lim_{r \to 0} \frac{1}{\lambda(B(x,r))} \int_{B(x,r)} |f(y) - f(x)|^p dy = 0.$$

Remark: This is indeed a better result when $1 < p$, because Hölder's inequality implies

$$\frac{1}{\lambda(B(x,r))} \int_{B(x,r)} |f(y) - f(x)| dy \le \left(\frac{1}{\lambda(B(x,r))} \int_{B(x,r)} |f(y) - f(x)|^p dy \right)^{1/p}$$

Proof: We simply follow the outline of the proof of Lebesgue's theorem in Section C. We assume $f \in L^p(\mathbb{R})$ and define

$$f^*(x) = \limsup_{r \to 0} \left(\frac{1}{\lambda(B(x,r))} \int_{B(x,r)} |f(y) - f(x)|^p dy \right)^{1/p}$$

The properties follow as before, with few changes.

    1. $f^* \geq 0$.

    2. $(f + g)^* \leq f^* + g^*$. This now uses Minkowski's inequality.

    3. g continuous $\Rightarrow g^* = 0$. No change.

    4. g continuous $\Rightarrow (f - g)^* = f^*$. No change.

    5. $f^* \leq (M|f|^p)^{1/p} + |f|$.

    This holds because Minkowski's inequality implies

$$\left(\frac{1}{\lambda(B(x,r))} \int_{B(x,r)} |f(y) - f(x)|^p dy \right)^{1/p} \leq \left(\frac{1}{\lambda(B(x,r))} \int_{B(x,r)} |f(y)|^p dy \right)^{1/p}$$
$$+ |f(x)|$$
$$\leq (M|f|^p)^{1/p} + |f(x)|.$$

    6. $\lambda^*(\{x \mid f^*(x) > t\}) \leq 2^p(3^n + 1)t^{-p}\|f\|_p^p$.

    This is proved in the same way, using the Hardy-Littlewood maximal theorem in the following way:

$$\lambda(\{x \mid (M|f|^p)^{1/p} > t/2\}) = \lambda(\{x \mid M(|f|^p) > (t/2)^p\})$$
$$\leq \frac{3^n}{(t/2)^p} \| |f|^p \|_1$$
$$= \frac{2^p 3^n}{t^p} \|f\|_p^p.$$

    The rest of the proof is the same, depending only on approximating by continuous functions in the L^p norm.   **QED**

    As an example of the type of application which makes use of the Lebesgue set of order p, we return to our discussion of approximate identities in Section F. We retain all the notation of that section. The crucial hypothesis we used there was the assumption

$$|\phi_a(x)| \leq a^{-n}\psi\left(\frac{|x|}{a}\right).$$

The function ψ was decreasing and $\psi(|x|)$ was integrable on $\mathbb{R}^n$. We noted that if ψ is bounded, then the approximate identity works in the nontangential sense for any $f \in L^1$; and that if $\psi \in L^1$ it may happen that the nontangential convergence fails. Now we give an intermediate result.

> **Theorem:**   *Assume $\psi \in L^1 \cap L^{p'}(\mathbb{R}^n)$ and $f \in L^p(\mathbb{R}^n)$, where $1 \leq p < \infty$ and p' is the Hölder conjugate of p. Then for almost every $x \in \mathbb{R}^n$ it is true that*
>
> $$\lim_{\substack{a \to 0 \\ |x'-x|<ma}} f * \phi_a(x') = cf(x).$$

Proof: The case $p = 1$ was handled in the theorem on p.471. The proof of the present result is the same except for the handling of the term involving $\psi(0)$ in the previous proof. In the present case we treat that term by exploiting the Lebesgue set of f of order p. Thus we assume x satisfies

$$\gamma(a) = \left(\frac{1}{a^n} \int_{|y|<a} |f(x+y) - A|^p dy\right)^{1/p} \to 0 \quad \text{as } a \to 0.$$

In the notation used in the earlier proof, we conclude that

$$|f * \phi_a(x') - c_a A| \leq \int_{|y|/a<1} |f(x'-y) - A|a^{-n}\psi\left(\frac{|y|}{a}\right) dy$$
$$+ \sum_{k=0}^{\infty} \psi(2^k)(2^{k+1} + m)^n g((2^{k+1} + m)a).$$

We must now prove the first term on the right side tends to zero as $a \to 0$, and the proof will be completed. We apply Hölder's inequality to estimate it by

$$\left(a^{-n} \int_{|y|/a<1} |f(x'-y)-A|^p dy \right)^{1/p} \left(a^{-n} \int_{|y|/a<1} \psi\left(\frac{|y|}{a}\right)^{p'} dy \right)^{1/p'}$$

The second factor equals

$$\left(\int_{|y|<1} \psi(|y|)^{p'} dy \right)^{1/p'} \le \|\psi\|_{p'}.$$

The first factor is treated by the change of variable $x' - y = x - z$, so that $|z| \le |y| + |x' - x| < a + ma$. Thus, the first term, which we are concerned with, is bounded by

$$\|\psi\|_{p'} \left(a^{-n} \int_{|z|<(1+m)a} |f(x-z)-A|^p dz \right)^{1/p}$$

$$= \|\psi\|_{p'} \gamma((1+m)a)(1+m)^{n/p},$$

and this tends to zero as $a \to 0$.   **QED**

J. Change of Variables

In this section we are going to deal with a fixed function Φ defined on an open subset of $\mathbb{R}^n$ and having values in $\mathbb{R}^n$. We require the following definition from calculus:

Definition: Φ is *differentiable* at a point x of its domain if there exists an $n \times n$ matrix T such that for every $\epsilon > 0$ there corresponds $\delta > 0$ such that

$$|\Phi(y) - \Phi(x) - T(y-x)| \le \epsilon|y-x| \quad \text{if } |y-x| \le \delta.$$

It is easily seen that if the components of Φ are $\Phi_1, \ldots, \Phi_n$, and if Φ is differentiable at x, then the following partial derivatives exist and are given by the entries of T:

$$\frac{\partial \Phi_i}{\partial x_j}(x) = t_{ij}.$$

It is not true conversely that if $\dfrac{\partial \Phi_i}{\partial x_j}(x)$ all exist, then Φ is differentiable.

However, it is shown in calculus that if these partial derivatives all exist and are *continuous* on an open set, then Φ is differentiable at every point of that set.

Notation: If Φ is differentiable at x, then in the notation of the above definition, we set $T = \Phi'(x)$. We also denote

$$J(x) = \det \Phi'(x).$$

This is called the *Jacobian* determinant of Φ at x.

Lemma: *Assume Φ is differentiable at x and $\epsilon > 0$. Then there exists $\delta > 0$ such that for $0 < r \leq \delta$*

$$\lambda^*(\Phi(B(x,r))) \leq (|J(x)| + \epsilon)\lambda(B(x,r)).$$

Proof: The proof splits naturally into two cases, depending on whether or not the matrix $T = \Phi'(x)$ is invertible. Since Lebesgue measure is translation invariant, we may assume that $x = 0$ and that $\Phi(0) = 0$. Then the existence of the derivative implies that for any $\epsilon_1 > 0$ there exists $\delta > 0$ such that

$$|\Phi(y) - Ty| \leq \epsilon_1 |y| \quad \text{if } |y| \leq \delta.$$

Case 1. T is not invertible.

In this case $J(0) = 0$. The vectors Ty must lie in a subspace of $\mathbb{R}^n$ with dimension less than n. We choose a constant c such that $|Ty| \leq c|y|$ for all $y \in \mathbb{R}^n$. Then for $y \in B(0,r)$, $|Ty| \leq cr$. Thus, if $r \leq \delta$, then all the vectors in $\Phi(B(0,r))$ lie within a distance $\epsilon_1 r$ of a ball in an $(n-1)$-dimensional subspace M whose radius is cr. This situation is illustrated in Figure 8. We could try to calculate the measure of the illustrated set, but an upper bound will suffice. The region is surely contained in a rectangle for which $n - 1$ sides have length $2(cr + \epsilon_1 r)$ and the other side has length $2\epsilon_1 r$. Thus,

$$\lambda^*(\Phi(B(0,r))) \leq 2^n (c + \epsilon_1)^{n-1} \epsilon_1 r^n.$$

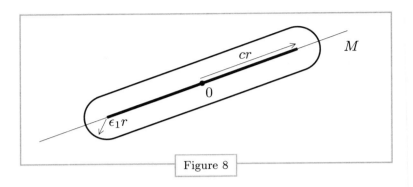

Figure 8

This estimate will clearly be smaller than $\epsilon\lambda(B(0,r))$ if ϵ_1 is chosen sufficiently small.

Case 2. *T is invertible.*

In this case there exists an inverse matrix T^{-1}. Choose a constant c such that $|T^{-1}z| \leq c|z|$ for all $z \in \mathbb{R}^n$. Then

$$|T^{-1}\Phi(y) - y| \leq c\epsilon_1|y| \quad \text{if } |y| \leq \delta.$$

Therefore,
$$|T^{-1}\Phi(y)| \leq (1 + c\epsilon_1)|y| \quad \text{if } |y| \leq \delta.$$

This implies that for $0 < r \leq \delta$

$$T^{-1}\Phi(B(0,r)) \subset B(0, (1 + c\epsilon_1)r),$$

and thus
$$\lambda^*(T^{-1}\Phi(B(0,r))) \leq \lambda(B(0, (1 + c\epsilon_1)r)$$
$$= (1 + c\epsilon_1)^n \lambda(B(0,r)).$$

Now we simply apply the theorem on p.76 as follows:

$$\lambda^*(\Phi(B(0,r))) = |\det T|\lambda^*(T^{-1}\Phi(B(0,r)))$$
$$\leq |\det T|(1 + c\epsilon_1)^n \lambda(B(0,r)).$$

Finally, choose ϵ_1 so small that

$$|\det T|(1 + c\epsilon_1)^n \leq |\det T| + \epsilon.$$

QED

Lemma: *Assume $\Omega \subset \mathbb{R}^n$ is open and $\Phi : \Omega \to \mathbb{R}^n$. Assume $E \subset \Omega$ and Φ is differentiable at every point of E. Assume the Jacobian determinant satisfies*

$$|J(x)| \leq M,$$

where $0 \leq M < \infty$ is a constant. Then

$$\lambda^*(\Phi(E)) \leq M\lambda^*(E).$$

Proof: First we show that we can assume E is bounded. Let $E_k = E \cap B(0, k)$ and assume we already know

$$\lambda^*(\Phi(E_k)) \leq M\lambda^*(E_k).$$

Then $\lambda^*(E_k) \leq \lambda^*(E)$. As $\Phi(E)$ is the increasing union

$$\Phi(E) = \bigcup_{k=1}^{\infty} \Phi(E_k),$$

Problem 2.40 implies that $\lambda^*(\Phi(E)) = \lim_{k \to \infty} \lambda^*(\Phi(E_k))$. Therefore, $\lambda^*(\Phi(E)) \leq M\lambda^*(E)$.

Therefore, we assume that E is bounded. Let $\epsilon > 0$. Then there exists an open set G such that $E \subset G \subset \Omega$ and $\lambda(G) < \lambda^*(E) + \epsilon$. By the preceding lemma, for each $x \in E$ there exists $\delta(x) > 0$ such that for $0 < r \leq \delta(x)$ the ball $B(x, r) \subset G$ and

$$\lambda^*(\Phi(B(x, r))) \leq (M + \epsilon)\lambda(B(x, r)).$$

The balls $B(x, r)$ with $x \in E$ and $0 < r \leq \delta(x)/5$ form a collection $\mathcal{F}$ which satisfies the Vitali condition relative to E (Section G). (The balls happen to be open, which is unimportant, but Problem 20 takes care of that anyway.) Therefore, the infinitesimal version of the Vitali covering theorem implies there exist disjoint balls $B_1, B_2, \ldots$ in $\mathcal{F}$ such that

$$E \subset \bigcup_{\alpha=1}^{\infty} B_\alpha$$

except for a null set. The *proof* of the Vitali theorem shows more: For any $k \in \mathbb{N}$

$$E \subset \bigcup_{\alpha=1}^{k-1} B_\alpha \cup \bigcup_{\alpha=k}^{\infty} 5B_\alpha.$$

Therefore,

$$\Phi(E) \subset \bigcup_{\alpha=1}^{k-1} \Phi(B_\alpha) \cup \bigcup_{\alpha=k}^{\infty} \Phi(5B_\alpha).$$

Thus,

$$\lambda^*(\Phi(E)) \leq \sum_{\alpha=1}^{k-1} \lambda^*(\Phi(B_\alpha)) + \sum_{\alpha=k}^{\infty} \lambda^*(\Phi(5B_\alpha))$$

$$\leq \sum_{\alpha=1}^{k-1} (M + \epsilon)\lambda(B_\alpha) + \sum_{\alpha=k}^{\infty} (M + \epsilon)\lambda(5B_\alpha)$$

$$= (M + \epsilon) \sum_{\alpha=1}^{k-1} \lambda(B_\alpha) + (M + \epsilon) \sum_{\alpha=k}^{\infty} 5^n \lambda(B_\alpha).$$

The balls B_α are disjoint and contained in G. Thus,

$$\sum_{\alpha=1}^{\infty} \lambda(B_\alpha) \leq \lambda(G)$$

so if we let $k \to \infty$ we obtain

$$\lambda^*(\Phi(E)) \leq (M + \epsilon)\lambda(G)$$
$$< (M + \epsilon)(\lambda^*(E) + \epsilon).$$

Since ϵ is arbitrary, the lemma is proved.   **QED**

Corollary (Sard's Theorem): *Assume $\Omega \in \mathbb{R}^n$ is open and $\Phi : \Omega \to \mathbb{R}^n$. Assume $E \subset \Omega$ and that for every point $x \in E$, Φ is differentiable at x and $J(x) = 0$. Then $\Phi(E)$ is a null set.*

Proof: This follows immediately from the lemma with $M = 0$.   **QED**

A point $y \in \mathbb{R}^n$ is called a *critical value* of Φ if there exists $x \in \Omega$ such that $\Phi(x) = y$, Φ is differentiable at x, and $J(x) = 0$. Sard's theorem can thus be expressed in the following way: *The set of critical values of Φ is a null set.*

Lemma: *If each component of Φ is measurable on Ω and Φ is differentiable at every point of the measurable set E, then J is measurable on E.*

Proof: Note that by extending Φ to be zero on Ω^c, we can assume with no loss of generality that Φ is defined and measurable on all of $\mathbb{R}^n$. Since $J(x) = \det \Phi'(x)$ is a certain algebraic combination of the partial derivatives $\partial \Phi_i / \partial x_j$, it is sufficient to prove that each such partial derivative is measurable. This is very similar to Problem 5.20. Since Φ_i is measurable on Ω, it follows that $\Phi_i(x + he_j)$ is measurable as a function of x, where e_j is the unit coordinate vector in the x_j-direction. Therefore,

$$\frac{\partial \Phi_i}{\partial x_j}(x) = \lim_{h \to 0} \frac{\Phi_i(x + he_j) - \Phi_i(x)}{h}$$

is also measurable on E.   **QED**

Proposition: *If Φ is measurable on Ω and differentiable at every point of the measurable set $E \subset \Omega$, then*

$$\lambda^*(\Phi(E)) \leq \int_E |J(x)| dx.$$

Proof: We prove this first under the assumption that $\lambda(E) < \infty$. Let $\epsilon > 0$ and define

$$E_k = \{x \in E \mid (k-1)\epsilon \leq |J(x)| < k\epsilon\}, \quad k \in \mathbb{N}.$$

Then the second lemma of this section implies

$$\lambda^*(\Phi(E_k)) \leq k\epsilon\lambda(E_k).$$

Therefore,

$$
\begin{aligned}
\lambda^*(\Phi(E)) &= \lambda^* \left(\bigcup_{k=1}^{\infty} \Phi(E_k) \right) \\
&\leq \sum_{k=1}^{\infty} \lambda^*(\Phi(E_k)) \\
&\leq \sum_{k=1}^{\infty} k\epsilon\lambda(E_k) \\
&= \sum_{k=1}^{\infty} (k-1)\epsilon\lambda(E_k) + \epsilon\sum_{k=1}^{\infty} \lambda(E_k) \\
&\leq \sum_{k=1}^{\infty} \int_{E_k} |J(x)| dx + \epsilon\lambda(E) \\
&= \int_E |J(x)| dx + \epsilon\lambda(E).
\end{aligned}
$$

Since $\lambda(E) < \infty$ and ϵ is arbitrary, the proof of this case is completed.

In case $\lambda(E) = \infty$, choose any sequence $A_1 \subset A_2 \subset \ldots$ of measurable sets with $\lambda(A_k) < \infty$ and $\bigcup\limits_{k=1}^{\infty} A_k = E$. By Problem 2.40

$$\lambda^*(\Phi(E)) = \lim_{k \to \infty} \lambda^*(\Phi(A_k))$$

$$\leq \lim_{k \to \infty} \int\limits_{A_k} |J(x)|dx$$

$$= \int\limits_E |J(x)|dx.$$

QED

Corollary: *Under the same assumptions, if $E \subset \Omega$ is a null set, then $\Phi(E)$ is a null set.*

Proof: Obvious.   **QED**

Corollary: *Under the same assumptions, if $E \subset \Omega$ is measurable, then $\Phi(E)$ is measurable.*

Proof: By Problem 2.48 it is possible to express E as a union of the form

$$E = \bigcup_{j=1}^{\infty} K_j \cup N,$$

where each K_j is compact and N is a null set. Since Φ is continuous on E and K_j is compact, it follows from the theorem on p.17 that $\Phi(K_j)$ is compact. The preceding corollary implies $\Phi(N)$ is a null set. Therefore, $\Phi(K_j)$ and $\Phi(N)$ are measurable. Therefore,

$$\Phi(E) = \bigcup_{j=1}^{\infty} \Phi(K_j) \cup \Phi(N)$$

is also measurable.   **QED**

Remark: The preceding corollary is definitely interesting. See the remark on p.110 for an example to show that if E is measurable and it is assumed only that Φ is continuous (not differentiable), then it may happen that $\Phi(E)$ is not measurable.

Corollary: *If Φ is differentiable on Ω and $E \subset \Omega$ is measurable, then $\Phi(E)$ is measurable and*

$$\lambda(\Phi(E)) \leq \int\limits_{E} |J(x)|dx.$$

Proof: This is only a restatement of the above proposition together with the new information that $\Phi(E)$ is measurable.   **QED**

Theorem: *Assume $\Phi : \Omega \to \mathbb{R}^n$ is differentiable on the open set $\Omega \subset \mathbb{R}^n$. Assume $f \geq 0$ is a Borel measurable function on $\mathbb{R}^n$. Then $f \circ \Phi$ is Borel measurable and*

$$\int\limits_{\Phi(\Omega)} f(y)dy \leq \int\limits_{\Omega} f(\Phi(x))|J(x)|dx.$$

Proof: Suppose first that $f = \chi_B$, where $B \subset \mathbb{R}^n$ is a Borel set. Then $f \circ \Phi = \chi_{\Phi^{-1}(B)}$. Since Φ is continuous, $\Phi^{-1}(B)$ is a Borel set, as shown by the theorem on p.109. Now apply the preceding corollary to the set $E = \Phi^{-1}(B)$. Then $\Phi(E) = \Phi(\Omega) \cap B$, so we obtain

$$\lambda(\Phi(\Omega) \cap B) \leq \int\limits_{\Phi^{-1}(B)} |J(x)|dx.$$

That is,

$$\int\limits_{\mathbb{R}^n} \chi_{\Phi(\Omega) \cap B}(y)dy \leq \int\limits_{\Omega} \chi_{\Phi^{-1}(B)}(x)|J(x)|dx.$$

That is,

$$\int\limits_{\Phi(\Omega)} \chi_B(y)dy \leq \int\limits_{\Omega} \chi_B(\Phi(x))|J(x)|dx.$$

This is just the statement of theorem for the case $f = \chi_B$.

The result is therefore true for the case in which f is a Borel measurable simple function. The general case follows from the theorem on p.118 and LICT.   **QED**

Now we can state the change of variables formula.

Theorem: *Assume Ω_1 and Ω_2 are open sets in $\mathbb{R}^n$. Assume that*

$$\Omega_1 \xrightarrow{\Phi} \Omega_2$$

is a bijection of class C^1 whose inverse is also of class C^1. Assume that f is a Lebesgue measurable function on Ω_2. Then $f \circ \Phi$ is Lebesgue measurable on Ω_1 and

$$\int\limits_{\Omega_2} f(y)dy = \int\limits_{\Omega_1} f(\Phi(x))|J(x)|dx.$$

This formula is valid in two senses: If $f \geq 0$, then it is true without further qualification. In general, $f \in L^1(\Omega_2)$ if and only if $f \circ \Phi\,|J| \in L^1(\Omega_1)$, and then the formula is valid.

Proof: Assume first that $f \geq 0$ and f is Borel measurable. The preceding theorem then implies

$$\int\limits_{\Omega_2} f(y)dy \leq \int\limits_{\Omega_1} f(\Phi(x))|J(x)|dx.$$

In the present situation we can also apply this result to Φ^{-1} and to any nonnegative Borel measurable function g on Ω_1:

$$\int\limits_{\Omega_1} g(x)dx \leq \int\limits_{\Omega_2} g(\Phi^{-1}(y))|\widetilde{J}(y)|dy,$$

where $\widetilde{J}$ is the Jacobian determinant for Φ^{-1}. Thus,

$$\begin{aligned}
\widetilde{J}(y) &= \det(\Phi^{-1})'(y) \\
&= \det(\Phi'(\Phi^{-1}(y)))^{-1} \\
&= \frac{1}{\det \Phi'(\Phi^{-1}(y))} \\
&= \frac{1}{J(\Phi^{-1}(y))}.
\end{aligned}$$

Now simply take
$$g(x) = f(\Phi(x))|J(x)|.$$

Thus,
$$g(\Phi^{-1}(y))|\widetilde{J}(y)| = f(y)|J(\Phi^{-1}(y))||\widetilde{J}(y)|$$
$$= f(y),$$

and we obtain
$$\int_{\Omega_1} f(\Phi(x))|J(x)|dx \le \int_{\Omega_2} f(y)dy.$$

The theorem is therefore established in case f is Borel measurable, $f \ge 0$.

   If f is only Lebesgue measurable, then there exists a Borel measurable f_1 such that $f = f_1$ a.e., as is shown by the theorem on p.118. Thus, there exists a null set $N \subset \Omega_2$ such that $f(y) = f_1(y)$ if $y \notin N$. Therefore, $f(\Phi(x)) = f_1(\Phi(x))$ if $x \notin \Phi^{-1}(N)$. Apply the first corollary of the proposition to Φ^{-1} to conclude $\Phi^{-1}(N)$ is also a null set. Thus, $f(\Phi(x)) = f_1(\Phi(x))$ a.e., and the theorem is established in general if $f \ge 0$.

   Finally, the case of general $f \in L^1(\Omega_2)$ follows by expressing f as a combination of nonnegative functions.   **QED**

   Remark: This result is termed a "change of variables" formula because it can be viewed as a transformation of the integral

$$\int_{\Omega_2} f(y)dy$$

by making the substitution $y = \Phi(x)$. We then replace $f(y)$ by $f(\Phi(x))$, Ω_2 by $\Phi^{-1}(\Omega_2) = \Omega_1$, and dy by $|\det \Phi'(x)|dx = |J(x)|dx$.

   Note that the linear version of this theorem appears in Section 7.B.

Problem 25 (SPHERICAL COORDINATES). Let $\Omega_1 \subset \mathbb{R}^n$ be the set
$$\Omega_1 = (0, \infty) \times (0, \pi)^{n-2} \times (0, 2\pi).$$

Here $n \ge 2$ and we denote the coordinates of a point in Ω_1 by

$r, \theta_1, \ldots, \theta_{n-2}, \theta_{n-1}$, respectively. Thus,

$$0 < r < \infty,$$
$$0 < \theta_k < \pi \quad \text{for } 1 \le k \le n - 2,$$
$$0 < \theta_{n-1} < 2\pi.$$

Then define

$$\Omega_1 \xrightarrow{\Phi} \mathbb{R}^n$$

by the spherical coordinate formulas: If $x = \Phi(r, \theta)$, then

$$x_k = r \sin \theta_1 \ldots \sin \theta_{k-1} \cos \theta_k \quad \text{for } 1 \le k \le n,$$

where we define $\theta_n = 0$, so that $x_n = r \sin \theta_1 \ldots \sin \theta_{n-1}$. Prove that Φ is a bijection of Ω_1 onto the open set

$$\Omega_2 = \mathbb{R}^n \sim (\mathbb{R}^{n-2} \times [0, \infty) \times \{0\}).$$

(**HINT**: It is easy to see that the image $\Phi(\Omega_1)$ is contained in Ω_2. Conversely, if $x \in \Omega_2$, first show that $r = |x|$ and θ_1 are uniquely determined. Then consider the vector

$$\left(\frac{x_2}{r \sin \theta_1}, \ldots, \frac{x_n}{r \sin \theta_1} \right) \in \mathbb{R}^{n-1}$$

and proceed inductively.)

Problem 26. Prove that the formula for integration in spherical coordinates is

$$\int_{\mathbb{R}^n} f(x)dx =$$

$$\int_0^\infty \int_0^\pi \cdots \int_0^\pi \int_0^{2\pi} f(\Phi(r,\theta)) r^{n-1} \sin^{n-2} \theta_1 \ldots \sin^2 \theta_{n-3} \sin \theta_{n-2} d\theta_{n-1} \ldots d\theta_1 dr.$$

Be sure you explain why the region of integration on the left side is $\mathbb{R}^n$ instead of Ω_2.

Problem 27. Prove that in the notation of p.206

$$\omega_n = \int_0^\pi \sin^{n-2}\theta_1 d\theta_1 \ldots \int_0^\pi \sin^2\theta_{n-3} d\theta_{n-3} \int_0^\pi \sin\theta_{n-2} d\theta_{n-2} \int_0^{2\pi} d\theta_{n-1}.$$

Problem 28. Prove that if f is a function of x_1 and $|x|$ only, say

$$f(x) = g(x_1, |x|),$$

then

$$\int_{\mathbb{R}^n} g(x_1, |x|) dx = \omega_{n-1} \int_0^\infty \int_0^\pi g(r\cos\theta, r) r^{n-1} \sin^{n-2}\theta\, d\theta\, dr.$$

Problem 29. Generalize the previous problem: Suppose σ is a fixed unit vector in $\mathbb{R}^n$, and prove

$$\int_{\mathbb{R}^n} g(x \cdot \sigma, |x|) dx = \omega_{n-1} \int_0^\infty \int_0^\pi g(r\cos\theta, r) r^{n-1} \sin^{n-2}\theta\, d\theta\, dr.$$

K. Noninvertible Mappings

Throughout this section we assume that Ω is an open subset of $\mathbb{R}^n$ and that $\Phi : \Omega \to \mathbb{R}^n$ is of class C^1. We continue to use the notation of the preceding section for the Jacobian determinant,

$$J(x) = \det \Phi'(x).$$

Since we are not going to assume that Φ is an injection, it is reasonable to introduce the following function. If $E \subset \Omega$ and $y \in \mathbb{R}^n$,

$$\#(E, y) = \text{ the number of points } x \in E \text{ such that } \Phi(x) = y.$$

In case $\Phi(x) = y$ for infinitely many $x \in E$, we set $\#(E, y) = \infty$. The basic result we want to establish is the following theorem.

Theorem: *If $E \subset \Omega$ is measurable, then $\#(E, y)$ is a measurable function of $y \in \mathbb{R}^n$, and*

$$\int_E |J(x)| dx = \int_{\mathbb{R}^n} \#(E, y) dy.$$

Remark: This theorem can be regarded as a sharpened version of the proposition of the preceding section. The reason is this: $y \in \Phi(E) \Leftrightarrow \#(E, y) \geq 1$. Therefore, $\#(E, y) \geq \chi_{\Phi(E)}(y)$, so our present theorem implies

$$\int_E |J(x)| dx \geq \int_{\mathbb{R}^n} \chi_{\Phi(E)}(y) dy = \lambda(\Phi(E)),$$

which is the inequality of the proposition.

Proof: We shall give the proof in several stages.
    $E = \Omega$ and J never vanishes.
    In this case consider an arbitrary $x \in \Omega$. Since $J(x) \neq 0$, the derivative $\Phi'(x)$ is invertible. We now apply the *inverse function theorem* of the theory of calculus on $\mathbb{R}^n$. It guarantees the existence of a number $\delta(x) > 0$ such that for all $0 < r \leq \delta(x)$ the mapping Φ is a bijection of $B(x, r)$ onto a neighborhood of $\Phi(x)$, and this bijection has a C^1 inverse mapping. Therefore, the change of variables formula of the preceding section implies

$$\lambda(\Phi(B(x, r))) = \int_{B(x,r)} |J| d\lambda \quad \text{for } 0 < r \leq \delta(x).$$

Now consider the collection of all such balls. These balls cover Ω and satisfy the Vitali condition of Section G. Therefore, the infinitesimal version of the Vitali covering theorem implies the existence of a disjoint sequence B_1, B_2, ... of these balls such that

$$\Omega = \bigcup_{\alpha \geq 1} B_\alpha \cup N,$$

where N is a null set. Since for all α

$$\lambda(\Phi(B_\alpha)) = \int_{B_\alpha} |J| d\lambda,$$

we can sum over α to obtain

$$\int_{\mathbb{R}^n} \sum_{\alpha \geq 1} \chi_{\Phi(B_\alpha)} d\lambda = \int_{\underset{\alpha \geq 1}{\bigcup} B_\alpha} |J| d\lambda$$

$$= \int_\Omega |J| d\lambda,$$

the last equality holding because N is a null set. Since the balls B_α are disjoint, $\sum_{\alpha \geq 1} \chi_{\Phi(B_\alpha)}(y)$ is equal to the number of points $x \in \bigcup_{\alpha \geq 1} B_\alpha$ such that $\Phi(x) = y$. (Remember that Φ is one-to-one on each B_α!) Therefore,

$$\sum_{\alpha \geq 1} \chi_{\Phi(B_\alpha)}(y) \leq \#(\Omega, y);$$

moreover, if for a given y the inequality sign is strict, then there must exist a point $x \in \Omega \sim \bigcup_{\alpha \geq 1} B_\alpha$ such that $\Phi(x) = y$. Thus, $y \in \Phi(N)$.
The first corollary of the proposition of the preceding section shows that $\Phi(N)$ is a null set. Therefore,

$$\sum_{\alpha \geq 1} \chi_{\Phi(B_\alpha)}(y) = \#(\Omega, y) \quad \text{for a.e. } y,$$

and we conclude that

$$\int_{\mathbb{R}^n} \#(\Omega, y) dy = \int_\Omega |J| d\lambda,$$

and, incidentally, that $\#(\Omega, y)$ is measurable.
    $E = \Omega$.
    Apply the preceding result to the open set $\Omega_1 = \{x \in \Omega \mid J(x) \neq 0\}$. Thus,

$$\int_{\Omega_1} |J| d\lambda = \int_{\mathbb{R}^n} \#(\Omega_1, y) dy.$$

Clearly, $\int_{\Omega_1} |J| d\lambda = \int_\Omega |J| d\lambda$. We therefore must prove that

$$\int_{\mathbb{R}^n} \#(\Omega_1, y) dy = \int_{\mathbb{R}^n} \#(\Omega, y) dy.$$

Since $\#(\Omega_1, y) \le \#(\Omega, y)$, we must prove that

$$\#(\Omega_1, y) = \#(\Omega, y) \quad \text{for a.e. } y.$$

If for a given $y \in \mathbb{R}^n$ this equality does not hold, there must exist $x \in \Omega \sim \Omega_1$ such that $\Phi(x) = y$. That is, $J(x) = 0$ and $\Phi(x) = y$. That is, y is a *critical value* of Φ. Sard's theorem states that the critical values of Φ form a null set, so this case is handled.

E open in Ω.

This case is now trivial. Apply the preceding result to the restriction of Φ to E.

E compact in Ω.

If E is compact, $E \subset \Omega$, then there exists a bounded open set G such that $E \subset G \subset G^- \subset \Omega$. Apply the preceding case to the open sets G and $G \sim E$:

$$\int\limits_{G} |J| d\lambda = \int\limits_{\mathbb{R}^n} \#(G, y) dy;$$

$$\int\limits_{G \sim E} |J| d\lambda = \int\limits_{\mathbb{R}^n} \#(G \sim E, y) dy.$$

These integrals are all finite since G^- is bounded and contained in Ω, and $|J|$ is continuous. In particular, $\#(G, y) < \infty$ for a.e. y, so that

$$\#(G, y) - \#(G \sim E, y) = \#(E, y) \quad \text{a.e.}$$

The result in this case therefore follows by subtraction.

$E \subset \Omega$ is a null set.

In this case $\#(E, y) > 0 \Rightarrow y \in \Phi(E)$. As $\Phi(E)$ is a null set, we conclude that $\#(E, y) = 0$ a.e.

General case.

If $E \subset \Omega$ is a measurable set, we apply Problem 2.48 to express

$$E = \bigcup_{j=1}^{\infty} K_j \cup N,$$

where $K_1 \subset K_2 \subset K_3 \subset \ldots$ are compact and N is a null set. We also take N to be disjoint from $\bigcup_{j=1}^{\infty} K_j$. By the two preceding cases,

$$\int\limits_{K_j} |J| d\lambda = \int\limits_{\mathbb{R}^n} \#(K_j, y) dy;$$

$$\int\limits_{N} |J| d\lambda = \int\limits_{\mathbb{R}^n} \#(N, y) dy.$$

Let $j \to \infty$, and add the second equation to obtain

$$\int_E |J| d\lambda = \int_{\mathbb{R}^n} \#(E, y) dy.$$

QED

If $B \subset \mathbb{R}^n$ is a Borel set, then we can apply this theorem to the Borel set $E = \Phi^{-1}(B)$. The left side becomes

$$\int_{\Phi^{-1}(B)} |J(x)| dx = \int_{\Omega} \chi_{\Phi^{-1}(B)}(x) |J(x)| dx$$

$$= \int_{\Omega} \chi_B(\Phi(x)) |J(x)| dx.$$

We also have

$$\#(\Phi^{-1}(B), y) = \text{ number of } x \text{ such that } \Phi(x) \in B \text{ and } \Phi(x) = y$$
$$= \#(\Omega, y) \chi_B(y).$$

Therefore, the right side of the theorem becomes

$$\int_{\mathbb{R}^n} \#(\Omega, y) \chi_B(y) dy.$$

Thus, we obtain

$$\int_{\mathbb{R}^n} \#(\Omega, y) \chi_B(y) dy = \int_{\Omega} \chi_B(\Phi(x)) |J(x)| dx$$

for any Borel set B. The usual extension process proves the following result.

Corollary: *If $f \geq 0$ is a Borel measurable function on $\mathbb{R}^n$,*

$$\int_{\mathbb{R}^n} \#(\Omega, y) f(y) dy = \int_{\Omega} f(\Phi(x)) |J(x)| dx.$$

Problem 30. Apply the theorem to any measurable $E \subset \Omega$ and generalize it suitably to prove that for any g which is nonnegative and measurable on Ω,

$$\int_{\mathbb{R}^n} \left(\sum_{\Phi(x)=y} g(x) \right) dy = \int_{\Omega} g(x)|J(x)|dx.$$

Problem 31. Demonstrate that the corollary is a special case of Problem 30.

Differentiation for Functions on ℝ

There are many special and interesting results concerned with the differentiability properties of functions of one real variable. Many of these properties will be treated in the present chapter.

A. Monotone Functions

A real-valued function f on an interval in ℝ is *increasing* if

$$x < y \Rightarrow f(x) \le f(y).$$

(Some authors describe this property by the word "nondecreasing.") If it is even true that

$$x < y \Rightarrow f(x) < f(y),$$

then f is said to be *strictly increasing*. In the same way we define *decreasing* and *strictly decreasing* functions. A function is said to be *monotone* if it is either an increasing function or a decreasing function. In order to illustrate how complicated monotone functions can be, we give two examples, one of which is discussed in Problem 2.

Example: Let $\mathbb{Q} = \{r_1, r_2, \ldots\}$ be an enumeration of the rational numbers. Define

$$f(x) = \sum_{r_k \le x} 2^{-k} \quad \text{for } x \in \mathbb{R}.$$

That is, $f(x)$ is the sum of the infinite series consisting of all numbers 2^{-k} for those integers k such that $r_k \le x$. Obviously, f is strictly increasing and $0 < f(x) < 1$ for all $x \in \mathbb{R}$. The upper bound follows from the fact that

$$\sum_{k=1}^{\infty} 2^{-k} = 1.$$

We shall often use the notation introduced on p.353,

$$f(x+) = \lim_{\substack{y \to x \\ y > x}} f(y) \text{ if the limit exists;}$$

likewise,

$$f(x-) = \lim_{\substack{y \to x \\ y < x}} f(y).$$

Of course, these limits do exist if f is monotone. If f is increasing, then

$$f(x-) \le f(x) \le f(x+),$$

so that f is continuous at $x \iff f(x-) = f(x+)$.

Problem 1. For the function introduced in the above example, prove that f is *right-continuous*; i.e., that

$$f(x+) = f(x) \quad \text{for all } x \in \mathbb{R}.$$

Prove also that f is continuous at $x \iff x$ is irrational. Show finally that for rational x

$$f(x) - f(x-) = 2^{-k} \quad \text{if } x = r_k.$$

Problem 2. Here is a closely related example which is based on the *dyadic* rationals in the interval $(0, 1)$ (cf. Section 4.C). Each such rational number has a unique representation as a proper fraction of the form $(2k-1)2^{-n}$, where $n \in \mathbb{N}$ and $k = 1, 2, 3, \ldots, 2^{n-1}$. Define the function g on $(0, 1)$ by

$$g(x) = \sum_{0 < (2k-1)2^{-n} \le x} 2^{-2n}.$$

Then g is strictly increasing. Prove that $0 < g(x) < \frac{1}{2}$. Also show that $g(0+) = 0$ and $g(1-) = \frac{1}{2}$.

These examples show that monotone functions can be discontinuous on a *dense* set. Each of them is, however, discontinuous only on a countable set. The next problem shows that this situation is typical.

Problem 3. Prove that if f is monotone, then f is discontinuous only at a countable set of points (see also Problem 7.9).

Problem 4. If $E \subset \mathbb{R}$ is countable, construct a monotone function which is discontinuous at each point of E and continuous at each point of E^c.

The first theorem we shall prove is an amazing theorem of Lebesgue to the effect that monotone functions are differentiable almost everywhere. Before doing that, let us calculate the derivatives of the function g in Problem 2. First, we show that the *right-hand* derivative is zero for all x:

$$\lim_{\substack{h \to 0 \\ h > 0}} \frac{g(x + h) - g(x)}{h} = 0.$$

To prove this, let $x \in (0, 1)$ be arbitrary. If $N > 0$, there exists $\delta > 0$ such that the interval $(x, x + \delta)$ contains no dyadic rational with denominator $1, 2, 4, \ldots, 2^N$. That is, if $(2k - 1)2^{-n} \in (x, x + \delta)$, then $n > N$. For $h > 0$

$$g(x + h) - g(x) = \sum_{x < (2k-1)2^{-n} \leq x+h} 2^{-2n}.$$

For any fixed n, the integers k which satisfy the given inequalities must satisfy

$$2^{n-1}x + \frac{1}{2} < k \leq 2^{n-1}x + 2^{n-1}h + \frac{1}{2}.$$

As the length of this interval is $2^{n-1}h$, there can be at most $2^{n-1}h$ such integers k. Therefore, assuming $0 < h < \delta$,

$$g(x + h) - g(x) \leq \sum_{n > N} 2^{n-1}h2^{-2n}$$

$$= h \sum_{n=N+1}^{\infty} 2^{-n-1}$$

$$= h2^{-N-1}.$$

Thus, $0 < h < \delta \Rightarrow$

$$0 \leq \frac{g(x + h) - g(x)}{h} \leq 2^{-N-1}.$$

Since N is arbitrary, we conclude that the right-hand derivative of g at x is zero.

Problem 5. By the same sort of argument, show that if $x \in (0, 1)$ is *not* a dyadic rational, then the left-hand derivative at x is zero:

$$\lim_{\substack{h \to 0 \\ h < 0}} \frac{g(x+h) - g(x)}{h} = 0.$$

In summary, the function g is strictly increasing and is discontinuous precisely at the dyadic rationals in $(0, 1)$. Of course, it cannot be differentiable at any point of discontinuity. However, for all $x \in (0, 1)$ except for the dyadic rationals, $g'(x) = 0$.

> **Theorem (Lebesgue):** *If f is monotone, then f is differentiable a.e.*

Proof: With no loss of generality we assume f is increasing on the closed interval $[a, b]$. Since the proof will be rather long, we divide it into several smaller pieces.

1. We introduce some notation:

$$Df(x) = \lim_{\delta \to 0} \sup \left\{ \frac{f(z) - f(y)}{z - y} \,\middle|\, a \leq y \leq x \leq z \leq b, 0 < z - y < \delta \right\};$$

$$df(x) = \lim_{\delta \to 0} \inf \left\{ \frac{f(z) - f(y)}{z - y} \,\middle|\, a \leq y \leq x \leq z \leq b, 0 < z - y < \delta \right\}.$$

Of course,

$$0 \leq df(x) \leq Df(x) \leq \infty.$$

What we must prove is precisely that for a.e. $x \in [a, b]$,

$$df(x) = Df(x) < \infty. \quad \text{(See Problem 6 below.)}$$

This common value is of course exactly the derivative $f'(x)$.

2. Obviously,

$$\{x \mid Df(x) = \infty\} = \bigcap_{k=1}^{\infty} \{x \mid Df(x) > k\}$$

and

$$\{x \mid df(x) < Df(x)\} = \bigcup_{\substack{s < t \\ s, t \in \mathbb{Q}}} \{x \mid df(x) < s < t < Df(x)\}.$$

Therefore, if we define the sets for fixed $k > 0$ and $0 < s < t < \infty$,

$$E = \{x \in [a, b] \mid Df(x) > k\}$$

and

$$F = \{x \in [a, b] \mid df(x) < s < t < Df(x)\},$$

then it is sufficient to prove

$$\lambda^*(E) \leq \frac{\text{constant}}{k},$$
$$\lambda^*(F) = 0.$$

3. First we estimate $\lambda^*(E)$. For any $x \in E$, $Df(x) > k$. Therefore, there exist arbitrarily small nondegenerate closed intervals $[y, z]$ such that $x \in [y, z] \subset [a, b]$ and

$$\frac{f(x) - f(y)}{z - y} > k.$$

It is convenient to introduce a notation for the interval $(f(y), f(z))$; for lack of a better one, let

$$\widetilde{[y, z]} = (f(y), f(z)).$$

Then the above inequality can be written in the form

$$\lambda(\widetilde{I}) > k\lambda(I), \quad \text{where } I = [y, z].$$

Assuming that E is not a null set, we apply the Vitali covering theorem of p.479. We conclude that there exist disjoint closed intervals (balls) $I_1, I_2, \ldots$, satisfying the above inequality, such that

$$E \subset \bigcup_{\alpha \geq 1} I_\alpha \text{ a.e.}$$

Thus,

$$\lambda^*(E) \leq \sum_{\alpha \geq 1} \lambda(I_\alpha)$$
$$< k^{-1} \sum_{\alpha \geq 1} \lambda(\widetilde{I}_\alpha).$$

Since f is increasing and the intervals I_α are disjoint, it follows that the (open) intervals $\widetilde{I}_\alpha$ are also disjoint. Therefore,

$$\lambda^*(E) < k^{-1}\lambda\left(\bigcup_{\alpha \geq 1} \widetilde{I}_\alpha\right)$$
$$\leq k^{-1}\lambda\left((f(a), f(b))\right)$$
$$= \frac{f(b) - f(a)}{k}.$$

This is precisely the type of inequality for $\lambda^*(E)$ that we needed to establish.

4. Finally, we turn to the considerably more difficult estimation of $\lambda^*(F)$. First, for any $\epsilon > 0$ there exists an open set $G \subset \mathbb{R}$ such that $F \subset G$ and $\lambda(G) < \lambda^*(F) + \epsilon$. Now we shall have to employ the Vitali covering theorem twice.

a. For any $x \in F$, there exist arbitrarily small nondegenerate closed intervals $[y, z]$ such that $x \in [y, z] \subset G \cap [a, b]$ and

$$\frac{f(z) - f(y)}{z - y} < s.$$

By the Vitali covering theorem of p.479, there exist disjoint closed intervals $I_1, I_2, \ldots$ of this type such that $F \subset \bigcup_{\alpha \geq 1} I_\alpha$ a.e. Thus,

$$\lambda\left(\bigcup_{\alpha \geq 1} \widetilde{I}_\alpha\right) = \sum_{\alpha \geq 1} \lambda(\widetilde{I}_\alpha)$$
$$< \sum_{\alpha \geq 1} s\lambda(I_\alpha)$$
$$= s\lambda\left(\bigcup_{\alpha \geq 1} I_\alpha\right)$$
$$\leq s\lambda(G)$$
$$< s(\lambda^*(F) + \epsilon).$$

Note also that

$$F \subset \bigcup_{\alpha \geq 1} I_\alpha^\circ \text{ a.e.}$$

b. For any $x \in F \cap \bigcup_{\alpha \geq 1} I_\alpha^o$, there exist arbitrarily small nondegenerate closed intervals $[y, z]$ such that $x \in [y, z]$,

$$\frac{f(z) - f(y)}{z - y} > t,$$

and $[y, z]$ is entirely contained in some I_α^o. We again apply the Vitali covering theorem, and we conclude that there exist disjoint closed intervals $J_1, J_2, \ldots$ of this type such that

$$F \cap \bigcup_{\alpha \geq 1} I_\alpha^o \subset \bigcup_{\beta \geq 1} J_\beta \quad \text{a.e.}$$

We also know that

$$F \subset \bigcup_{\beta \geq 1} J_\beta \quad \text{a.e.}$$

and that each J_β is entirely contained in some I_α. Thus,

$$
\begin{aligned}
\lambda^*(F) &\leq \sum_{\beta \geq 1} \lambda(J_\beta) \\
&< t^{-1} \sum_{\beta \geq 1} \lambda(\widetilde{J}_\beta) \\
&= t^{-1} \lambda \left(\bigcup_{\beta \geq 1} \widetilde{J}_\beta \right) \\
&\leq t^{-1} \lambda \left(\bigcup_{\alpha \geq 1} \widetilde{I}_\alpha \right) \quad (f \text{ is increasing}) \\
&< t^{-1} s(\lambda^*(F) + \epsilon);
\end{aligned}
$$

at the last step we used the inequality derived in part a. Since ϵ is arbitrary, we conclude that

$$\lambda^*(F) \leq \frac{s}{t} \lambda^*(F).$$

Since $\dfrac{s}{t} < 1$, it follows that $\lambda^*(F) = 0$, and that is what we needed to prove about $\lambda^*(F)$.   **QED**

Problem 6. This problem justifies the notation used at the beginning of the preceding proof. Prove that f is differentiable at $x \iff$ there exists

$$\lim \frac{f(z) - f(y)}{z - y},$$

where $y \le x \le z$, $z - y > 0$, and $z - y \to 0$. That is, f is differentiable at $x \iff df(x) = Df(x) < \infty$.

Lebesgue's theorem that we have just proved has the strongest possible conclusion, in the following precise sense.

Theorem: *Let $N \subset \mathbb{R}$ be a null set. Then there exists a continuous increasing function f on $\mathbb{R}$ such that $f'(x) = \infty$ for all $x \in N$.*

Proof: Since $\lambda^*(N) = 0$, for any $k \in \mathbb{N}$ there exists an open set G_k such that $N \subset G_k$ and $\lambda(G_k) \le 2^{-k}$. Let

$$f_k(x) = \int\limits_{-\infty}^{x} \chi_{G_k}(t)dt = \lambda(G_k \cap (-\infty, x]).$$

Then f_k is continuous and increasing on $\mathbb{R}$, and $0 \le f_k(x) \le 2^{-k}$. Thus, the infinite series

$$f(x) = \sum_{k=1}^{\infty} f_k(x)$$

converges uniformly on $\mathbb{R}$, so that f is continuous and increasing. Now let $x \in N$ and let $m \in \mathbb{N}$. Since x belongs to the open set $\bigcap\limits_{k=1}^{m} G_k$, there exists $\delta > 0$ such that $[x - \delta, x + \delta] \subset \bigcap\limits_{k=1}^{m} G_k$. Thus, if $x - \delta \le y \le x \le$

$z \leq x + \delta$ and $y < z$,

$$\frac{f(z) - f(y)}{z - y} = \sum_{k=1}^{\infty} \frac{f_k(z) - f_k(y)}{z - y}$$

$$\geq \sum_{k=1}^{m} \frac{f_k(z) - f_k(y)}{z - y}$$

$$= \sum_{k=1}^{m} \frac{1}{z - y} \int_{y}^{z} \chi_{G_k}(t) dt$$

$$= \sum_{k=1}^{m} \frac{z - y}{z - y}$$

$$= m.$$

Since m is arbitrary, $f'(x) = \infty$ (in the notation of the proof of Lebesgue's theorem, $df(x) = \infty$).   **QED**

The following result is quite simple and depends only on the conclusion of Lebesgue's theorem.

Theorem: *Assume f is increasing on $[a, b]$. Then f' is integrable, and*

$$\int_{a}^{b} f'(x) dx \leq f(b) - f(a).$$

Proof: For convenience extend the definition of f by defining $f(x) = f(b)$ for $x > b$. By the theorem of Lebesgue above, $f'(x)$ exists for a.e. x in $[a, b]$. Thus,

$$f'(x) = \lim_{k \to \infty} k \left[f \left(x + \frac{1}{k} \right) - f(x) \right] \quad \text{for a.e. } x.$$

Note that

$$\int_a^b k\left[f\left(x+\frac{1}{k}\right)-f(x)\right]dx = k\int_{a+1/k}^{b+1/k} f(x)dx - k\int_a^b f(x)dx$$

$$= k\int_b^{b+1/k} f(x)dx - k\int_a^{a+1/k} f(x)dx$$

$$= f(b) - k\int_a^{a+1/k} f(x)dx$$

$$\leq f(b) - f(a).$$

Now Fatou's lemma of p.129 implies

$$\int_a^b f'(x)dx \leq \liminf_{k\to\infty} \int_a^b k\left[f\left(x+\frac{1}{k}\right)-f(x)\right]dx$$

$$\leq f(b) - f(a).$$

$$\text{QED}$$

Problem 7. Prove that the conclusion of this theorem can be slightly strengthened to

$$\int_a^b f'(x)dx \leq f(b-) - f(a+).$$

Problem 8. Prove that if f is increasing on $[a,b]$ and f is *not* continuous on $[a,b]$ then

$$\int_a^b f'(x)dx < f(b) - f(a).$$

Naturally, we are very interested in the situation of equality in the preceding theorem:

$$\int_a^b f'(x)dx = f(b) - f(a).$$

Problem 8 shows that a monotone function cannot satisfy this equation unless it is continuous. The reason is essentially that a jump discontinuity is not accounted for by f', which does not exist at a discontinuity. A more subtle fact is that the continuity of f does not guarantee equality either. The most famous example is the Lebesgue function for the Cantor ternary set. By consulting the sketch in Figure 3 on p.87 it is seen obviously that the Lebesgue function is constant on all the excluded open middle third intervals and therefore has zero derivative there. Since all these open intervals constitute a set of measure 1, the Lebesgue function f satisfies:

f is continuous and increasing on $[0, 1]$,

$f' = 0$ a.e. on $[0, 1]$,

$$0 = \int_0^1 f'(x)dx < f(1) - f(0) = 1.$$

This is an extremely interesting phenomenon, about which we shall say more after we discuss absolute continuity.

Problem 9. Let f be the Lebesgue function for the Cantor ternary set C. Prove that for all $x \in C$, $Df(x) = \infty$.

(**HINT**: Use the formula for f given in Problem 4.9. In that notation, if $\alpha_k = 0$, consider $x + 2/3^k$; if $\alpha_k = 2$, consider $x - 2/3^k$.)

B. Jump Functions

In this section we shall treat increasing functions on *open* intervals. The corresponding results for the situation of compact intervals are somewhat simpler because of the fact that monotone functions on compact intervals are bounded.

Definition: An *elementary increasing jump function* is a function σ defined on $\mathbb{R}$ which has the following form:

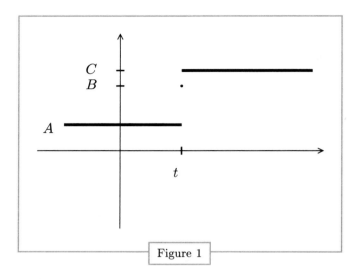

Figure 1

$$\sigma(x) = \begin{cases} A & \text{if } x < t, \\ B & \text{if } x = t, \\ C & \text{if } x > t. \end{cases}$$

Since σ is increasing, we have $A \leq B \leq C$. We also assume $A < C$.

Definition: Let $I \subset \mathbb{R}$ be an open interval. An *increasing jump function* on I is a function $s : I \to \mathbb{R}$ which has the following sort of representation: There exist elementary increasing jump functions $\sigma_1, \sigma_2, \ldots$ such that

$$s(x) = \sum_{k=1}^{\infty} \sigma_k(x) \qquad \text{for all } x \in I.$$

We have already seen two examples of such functions in the preceding section.

Problem 10. Demonstrate that the function of Problem 1 is an increasing jump function.

Problem 11. Suppose s is an increasing jump function, represented as above.

(a) Prove that if $\displaystyle\sum_{k=1}^{\infty} \sigma_k(x)$ converges absolutely at some point of I, then it converges absolutely at every point of I.

(b) Give an example showing that absolute convergence does not necessarily hold in the representation of $s(x)$.

(c) Prove that every increasing jump function can be represented as an absolutely convergent series of elementary increasing jump functions.

(HINT: For any x, $x_0 \in I$,

$$s(x) - s(x_0) = \sum_{k=1}^{\infty} [\sigma_k(x) - \sigma_k(x_0)].)$$

Problem 12. In the above notation prove that

$$s(x+) = \sum_{k=1}^{\infty} \sigma_k(x+)$$

and

$$s(x-) = \sum_{k=1}^{\infty} \sigma_k(x-)$$

Problem 13. Let s be an increasing jump function on the open interval I, and assume s has a representation as in the definition. Prove that s is discontinuous at the discontinuity of each σ_k and is continuous elsewhere.

Now suppose that f is an increasing function on I. We are going to associate a jump function with f which incorporates all the discontinuities of f. Suppose that f is discontinuous at a point $t \in I$. Then we define

$$\sigma(x) = \begin{cases} f(t-) & \text{for } x < t, \\ f(t) & \text{for } x = t, \\ f(t+) & \text{for } x > t. \end{cases}$$

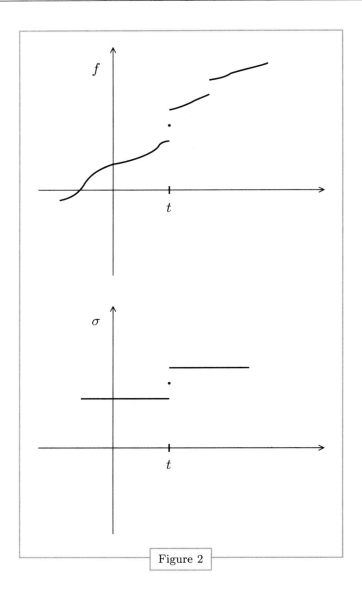

Figure 2

In Figure 2 we have illustrated the graph of σ right below the graph of f. Note that σ is increasing, $f - \sigma$ is continuous at t, and $f - \sigma$ is also increasing.

By Problem 2 the function f has at most countably many discontinuities. Let us denote them t_1, t_2, t_3, $\ldots$. Let σ_k be the jump function illustrated in Figure 2 associated with the point t_k. Also let $x_0 \in I$ be an arbitrary point chosen as reference point. We then define for $n \in \mathbb{N}$

$$f_n(x) = f(x) - \sum_{k=1}^{n} (\sigma_k(x) - \sigma_k(x_0)).$$

Note that f_n is an increasing function on I. We shall now investigate the convergence of the series

$$s(x) = \sum_{k=1}^{\infty} (\sigma_k(x) - \sigma_k(x_0)), \quad x \in I.$$

Suppose that $x_0 < x$. Then $f_n(x_0) \le f_n(x)$, so that

$$f(x_0) \le f(x) - \sum_{k=1}^{n} (\sigma_k(x) - \sigma_k(x_0)),$$

or

$$\sum_{k=1}^{n} (\sigma_k(x) - \sigma_k(x_0)) \le f(x) - f(x_0).$$

This sum of nonnegative numbers is thus bounded by the number $f(x) - f(x_0)$, independently of n, so that there exists

$$s(x) \le f(x) - f(x_0) \quad \text{for } x \in I, x_0 < x.$$

Likewise, there exists

$$s(x) \ge f(x) - f(x_0) \quad \text{for } x \in I, x < x_0,$$

and $s(x)$ is a series of nonpositive terms in this case.
   We also define
$$\phi(x) = f(x) - s(x).$$

Obviously, s is increasing. Also, ϕ is increasing as it is the limit as $n \to \infty$ of the increasing functions f_n. The important observation is that ϕ is *continuous*. To see this let $x \in I$ be fixed. Then if $y < x < z$ and $y, z \in I$, $\phi(y) \le \phi(z)$ so that

$$f(y) - s(y) \le f(z) - s(z),$$

or

$$s(z) - s(y) \le f(z) - f(y).$$

Now let $y \to x$ and $z \to x$:

$$s(x+) - s(x-) \leq f(x+) - f(x-).$$

We now prove on the other hand that

$$s(z) - s(y) \geq f(x+) - f(x-).$$

If f is continuous at x, this inequality is trivial from the fact that s is increasing. If f is discontinuous at x, then $x = t_m$ for some m. Therefore, since $y < t_m < z$,

$$\begin{aligned} s(z) - s(y) &= \sum_{k=1}^{\infty} (\sigma_k(z) - \sigma_k(y)) \\ &\geq \sigma_m(z) - \sigma_m(y) \\ &= f(x+) - f(x-). \end{aligned}$$

Now let $y \to x$ and $z \to x$:

$$s(x+) - s(x-) \geq f(x+) - f(x-).$$

We conclude that

$$s(x+) - s(x-) = f(x+) - f(x-),$$

or

$$\phi(x-) = \phi(x+).$$

Therefore, ϕ is continuous at x. We have now completely proved the following result:

Theorem: *Let $I \subset \mathbb{R}$ be an open interval, and assume $f : I \to \mathbb{R}$ is increasing. Let s be the increasing jump function associated with f by the above construction. Then*

$$f(x) = \phi(x) + s(x),$$

where s is an increasing jump function and ϕ is an increasing continuous function.

Problem 14. Prove the same result if I is a compact interval, and show that you may assume $s = 0$ at the left endpoint of I.

Problem 15. Let f be an increasing function on any interval I. Prove that the representation of f in the form $f = \phi + s$, where s is an increasing jump function and ϕ a continuous function is unique except for the addition of constants to s and ϕ.

C. Another Theorem of Fubini

The result we are going to handle in this section is concerned with the differentiation of infinite series. We shall give two applications of it.

Theorem (Fubini): *Assume $I \subset \mathbb{R}$ is an interval and that for $k \in \mathbb{N}$, $f_k : I \to \mathbb{R}$ is an increasing function. Assume*

$$s(x) = \sum_{k=1}^{\infty} f_k(x) \quad \text{exists for all } x \in I.$$

Then

$$s'(x) = \sum_{k=1}^{\infty} f_k'(x) \quad \text{for a.e. } x \in I.$$

Proof: Without loss of generality we can assume $I = [a, b]$ is compact. Since

$$s(x) - s(a) = \sum_{k=1}^{\infty} [f_k(x) - f_k(a)],$$

we can further assume that $f_k(a) = 0$ for all k. Let E be the set of points $x \in (a, b)$ such that the derivatives

$$s'(x), f_1'(x), f_2'(x), f_3'(x), \ldots$$

all exist. By Lebesgue's theorem of Section A, $[a, b] \sim E$ is a null set. Suppose $x \in E$ and $h > 0$ is sufficiently small that $x + h \in I$. Then

$$\frac{s(x + h) - s(x)}{h} = \sum_{k=1}^{\infty} \frac{f_k(x + h) - f_k(x)}{h}.$$

We can now let $h \to 0$ and conclude that there is an inequality

$$s'(x) \geq \sum_{k=1}^{\infty} f_k'(x).$$

This follows immediately from Fatou's lemma for counting measure on $\mathbb{N}$. (Alternatively, a direct proof is quite simple: For any N

$$\frac{s(x+h) - s(x)}{h} \geq \sum_{k=1}^{N} \frac{f_k(x+h) - f_k(x)}{h};$$

now let $h \to 0$ to conclude

$$s'(x) \geq \sum_{k=1}^{N} f_k'(x).$$

Finally, let $N \to \infty$ to obtain the desired inequality.)

Actually, the only fact we require from this part of the proof is that

$$\lim_{k \to \infty} f_k'(x) = 0 \quad \text{for a.e. } x \in [a, b].$$

For the second stage of the proof we define the partial sums

$$s_N(x) = \sum_{k=1}^{N} f_k(x).$$

Since $\lim_{N \to \infty} s_N(b) = s(b)$, there exists an increasing sequence N_j such that

$$s(b) - s_{N_j}(b) \leq 2^{-j}.$$

Since $s - s_{N_j}$ is an increasing function, we thus conclude that

$$0 \leq s(x) - s_{N_j}(x) \leq 2^{-j} \quad \text{for all } x \in [a, b].$$

Therefore, the series of increasing functions

$$\sum_{j=1}^{\infty} (s - s_{N_j})$$

converges on $[a, b]$. The first stage of the proof therefore implies

$$\lim_{j \to \infty} (s'(x) - s'_{N_j}(x)) = 0 \quad \text{for a.e. } x \in [a, b].$$

That is,

$$\lim_{j \to \infty} \sum_{k=1}^{N_j} f'_k(x) = s'(x) \quad \text{for a.e. } x \in [a, b].$$

Since $f'_k(x) \geq 0$ wherever the derivative exists, the last result implies that

$$\lim_{N \to \infty} \sum_{k=1}^{N} f'_k(x) = s'(x) \quad \text{for a.e. } x \in [a, b].$$

QED

Corollary: *If s is any increasing jump function, then $s' = 0$ a.e.*

Proof: We know that $s = \sum_{k=1}^{\infty} \sigma_k$, where each σ_k is increasing and each σ_k satisfies $\sigma'_k = 0$ except for one point. The theorem of Fubini implies $s' = \sum_{k=1}^{\infty} \sigma'_k = 0$ a.e.

QED

In particular, we can now say that the function of Problem 1 satisfies $f' = 0$ a.e.

A particularly spectacular application of the theorem is contained in the following example.

Example: We shall construct a function $g : \mathbb{R} \to (0, 1)$ which is continuous, *strictly* increasing, and which satisfies $g' = 0$ a.e.

To do this, let f be the Lebesgue function for the Cantor ternary set, extended so that $f(x) = 0$ for $x < 0$ and $f(x) = 1$ for $x > 1$. Enumerate the rationals $\mathbb{Q} = \{r_1, r_2, \ldots\}$. Then define

$$g(x) = \sum_{k=1}^{\infty} 2^{-k} f(x - r_k).$$

By the uniform convergence of the series, g is continuous on $\mathbb{R}$. Clearly, $0 < g(x) < 1$. The Fubini theorem implies

$$g'(x) = \sum_{k=1}^{\infty} 2^{-k} f'(x - r_k) \text{ a.e.}$$

Since $f' = 0$ a.e., also $g' = 0$ a.e. Finally, if $x < y$, then there exists r_k such that $x < r_k < y$. Thus, $f(x - r_k) = 0 < f(y - r_k)$, so $g(x) < g(y)$.

One might expect that if s is an increasing jump function, then $s' = 0$ except at the discontinuities of s. If this were true, then the preceding corollary would be extremely unimpressive. However, the next problem indicates that the situation is much more complicated than one might at first imagine.

Problem 16. Construct an increasing jump function s on $\mathbb{R}$ such that $s'(0) = 1$.

D. Bounded Variation

In this section it will be advantageous to allow the functions to be vector-valued. Thus, we shall consider $f : [a, b] \rightarrow \mathbb{R}^n$, and we shall use the Euclidean norm on $\mathbb{R}^n$.

Definition: Let $f : [a, b] \rightarrow \mathbb{R}^n$. Consider any partition

$$a = x_0 < x_1 < x_2 < \cdots < x_m = b,$$

and form the sum

$$V = \sum_{i=1}^{m} |f(x_i) - f(x_{i-1})|.$$

The least upper bound of the set of all numbers V formed this way is called the *total variation* of f on $[a, b]$ and is denoted $V_f(a, b)$. In case $V_f(a, b) < \infty$, we say that f has *bounded variation* on $[a, b]$. Frequently we abbreviate this by writing $f \in BV$.

We now list a number of properties of functions which have bounded variation.

BV1 If $f : [a, b] \rightarrow \mathbb{R}$ is monotone, then $f \in BV$ and

$$V_f(a, b) = |f(b) - f(a)|.$$

This is trivial: For instance, if f is decreasing then each sum V is exactly

$$\sum_{i=1}^{m} [f(x_{i-1}) - f(x_i)] = f(x_0) - f(x_m)$$

$$= f(a) - f(b)$$
$$= |f(b) - f(a)|.$$

BV2 If $f : [a, b] \to \mathbb{R}^n$ has components $f = (f_1, f_2, \ldots, f_n)$, then $f \in BV \iff$ each $f_k \in BV$.

This follows from the inequalities valid for $y \in \mathbb{R}^n$:

$$|y_k| \leq |y| \leq |y_1| + \cdots + |y_n|.$$

Thus,

$$V_{f_k}(a, b) \leq V_f(a, b) \leq V_{f_1}(a, b) + \cdots + V_{f_n}(a, b).$$

BV3 $|f(b) - f(a)| \leq V_f(a, b)$.

Use the definition with $m = 1$, $x_0 = a$, $x_1 = b$.

BV4 If $f \in BV$, then f is bounded.

To see this, let $a < x < b$ and use the definition with $m = 2$, $x_0 = a$, $x_1 = x$, $x_2 = b$:

$$|f(x) - f(a)| + |f(b) - f(x)| \leq V_f(a, b).$$

Therefore,

$$|f(x)| \leq |f(a)| + V_f(a, b).$$

BV5 If f is of class C^1 on $[a, b]$, then $f \in BV$.

By BV2 we may assume f is real-valued in proving this. Since f' is continuous on the compact interval $[a, b]$, there exists a constant C such that $|f'| \leq C$. By the mean value theorem

$$\begin{aligned} |f(x_i) - f(x_{i-1})| &= |f'(\xi)(x_i - x_{i-1})| \\ &\leq C(x_i - x_{i-1}). \end{aligned}$$

Therefore, any of the sums V in the definition is bounded by

$$\sum_{i=1}^{m} C(x_i - x_{i-1}) = C(b - a).$$

Thus,

$$V_f(a, b) \leq C(b - a).$$

BV6 The continuity of f on $[a, b] \;\not\!\!\Longrightarrow\; f$ has bounded variation.

Here is an example. Let $f(x) = \begin{cases} x \sin \dfrac{1}{x} & \text{for } 0 < x \le 1, \\ 0 & \text{for } x = 0. \end{cases}$

Then if $x_i = \dfrac{1}{(i+\frac{1}{2})\pi}$, $f(x_i) = \dfrac{(-1)^i}{(i+\frac{1}{2})\pi}$. Thus,

$$|f(x_i) - f(x_{i-1})| = \frac{1}{(i+\frac{1}{2})\pi} + \frac{1}{(i-\frac{1}{2})\pi} > \frac{2}{i\pi}.$$

Therefore, one of the possible sums is

$$V = |f(x_n) - f(0)| + |f(x_{n-1}) - f(x_n)| + \cdots +$$

$$|f(x_0) - f(x_1)| + |f(1) - f(x_0)|$$

$$\ge \sum_{i=1}^{n} |f(x_{i-1}) - f(x_i)|$$

$$> \sum_{i=1}^{n} \frac{2}{i\pi},$$

which is unbounded as $n \to \infty$. Therefore, $f \notin BV$.

Problem 17. Prove that for the function f which has just been defined, the composite function $f(x^2)$ is *differentiable* on $[0, 1]$ and yet does not have bounded variation.

BV7   If f and g have bounded variation, so does $f + g$.

Indeed, the triangle inequality for $\mathbb{R}^n$ makes it easy to show that

$$V_{f+g}(a, b) \le V_f(a, b) + V_g(a, b).$$

BV8   Suppose $f : [a, b] \to \mathbb{R}^n$ and $g : [a, b] \to \mathbb{R}$ both have bounded variation. Then $gf \in BV$. If also $|g(x)| \ge c > 0$ for all x, then $f/g \in BV$.

The proof is routine. For example, we prove the second statement. By BV4 we know $|f(x)| \le M$ for all x. Therefore,

$$\left| \frac{f(x_i)}{g(x_i)} - \frac{f(x_{i-1})}{g(x_{i-1})} \right| = \frac{|g(x_{i-1})f(x_i) - g(x_i)f(x_{i-1})|}{|g(x_i)g(x_{i-1})|}$$

$$\le \frac{|f(x_i) - f(x_{i-1})|}{|g(x_i)|} + |f(x_{i-1})|\frac{|g(x_{i-1}) - g(x_i)|}{|g(x_i)g(x_{i-1})|}$$

$$\le c^{-1}|f(x_i) - f(x_{i-1})| + Mc^{-2}|g(x_i) - g(x_{i-1})|.$$

Thus,

$$V_{f/g}(a, b) \le c^{-1}V_f(a, b) + Mc^{-2}V_g(a, b).$$

BV9   If $a < c < b$, then $V_f(a, b) = V_f(a, c) + V_f(c, b)$.

First suppose we are given partitions of $[a, c]$ and of $[c, b]$:

$$a = x_0 < x_1 < \cdots < x_m = c,$$

$$c = y_0 < y_1 < \cdots < y_k = b.$$

Then we obtain a partition of $[a, b]$ as well, so that

$$\sum_{i=1}^{m}|f(x_i) - f(x_{i-1})| + \sum_{j=1}^{k}|f(y_j) - f(y_{j-1})| \le V_f(a, b).$$

Therefore, we obtain the inequality

$$V_f(a, c) + V_f(c, b) \le V_f(a, b).$$

On the other hand, suppose we begin with an arbitrary partition of $[a, b]$:

$$a = z_0 < z_1 < \cdots < z_l = b.$$

If c is not one of these division points, we can insert c as a new division point without decreasing the corresponding sum. Specifically, if $z_{\alpha-1} < c < z_\alpha$, then

$$|f(z_\alpha) - f(z_{\alpha-1})| \le |f(c) - f(z_{\alpha-1})| + |f(z_\alpha) - f(c)|.$$

Therefore, we conclude that

$$\sum_{i=1}^{l} |f(z_i) - f(z_{i-1})| \leq V_f(a, c) + V_f(c, b).$$

Consequently, we obtain the inequality

$$V_f(a, b) \leq V_f(a, c) + V_f(c, b).$$

BV10 Assume $f : [a, b] \to \mathbb{R}^n$ has bounded variation. Consider the function of $x \in [a, b]$ whose value at x is $V_f(a, x)$. The preceding property shows that $V_f(a, x)$ is an increasing function of x. Moreover, f is continuous at $x \iff V_f(a, \cdot)$ is continuous at x.

Properties BV3 and BV9 show immediately that the continuity of V_f implies that of f: If $x < y$, then

$$|f(y) - f(x)| \leq V_f(x, y) = V_f(a, y) - V_f(a, x);$$

if $y < x$, then

$$|f(y) - f(x)| \leq V_f(y, x) = V_f(a, x) - V_f(a, y).$$

Conversely, assume that f is continuous at x. Then we must show $V_f(a, \cdot)$ is continuous at x. We shall content ourselves with the situation $a \leq x < b$ and the proof that $V_f(a, \cdot)$ is right-continuous at x. Let $\epsilon > 0$. Then there exists a partition $x = x_0 < x_1 < x_2 < \cdots < x_m = b$ such that

$$\sum_{i=1}^{m} |f(x_i) - f(x_{i-1})| > V_f(x, b) - \frac{\epsilon}{2}.$$

By inserting an additional division point between x_0 and x_1, if necessary, we can assume that

$$|f(x_1) - f(x_0)| < \frac{\epsilon}{2}.$$

Therefore,

$$V_f(x, b) < \frac{\epsilon}{2} + \sum_{i=1}^{m} |f(x_i) - f(x_{i-1})|$$

$$< \epsilon + \sum_{i=2}^{m} |f(x_i) - f(x_{i-1})|$$

$$\leq \epsilon + V_f(x_1, b).$$

By BV9, this inequality is exactly

$$V_f(a, b) - V_f(a, x) < \epsilon + V_f(a, b) - V_f(a, x_1).$$

That is,

$$V_f(a, x_1) < V_f(a, x) + \epsilon.$$

Since $V_f(a, \cdot)$ is increasing, this implies that for $x \le y \le x_1$

$$V_f(a, x) \le V_f(a, y) < V_f(a, x) + \epsilon.$$

Therefore, $V_f(a, \cdot)$ is right-continuous at x.

Problem 18. Finish this proof by showing that if f is left-continuous at x, then $V_f(a, \cdot)$ is left-continuous at x.

We can now quickly prove one of the most important elementary results about BV.

> **Theorem:** *Assume* $f : [a, b] \to \mathbb{R}$. *Then* f *has bounded variation* $\Longleftrightarrow f$ *is equal to the difference of two increasing functions.*

Proof: Properties BV1 and BV7 render half of this assertion trivial. Conversely, assume $f \in BV$. Define the function g on $[a, b]$ by the equation

$$f(x) = V_f(a, x) - g(x).$$

Since $V_f(a, \cdot)$ is increasing, the proof will be finished as soon as we show that g is increasing. If $a \le x < y \le b$, BV9 and 3 imply

$$g(y) - g(x) = [V_f(a, y) - f(y)] - [V_f(a, x) - f(x)]$$

$$= [V_f(a, y) - V_f(a, x)] - [f(y) - f(x)]$$

$$= V_f(x, y) - [f(y) - f(x)]$$

$$\ge |f(y) - f(x)| - [f(y) - f(x)]$$

$$\ge 0.$$

QED

> ***Corollary:*** *Assume* $f : [a, b] \to \mathbb{R}^n$ *has bounded variation. Then* f *is continuous except on a countable set in* $[a, b]$. *Moreover,* f' *exists a.e. in* $[a, b]$ *and* $|f'|$ *is integrable.*

Proof: By BV2 it suffices to consider the case $n = 1$. By the theorem, f is the difference of two increasing functions. Since the assertions are all known for increasing functions (Problem 3, Lebesgue's theorem of Section A, the last theorem in Section A), the corollary follows.   **QED**

Problem 19. Assume $f : [a, b] \to \mathbb{R}^n$ has bounded variation. Prove that for $0 < h < b - a$,

$$\int_a^{b-h} |f(x + h) - f(x)| \, dx \leq h V_f(a, b).$$

The next very interesting result has a simple covering argument in its proof.

> ***Theorem:*** *Assume* $f : [a, b] \to \mathbb{R}^n$ *has bounded variation. Then for a.e.* $x \in [a, b]$
> $$|f'(x)| = V_f'(a, x).$$

Proof: The corollary shows that f' exists a.e. Since $V_f(a, x)$ is increasing, also $V_f'(a, x)$ exists a.e. Property BV3 implies that $|f'(x)| \leq V_f'(a, x)$ wherever both derivatives exist. Now define the set A by

$$x \in A \iff f'(x) \text{ and } V_f'(a, x) \text{ exist and } V_f'(a, x) > |f'(x)|.$$

We have to prove that A is a null set. The set A can be expressed as a union $A = \bigcup_{k=1}^{\infty} A_k$, where

$$x \in A_k \iff f'(x) \text{ and } V_f'(a, x) \text{ exist and } V_f'(a, x) - |f'(x)| > k^{-1}.$$

Thus, we need only prove that each A_k is a null set. If $x \in A_k$,

$$\lim_{\substack{y \leq x \leq z \\ 0 < z - y \to 0}} \left[\frac{V_f(y, z)}{z - y} - \frac{|f(z) - f(y)|}{z - y} \right] > k^{-1};$$

in particular, there exists $j \in \mathbb{N}$ such that

$$\inf_{\substack{y \leq x \leq z \\ 0 < z - y \leq j^{-1}}} \frac{V_f(y, z) - |f(z) - f(y)|}{z - y} > k^{-1}.$$

Now replace j^{-1} by s and k^{-1} by t. Then $0 < s$ and $0 < t$, and A is contained in a countable union of sets of the form

$$E = \left\{ x \mid \text{if } y \leq x \leq z \text{ and } 0 < z - y \leq s, \right.$$

$$\left. \text{then } \frac{V_f(y, z) - |f(z) - f(y)|}{z - y} \geq t \right\}.$$

Thus, we need only prove that E is a null set.

Let $\epsilon > 0$. Then there exists a partition $a = x_0 < x_1 < \cdots < x_m = b$ such that $x_i - x_{i-1} \leq s$ for all i and

$$V = \sum_{i=1}^{m} |f(x_i) - f(x_{i-1})| \geq V_f(a, b) - \epsilon.$$

If for a given i the set $E \cap [x_{i-1}, x_i] \neq \emptyset$, then we can use $y = x_{i-1}$ and $z = x_i$ in the expression defining E, and conclude that

$$t \leq \frac{V_f(x_{i-1}, x_i) - |f(x_i) - f(x_{i-1})|}{x_i - x_{i-1}}.$$

That is,

$$x_i - x_{i-1} \leq t^{-1}[V_f(x_{i-1}, x_i) - |f(x_i) - f(x_{i-1})|].$$

Therefore,

$$\lambda^*(E \cap [x_{i-1}, x_i]) \leq t^{-1}[V_f(x_{i-1}, x_i) - |f(x_i) - f(x_{i-1})|].$$

This inequality has been derived under the assumption that $E \cap [x_{i-1}, x_i]$ is not empty, but if this set is empty, the inequality is valid anyway because the right side is nonnegative. Therefore, the inequality is true for all i. Thus

$$\lambda^*(E) \le \sum_{i=1}^{m} \lambda^*(E \cap [x_{i-1}, x_i])$$

$$\le t^{-1} \sum_{i=1}^{m} [V_f(x_{i-1}, x_i) - |f(x_i) - f(x_{i-1})|]$$

$$= t^{-1}[V_f(a, b) - V]$$

$$\le t^{-1} \epsilon.$$

Since ϵ is arbitrary, $\lambda^*(E) = 0$.   **QED**

Corollary: *Let* $f : [a, b] \to \mathbb{R}^n$ *have bounded variation. Then*

$$\int_a^b |f'(x)| dx \le V_f(a, b).$$

Proof: From the theorem we know that almost everywhere

$$|f'(x)| = V_f'(a, x).$$

(Actually, we only require the easy inequality $|f'(x)| \le V_f'(a, x)$.) Therefore,

$$\int_a^b |f'(x)| dx = \int_a^b V_f'(a, x) dx.$$

Since $V_f(a, x)$ is an increasing function of x, the theorem on p.519 implies

$$\int_a^b V_f'(a, x) dx \le V_f(a, b) - V_f(a, a)$$

$$= V_f(a, b).$$

By the way, we could also prove this corollary directly from Problem 19.

QED

Problem 20. Let $(a, b) \subset \mathbb{R}$ be an *open* interval, and assume $f :$ $(a, b) \to \mathbb{R}^n$. Define the *total variation* of f on (a, b) to be the least upper bound of the sums

$$\sum_{i=1}^{m} |f(x_i) - f(x_{i-1})|,$$

where $a < x_0 < x_1 < \cdots < x_m < b$. Call this total variation $V_f(a+, b-)$. If it is finite, we say that f has bounded variation on (a, b).

(a) Prove that $V_f(a+, b-) = \sup\{V_f(c, d) \mid a < c < d < b\}$.

(b) If f has bounded variation, prove the limits $f(a+)$, $f(b-)$ exist.

(c) If $f : [a, b] \to \mathbb{R}^n$, what is the relation between $V_f(a+, b-)$ and $V_f(a, b)$?

The next theorem is important partly because it allows us to compute the actual variation of a function in some instances.

Theorem: *Let f be a vector-valued function in $L^1(a, b)$. Define $F = [a, b] \to \mathbb{R}^n$ by the expression*

$$F(x) = \int_a^x f(t) dt.$$

Then $F \in BV$ and

$$V_F(a, b) = \int_a^b |f(t)| dt.$$

Proof: First, it is not difficult to prove that a norm inequality is valid for the integration of vector-valued functions:

$$\left| \int_a^b f(t)dt \right| \le \int_a^b |f(t)|dt.$$

This can be proved directly, or we can simply notice that it is a special case of the generalized Minkowski inequality on p.271. Therefore, for any partition $a = x_0 < x_1 < \cdots < x_m = b$,

$$\sum_{i=1}^m |F(x_i) - F(x_{i-1})| = \sum_{i=1}^m \left| \int_{x_{i-1}}^{x_i} f(t)dt \right|$$

$$\le \sum_{i=1}^m \int_{x_{i-1}}^{x_i} |f(t)|dt$$

$$= \int_a^b |f(t)|dt.$$

Thus we have proved that $F \in BV$ and $V_F(a,b) \le \int_a^b |f(t)|dt$.

To establish the reverse inequality, suppose $\epsilon > 0$ is arbitrary. By the results on approximation in L^1 and the discussion of the Riemann integral in Chapter 7, there exist *step* functions σ_k corresponding to the components f_k of f such that

$$\int_a^b |f_k(t) - \sigma_k(t)|dt \le \epsilon/2n.$$

Let $\sigma = (\sigma_1, \ldots, \sigma_n)$. Then

$$\int_a^b |f(t) - \sigma(t)|dt \le \sum_{k=1}^n \int_a^b |f_k(t) - \sigma_k(t)|dt$$

$$\le \epsilon/2.$$

Let

$$\Sigma(x) = \int_a^x \sigma(t)dt.$$

The vector-valued function σ is of course *constant* on certain intervals (x_{i-1}, x_i), where $a = x_0 < x_1 < \cdots < x_m = b$. Therefore,

$$V_\Sigma(a, b) \geq \sum_{i=1}^{m} |\Sigma(x_i) - \Sigma(x_{i-1})|$$

$$= \sum_{i=1}^{m} \left| \int_{x_{i-1}}^{x_i} \sigma(t)dt \right|$$

$$= \sum_{i=1}^{m} \int_{x_{i-1}}^{x_i} |\sigma(t)|dt$$

(in the last step we used the fact that $\sigma(t)$ is constant for $x_{i-1} < t < x_i$). Thus,

$$V_\Sigma(a, b) \geq \int_a^b |\sigma(t)|dt.$$

Therefore,

$$\int_a^b |f(t)|dt \leq \int_a^b |\sigma(t)|dt + \frac{\epsilon}{2}$$

$$\leq V_\Sigma(a, b) + \frac{\epsilon}{2}$$

$$\leq V_F(a, b) + V_{\Sigma-F}(a, b) + \frac{\epsilon}{2} \quad \text{(Property BV7)}$$

$$\leq V_F(a, b) + \int_a^b |\sigma(t) - f(t)|dt + \frac{\epsilon}{2}$$

$$\leq V_F(a, b) + \epsilon.$$

(Notice that in the penultimate inequality we used the inequality established in the first part of this proof.) Since ϵ is arbitrary,

$$\int_a^b |f(t)|dt \leq V_F(a, b).$$

QED

Example: Take $n = 2$, and let $F(x) = (\cos x, \sin x)$ for $0 \leq x \leq 2\pi$. Then $F'(x) = (-\sin x, \cos x)$, so that

$$F(x) = (1, 0) + \int\limits_0^x (-\sin t, \cos t)dt.$$

The theorem may be applied since the addition of a constant $(1, 0)$ does not affect the variation. Thus,

$$V_F = \int\limits_0^{2\pi} |(-\sin t, \cos t)|dt = 2\pi.$$

In complex notation, $F(x) = e^{ix}$ and $f(t) = F'(t) = ie^{it}$.
   Example: Again take $n = 2$, and use complex notation. Let

$$F(x) = \begin{cases} x^2 e^{i/x} & \text{for } 0 < x \leq 1, \\ 0 & \text{for } x = 0. \end{cases}$$

Then for $0 < x \leq 1$,

$$F'(x) = -ie^{i/x} + 2xe^{i/x},$$

so that

$$|F'(x)| = |(-i + 2x)e^{i/x}|$$

$$= |-i + 2x|$$

$$= \sqrt{1 + 4x^2}.$$

Thus,

$$V_F(0, x) = \int\limits_0^x \sqrt{1 + 4t^2}dt.$$

Notice also that

$$F'(0) = \lim_{x \to 0} \frac{F(x) - F(0)}{x}$$

$$= \lim_{x \to 0} xe^{i/x}$$

$$= 0.$$

This gives an example which illuminates the second theorem of this section, which implies that

$$|F'(x)| = V_F'(0,x) \quad \text{for a.e. } x \in [0,1].$$

In the present example this equation is valid for $0 < x \leq 1$, but

$$F'(0) = 0, \quad V_F'(0,0) = 1.$$

Problem 21. In presenting the preceding example we omitted the verification that

$$F(x) = \int\limits_0^x F'(t)dt.$$

Prove that this is valid.

Problem 22. Modify the above example by setting $F(x) = x^\alpha e^{i/x}$ for $0 < x \leq 1$. Prove the following:

$$0 \leq \alpha \leq 1: \ F \notin BV.$$

$$1 < \alpha < 2: \ F'(0) = 0, V_F'(0,0) = \infty.$$

$$\alpha = 2: \ F'(0) = 0, V_F'(0,0) = 1.$$

$$2 < \alpha < \infty: \ F'(0) = 0, V_F'(0,0) = 0.$$

Problem 23. In this problem let $n = 1$ and define

$$F(x) = \begin{cases} x^\alpha \cos x^{-1} & \text{for } 0 < x \leq 1, \\ 0 & \text{for } x = 0. \end{cases}$$

Prove the following:

$$0 \leq \alpha \leq 1: \ F \notin BV.$$

$$1 < \alpha < 2: \ V_F'(0,0) = \infty.$$

$$\alpha = 2: \ V_F'(0,0) = 2/\pi.$$

$$2 < \alpha < \infty: \ V_F'(0,0) = 0.$$

E. Absolute Continuity

We now return to the discussion of monotone functions. Suppose that f is an increasing real-valued function on the interval $[a, b]$. In Section B we proved that f can be expressed in the form

$$f = \phi + s,$$

where s is an increasing jump function and ϕ is an increasing continuous function. In Section C we showed that $s' = 0$ a.e., so we know $f' = \phi'$ a.e. Now we investigate the continuous function ϕ. Define

$$F(x) = \int\limits_a^x f'(t)dt$$

(remember that f' is integrable by the theorem on p.519). Then $F' = f' = \phi'$ a.e. Thus, if we write

$$\phi = F + g,$$

we find that g is continuous and $g' = 0$ a.e. Moreover, g is increasing. To see this, suppose $a \leq x < y \leq b$. Then

$$g(x) - g(y) = \phi(x) - \phi(y) + F(y) - F(x)$$

$$= \phi(x) - \phi(y) + \int\limits_x^y \phi'(t)dt$$

$$\leq \phi(x) - \phi(y) + \phi(y) - \phi(x)$$
$$= 0$$

by the theorem on p.519. We now summarize these results in the following statement. The uniqueness follows from Problem 15.

Proposition: *Assume $f : [a, b] \to \mathbb{R}$ is increasing. Then f can be expressed in the form*

$$f(x) = \int\limits_a^x f'(t)dt + g(x) + s(x),$$

where g is increasing, continuous, and satisfies $g' = 0$ a.e., and s is an increasing jump function (and thus $s' = 0$ a.e.). In this formula for f the functions g and s are unique to within additive constants.

Corollary: *Assume $f : [a,b] \to \mathbb{R}$ is increasing. Then*

$$\int_a^b f'(t)dt = f(b) - f(a),$$

if and only if

$$f(x) = f(a) + \int_a^x f'(t)dt \quad \text{for all } x \in [a,b].$$

Proof: Rewrite the proposition in the form

$$f(x) = f(a) + \int_a^x f'(t)dt + h(x),$$

where h is an increasing function with $h(a) = 0$. The assumption that

$$\int_a^b f'(t)dt = f(b) - f(a)$$

implies

$$h(b) = f(b) - f(a) - \int_a^b f'(t)dt = 0.$$

Since $h(a) = 0$ and h is increasing, $h(x) = 0$ for all x.   **QED**

The possibility of being able to express a continuous funtion f on $[a,b]$ as an indefinite integral is very important. It is thus of great interest to determine a criterion which can be applied to f to decide if indeed

$$f(x) = f(a) + \int_a^x f'(t)dt.$$

There is in fact a remarkable necessary and sufficient condition, which we now begin to discuss.

Definition: Let $f : [a, b] \to \mathbb{R}$. Then f is *absolutely continuous* if for every $\epsilon > 0$ there exists $\delta > 0$ such that the following condition is valid:

Whenever $a \le x_1 < y_1 \le x_2 < y_2 \le \cdots \le x_m < y_m \le b$

and $\displaystyle\sum_{i=1}^{m}(y_i - x_i) < \delta$,

then $\displaystyle\sum_{i=1}^{m}|f(y_i) - f(x_i)| < \epsilon$.

Proposition: *Any absolutely continuous function is continuous and has bounded variation.*

Proof: Suppose $f : [a, b] \to \mathbb{R}$ is absolutely continuous. Let $\epsilon > 0$. Then there exists $\delta > 0$ corresponding to the above definition. In particular, the case $m = 1$ implies that

$$a \le x < y \le b \text{ and } y - x < \delta \implies |f(y) - f(x)| < \epsilon.$$

Thus, f is (uniformly) continuous.

Next, subdivide $[a, b]$ in any way, $a = t_0 < t_1 < \cdots < t_N = b$, such that $t_i - t_{i-1} < \delta$ for all i. Restricting attention to the interval $[t_{i-1}, t_i]$, we can use the choice of δ to estimate the variation of f. The result is

$$V_f(t_{i-1}, t_i) \le \epsilon.$$

Therefore,

$$V_f(a, b) = \sum_{i=1}^{N} V_f(t_{i-1}, t_i) \le N\epsilon < \infty.$$

QED

Proposition: *Suppose f is absolutely continuous on $[a, b]$ and suppose $E \subset [a, b]$ is a null set. Then $f(E)$ is a null set.*

Proof: Let $\epsilon > 0$ and select $\delta > 0$ to satisfy the condition in the definition of absolute continuity. There exists an open set G such that $E \subset G$ and $\lambda(G) < \delta$. Since $f(\{a\})$ and $f(\{b\})$ are null sets, we can assume $E \subset (a, b)$ and thus also can assume $G \subset (a, b)$. By Problem 2.6, G can be expressed as a countable disjoint union of open intervals; thus,

$$E \subset \bigcup_{k \geq 1} (a_k, b_k) \subset (a, b),$$

and

$$\sum_{k \geq 1} (b_k - a_k) = \lambda(G) < \delta.$$

Now choose c_k, $d_k \in [a_k, b_k]$ to be extreme points of f on $[a_k, b_k]$:

$$f([a_k, b_k]) \subset [f(c_k), f(d_k)].$$

Since

$$\sum_{k=1}^{m} |d_k - c_k| \leq \sum_{k=1}^{m} (b_k - a_k) < \delta$$

for any m, the choice of δ implies

$$\sum_{k=1}^{m} |f(d_k) - f(c_k)| < \epsilon.$$

Since m is arbitrary,

$$\sum_{k \geq 1} |f(d_k) - f(c_k)| \leq \epsilon.$$

Therefore, since

$$f(E) \subset \bigcup_{k \geq 1} f((a_k, b_k))$$

$$\subset \bigcup_{k \geq 1} [f(c_k), f(d_k)],$$

we conclude that

$$\lambda^*(f(E)) \leq \sum_{k \geq 1} [f(d_k) - f(c_k)]$$

$$\leq \epsilon.$$

Since ϵ is arbitrary, we conclude that $\lambda^*(f(E)) = 0$. Therefore, $f(E)$ is a null set.   **QED**

Proposition: *Suppose f and g are absolutely continuous on $[a, b]$. Then so are the functions $f + g$, fg, $|f|^\alpha$ (if $\alpha \geq 1$), and f/g (if $g(x)$ is never 0).*

We omit the routine proof of this proposition, except to note that the proof for $|f|^\alpha$ relies on the following estimate: If $|f(x)| \leq M$ for all x, then

$$\Big|\, |f(y)|^\alpha - |f(x)|^\alpha \,\Big| \leq \alpha M^{\alpha - 1} |f(y) - f(x)|.$$

Problem 24. If f is absolutely continuous and $f > 0$ on $[a, b]$, prove that f^α is absolutely continuous for any $\alpha \in \mathbb{R}$.

Problem 25. Recall that a function f on $[a, b]$ is said to satisfy a *Lipschitz condition* if there exists a constant C such that

$$|f(x) - f(y)| \leq C|x - y|.$$

(See Problem 1.49.) Prove that if f is of class C^1 on $[a, b]$, then f satisfies a Lipschitz condition. Prove that if f satisfies a Lipschitz condition, then f is absolutely continuous.

Problem 26. Let $E \subset \mathbb{R}$ and let $f(x) = d(x, E)$ as defined on p.20. Prove that f satisfies a Lipschitz condition, so that f' exists a.e. Prove that $f' = -1$, 0, or 1 a.e. Do this by showing that if $f'(x)$ exists, then $f'(x) = -1$, 0, or 1.

Problem 27. We were careful in the definition of absolute continuity to require the intervals (x_i, y_i) to be disjoint. If we had omitted this requirement, we would have defined the Lipschitz condition. Prove this. That is, assume that there exists $\delta > 0$ (we have let $\epsilon = 1$) such that whenever $a \leq x_i < y_i \leq b$ for $1 \leq i \leq m$ and $\sum_{i=1}^{m} (y_i - x_i) < \delta$, then $\sum_{i=1}^{m} |f(y_i) - f(x_i)| < 1$; and then prove that f is Lipschitz continuous.

Proposition: *Let $h \in L^1(a, b)$ and define*

$$f(x) = \int_a^x h(t)\,dt \quad \text{for } a \leq x \leq b.$$

Then f is absolutely continuous.

Proof: This was proved long ago. It is an immediate consequence of the theorem on absolute continuity on p.141.   **QED**

The major task of this section is essentially to prove the converse of the above proposition. To see what will be involved, suppose f is given to be absolutely continuous on $[a, b]$, and we want to prove that for some $h \in L^1(a, b)$

$$f(x) = f(a) + \int_a^x h(t)dt.$$

By Lebesgue's theorem on differentiation, it follows that $f' = h$ a.e. Thus, the function h is required to be equal to f', which is known to exist a.e. and to be integrable because $f \in BV$. What now remains to be proved is that the function

$$f(x) - \int_a^x f'(t)dt.$$

is *constant*. This function is absolutely continuous and has zero derivative a.e. Thus, the following lemma will be decisive.

Lemma: *Let f be absolutely continuous on $[a, b]$ and $f' = 0$ a.e. Then f is constant.*

Proof: Let

$$A = \{x \in (a, b) \mid f'(x) = 0\}.$$

According to the hypothesis, $[a, b] \sim A$ is a null set. Therefore, the absolute continuity implies $f([a, b] \sim A)$ is also a null set, thanks to a previous proposition. On the other hand, Sard's theorem on p.498 implies $f(A)$ is a null set. Combining these two facts, we see that $f([a, b])$ is a null set. Since f is continuous, $f([a, b])$ is an *interval*. Thus, $f([a, b])$ is a single point.   **QED**

The next theorem was completely proved in the discussion just preceding the lemma. We state it now for the record.

Theorem: *Assume $f : [a, b] \to \mathbb{R}$. Then f is absolutely continuous if and only if there exists $h \in L^1(a, b)$ such that*

$$f(x) = f(a) + \int_a^x h(t)dt.$$

It follows of course that $h = f'$ a.e.

Now let us restate the first proposition of this section and its corollary.

Theorem: *Assume $f : [a, b] \to \mathbb{R}$ is increasing. Then f can be expressed in the form*

$$f = F + g + s,$$

where

F *is increasing and absolutely continuous;*

g *is increasing and continuous and $g' = 0$ a.e.;*

s *is an increasing jump function (and $s' = 0$ a.e.).*

In this decomposition of f, the components F, g, and s are unique to within additive constants. The function f is absolutely continuous if and only if

$$\int_a^b f'(t)dt = f(b) - f(a).$$

Proof: The only thing we must prove at this juncture is the uniqueness assertion. Suppose then that $f = F_1 + g_1 + s_1$ is another representation of the same variety. Then $f' = F'$ and $f' = F_1'$ a.e. $\Rightarrow F' = F_1'$ a.e. Apply the lemma to the absolutely continuous function $F - F_1$ to conclude that $F - F_1 = $ constant. The remaining equalities $g - g_1 = $ constant and $s - s_1 = $ constant were both proved earlier.   **QED**

Corollary: *Assume that $f : [a, b] \to \mathbb{R}^n$ has bounded variation. Then f is absolutely continuous $\iff V_f(a, x)$ is absolutely continuous.*

Proof: Of course, when we say that the vector-valued function f is absolutely continuous, we mean simply that each component of f is absolutely continuous. Assume first that $V_f(a, x)$ is absolutely continuous. Since the inequalities $a \le x_1 < y_1 \le x_2 < y_2 \le \cdots \le x_m < y_m \le b$ imply $|f(y_i) - f(x_i)| \le V_f(a, y_i) - V_f(a, x_i)$ (see Property BV3), we have

$$\sum_{i=1}^{m} |f(y_i) - f(x_i)| \le \sum_{i=1}^{m} [V_f(a, y_i) - V_f(a, x_i)],$$

and the absolute continuity of f follows immediately from the definition. Conversely, assume f is absolutely continuous. Then

$$f(x) = f(a) + \int_a^x f'(t)dt,$$

so the last theorem in Section D implies

$$V_f(a, x) = \int_a^x |f'(t)|dt.$$

Therefore, $V_f(a, x)$ is absolutely continuous.   **QED**

Corollary: *Assume that $f : [a, b] \to \mathbb{R}^n$ has bounded variation. Then f is absolutely continuous $\Longleftrightarrow$*

$$V_f(a, b) = \int_a^b |f'(x)|dx.$$

Proof: If f is absolutely continuous, we have just shown the equality holds. Conversely, suppose the equality holds. The second theorem in Section D implies $|f'(x)| = V_f'(a, x)$ a.e., so we conclude

$$V_f(a, b) = \int_a^b V_f'(a, x)dx.$$

Now the last assertion of the preceding theorem implies $V_f(a, x)$ is absolutely continuous. By the preceding corollary, f is absolutely continuous.
                                                                       QED

Definition: A *continuous singular* function is a continuous function whose derivative exists and is zero almost everywhere.

Definition: A *jump function* is a function which is equal to the difference of two increasing jump functions. Alternatively, it is a function which can be expressed as an absolutely convergent series $\sum_{k=1}^{\infty} \sigma_k$, where σ_k is an elementary (increasing or decreasing) jump function. (For the absolute convergence see Problem 11.)

Theorem: *Assume $f : [a,b] \to \mathbb{R}$ has bounded variation. Then f can be expressed in the form*

$$f = F + g + s,$$

where

$$F \text{ is absolutely continuous,}$$

$$g \text{ is a continuous singular function,}$$

$$s \text{ is a jump function.}$$

These functions F, g, and s are unique to within additive constants.

Problem 28. Prove this theorem.

Problem 29. Assume that f is continuous and has bounded variation on $[a,b]$. Assume also that for any $a < c < b$, f is absolutely continuous on $[c,b]$. Prove that f is absolutely continuous on $[a,b]$.

Problem 30. Assume $f \in L^1(a,b)$. Prove that there exists a unique $g \in L^1(a,b)$ such that

$$\int_a^x g(t)dt = \left(\int_a^x f(t)dt \right)^2 , \quad a \leq x \leq b.$$

F. Further Discussion of Absolute Continuity

In Section E we completed our handling of the basic properties of absolutely continuous functions, but in the present section we shall combine several other interesting features.

1. Integration by Parts

> **Theorem:** *Assume that f and g are absolutely continuous on $[a, b]$. Then*
> $$\int_a^b fg'\,dx = f(b)g(b) - f(a)g(a) - \int_a^b f'g\,dx.$$

Proof: Since fg is absolutely continuous,

$$\int_a^b (fg)'\,dx = f(b)g(b) - f(a)g(a).$$

Now apply the product rule to $(fg)'$.   **QED**

2. *N*-Functions

Definition: Let $f : [a, b] \to \mathbb{R}$. Then f is an *N-function* if for every null set $E \subset [a, b]$, $f(E)$ is a null set.

Proposition: *Let $f : [a, b] \to \mathbb{R}$ be continuous. Then f is an N-function if and only if for every measurable set $E \subset [a, b]$, $f(E)$ is measurable.*

Proof: The proof of the corollary on p.500 carries over to establish the "only if" assertion. Conversely, assume that f is not an N-function. Then there exists a null set $N \subset [a, b]$ such that $f(N)$ is not a null set. Now apply the corollary on p.82: If $f(N)$ is measurable, it contains a nonmeasurable subset; if $f(N)$ is nonmeasurable, it also contains (is) a nonmeasurable subset. Thus, there exists a nonmeasurable set $A \subset f(N)$. Let $E = f^{-1}(A) \cap N$. Then $f(E) = A$.

The set E is measurable, since $E \subset N$, but $f(E)$ is not measurable.

QED

Problem 31. Let $f : [a,b] \to \mathbb{R}$. Prove that f is an N-function if and only if for every null set $E \subset [a,b]$, $f(E)$ is measurable.

Theorem: Let $f : [a,b] \to \mathbb{R}$. Then f is absolutely continuous if and only if the following four conditions are satisfied:

(1) f is continuous;

(2) f' exists a.e.;

(3) $f' \in L^1(a,b)$;

(4) f is an N-function.

Proof: If f is absolutely continuous, we already know all the properties are valid. The fact that f is an N-function is contained in the proposition on p.546.

Conversely, assume f satisfies the given conditions. Let $\epsilon > 0$. Then (3) implies there exists $\delta > 0$ such that if $E \subset [a,b]$ and $\lambda(E) < \delta$, then

$$\int_E |f'(x)| dx < \epsilon.$$

For this we have used the theorem on absolute continuity on p.141. (That is merely the name of the theorem — we have not assumed anything besides the integrability of f'.) Assume that $a \le x_1 < y_1 \le x_2 < y_2 \le \cdots \le x_m < y_m \le b$ and

$$\sum_{i=1}^m (y_i - x_i) < \delta.$$

Therefore,

$$\sum_{i=1}^m \int_{[x_i, y_i]} |f'(x)| dx < \epsilon.$$

Let $A = \{x \in [a,b] | f'(x) \text{ exists}\}$. By (2), $[a,b] \sim A$ is a null set. By (4),

$f([a,b] \sim A)$ is also a null set. Therefore,

$$\sum_{i=1}^{m} |f(y_i) - f(x_i)| \leq \sum_{i=1}^{m} \lambda(f([x_i, y_i])) \quad \text{(by (1))}$$

$$= \sum_{i=1}^{m} \lambda(f([x_i, y_i] \sim A))$$

$$\leq \sum_{i=1}^{m} \int_{[x_i, y_i] \sim A} |f'(x)| dx$$

$$= \sum_{i=1}^{m} \int_{[x_i, y_i]} |f'(x)| dx$$

$$< \epsilon.$$

This proves f is absolutely continuous. The middle inequality in the above analysis is a direct consequence of the proposition on p.499, which implies that if $B \subset [a,b]$ is a measurable set on which f' exists, then

$$\lambda(f(B)) \leq \int_{B} |f'(x)| dx.$$

QED

Corollary: If $f : [a,b] \to \mathbb{R}$ *is continuous, has bounded variation, and is an N-function, then f is absolutely continuous.*

Proof: Since $f \in BV$, f' exists a.e. and f' is integrable.   **QED**

Problem 32. Let $N \subset [0, \infty)$ be a null set. Prove that $\sqrt{N}$ is a null set.

Problem 33. Let $f : [a,b] \to [0, \infty)$ be monotone and absolutely continuous. Prove that $\sqrt{f}$ is absolutely continuous.

Problem 34. Let f be defined as follows:

$$f(x) = \begin{cases} x^2 \cos^2 x^{-1} & \text{for } 0 < x \le 1, \\ 0 & \text{for } x = 0. \end{cases}$$

Prove that f is absolutely continuous but $\sqrt{f}$ is not absolutely continuous.

A very impressive corollary of the theorem of this section is the following result on integration as the inverse of differentiation. The result appears to be quite simple, but the proof is based on rather deep facts.

Corollary: *Assume* $f : [a, b] \to \mathbb{R}$ *is differentiable at every point in* $[a, b]$. *Assume* $f' \in L^1(a, b)$. *Then*

$$f(x) = f(a) + \int_a^x f'(t)dt \quad \text{for } a \le x \le b.$$

Proof: Obviously, (1), (2), and (3) of the theorem are fulfilled. We need only prove that f is absolutely continuous, of course; thus we need only prove that f is an N-function. This follows immediately from the corollary on p.500. **QED**

Problem 35. Give an example of $f : [a, b] \to \mathbb{R}$ which is differentiable at every point of $[a, b]$ but for which f' is not integrable.

Problem 36. Assume $f : [a, b] \to \mathbb{R}$ is continuous. Assume f is differentiable except on a countable subset of $[a, b]$, and assume f' is integrable. Prove that

$$f(x) = f(a) + \int_a^x f'(t)dt \quad \text{for } a \le x \le b.$$

Problem 37. Assume f is a continuous strictly increasing function on $[a, b]$. Then the inverse function f^{-1} is also continuous and strictly increasing. Prove that f is singular $\iff f^{-1}$ is singular.

3.   Counterexamples

The preceding section shows that absolutely continuous functions enjoy the following mapping properties: If E is measurable, then $f(E)$ is measurable; if E is a null set, then $f(E)$ is a null set. In the present section we give two examples to show that absolute continuity is not generally preserved under composition of functions. Both examples are based on Cantor sets.

We refer to Section 4.B for details on the Cantor sets we shall use. Let A be a Cantor set of the type constructed there. At the kth stage of that construction there are 2^k closed intervals of length l_k each, contained in $[0, 1]$, and

$$\lambda(A) = \lim_{k \to \infty} 2^k l_k.$$

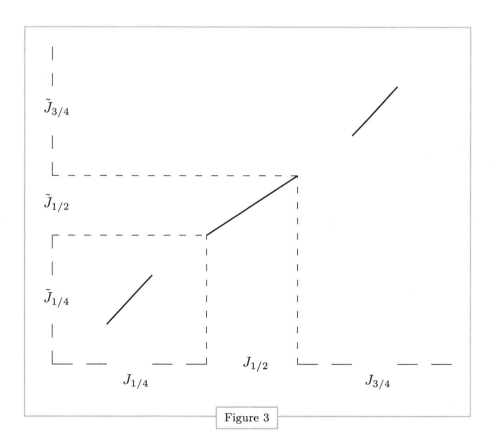

Figure 3

We assume $\lambda(A) > 0$. Let $\widetilde{A}$ be another Cantor set constructed in the same way but with $\lambda(\widetilde{A}) = 0$. We are now going to define a function

$$u : [0, 1] \to [0, 1],$$

which is continuous, strictly increasing, and a bijection of A onto $\widetilde{A}$. The construction is similar to the construction of the Lebesgue functions in Section 4.C, so we shall not give complete details. Figure 3 shows the first two stages in the construction of u. First, the excluded intervals $J_{1/2}$ and $\widetilde{J}_{1/2}$ are mapped onto one another linearly. Then $J_{1/4}$ is mapped onto $\widetilde{J}_{1/4}$ and $J_{3/4}$ onto $\widetilde{J}_{3/4}$, etc.

The resulting function is continuous and strictly increasing, and provides a bijection between A and $\widetilde{A}$.

Problem 38. Every $x \in A$ has a unique representation of the form

$$x = \sum_{j=1}^{\infty} \epsilon_j (l_{j-1} - l_j),$$

where $\epsilon_j = 0$ or 1. Prove that, with an obvious notation,

$$u(x) = \sum_{j=1}^{\infty} \epsilon_j (\tilde{l}_{j-1} - \tilde{l}_j).$$

Observe that u' is constant on each open interval J_r, and u maps J_r onto $\widetilde{J}_r$. Therefore,

$$\int_{J_r} u'(x)dx = \lambda(\widetilde{J}_r).$$

Since $\bigcup_r J_r = [0, 1] \sim A$ and $\bigcup_r \widetilde{J}_r = [0, 1] \sim \widetilde{A}$, we conclude that

$$\int_{[0,1]\sim A} u'(x)dx = 1 - \lambda(\widetilde{A}).$$

By symmetry (we have not yet used any assumption regarding the measures of A and $\widetilde{A}$), the inverse u^{-1} also satisfies

$$\int_{[0,1]\sim\widetilde{A}} (u^{-1})'(y)dy = 1 - \lambda(A).$$

Now we use the facts $\lambda(A) > 0$ and $\lambda(\widetilde{A}) = 0$. We conclude that

$$\int\limits_{[0,1] \sim A} u'(x)dx = 1.$$

Since $\int\limits_0^1 u'(x)dx \le u(1) - u(0)$, it follows that $u' = 0$ a.e. on A and that

$$\int\limits_0^1 u'(x)dx = 1.$$

Therefore, u is *absolutely continuous*. On the other hand,

$$\int\limits_0^1 (u^{-1})'(y)dy = 1 - \lambda(A) < 1,$$

so u^{-1} is *not* absolutely continuous. Thus, our first example is a strictly increasing absolutely continuous function whose inverse is not absolutely continuous.

For the second example, let $E \subset A$ be a nonmeasurable set. This exists by the corollary on p.82. Let $\widetilde{E} = u(E)$. This set is measurable, since $\widetilde{E} \subset u(A) = \widetilde{A}$ and $\widetilde{A}$ is a null set. Thus,

$$\chi_{\widetilde{E}} \text{ is measurable, } \quad \chi_{\widetilde{E}} \circ u \text{ is not measurable.}$$

(Simply note that $\chi_{\widetilde{E}} \circ u = \chi_E$.) It is important to notice that the product

$$\chi_{\widetilde{E}}(u(x))u'(x)$$

is measurable. This is seen because this function is $\chi_E u'$ and $u' = 0$ a.e. on $A \supset E$.

Problem 39. Use the same notation as has just been introduced. Define a function $g : [0, 2] \to [0, 2]$ as follows, assuming $0 \notin E$ and $1 \notin E$

$$g(x) = \begin{cases} u(x) & \text{if } x \in [0, 1] \sim E, \\ u(x) + 1 & \text{if } x \in [0, 1] \cap E, \\ u(x - 1) + 1 & \text{if } x - 1 \in (0, 1] \sim E, \\ u(x - 1) & \text{if } x - 1 \in (0, 1] \cap E. \end{cases}$$

Prove that g is a bijection, that g^{-1} is measurable, but g is not measurable.

4.   Change of Variable

In this discussion we assume $u : [a, b] \to \mathbb{R}$ is an increasing absolutely continuous function.

Theorem: *Assume* $f \in L^1(u(a), u(b))$. *Then* $f \circ u \cdot u' \in L^1(a, b)$ *and*

$$\int\limits_{u(a)}^{u(b)} f(y)dy = \int\limits_{a}^{b} f(u(x))u'(x)dx.$$

Remark: A striking feature of this theorem is the very measurability of the function $f \circ u \cdot u'$, for an example in the preceding section shows that $f \circ u$ itself might not be measurable.

Proof: We first prove the result in the case where f is the characteristic function of an open interval $(c, d) \subset (u(a), u(b))$. Choose the largest α and smallest β in $[a, b]$ such that $u(\alpha) = c$, $u(\beta) = d$. From this, $c < u(x) < d \iff \alpha < x < \beta$, so we compute

$$\int\limits_{a}^{b} f(u(x))u'(x)dx = \int\limits_{\alpha}^{\beta} u'(x)dx$$
$$= u(\beta) - u(\alpha)$$
$$= d - c$$
$$= \int\limits_{u(a)}^{u(b)} f(y)dy.$$

Second, since every open set is a countable disjoint union of open intervals, the result is seen to be valid if $f = \chi_G$ for any open set G. By taking complements, it can be seen to be valid for $f = \chi_K$ for any compact set K.

Now let $E \subset [u(a), u(b)]$ be a measurable set. There exist compact sets K_j and open sets G_j such that

$$K_1 \subset K_2 \subset \cdots \subset E \subset \cdots \subset G_2 \subset G_1,$$

and

$$\lambda(G_j \sim K_j) \to 0.$$

Let

$$\phi_j(x) = \chi_{K_j}(u(x))u'(x),$$
$$\psi_j(x) = \chi_{G_j}(u(x))u'(x).$$

Then let

$$g(x) = \chi_E(u(x))u'(x).$$

We see that

$$\phi_1 \leq \phi_2 \leq \cdots \leq g \leq \cdots \leq \psi_2 \leq \psi_1.$$

By what we have already proved the ϕ_j's and ψ_j's are measurable and

$$\int_a^b \phi_j(x)dx = \int_{u(a)}^{u(b)} \chi_{K_j}(y)dy = \lambda(K_j),$$
$$\int_a^b \psi_j(x)dx = \int_{u(a)}^{u(b)} \chi_{G_j}(y)dy = \lambda(G_j \cap [u(a), u(b)]).$$

Thus,

$$\int_a^b \lim \phi_j(x)dx = \lambda(E) = \int_a^b \lim \psi_j(x)dx.$$

Since

$$\lim \phi_j \leq g \leq \lim \psi_j,$$

this proves that g is measurable and

$$\int_a^b g(x)dx = \lambda(E).$$

Thus, the theorem is proved for any $f = \chi_E$, where E is measurable.

The extension to general nonnegative measurable f and then to general $f \in L^1(u(a), u(b))$ is routine, and we omit the details.   **QED**

5. Cantor Sets

Once again we examine a Cantor set of the type constructed in Section 4.B. In the notation of that section, the Cantor set is A and

$$\lambda(A) = \lim_{k \to \infty} 2^k l_k.$$

Now let f be the corresponding *Lebesgue function*, as defined in Section 4.C. This function is continuous and increasing on $[0, 1]$, $f(0) = 0$, $f(1) = 1$, and $f' = 0$ on the open set $[0, 1] \sim A$. Thus, if $\lambda(A) = 0$, f is a continuous singular function.

Theorem: If $\lambda(A) = 0$, the Lebesgue function is singular. If $\lambda(A) > 0$, the Lebesgue function is absolutely continuous.

Proof: By the above remarks, we are to treat the case $\lambda(A) > 0$. Then we shall see that f is even *Lipschitz* continuous. In Section 4.C it was proved that $|x - y| \le l_k \Rightarrow |f(x) - f(y)| \le 2^{-k}$. Suppose that x and y are distinct numbers in $[0, 1]$, and choose the largest k such that $|x - y| \le l_k$. Therefore, $l_{k+1} < |x - y|$, and we conclude

$$|f(x) - f(y)| \le 2^{-k}$$

$$= \frac{2 l_{k+1}}{2^{k+1} l_{k+1}}$$

$$< \frac{2 l_{k+1}}{\lambda(A)}$$

$$< \frac{2|x - y|}{\lambda(A)}.$$

Thus, f satisfies a Lipschitz condition.   **QED**

Remark: We can actually prove a much better fact about f in the case of $\lambda(A) > 0$. Suppose $x \in A$. Then for every $k \in \mathbb{N}$, x belongs to exactly one of the remaining 2^k disjoint closed intervals of length l_k at that stage of the construction of A. Suppose that the endpoints of this interval are $y_k < z_k$. The definition of f implies that $f(z_k) - f(y_k) = 2^{-k}$. Thus,

$$\lim_{k \to \infty} \frac{f(z_k) - f(y_k)}{z_k - y_k} = \lim_{k \to \infty} \frac{2^{-k}}{l_k}$$

$$= \frac{1}{\lambda(A)}.$$

This does not prove that $f'(x)$ exists. What it does prove is that *if* $f'(x)$ exists, then $f'(x) = 1/\lambda(A)$. Since we know f' exists a.e., we conclude that $f' = 1/\lambda(A)$ almost everywhere on A. Since $f' = 0$ on A^c, we conclude that

$$f' = \frac{1}{\lambda(A)} \chi_A \text{ a.e. on } [0,1].$$

Since f is absolutely continuous, this gives a remarkable formula for the Lebesgue function in this case:

$$f(x) = \frac{\lambda(A \cap [0, x])}{\lambda(A)}, \quad 0 \le x \le 1.$$

In particular, the Lipschitz condition becomes $|f(x) - f(y)| \le |x - y|/\lambda(A)$.

G. Arc Length

This section essentially continues the discussion of bounded variation, but now the emphasis is on *continuous* functions.

Definition: A *curve* in $\mathbb{R}^n$ is a continuous function $f : [a, b] \to \mathbb{R}^n$.

The interval $[a, b]$ is called the parameter interval for the curve f, and frequently f is called a *parametrized* curve. In this section we shall consistently use the letter t to denote the parameter, $a \le t \le b$.

We now give the definition of the length of the curve f. Consider any partition of the parameter interval:

$$a = t_0 < t_1 < t_2 < \cdots < t_m = b.$$

These points correspond to points on (the graph of) the curve f, namely $(t_i, f(t_i))$ for $0 \leq i \leq m$. We then calculate the length of the polygon obtained by connecting in $\mathbb{R}^n$ the vertices $f(t_0)$, $f(t_1)$, ..., $f(t_m)$ in order. We obtain

$$\sum_{i=1}^{m} |f(t_i) - f(t_{i-1})|$$

as the length of this inscribed polygon. Then we define the *length* of f to be the least upper bound of lengths of such inscribed polygons.

Notice that all we have done is introduce new words for concepts introduced back in Section D. Thus, the *length* of the curve f is precisely the total variation $V_f(a, b)$. If this length is finite, we say the curve is *rectifiable*. Thus, f is rectifiable $\Longleftrightarrow$ f has bounded variation.

Problem 40. Prove that length is independent of the parameter. That is, suppose $f : [a, b] \to \mathbb{R}^n$ is a curve, and suppose $u : [\alpha, \beta] \to [a, b]$ is a continuous increasing surjection. Prove that f and $f \circ u$ have the same length.

Definition: Let $f : [a, b] \to \mathbb{R}^n$ be a rectifiable curve. The *arc length function* of f is the function $s : [a, b] \to \mathbb{R}$ defined by

$$s(t) = V_f(a, t) \quad \text{for } a \leq t \leq b.$$

We now quickly summarize the results we have obtained which pertain to this situation:

(a) s is increasing;

(b) If $t < t'$, $V_f(t, t') = s(t') - s(t)$;

(c) s is continuous;

(d) $|f'(t)| = s'(t)$ for a.e. t (norm of velocity equals speed);

(e) s is absolutely continuous $\Longleftrightarrow$ f is absolutely continuous;

(f) If L is the length of f,

$$\int_a^b s'(t)dt = \int_a^b |f'(t)|dt \leq L,$$

and equality holds $\Longleftrightarrow$ f is absolutely continuous.

Problem 41. Let $f : [a, b] \to \mathbb{R}^n$ be a rectifiable curve with length L. Prove there exists a unique curve $\phi : [0, L] \to \mathbb{R}^n$ such that

$$f(t) = \phi(s(t)), \ a \leq t \leq b.$$

(This curve ϕ is called the parametrization of f by means of its arc length.)

Problem 42. Continuing with Problem 41, prove that $V_\phi(0, s) = s$ for $0 \leq s \leq L$. Prove also that

$$|\phi'(s)| = 1 \text{ a.e.}$$

Now we are going to prove two special results which are valid in the context of *continuous* functions of bounded variation. The first one shows that any sufficiently fine partition generates a good approximation to the length.

> **Theorem:** *Let $f : [a, b] \to \mathbb{R}^n$ be a rectifiable curve. Then for any $\epsilon > 0$ there exists $\delta > 0$ such that if*
>
> $$a = t_0 < t_1 < t_2 < \cdots < t_m = b,$$
>
> *and*
>
> $$t_i - t_{i-1} < \delta \quad for \ 1 \leq i \leq m,$$
>
> *then*
>
> $$\sum_{i=1}^{m} |f(t_i) - f(t_{i-1})| > V_f(a, b) - \epsilon.$$

Proof: First choose a partition
$$a = T_0 < T_1 < \cdots < T_M = b$$
such that the corresponding sum satisfies
$$V_0 = \sum_{i=1}^{M} |f(T_i) - f(T_{i-1})| > V_f(a, b) - \frac{\epsilon}{2}.$$
Since f is uniformly continuous on $[a, b]$, there exists $\delta > 0$ such that if $|t - t'| < \delta$, then
$$|f(t) - f(t')| \leq \frac{\epsilon}{4(M - 1)}.$$

Now consider any partition $a = t_0 < t_1 < \cdots < t_m = b$ with all $t_i - t_{i-1} < \delta$. Let

$$V = \sum_{i=1}^{m} |f(t_i) - f(t_{i-1})|.$$

Consider the partition of $[a, b]$ which is the common refinement of t_0, t_1, ..., t_m and T_0, T_1, ..., T_M. This partition has for its division points t_0, t_1, ..., t_m, T_0, T_1, ..., T_M (with repetitions ignored). We denote the corresponding sum by V'. The triangle inequality implies that $V' \geq V$ and $V' \geq V_0$. On the other hand, let us examine the effect of adjoining one T_i at a time to the points t_0, t_1, ..., t_m. If $t_{j-1} < T_i < t_j$, then we wish to compare

$$\sum_{k=1}^{j-1} |f(t_k) - f(t_{k-1})| + |f(T_i) - f(t_{j-1})| + |f(t_j) - f(T_i)|$$

$$+ \sum_{k=j+1}^{m} |f(t_k) - f(t_{k-1})|$$

with the original sum

$$\sum_{k=1}^{m} |f(t_k) - f(t_{k-1})|.$$

The difference in the larger and the smaller sums is precisely

$$|f(T_i) - f(t_{j-1})| + |f(t_j) - f(T_i)| - |f(t_j) - f(t_{j-1})|,$$

and this is no larger than

$$|f(T_i) - f(t_{j-1})| + |f(t_j) - f(T_i)|.$$

Since $t_j - t_{j-1} < \delta$, this sum in turn is no larger than

$$2\frac{\epsilon}{4(M-1)} = \frac{\epsilon}{2(M-1)}.$$

Thus, adjoining a single T_i increases V by at most $\epsilon/(2(M-1))$. Since at most $M - 1$ of the T_i's have to be adjoined, we conclude that

$$V' \leq V + (M-1)\frac{\epsilon}{2(M-1)}$$

$$= V + \frac{\epsilon}{2}.$$

Therefore,

$$V \geq V' - \frac{\epsilon}{2}$$
$$\geq V_0 - \frac{\epsilon}{2}$$
$$> V_f(a, b) - \epsilon.$$

QED

Problem 43. Prove that this theorem is not valid without the assumption of continuity.

The second special result provides a good illustration of the relation between absolute continuity and singularity.

Theorem: *Assume* $f : [a, b] \to \mathbb{R}^n$ *is absolutely continuous and* $g : [a, b] \to \mathbb{R}^n$ *has bounded variation and* $g' = 0$ *a.e. Then*

$$V_{f+g}(a, b) = V_f(a, b) + V_g(a, b).$$

Proof: Define the real-valued function ϕ on $[a, b]$ by the equation

$$\phi(x) = V_{f+g}(a, x) - V_g(a, x) \quad \text{for } a \leq x \leq b.$$

Property BV7 in Section D implies that

$$V_{f+g}(a, b) - V_g(a, b) \leq V_f(a, b).$$

Since $g = (f + g) + (-f)$, we also have an inequality

$$V_g(a, b) - V_{f+g}(a, b) \leq V_{-f}(a, b) = V_f(a, b).$$

Therefore,

$$|V_{f+g}(a, b) - V_g(a, b)| \leq V_f(a, b).$$

Therefore, we have more generally for $x < y$

$$\begin{aligned}
|\phi(y) - \phi(x)| &= |V_{f+g}(a, y) - V_g(a, y) - V_{f+g}(a, x) + V_g(a, x)| \\
&= |V_{f+g}(x, y) - V_g(x, y)| \\
&\leq V_f(x, y) \\
&= V_f(a, y) - V_f(a, x).
\end{aligned}$$

Since $V_f(a, x)$ is absolutely continuous by the corollary on p.550, this inequality implies that ϕ is absolutely continuous.

Next, the theorem on p.536 implies that almost everywhere

$$\phi'(x) = |f'(x) + g'(x)| - |g'(x)|$$

$$= |f'(x)| \quad \text{(since } g' = 0 \text{ a.e.)}$$

$$= V_f'(a, x).$$

Since $\phi(x)$ and $V_f(a, x)$ are absolutely continuous and have the same derivative a.e., the lemma on p.549 implies

$$\phi(x) = V_f(a, x).$$

That is, $V_{f+g}(a, x) = V_g(a, x) + V_f(a, x)$. Take $x = b$ to obtain the conclusion.   **QED**

Example: Let $f : [0, 1] \to \mathbb{R}$ be a continuous function with bounded variation. We then examine the length of the *graph* of f, $y = f(x)$. That is, consider the curve $(t, f(t))$. The last theorem in Section E shows that

$$f(t) = F(t) + g(t),$$

where F is absolutely continuous and g is continuous singular. Thus, the curve we are considering is equal to a sum

$$(t, f(t)) = (t, F(t)) + (0, g(t))$$

of an absolutely continuous curve and a continuous singular curve. The length of the absolutely continuous part is

$$\int_0^1 |(1, F'(t))| dt = \int_0^1 \sqrt{1 + F'(t)^2} dt$$

$$= \int_0^1 \sqrt{1 + f'(t)^2} dt,$$

and the length of the singular part is

$$V_{(0,g)}(0, 1) = V_g(0, 1).$$

Thus, the length of the graph $y = f(x)$ is given by

$$L = \int_0^1 \sqrt{1 + f'(x)^2}\,dx + V_g(0,1).$$

In particular, if f is increasing as well, then so is g, and the length is

$$L = \int_0^1 \sqrt{1 + f'(x)^2}\,dx + g(1) - g(0).$$

For example, suppose f is the Lebesgue function associated with a Cantor set A, as we discussed at the end of Section F. If $\lambda(A) > 0$, then f is absolutely continuous and $f' = \lambda(A)^{-1}\chi_A$ a.e., so

$$L = \int_A \sqrt{1 + \lambda(A)^{-2}}\,dx + \int_{[0,1]\sim A} dx$$

$$= \lambda(A)\sqrt{1 + \lambda(A)^{-2}} + \lambda([0,1] \sim A)$$

$$= \sqrt{\lambda(A)^2 + 1} + 1 - \lambda(A).$$

On the other hand, if $\lambda(A) = 0$, then f is singular, so $g = f$ and

$$L = 1 + f(1) = 2.$$

Thus, in either case, but for different reasons, we have

$$L = \sqrt{\lambda(A)^2 + 1} + 1 - \lambda(A).$$

Problem 44. Let $f : [0,1] \to \mathbb{R}$ be continuous and increasing, and assume $f(0) = 0$, $f(1) = 1$. Let L be the length of the graph $y = f(x)$. Prove that $L \leq 2$, and that $L = 2 \iff f$ is singular.

(**HINT:** $\sqrt{1 + f'(t)^2} \leq 1 + f'(t)$. When does equality hold?)

H. Nowhere Differentiable Functions

In any discussion of differentiation we should keep our perspective by realizing that there exist continuous functions which are differentiable at no point. The example we are going to consider now is due essentially to Weierstrass from about 1875. The particularly elegant analysis presented here I first saw in the book by Jack Peetre, *New Thoughts on Besov Spaces*, Duke Univ. Math. Series I, 1976.

Before giving the example we recall some terminology already introduced in Problem 14.40.

Definition: Let $f : \mathbb{R} \to \mathbb{C}$ and let $0 < \alpha \leq 1$. The function f is *Hölder continuous of order* α if there exists a constant c such that

$$|f(x) - f(y)| \leq c|x - y|^{\alpha} \quad \text{for all } x, y \in \mathbb{R}.$$

(Notice that Hölder continuity of order 1 is identical to Lipschitz continuity.) The function is said to be Hölder continuous of order α *at the point* x if

$$|f(x) - f(y)| \leq c|x - y|^{\alpha} \quad \text{for all } y \in \mathbb{R} \text{ in a neighborhood of } x.$$

Problem 45. Show that if $\alpha > 1$, then a function would have to be constant to be Hölder continuous of order α.

All the examples we are going to discuss have the following form. The most important parameter is a number $b > 1$. Then let

$$f(x) = \sum_{k=0}^{\infty} c_k e^{ib^k x} + \sum_{k=-\infty}^{-1} c_k e^{i\lambda_k x}.$$

We assume throughout that all $\lambda_k < 0$, that $c_k \in \mathbb{C}$, and that the series converges absolutely:

$$\sum_{-\infty}^{\infty} |c_k| < \infty.$$

Therefore, it converges uniformly, and we conclude that f is continuous on $\mathbb{R}$. Thus, $f : \mathbb{R} \to \mathbb{C}$ is bounded and continuous.

> **Theorem:** *Let f be as described above.*
>
> *(a) Assume $0 < \alpha \le 1$ and assume f is Hölder continuous of order α at one point. Then*
> $$c_k b^{k\alpha} \text{ is bounded for } k \ge 0.$$
>
> *(b) Assume f is differentiable at one point. Then*
> $$\lim_{k \to \infty} c_k b^k = 0.$$
>
> *Conversely, assume $c_k = 0$ for $k < 0$.*
>
> *(a) Assume $0 < \alpha < 1$ and $c_k b^{k\alpha}$ is bounded. Then f is Hölder continuous of order α.*
>
> *(b) Assume $\sum_0^\infty |c_k| b^k < \infty$. Then f is continuously differentiable.*

The converse result is very straightforward, so we shall prove it first.

Proof of converse: For the converse we are assuming

$$f(x) = \sum_{k=0}^\infty c_k e^{ib^k x}.$$

The second assertion is very easily checked: Since the differentiated series converges absolutely uniformly,

$$f'(x) = \sum_{k=0}^\infty c_k i b^k e^{ib^k x},$$

and thus f' is continuous. To prove the first assertion we assume $0 < \alpha < 1$ and

$$|c_k| \le C b^{-k\alpha}.$$

Let $h > 0$. Then

$$|f(x+h) - f(x)| = \Big| \sum_{k=0}^{\infty} c_k \Big[e^{ib^k(x+h)} - e^{ib^k x} \Big] \Big|$$

$$\leq \sum_{k=0}^{\infty} C b^{-k\alpha} \Big| e^{ib^k x} \Big[e^{ib^k h} - 1 \Big] \Big|$$

$$= C \sum_{k=0}^{\infty} b^{-k\alpha} \Big| e^{ib^k h} - 1 \Big|.$$

Now $|e^{i\theta} - 1| \leq |\theta|$ for real θ; also $|e^{i\theta} - 1| \leq 2$. Therefore,

$$|f(x+h) - f(x)| \leq C \sum_{k=0}^{\infty} b^{-k\alpha} \min(b^k h, 2)$$

$$\leq C \sum_{b^k h \leq 1} b^{-k\alpha} b^k h + C \sum_{b^k h > 1} 2 b^{-k\alpha}.$$

We can clearly assume $h \leq 1$. Then let m be the largest integer such that $b^m h \leq 1$; it follows that $m \geq 0$ and $b^{m+1} h > 1$. Thus,

$$\sum_{b^k h \leq 1} b^{-k\alpha} b^k h = h \sum_{k=0}^{m} b^{(1-\alpha)k}$$

$$= h \frac{b^{(1-\alpha)(m+1)} - 1}{b^{1-\alpha} - 1}$$

$$\leq h \frac{b^{1-\alpha} (h^{-1})^{1-\alpha}}{b^{1-\alpha} - 1}$$

$$= \frac{h^{\alpha}}{1 - b^{\alpha-1}}.$$

Also,

$$\sum_{b^k h > 1} b^{-k\alpha} = \sum_{k=m+1}^{\infty} b^{-k\alpha}$$

$$= \frac{b^{-(m+1)\alpha}}{1 - b^{-\alpha}}$$

$$< \frac{h^{\alpha}}{1 - b^{-\alpha}}.$$

Therefore,

$$|f(x+h) - f(x)| \leq C \left(\frac{1}{1 - b^{\alpha - 1}} + \frac{2}{1 - b^{-\alpha}} \right) h^{\alpha}.$$

(QED for converse result)

Proof of main part of theorem: Suppose the one point of Hölder continuity or differentiability is x_0. Then

$$f(x_0 + h) = \sum_{k=0}^{\infty} c'_k e^{ib^k h} + \sum_{k=-\infty}^{-1} c'_k e^{i\lambda_k h},$$

where $c'_k = c_k e^{ib^k x_0}$ for $k \geq 0$ and $c'_k = c_k e^{i\lambda_k x_0}$ for $k < 0$. This function of h has the same form as the original function, $|c'_k| = |c_k|$, and the new function is Hölder continuous or differentiable at $h = 0$. Thus, we assume with no loss of generality that the original function f is Hölder continuous or differentiable at $x = 0$.

We are going to use a function in C_c^{∞} which vanishes outside the interval $[b^{-1}, b]$, and which equals 1 at 1. Since such a function is in $\mathcal{S}$ in particular, it is the Fourier transform of a function in $\mathcal{S}$. Thus, there exists $\phi \in \mathcal{S}$ such that $\widehat{\phi}$ has the desired properties. The graph of $\widehat{\phi}$ is sketched in Figure 4.

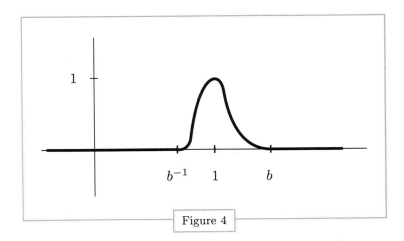

Figure 4

Note that

$$\int_{\mathbb{R}} \phi dx = \widehat{\phi}(0) = 0,$$

$$\int_{\mathbb{R}} -ix\phi dx = (\widehat{\phi})'(0) = 0.$$

Now for any $n \geq 0$ we have

$$f(-b^{-n}x) = \sum_{k=0}^{\infty} c_k e^{-ib^{k-n}x} + \sum_{k=-\infty}^{-1} c_k e^{-i\lambda_k b^{-n}x}.$$

Multiply this equation by $\phi(x)$ and integrate to obtain

$$\int_{\mathbb{R}} \phi(x)f(-b^{-n}x)dx = \sum_{k=0}^{\infty} c_k \widehat{\phi}(b^{k-n}) + \sum_{k=-\infty}^{-1} c_k \widehat{\phi}(\lambda_k b^{-n}).$$

Since all $\lambda_k < 0$, the second sum vanishes. In the first sum only $\widehat{\phi}(1)$ is not zero, so we obtain

$$\int_{\mathbb{R}} \phi(x)f(-b^{-n}x)dx = c_n.$$

Since $\int_{\mathbb{R}} \phi dx = 0$,

$$c_k = \int_{\mathbb{R}} \phi(-x)[f(b^{-k}x) - f(0)]dx \quad \text{for } k \geq 0.$$

Now we prove (a). Since f is bounded, we have an inequality of the form

$$|f(x) - f(0)| \leq C|x|^{\alpha} \quad \text{for all } x \in \mathbb{R}.$$

Therefore,

$$|c_k| \leq \int_{\mathbb{R}} |\phi(-x)|C|b^{-k}x|^{\alpha}dx$$

$$= Cb^{-k\alpha} \int_{\mathbb{R}} |\phi(x)| \, |x|^{\alpha}dx.$$

Thus, $|c_k|b^{k\alpha} \leq$ constant, and (a) is proved.

In order to prove (b) we further write

$$c_k = \int_{\mathbb{R}} \phi(-x)\frac{f(b^{-k}x) - f(0)}{b^{-k}x}b^{-k}x dx;$$

$$c_k b^k = \int_{\mathbb{R}} x\phi(-x)\frac{f(b^{-k}x) - f(0)}{b^{-k}x}dx.$$

Since f is differentiable at the origin and the difference quotient in the integrand is bounded, LDCT implies

$$\lim_{k \to \infty} c_k b^k = \int_{\mathbb{R}} x\phi(-x)f'(0)dx$$

$$= -f'(0)\int_{\mathbb{R}} x\phi(x)dx$$

$$= 0. \qquad\qquad \textbf{QED}$$

Corollary: *Assume $b > 1$ and let $a \in \mathbb{C}$, $|a| < 1$. Let*

$$f(x) = \sum_{k=0}^{\infty} a^k e^{ib^k x}.$$

Then

(a) *if $|a|b < 1$, f is of class C^1;*

(b) *if $|a|b \geq 1$, f is nowhere differentiable;*

(c) *if $|a|b > 1$, f is Hölder continuous of order $-\log|a|/\log b$ and is nowhere Hölder continuous of higher order.*

Proof: This is now virtually obvious. Certainly parts (a) and (b) are trivial consequences of the theorem. To prove (c), suppose f is Hölder continuous of order α at one point. Then the theorem implies

$$|a|^k b^{k\alpha} \leq C, \ k \geq 0.$$

This holds if and only if $|a|b^\alpha \leq 1$, which is equivalent to

$$\alpha \leq \frac{-\log|a|}{\log b}.$$

On the other hand, if

$$\alpha = \frac{-\log|a|}{\log b},$$

then $0 < \alpha < 1$ and the converse part of the theorem implies f is Hölder continuous of order α.   **QED**

Corollary:*Assume $b > 1$, $|a| < 1$, and $|a|b \geq 1$. Then the function*

$$\sum_{k=1}^{\infty} a^k \sin(b^k x)$$

is nowhere differentiable.

Proof: This function is equal to $\displaystyle\sum_{k=1}^{\infty} \frac{a^k}{2i} e^{ib^k x} + \sum_{k=-\infty}^{-1} \frac{-a^{-k}}{2i} e^{-ib^{-k} x}$, so the theorem applies if we take $\lambda_k = -b^{-k}$.   **QED**

I.   Convex Functions

In Section 4.D we discussed very briefly the concept of *concavity*. Now we develop this more fully, as a convex function is just the negative of a concave function.

Definition: Let $I \subset \mathbb{R}$ be an *open* interval. A function $f : I \to \mathbb{R}$ is *convex* if any chord inscribed in the graph of f lies above the graph. That is, if $a < b < c$ are points in I, then

$$f(b) \leq \frac{c-b}{c-a} f(a) + \frac{b-a}{c-a} f(c).$$

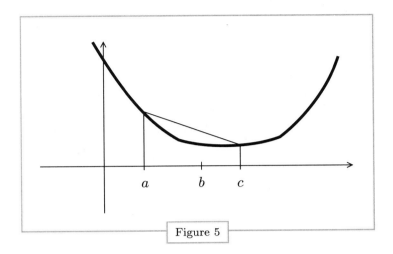

Figure 5

Several remarkable facts are consequences of this simple definition. We shall now develop them, and we shall conclude with a characterization of convex functions in terms of integration.

First, we note that the inequality in the definition is equivalent to

$$0 \le \frac{c-b}{c-a}[f(a) - f(b)] + \frac{b-a}{c-a}[f(c) - f(b)].$$

We rearrange this to conclude that

$$\frac{f(b) - f(a)}{b - a} \le \frac{f(c) - f(b)}{c - b}.$$

This has an obvious geometric interpretation in terms of slopes of chords increasing as one moves with increasing x, as illustrated in the figure:

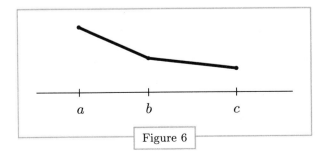

Figure 6

By considering a third interval, we find that the slope of the chord over $[a, b]$ is not greater than the slope of the chord over $[c, d]$, if $b < c$:

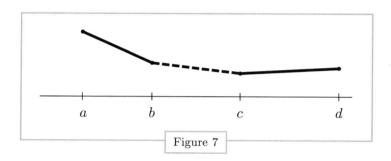

Figure 7

Now consider any *compact* interval J contained in the open interval I. Choose points a, b, c, d all in I, such that $a < b$ are situated to the left of J and $c < d$ are situated to the right of J. Then we conclude for any $x < y$ in J

$$\frac{f(b) - f(a)}{b - a} \leq \frac{f(y) - f(x)}{y - x} \leq \frac{f(d) - f(c)}{d - c}.$$

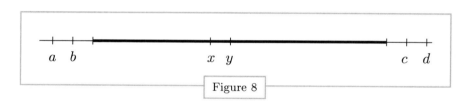

Figure 8

Now regard a, b, c, d as fixed. The conclusion is that there exists a constant C which depends only on J (and f) such that

$$|f(y) - f(x)| \leq C|y - x| \quad \text{for all } x, y \in J.$$

That is, f is *Lipschitz continuous* on J, and is therefore also absolutely continuous on J. Since this is valid for any compact interval $J \subset I$, we say that the function f is *locally Lipschitz continuous* on I.

We now know that the convex function f on I is locally absolutely continuous on I, and thus f' exists almost everywhere on I and

$$f(x) = f(x_0) + \int_{x_0}^{x} f'(t)dt \quad \text{for all } x \in I.$$

Here x_0 is any fixed point in I. Not only does f' exist a.e., but it is an *increasing* function. This follows from Figure 7: Let $a < c$ be points where f' exists. Use the inequality implied by Figure 7, and let $b \to a+$ and $d \to c+$ to conclude

$$f'(a) \le f'(c).$$

Since f' is increasing, Problem 3 implies that it is discontinuous at only countably many points. Therefore, the integral representation above actually implies f' *exists* except for countably many points.

We now summarize our findings: If f is convex on an open interval I, then

(a) f is locally Lipschitz continuous,

(b) f' exists except on a countable set,

(c) f' is an increasing function, and

(d) for any $x_0 \in I$

$$f(x) = f(x_0) + \int_{x_0}^{x} f'(t)dt \quad \text{for } x \in I.$$

The converse of this is also valid. Namely, suppose h is an increasing function defined a.e. on I, and define

$$f(x) = \alpha + \int_{x_0}^{x} h(t)dt \quad \text{for } x \in I,$$

where $\alpha \in \mathbb{R}$ and $x_0 \in I$ are arbitrary. Then f is convex. The proof is simple. If $a < b < c$, we want to verify

$$\frac{f(b) - f(a)}{b - a} \le \frac{f(c) - f(b)}{c - b}.$$

That is,

$$\frac{1}{b - a} \int_{a}^{b} h(t)dt \le \frac{1}{c - b} \int_{b}^{c} h(s)ds.$$

This inequality follows because $h(t) \le h(s)$ for a.e. t, s in the indicated intervals. Thus, there exists $A \in \mathbb{R}$ such that $h(t) \le A \le h(s)$. Therefore,

$$\frac{1}{b - a} \int_{a}^{b} h(t)dt \le A \le \frac{1}{c - b} \int_{b}^{c} h(s)ds.$$

Problem 46. Suppose f is of class C^2 on I. Prove that f is convex if and only if $f'' \geq 0$.

Problem 47. Suppose f is convex on I. Then for every $x \in I$ there exists a linear function $l_x(t) = at + b$ such that $l_x \leq f$ on I and $l_x(x) = f(x)$.

Problem 48. Conversely, assume f is a real-valued function on I such that for every $x \in I$ there exists a linear function l_x such that $l_x \leq f$ on I and $l_x(x) = f(x)$. Prove that f is convex.

Index

Symbol Index

Assorted Facts

$$\Gamma(a) = \int\limits_0^\infty x^{a-1}e^{-x}dx \qquad \text{GAMMA FUNCTION} \qquad 197$$

$$\frac{1}{\Gamma(a)} = \lim_{n\to\infty} \frac{a(a+1)\dots(a+n)}{n^a n!} \qquad 207$$

$$\frac{1}{\Gamma(a)} = ae^{\gamma a} \prod_{k=1}^\infty \left(1 + \frac{a}{k}\right) e^{-a/k} \qquad 209$$

$$\Gamma(na) = (2\pi)^{(1-n)/2} n^{na-1/2} \Gamma(a)\Gamma\left(a + \frac{1}{n}\right)\dots\Gamma\left(a + \frac{n-1}{n}\right) \qquad 213$$

$$\Gamma(a)\Gamma(1-a) = \frac{\pi}{\sin \pi a} \qquad 216$$

$$\Gamma\left(\frac{1}{2}\right) = \sqrt{\pi} \qquad 200$$

$$\Gamma(a+b) \sim \sqrt{2\pi}a^{a+b-1/2}e^{-a} \text{ as } a \to \infty \quad \text{STIRLING APPROXIMATION} \quad 213$$

$$\gamma = \lim_{n\to\infty}\left(\sum_{k=1}^n \frac{1}{k} - \log n\right) \qquad \text{EULER'S CONSTANT} \qquad 208$$

$$\Gamma'(1) = -\gamma \qquad 209$$

$$\sin \pi a = \pi a \prod_{n=1}^\infty \left(1 - \frac{a^2}{n^2}\right) \qquad 216, 402$$

$$\frac{\pi^2}{\sin^2 \pi t} = \sum_{n=-\infty}^\infty \frac{1}{(t-n)^2} \qquad 423$$

$$\frac{\pi}{2} = \frac{2}{1}\cdot\frac{2}{3}\cdot\frac{4}{3}\cdot\frac{4}{5}\cdot\frac{6}{5}\cdot\frac{6}{7}\dots \qquad \text{WALLIS' FORMULA} \qquad 208$$